DESIGN OF PRESTRESSED CONCRETE

Chillon viaduct at Lake Geneva, Switzerland.

DESIGN OF PRESTRESSED CONCRETE

ARTHUR H. NILSON

PROFESSOR OF STRUCTURAL ENGINEERING
CORNELL UNIVERSITY

JOHN WILEY AND SONS
New York   Santa Babara   Chichester   Brisbane   Toronto

5/93

3770856

Library of Congress Cataloging in Publication Data:

Nilson, Arthur H
  Design of prestressed concrete.

  Includes index.
  1. Prestressed concrete construction. I. Title.
TA683.9.N54   624′.1834   78-4929
ISBN 0-471-02034-6

Printed in the United States of America

10 9 8 7 6 5 4 3 2 1

To George Winter

PREFACE

Although the first proposal to apply prestressing to concrete was made as early as 1886, in the United States, it was only as a result of the studies of the renowned French engineer Eugene Freyssinet, in the 1930s, that prestressed concrete became a practical reality. In Europe, in the period of acute material shortages following World War II, Freyssinet and other pioneers such as Finsterwalder and Magnel demonstrated the remarkable possibilities of this new concept of design and set the stage for the development that was to take place in the years that followed.

Largely for economic reasons, the evolution of prestressed concrete in the United States has taken place along very different lines than in Europe. Until recently, the main interest had been in pretensioned precast units of short to medium span, which could be mass-produced at great savings in labor costs. Used for floors, roofs, and walls, these units have accounted for a significant fraction of new construction, and undoubtedly will continue to do so.

However, changing economic conditions are producing important changes in U.S. practice. Construction labor is not in such short supply as before. The cost of materials is constantly increasing, and there is serious concern for conservation of resources. Under such circumstances, it is natural that engineers should consider the suitability of more sophisticated designs, which more fully exploit the capability of prestressing. It has been found that prestressed concrete now competes successfully with other forms of construction for medium- and long-span bridges, tall buildings, long-span roofs, and other types of one-of-a-kind construction.

Such changes in conditions of practice have created the need for engineers who have a firm understanding of the fundamental principles of prestressed concrete behavior and design, who can not only act effectively to optimize existing forms of construction, but who can also apply fundamental concepts with confidence in unusual and challenging situations.

I hope that this textbook may be effective in developing that basic understanding. The book has grown from a set of lecture notes that I developed while teaching prestressed concrete to civil engineering students at Cornell University over a 15-year period. Every effort has been made to insure a thorough understanding of basic mechanics and behavior. Although the book is intended mainly as a college textbook at the fourth- or fifth-year level, a special effort has been made to develop a clear, self-contained presentation, so that the book may be useful to engineers who wish to improve their knowledge of this relatively new field by self-study. The material has been carefully coordinated with codes and specifications governing U.S. practice, notably the ACI Building Code, but also the AASHTO Specification for highway structures and the AREA Design Manual for railway construction.

It is assumed that the student has had prior exposure to the basic aspects of reinforced concrete behavior and design. Certain fundamentals, encountered first in the design of reinforced concrete, are not developed fully here; in such cases references are given to other sources.

The arrangement of the material follows that of my lectures. After an introduction to basic concepts and properties of materials, in Chapters 1 and 2, the analysis and design of beams is presented in Chapters 3 to 5. Losses of prestress force are considered in Chapter 6. It may be argued that analysis of losses should precede beam analysis and design, but I have concluded that, from a pedagogical point of view, there are advantages to getting on with the business of design early. In many practical cases, losses must be considered in no more detail than in Chapters 3 and 4.

The study of deflections (Chapter 9) and the design of slabs (Chapter 10) are fundamental and should be included in a first course of study. However, the teacher may not find time to cover composite beams or continuous members (Chapter 7 and 8, respectively). These topics, as well as the treatment of axially loaded members (Chapter 11), may be deferred until a later course or taken up through self-study.

Chapters 12 and 13, which deal, respectively, with precast construction and applications, have been written to permit their assignment as outside reading.

Appendix A contains a variety of design aids. These are useful in connection with examples and problems to be assigned, and may also make the book a useful desk aid for the practicing engineer. Appendix B contains engineering data for certain common post-tensioning systems. No attempt has been made to be encyclopedic here, but only to present sufficient detail to permit realistic proportioning of members in practice problems.

A word is in order relative to the units of measurement used. Nationwide, there is a movement toward adoption of the International System (SI) of metric units. In many cases, basic science and engineering science courses are now taught in SI units. Certain industries have already converted. However, in current U.S. structural practice, the familiar "English" or "customary" units are still almost universally used. Conversion to metric units will follow by at least several years the metrication of design codes and specifications. Yet the new edition of the ACI Code, governing the greatest part of U.S. concrete design and construction, is written entirely in customary units.

Recognizing that the users of this textbook may have become familiar with SI units in preparatory courses, but will soon enter design offices in which customary units prevail, I have proceeded as follows: (1) all graphs and tabulated information of a fundamental nature are given in dual units; (2) all dimensionally inconsistent equations are given in customary units, but SI equivalents are given in the separate Appendix C; (3) examples are given in customary units, but SI equivalents are provided, in parentheses, for input data and key answers; and (4) design aids in Appendix A are given in customary units only. This is a reasonable compromise between encouragement to adopt the obviously superior International System of units, and recognition of the probable facts of professional practice over the next 5 to 10 years.

Many persons and organizations have contributed to this volume. Significant contributions have been made by former students, particularly by Charles Dolan, of ABAM Engineers, Inc., who offered valuable comments and arranged for much illustrative material. Other illustrations were obtained through the cooperation of George Nasser, of the Prestressed Concrete Institute, Gene Corley, of the Portland Cement Association, Cliff Freyermuth, of the Post-Tensioning Institute, and many others. A substantial contribution was made by Edward Nawy, of Rutgers University, who reviewed the final manuscript.

Secretarial and other essential support was provided by Cornell University.

Finally, I would like to acknowledge the influence of George Winter, with whom an earlier book on reinforced concrete was coauthored. A long professional and personal association with him has had a profound effect in developing a point of view that I hope is reflected in the following pages.

Ithaca, New York   ARTHUR H. NILSON
March 1978

CONTENTS

xi

CHAPTER 6   PARTIAL LOSS OF PRESTRESS FORCE   221

Introduction; Lump Sum Estimates of Losses; Detailed Estimation of Losses; Anchorage Slip; Elastic Shortening of the Concrete; Losses Due to Friction; Creep of Concrete; Concrete Shrinkage; Relaxation of Steel; Example: Calculation of Separate Losses; Estimation of Losses by the Time Step Method.

CHAPTER 7   COMPOSITE BEAMS   241

Types of Composite Construction; Load Stages; Section Properties and Elastic Flexural Stresses; Flexural Strength; Horizontal Shear Transfer; Shear and Diagonal Tension.

CHAPTER 8   CONTINUOUS BEAMS AND FRAMES   261

Simple Spans versus Continuity; Tendon Profiles and Stressing Arrangements; Elastic Analysis for the Effects of Prestressing; Equivalent Load Analysis; Example: Indeterminate Prestressed Beam; Linear Transformation; Concordant Tendons; Concrete Stresses in the Elastic Range; Flexural Strength; Moment Redistribution and Limit Analysis; Indeterminate Frames.

CHAPTER 9   DEFLECTIONS   295

Introduction; Basis for the Calculations; Approximate Method for Deflection Calculation; Effective Moment of Inertia; Refined Calculations Using Incremental Time Steps; Example of Deflection Calculation; Composite Members; Allowable Deflections.

CHAPTER 10   SLABS   319

Introduction; One-Way Slabs; Two-Way Slabs with All Edges Supported: Behavior; Two-Directional Load Balancing for Edge-Supported Slabs; Practical Analysis for Unbalanced Loading; Deflection of Two-Way Slabs; Ultimate Strength of Two-Way Slabs; Example: Two-Way Wall-supported Slab; Prestressed Flat Plate Slabs; Behavior of Flat Plates; The Balanced Load Stage; The Equivalent Frame Method; Flexural Strength of Flat Plates; Shear in Flat Plates; Non-Prestressed Reinforcement; Deflection of Flat Plates; Example: Flat Plate Design.

CHAPTER 11   AXIALLY LOADED MEMBERS   389

Introduction; Behavior of Prestressed Columns; Example: Construction of Column Interaction Diagram; Non-Prestressed Reinforcement in Columns; Behavior of Slender Columns; Practical Consideration of Slenderness Effects; Behavior of Tension Members;

Example: Behavior of Prestressed Concrete Tension Element; Design of Tension Members; Example: Design of Rigid Frame Tie Member.

CHAPTER 1
BASIC CONCEPTS

1.1 INTRODUCTION

Prestressing can be defined in general terms as the preloading of a structure, before application of the required design loads, in such a way as to improve its overall performance. Although the principles and techniques of prestressing have been applied to structures of many types and materials, the most common application is in the design of structural concrete.

Concrete is essentially a compression material. Its strength in tension is much lower than that in compression, and in many cases in design the tensile resistance is discounted altogether. The prestressing of concrete, therefore, naturally involves application of a compressive loading, prior to applying the anticipated design loads, so that tensile stresses that otherwise would occur are reduced or eliminated.

In fact, the original concept of prestressing concrete was to introduce sufficient axial precompression in beams so that all tension in the concrete was eliminated in the loaded member. However, as knowledge of this relatively new form of construction has developed, it has become clear that this view is unnecessarily restrictive, and in present design practice tensile stress in the concrete, even some limited cracking, is permitted. By varying the amount of compressive prestress, the number and width of cracks can be limited to the desired degree. Of equal importance, the deflection of the member may be controlled. Beams may even be designed to have zero deflection at a specified combination of prestress and external loading. In the sense of improved serviceability, such partial prestressing represents a substantial improvement, not only over conventional reinforced concrete construction, but also over the original form of full prestressing which, while eliminating service-load cracking, often produced troublesome upward camber.

But it is not only through improved serviceability that prestressing has achieved its position of importance. By crack and deflection control at service loads, prestressing makes it possible to employ economical and efficient high tensile strength steel reinforcement and high strength concrete.

Crack widths in conventional reinforced concrete beams are roughly proportional to the stress in the tensile reinforcement, and for this reason steel stresses must be limited to values far less than could otherwise be used. In prestressed

1

beams, high steel stress is not accompanied by wide concrete cracks, because much of the strain is applied to the steel before it is anchored to the concrete, and before the member is loaded.

Deflection of ordinary reinforced concrete beams is also linked directly to stresses. If very high stresses were permitted, the accompanying high strains in the concrete and steel would inevitably produce large rotations of the cross sections along the member, which translate directly into large deflections. By prestraining the high tensile reinforcement of prestressed beams, the large rotations and deflections that would otherwise occur are avoided. In addition, the essentially uncracked concrete member is stiffer, for given section dimensions, than it would be if cracking were permitted to the extent typical of reinforced concrete construction.

Thus it is not only because of improvement of service load behavior, by controlling cracking and deflection, that prestressed concrete is attractive, but also because it permits utilization of efficient high strength materials. Smaller and lighter members may be used. The ratio of dead to live load is reduced, spans increased, and the range of possible application of structural concrete is greatly extended.

The dramatic improvements in the performance of concrete structures that could be obtained by prestressing were first recognized by the renowned French engineer Eugene Freyssinet. His studies of the time-dependent effects of shrinkage and creep of concrete, which began as early as 1911, led him to realize the importance of using steel at a high initial stress to prestress concrete members. In 1940 he introduced a system for prestressing using wedge-anchored high strength cables, an arrangement of great practicality that is still in wide use.

The remarkable bridge over the river Marne at Luzancy, France, shown in Figs. 1.1 and 1.2, illustrates the innovation and daring that was to be typical of Freyssinet's later designs. Built in 1941, this very flat, two-hinged portal frame structure has a span of 180 ft and a depth at midspan of only 4.17 ft, a ratio of span to depth of 43. The hinged supports of the bridge were provided with adjustments in order to compensate for the effects of shrinkage and creep.

The I-shaped bridge segments were precast. The flanges were cast first, and were connected by wires that were tensioned prior to casting the web, by jacking the flanges apart. After the webs were cast, the jacking force was released, precompressing the webs to counteract diagonal tensile stresses resulting from loads. Individual segments were then assembled into larger components, which were placed in final position by cableways, and the entire structure then post-tensioned. This structure, and five other nearly identical spans in the same region, provide the model for segmentally precast bridges now widely used.

Prestressing has been applied to great advantage in a wide variety of situations, a few of which are illustrated by the following photographs. Figure 1.3 shows the use of precast "double-tee" beams carrying a floor with clear span of about 20 ft. End support is provided by the precast L-section beam over the

Figure 1.1 Bridge of 180 ft span over the river Marne at Luzancy designed by Freyssinet and built in 1941.

Figure 1.2 View of the Luzancy bridge.

Figure 1.3 Precast prestressed double-tee floor beams.

Figure 1.4 Twin box girder bridge under construction using the segmentally cast cantilever method.

Figure 1.5 Highway crossing in Switzerland, continuous over three spans.

Figure 1.6 Segmentally precast post-tensioned rigid frames for the Olympic stadium in Montreal (courtesy Regis Trudeau and Associates, Inc., Montreal).

window, also prestressed. Such precast prestressed construction has been used extensively throughout the United States.

The construction of bridges by the cantilever method, in which newly completed segments are prestressed to completed construction, is illustrated by Fig. 1.4. The twin spans shown under construction, near Paris, will carry four lanes of traffic.

The two-lane bridge shown in Fig. 1.5, over the highway between Bern and Lausanne in Switzerland, illustrates the lightness and grace often associated with prestressed concrete structures.

The huge, segmentally precast frames shown in Fig. 1.6, recently completed for the 1976 Olympic Games in Montreal illustrate the versatility of prestressed concrete. To provide a sense of scale, note the construction worker atop the catwalk of the farther frame, just forward of the supporting leg.

1.2   EXAMPLE

Many important features of prestressing can be illustrated by a simple example. Consider first the plain, unreinforced concrete beam shown in Fig. 1.7a. It carries a single concentrated load at the center of its span. (The self-weight of the member will be neglected here.) As the load W is gradually applied, longitudinal flexural stresses are induced. Assuming that the concrete is stressed only within its elastic range, the flexural stress distribution at midspan will be linear, as shown.

At a relatively low load, the tensile stress in the concrete at the bottom of the member will reach the tensile strength of the material, f'_r, and a crack will form. Since no restraint is provided against upward extension of the crack, the member will collapse without further increase of load.

Now consider an otherwise identical beam, as in Fig. 1.7b, in which a longitudinal axial force P is introduced prior to the vertical loading. The longitudinal prestressing force will produce a uniform axial compressive stress $f_c = P/A_c$, where A_c is the cross-sectional area of the concrete. It is clear that the force can be adjusted in magnitude, so that, when the transverse load Q is applied, the superposition of stresses due to P and Q will result in zero tensile stress at the bottom of the beam, as shown. Tensile stress in the concrete may be eliminated in this way, or reduced to a specified amount.

But it would be more logical to apply the prestressing force near the bottom of the beam, so as to compensate more effectively for the load-induced tension. A possible design specification, for example, might be to introduce the maximum compression at the bottom of the member without causing tension at the top, when only the prestressing force acts. It is easily shown that, for a rectangular cross section beam, the corresponding point of application of the force is at the lower third point of the section depth. The load P, with the same

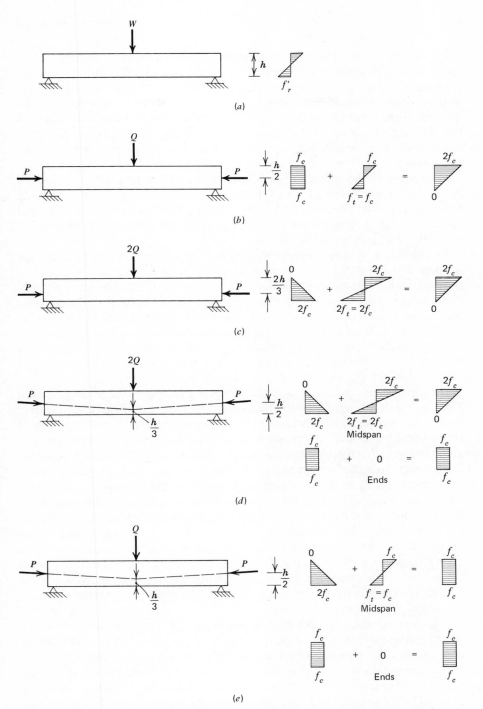

Figure 1.7 Alternative schemes for prestressing a rectangular concrete beam. (*a*) Plain concrete beam. (*b*) Axially prestressed beam. (*c*) Eccentrically prestressed beam. (*d*) Beam prestressed with variable eccentricity. (*e*) Balanced load stage for beam with variable eccentricity.

value as before, but applied with eccentricity $e = h/6$ relative to the concrete centroid, will produce a longitudinal compressive stress distribution varying from zero at the top surface to a maximum value of $2f_c = (P/A_c) + (Pec_2/I_c)$, at the bottom, where f_c is the concrete stress at the section centroid, c_2 is the distance from concrete centroid to the bottom face of the concrete, and I_c is the moment of inertia of the cross section. This is shown in Fig. 1.7c. The stress at the bottom will be exactly twice the value produced before by axial prestressing.

Consequently the transverse load may now be twice as great as before, or $2Q$, and still cause no tensile stress. In fact, the final stress distribution resulting from the superposition of load and prestressing force in Fig. 1.7c is identical to that of Fig. 1.7b, although the load is twice as great. The advantage of eccentric prestressing is obvious.

The methods by which concrete members are prestressed will be discussed in some detail in Art. 1.6 with further details given in Appendix B. For present purposes, it is sufficient to know that one common method of prestressing uses high strength steel wires passing through a conduit embedded in the concrete beam. The tendon is anchored to the concrete at one end, and is stretched at the far end by a hydraulic jack that reacts against the concrete. When the desired tension in the tendon is obtained, it is anchored against the concrete at the jacking end as well, and the jack is removed. The result is a self-contained system by which the force P of Fig. 1.7 may be applied.

If such a system is used, a significant improvement over the arrangement of Figs. 1.7b or 1.7c can be made, by using a variable eccentricity of prestress force, with respect to the centroid of the concrete section, along the length of the member. The load $2Q$ produces a bending moment that varies linearly along the span, from zero at the supports to maximum at the center. Intuitively, one suspects that the best arrangement of prestressing would produce a countermoment, acting in the opposite sense, which would vary in the same way. This is easily done, because the prestress moment is directly proportional to the eccentricity of the tendon, measured from the steel centroid to the concrete centroid. Accordingly, the tendon is now given an eccentricity that varies linearly from zero at the supports to maximum at the center of the span. Such an arrangement is shown in Fig. 1.7d. The stresses at midspan are the same as before, both when the load $2Q$ acts and when it does not. At the supports, where only the prestress force acts, with zero eccentricity, a uniform compressive stress f_c is obtained as shown.

It should be clear that, for each characteristic load arrangement, there is a "best" tendon profile in the sense that it produces a prestress moment diagram which corresponds to that of the applied load. It is of further interest to note that, if the prestress countermoment should be made exactly equal and opposite to the moment from the loads, all along the span, the result is a beam that is subject only to uniform axial compressive stress throughout for that particular loading. The beam would not only be free of cracking but (neglecting the influence of concrete shrinkage and creep) would deflect neither up nor down when that load is in place, compared to its unstressed position. Such a situation would be obtained for a load of $\frac{1}{2} \times (2Q) = Q$, as in Fig. 1.7e, for example. This condition is referred to as the balanced load stage.

Although this brief discussion has been presented with reference to the elimination of flexural tension and control of cracking and deflection in concrete beams, it should be recognized that prestressing may be used effectively in many other situations, such as to reduce or eliminate diagonal tensile stresses in beams, hoop tension in liquid storage vessels or pipes, tensile stresses due to loading or shrinkage in pavements, or tension from the eccentric loading of columns. The fundamental principles are broadly applicable and provide design engineers with a powerful means to improve the performance of structures of many types.

1.3   EQUIVALENT LOADS

The effect of a change in the vertical alignment of a prestressing tendon is to produce a transverse vertical force on the concrete member. That force, together with the prestressing forces acting at the ends of the member through the tendon anchorages, may be looked upon as a system of external forces in studying the effect of prestressing.

In Fig. 1.8a, for example, a tendon that applies force P at the centroid of the concrete section at the ends of a beam, and that has a uniform slope at angle θ between the ends and midspan, introduces the transverse force $2P \sin \theta$ at the point of change in tendon alignment at midspan. At the anchorages the vertical component of the prestressing force is $P \sin \theta$ and the horizontal component is $P \cos \theta$. The horizontal component is very nearly equal to the force P for the usual small slope angles. The moment diagram for the beam of Fig. 1.8a is seen to have the same form as that for any center-loaded simple span.

The beam of Fig. 1.8b, with a curved tendon, is subject to a transverse distributed load from the tendon, as well as the forces P at each end. The exact distribution of the load depends on the alignment of the tendon. A tendon with a parabolic profile, for example, will produce a uniformly distributed transverse load. In this case, the moment diagram will have a parabolic shape, as for a uniformly loaded simple span beam.

If a straight tendon is used with constant eccentricity e, as in Fig. 1.8c, there are no transverse forces on the concrete. But the member is subject to a moment Pe at each end, as well as the axial force P, and a diagram of constant moment results.

The end moment must also be accounted for in considering the beam of Fig. 1.8d, in which a parabolic tendon is used that does not pass through the

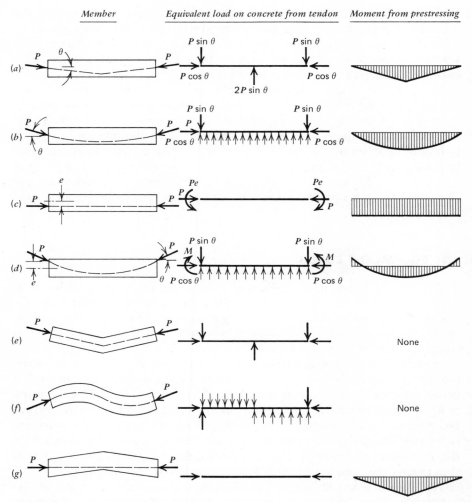

Figure 1.8   Equivalent loads and moments produced by prestressed tendons.

concrete centroid at the ends of the span. In this case, a uniformly distributed transverse load and end anchorage forces are produced, just as in Fig. 1.8b. But, in addition, the end moments $M = Pe \cos \theta$ must be considered.

The concept of equivalent transverse loading is a useful one, but it must be applied with care. In all of the cases considered thus far, the profile of the concrete centroid was straight. The concrete thrust was horizontal, consequently, and any change in alignment of the tendon produced an unbalanced force acting on the concrete at that section. If the beam axis is curved, as in Figs. 1.8e and 1.8f and, if the tendon and concrete centroid coincide at all sections, then the lateral force produced by the steel at any section is balanced by a resultant force in the opposite direction produced by the thrust from the adjacent concrete, and no bending moment results.

On the other hand, if the tendon is straight, but the concrete centroidal axis has some other alignment, as in Fig. 1.8*g*, then the lateral force produced by the concrete thrust is not balanced by the lateral forces from the steel, and bending moment is produced as shown.

It may be evident that, for any arrangement of applied loads, a tendon profile can be selected such that the equivalent loads acting on the beam from the tendon are just equal and opposite to the applied loads. The result would be a state of pure compression in the beam, as discussed in somewhat different terms at the end of the preceding article. An advantage of the equivalent loading concept is that it leads the designer to select what is probably the best tendon profile for any given load configuration.

It is worth emphasizing that *all* of the systems shown in Fig. 1.8 are self-equilibrating, and that the application of prestressing forces produce no external reactions. This is always true for statically determinate beams, but is not generally true for indeterminate spans, as will be discussed in Ch. 8.

1.4   OVERLOAD BEHAVIOR AND STRENGTH IN FLEXURE

In describing the effect of prestressing in the example of Art. 1.2, it was implied that the beam responded in a linear elastic way, and that the principle of superposition was valid. This requires that the beam remain uncracked, and that both the concrete and steel be stressed only within their elastic ranges. This may be the case up to approximately the level of *service load*, that is, the actual self-weight of the member plus those superimposed loads that may reasonably be expected to act during the life of the member. But should the loads be increased further, tensile stresses resulting from flexure will eventually exceed the tensile strength of the concrete, and cracks will form. These do not cause failure, because of the presence of the steel, and the loads generally can be increased well beyond the cracking load without producing distress.

Eventually, with loads increased still further, either the steel or the concrete, or both, will be stressed into their nonlinear range. The condition at incipient failure is represented by Fig. 1.9, which shows a beam carrying a *factored load*, equal to some multiple of the expected service load. In designing a member, the magnitude of the load factor can be selected to provide the desired degree of safety.

For the overloaded condition, the beam undoubtedly would be in a partially cracked state; a possible pattern of cracking is shown in Fig. 1.9. Only the concrete in compression is considered to be effective, just as in the analysis of ordinary reinforced concrete. The steel in tension works with the concrete in

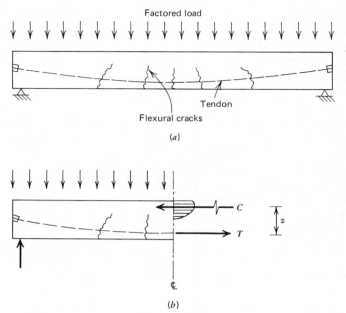

Figure 1.9 Prestressed concrete beam at ultimate flexural load. (*a*) Beam with factored load. (*b*) Equilibrium of forces on half-beam.

compression to form an internal force couple, which resists the moment from the applied load.

The concrete stress distribution in the compression zone at failure can be found by methods presented in Ch. 3, as can the magnitude of the compressive resultant C, the tensile force T in the steel, and the distance between the two. If the internal lever arm is z then the ultimate resisting moment is

$$M_n = Cz = Tz \qquad (1.1)$$

It will be recognized that, at the ultimate load stage, when the beam is at the point of incipient failure in flexure, it behaves very much as an ordinary reinforced concrete beam. The main difference is that the steel used has very high strength, and requires a very large strain to achieve a high stress level. If it were to be used without being prestressed (and prestrained) in tension, unacceptably large deformation and cracking of the beam would result.

It should be clear that no conclusions concerning the strength of prestressed beams can be formed by study of elastic stresses. Strength prediction requires the development of equations that account for both cracking and nonlinear material characteristics.

1.5   PARTIAL PRESTRESSING

Early designers of prestressed concrete focused on the complete elimination of tensile stresses in members at normal service load. This is defined as *full prestressing*. As experience has been gained with prestressed concrete construction, it has become evident that a solution intermediate between fully prestressed concrete and ordinary reinforced concrete offers many advantages. Such an intermediate solution, in which a controlled amount of concrete tension is permitted at full service load, is termed *partial prestressing*.

Although full prestressing offers the possibility of complete elimination of cracks at full service load, it may at the same time produce members with objectionably large camber, or negative deflection, at more typical loads less than the full value. A smaller amount of prestress force may produce improved deflection characteristics at load stages of interest. While cracks will usually form in partially prestressed beams, should the specified full service load be applied, these cracks are small and will close completely when the load is reduced.

In addition to improved deflection characteristics, partial prestressing may result in significant economy by reducing the amount of prestressed reinforcement, and by permitting use of cross section configurations with certain practical advantages, compared with those required by full prestressing.

Even though the amount of prestress force may be reduced through use of partial prestressing, a beam must still have an adequate factor of safety against failure. This will often require the addition of ordinary unstressed reinforcing bars in the tension zone. Alternatives are to provide the total steel area needed for strength by high strength tendons, but to stress those tendons to less than their full permitted value, or to leave some of the strands unstressed.

Partial prestressing is looked upon with increasing favor in the United States, as it offers the combined advantages of reinforced and prestressed concrete.

1.6   PRESTRESSING METHODS

Although many methods have been used to produce the desired state of precompression in concrete members, all prestressed concrete members can be placed in one of two categories: *pretensioned* or *post-tensioned*. Pretensioned prestressed concrete members are produced by stretching the tendons between external anchorages *before* the concrete is placed. As the fresh concrete hardens it bonds to the steel. When the concrete has reached the required strength, the jacking force is released, and the force is transferred by bond from steel to concrete. In the case of post-tensioned prestressed concrete members, the tendons are stressed *after* the concrete has hardened and achieved sufficient strength, by jacking against the concrete member itself.

A. PRETENSIONING

The greater part of prestressed concrete construction in the United States is pretensioned. The tendons, usually in the form of multiple-wire stranded cables, are stretched between abutments that are a permanent part of the plant facility, as shown in Fig. 1.10a. The extension of the strands is measured, as well as the jacking force.

With the forms in place, the concrete is cast around the stressed tendon. High early strength concrete is often used, together with steam curing to accelerate the hardening of the concrete. After sufficient strength is attained, the jacking pressure is released. The strands tend to shorten, but are prevented from doing so because they are bonded to the concrete. In this way, the pre-stress force is transferred to the concrete by bond, mostly near the ends of the

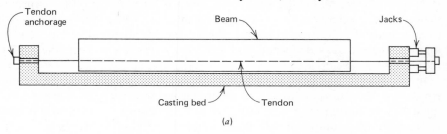

(a)

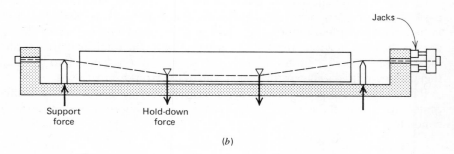

(b)

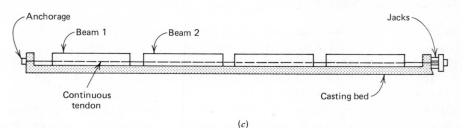

(c)

Figure 1.10 Methods of pretensioning. (a) Beam with straight tendon. (b) Beam with variable tendon eccentricity. (c) Long-line stressing and casting.

Figure 1.15   Post-tensioning a beam using multiple-strand tendons.

An alternative method of post-tensioning is shown in Fig. 1.13*b*. Here a hollow, cellular concrete beam is shown, with solid end blocks and intermediate diaphragms. Anchorage fittings are provided as before, but the tendons pass through the void spaces in the member. The desired cable profile is maintained by passing the steel through sleeves positioned in the intermediate diaphragms.

In many cases, particularly in relatively thin slabs, post-tensioning tendons are asphalt-coated and wrapped with asphalt-impregnated paper, as shown in Fig. 1.13*c*. Anchorage and jacking hardware is provided. The wrapping prevents the concrete from bonding to the steel. When the concrete has hardened, the tendons are stretched and anchored, and the jack removed. Obviously, bonding of the tendon by grouting is impossible with such an arrangement. Figure 1.16 shows a two-way slab under construction, which will be post-tensioned using the wrapped tendons shown in position.

Countless patented systems of post-tensioning are available, along with all necessary hardware. Explicit details of representative systems are found in Appendix B. A significant advantage of all post-tensioning schemes is the ease with which the tendon eccentricity can be varied along the span to provide the desired countermoment.

Figure 1.16 Two-way prestressed slab, using unbonded wrapped tendons, under construction (courtesy Post-Tensioning Institute).

1.7 CHANGES IN PRESTRESS FORCE

The magnitude of prestressing force in a concrete member is not constant, but assumes different values during the life of the member. Some of the changes are instantaneous or nearly so, some are time-dependent, and some are a function of the superimposed loading. All such changes must be accounted for in the design. Neglect of time-dependent losses, in particular, accounts for the lack of success of all early attempts to prestress concrete.

With the exception of conditions at severe overloading, the greatest force that acts is during the jacking operation. The *jacking force* will be referred to subsequently as P_j. For a post-tensioned member, this force is applied as a reaction directly upon the concrete member, while with pretensioning, the jacking force reacts against external anchorages and does not act on the concrete at all.

At the moment of transfer of prestress force from the jack to the anchorage fittings that grip the tendon, there is an immediate reduction in force. There is inevitably a small amount of slip as the wedges or grips seat themselves into the steel tendon, and the shortening of the tendon that results is accompanied by loss in tensile strain and stress. This is always a factor to consider in post-tensioned beams. Corresponding slip loss occurs in pretensioning too, because temporary grips are normally used at the jacking abutment to hold the strand as the concrete is poured. However, in beams pretensioned by the long-line method, slip loss is apt to be insignificant because of the great length of tendon over which the slip is distributed.

There is an instantaneous stress loss because of the elastic shortening of the concrete, as the prestress force is transferred to it. This always occurs in pretensioning, but occurs in post-tensioning only if there are two or more tendons, and if they are tensioned sequentially.

Another source of immediate loss of prestress force, applying to post-tensioned members only, is the friction between the steel and the conduit through which it passes, as the tendon is stretched. The tensile force at the jack will always be larger than that at the far end, where the tendon is anchored. This loss can be minimized by overstretching the steel slightly if necessary, then reducing the jacking force to the desired value. In some cases, tendons are jacked from both ends in order to minimize frictional losses, particularly when the tendon profile has several reversals of curvature.

As a consequence of all instantaneous losses, including those due to anchorage slip, elastic shortening, and friction, the jacking force P_j is reduced to a lower value P_i, defined as the *initial prestress force*.

With the passage of time, the steel stress is further reduced. The changes that cause this reduction occur rather rapidly at first, but the rate of change of stress soon decreases. A nearly constant stress level is approached, but only after many months, or even several years.

The main causes of time-dependent loss are shrinkage of the concrete, and concrete creep under sustained compressive stress. Both of these produce shortening of the member, which results in a reduction in steel strain and stress. In addition, the steel experiences a gradual relaxation of stress, as it is held at nearly constant strain. The result of all time-dependent effects, including concrete shrinkage and creep and steel relaxation, is that the initial prestress force is gradually reduced to what will be termed the *effective prestress force P_e*.

The sum of all losses, immediate and time-dependent, may be of the order of 20 to 35 percent of the original jacking force. All losses must be accounted for in the design of prestressed concrete. They will be examined in detail in Ch. 6.

Loading of a prestressed beam will generally produce an *increase* in stress in the tendon. As long as the member remains uncracked, the increase is so small that it is usually neglected in design. However, cracking of the concrete is accompanied by an instantaneous increase in steel stress, as the tensile force formerly carried by the concrete is transferred to the steel. If the load is increased further, the member behaves much as ordinary reinforced concrete, and the steel stress increases roughly in proportion to the load until the nonlinear range of material behavior is reached, followed by eventual failure. The steel may reach its ultimate tensile strength at failure, although this is not necessarily so.

1.8 LOADS, STRENGTH, AND STRUCTURAL SAFETY

A. LOADS

Loads that act on structures are usually classified as *dead loads* or *live loads*. Dead loads are fixed in location and constant in magnitude throughout the life of the structure. Usually the *self-weight* of a structure is the most important part of the dead load. This can be calculated closely, based on the dimensions of the structure and the unit weight of the material. Concrete density varies from about 90 to 120 pcf (14 to 19 kN/m^3) for lightweight concrete, and is about 145 pcf (23 kN/m^3) for normal concrete. In calculating the dead load of structural concrete, usually a 5 pcf (1 kN/m^3) increment is included with the weight of the concrete to account for the presence of the reinforcement.

Live loads are loads such as occupancy, snow, wind, or traffic loads, or seismic forces. They may be either fully or partially in place, or not present at all. They may also change in location.

Although it is the responsibility of the engineer to calculate dead loads, live loads are usually specified by local, regional, or national codes and specifications. Typical sources are the publications of the American National Standards Institute (ANSI, Ref. 1.1), the American Association of State Highway and Transportation Officials (AASHTO, Ref. 1.2) and, for wind loads, the recommendations of the ASCE Task Committee on Wind Forces (Ref. 1.3). Floor live loads and roof snow loads from Ref. 1.1 are presented in Table 1.1 and Fig. 1.17. More detailed information will be found in the excellent summary of structural loads in Ref. 1.4.

Specified live loads usually include some allowance for overload, and may include dynamic effects, explicitly or implicitly. Live loads can be controlled to some extent by measures such as posting of maximum loads for floors or bridges, but there can be no certainty that such loads will not be exceeded. It is often important to distinguish between the *specified load*, and what is termed the *characteristic load*, that is, the load that actually is in effect under normal conditions of service, which may be significantly less. In estimating the long-term deflection of a structure, for example, it is the characteristic load that is important, not the specified load.

The sum of the calculated dead load and the specified live load is called the *service load*, because this is the maximum load which may reasonably be expected to act during the service life of the structure. The *factored load*, or failure load which a structure must just be capable of resisting is a multiple of the service load.

B. STRENGTH

The strength of a structure depends on the strength of the materials from which it is made. Minimum material strengths are specified in certain, standardized ways. The properties of concrete and its components, the methods of mixing,

Table 1.1 Minimum Uniformly Distributed Live Loads (from Ref. 1.1, courtesy of American National Standards Institute)

Occupancy or Use	Live Load	
	psf	kN/m²
Apartments (see Residential)		
Armories and drill rooms	150	7.2
Assembly halls and other places of assembly:		
Fixed seats	60	2.9
Movable seats	100	4.8
Balcony (exterior)	100	4.8
Bowling alleys, poolrooms, and similar recreational areas	75	3.6
Corridors:		
First floor	100	4.8
Other floors, same as occupancy served except as indicated		
Dance halls	100	4.8
Dining rooms and restaurants	100	4.8
Dwellings (see Residential)		
Garages (passenger cars)	100	4.8
Floors shall be designed to carry 150 percent of the maximum wheel load anywhere on the floor.		
Grandstands (see Reviewing stands)		
Gymnasiums, main floors, and balconies	100	4.8
Hospitals:		
Operating rooms	60	2.9
Private rooms	40	1.9
Wards	40	1.9
Hotels (see Residential)		
Libraries:		
Reading rooms	60	2.9
Stack rooms	150	7.2
Manufacturing	125	6.0
Marquees	75	3.6
Office buildings:		
Offices	80	3.8
Lobbies	100	4.8
Penal institutions:		
Cell blocks	40	1.9
Corridors	100	4.8
Residential:		
Multifamily houses:		
Private apartments	40	1.9

Table 1.1 (*cont.*)

Occupancy or Use	Live Load psf	Live Load kN/m²
Public rooms	100	4.8
Corridors	60	2.9
Dwellings:		
First floor	40	1.9
Second floor and habitable attics	30	1.4
Uninhabitable attics	20	1.0
Hotels:		
Guest rooms	40	1.9
Public rooms	100	4.8
Corridors serving public rooms	100	4.8
Public corridors	60	2.9
Private corridors	40	1.9
Reviewing stands and bleachers	100	4.8
Schools:		
Classrooms	40	1.9
Corridors	100	4.8
Sidewalks, vehicular driveways, and yards subject to trucking	250	12.0
Skating rinks	100	4.8
Stairs, fire escapes, and exitways	100	4.8
Storage warehouse:		
Light	125	6.0
Heavy	250	12.0
Stores:		
Retail:		
First floor, rooms	100	4.8
Upper floors	75	3.6
Wholesale	125	6.0
Theaters:		
Aisles, corridors, and lobbies	100	4.8
Orchestra floors	60	2.9
Balconies	60	2.9
Stage floors	150	7.2
Yards and terraces, pedestrians	100	4.8

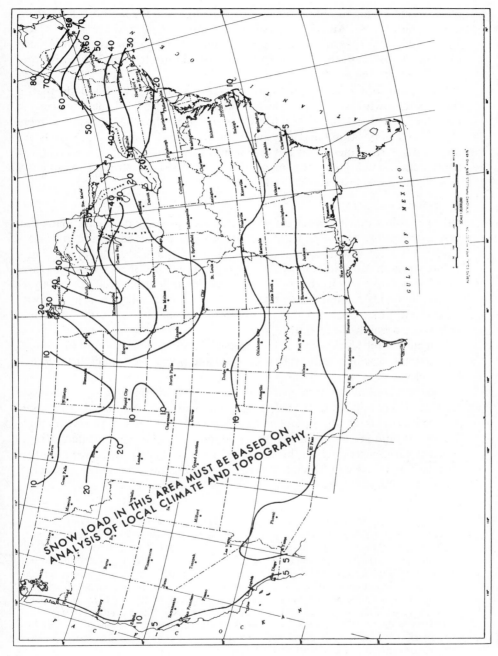

Figure 1.17 Estimated weight of seasonal snowpack (psf) equaled or exceeded one year in ten (from Ref. 1.1, courtesy of American National Standards Institute).

placing, and curing to obtain the required quality, and the methods for testing, are specified by the American Concrete Institute (ACI)* and are given in Ref. 1.5. Included by reference in the same document are standards of the American Society for Testing Materials (ASTM) pertaining to reinforcing and prestressing steels and concrete.

Strength also depends on the care with which the structure is built, that is, the accuracy with which the drawings and specifications of the engineer are followed. Member sizes may differ from specified dimensions, reinforcement may be out of position, or poor placement of concrete may result in voids. An important part of the job of the engineer is to provide proper supervision of construction. Slighting of this responsibility has had disastrous consequences in more than one instance (Ref. 1.7).

C. STRUCTURAL SAFETY

Safety requires that the strength of a structure be adequate for all loads that may conceivably act on it. If strength could be predicted accurately and if loads were known with equal certainty, then safety could be assured by providing strength just barely in excess of the requirements of the loads. But there are many sources of uncertainty in the estimation of loads as well as in analysis, design, and construction. These uncertainties require a safety margin.

In recent years engineers have come to realize that the matter of structural safety is probabilistic in nature, and the safety provisions of many current specifications reflect this view. The approach to safety that is found in the ACI Code (Ref. 1.5), which pertains to reinforced and prestressed concrete buildings, is as follows.

Separate consideration is given to loads and strength. *Load factors*, larger than unity, are applied to the calculated dead loads and estimated or specified service live loads, to obtain *factored loads* that the member must just be capable of sustaining at incipient failure. Load factors pertaining to different types of loads vary, depending on the degree of uncertainty associated with loads of various types, and with the likelihood of simultaneous occurrence of different loads. A summary of the ACI load factors is presented in Table 1.2.

---

* Throughout this text repeated reference will be made to the American Concrete Institute and its recommendations. As one part of its activity, the American Concrete Institute has published the *Building Code Requirements for Reinforced Concrete* (ACI 318–77) that serves as a guide in the design and construction of reinforced and prestressed concrete buildings. The Code has no official status in itself. However, it is generally regarded as an authoritative statement of current good practice. As a result it has been incorporated by law into countless municipal and regional building codes that do have legal status, and its provisions thereby attain, in effect, legal significance. Most structural concrete in the United States and in many other countries is designed in accordance with the ACI Building Code and its current amendments. A second publication, *Commentary on Building Code Requirements for Reinforced Concrete* (ACI 318–77C) provides background material and rationale for the Code provisions (Ref. 1.6).

Table 1.2 Load Factors from ACI Code[a]

1. The required strength U to resist dead load D and live load L shall be at least equal to

$$U = 1.4D + 1.7L \qquad \text{(ACI 9-1)}$$

2. If resistance to structural effects of a specified wind load W are included in design, the following combinations of D, L, and W shall be investigated to determine the greatest required strength U:

$$U = 0.75(1.4D + 1.7L + 1.7W) \qquad \text{(ACI 9-2)}$$

   where load combinations shall include both full value and zero value of L to determine the more severe condition, and

$$U = 0.9D + 1.3W \qquad \text{(ACI 9-3)}$$

   but for any combination of D, L, and W the required strength U shall not be less than Eq. (ACI 9-1).

3. If resistance to specified earthquake loads or forces E are included in design, load combinations of Section 2 shall apply, except that $1.1E$ shall be substituted for W.

4. If resistance to lateral earth pressure H is included in design, the required strength U shall be at least equal to

$$U = 1.4D + 1.7L + 1.7H \qquad \text{(ACI 9-4)}$$

   and where D or L reduce the effect of H, the following combinations of D, L, and H shall be investigated to determine the greatest required strength U:

D opposing H:	$U = 0.9D + 1.7L + 1.7H$	(ACI 9-5)
L opposing H:	$U = 1.4D + 1.7H$	(ACI 9-6)
D and L opposing H:	$U = 0.9D + 1.7H$	(ACI 9-7)

   but for any combination of D, L, and H the required strength U shall not be less than Eq. (ACI 9-1).

5. If resistance to lateral liquid pressure F is included in design, the load combination of Section 4 shall apply, except that $1.4F$ shall be substituted for $1.7H$. Vertical liquid pressure shall be considered as dead load D, with due regard to variation in liquid depth.

6. If resistance to impact effects are included in design, such effects shall be included with live load L.

Table 1.2 (*cont.*)

7. Where structural effects T of differential settlement, creep, shrinkage, or temperature change may be significant in design, the required strength U shall be at least equal to

$$U = 0.75(1.4D + 1.4T + 1.7L) \qquad \text{(ACI 9-8)}$$

but the required strength U shall not be less than

$$U = 1.4(D + T) \qquad \text{(ACI 9-9)}$$

Estimations of differential settlement, creep, shrinkage, or temperature change shall be based on a realistic assessment of such effects occurring in service.

[a] Adapted with permission of the American Concrete Institute from ACI Building Code 318–77.

Table 1.3 Strength Reduction Factors from ACI Code[a]

Kind of Stress	Strength Reduction Factor ϕ
Flexural, with or without axial tension	0.90
Axial tension	0.90
Axial compression, with or without flexure:	
Members with spiral reinforcement	0.75
Other reinforced members	0.70
except that for low values of axial load, ϕ may be increased in accordance with the following:	
For members in which f_y does not exceed 60,000 psi, with symmetrical reinforcement, and with $(h - d' - d_s)/h$ not less than 0.70, ϕ may be increased linearly to 0.90 as ϕP_n decreases from $0.10 f'_c A_g$ to zero.	
For other reinforced members, ϕ may be increased linearly to 0.90 as ϕP_n decreases from $0.10 f'_c A_g$ or ϕP_{nb} whichever is smaller, to zero.	
Shear and torsion	0.85
Bearing on concrete	0.70
Flexure in plain concrete	0.65

[a] Adapted with permission of the American Concrete Institute from ACI Building Code 318–77.

The *required strength*, should the structure be overloaded, must not exceed a conservative estimate of the actual strength of the structure. To obtain that estimate, the *nominal strength* of the structure is calculated according to the best current knowledge of structural behavior and material strength. That *nominal strength* is reduced by applying a *strength reduction factor* ϕ to obtain what is called the *design strength*. Thus:

$$M_u \leq \phi M_n$$
$$P_u \leq \phi P_n$$
$$V_u \leq \phi V_n$$

for example, where the subscripts n are associated with nominal strengths in bending, axial thrust, and shear, and the subscripts u are associated with required strengths, determined at factored loads.

The value of ϕ to be applied varies depending on several things, including the probable variation of material strengths, the particular mode of failure and how well it can be predicted, the nature of the failure should it occur, the importance of dimensional inaccuracies for the particular type of member, and the consequences of failure. Values of strength reduction factors specified in the ACI Code, for various circumstances, are summarized in Table 1.3. These provisions and those for load factors are based to some extent on statistical information, but to a much larger degree on engineering experience, intuition, and judgment.

REFERENCES

1.1 *Building Code Requirements for Minimum Design Loads in Buildings and Other Structures*, ANSI A58.1–1972, American National Standards Institute, New York, 1972.

1.2 *Standard Specifications for Highway Bridges*, 11th ed., American Association of State Highway and Transportion Officials, Washington, D.C., 1973.

1.3 *Wind Forces on Structures*, Task Committee on Wind Forces, Committee on Loads and Stresses, Structural Division, ASCE, *Trans. ASCE*, Vol. 126, 1961, pp. 1124–1198.

1.4 McGuire, William, *Steel Structures*, Prentice-Hall., Englewood Cliffs, New Jersey, 1968.

1.5 *Building Code Requirements for Reinforced Concrete* (ACI 318–77), American Concrete Institute, Detroit, 1977.

1.6 *Commentary on Building Code Requirements for Reinforced Concrete* (ACI 318–77C), American Concrete Institute, Detroit, 1977.

1.7 Feld, Jacob, *Lessons from Failures of Concrete Structures*, American Concrete Institute, Detroit, and the Iowa State University Press, Ames, 1964.

1.8 Cornell, C. Allin, "A Probability-Based Structural Code," *J. ACI*, Vol. 66, No. 12, December 1969, pp. 974–985.

1.9 Winter, George and Nilson, Arthur H., *Design of Concrete Structures*, 8th ed., McGraw-Hill, New York, 1972, 615 pp.

CHAPTER 2
MATERIALS

2.1 INTRODUCTION

The structures and component members to be considered are composed of concrete, prestressed with steel tendons. Supplemental non-prestressed reinforcement is also used for various purposes. Although the general characteristics of the materials are well known to students of structural engineering and to practicing engineers, certain special properties are of profound significance in the design of prestressed concrete. Indeed, it was the failure to consider some of these special properties that accounted for lack of success of all early efforts to prestress concrete. For example, it was only after Freyssinet established the significance of time-dependent shrinkage and creep of concrete that prestressed structures could be built successfully.

The use of very high strength steel for prestressing is necessary for basic physical reasons. The mechanical properties of this steel, as disclosed by stress-strain curves, are quite different from those of the steel used for ordinary reinforced concrete. In addition to the higher strength, the designer must account for differences in ductility, lack of a well-defined yield point, and other characteristics of great engineering significance.

Ordinary bar reinforcement, of the same type used for nonprestressed structures, also plays an important role in prestressed construction. It is used for web reinforcement, supplementary longitudinal reinforcement, and other purposes.

The concrete used in prestressed members is characteristically of higher strength than that used for non-prestressed structures. Differences in elastic modulus, strain capacity, and strength must be accounted for in design, and time-dependent characteristics assume crucial importance.

The increasing use of lightweight concrete in recent years has permitted reduction of dead loads, a matter of special significance in concrete structures, and has facilitated handling of large precast structural components. Advances in concrete technology have resulted in the development of lightweight aggregate concrete of strength comparable to normal density material. Its deformational characteristics, including time-dependent effects, must be fully understood before it can be used with confidence.

The following articles present engineering information pertaining to these materials.

31

2.2 IMPORTANCE OF HIGH STRENGTH STEEL

The reason for the lack of success of most early attempts to prestress concrete was the failure to employ steel at a sufficiently high stress and strain. The time-dependent length changes permitted by shrinkage and creep of the concrete were such as to completely relieve the steel of stress. The importance of high initial strain, and corresponding high initial stress, in the steel can be shown by a simple example.

Shown in Fig. 2.1(a) is a short concrete member that is to be axially prestressed using a steel tendon. In the unstressed state the concrete has length l_c and the unstressed steel has length l_s. After tensioning of the steel and transfer of force to the concrete through the end anchorages, the length of the concrete is shortened to l'_c and the length of the stretched steel is l'_s. These values must, of course, be identical, as indicated by the figure.

But the concrete experiences a shrinkage strain ε_{sh} with the passage of time and, in addition, if held under compression will suffer a creep strain ε_{cu}. The total length change in the member

$$\Delta l_c = (\varepsilon_{sh} + \varepsilon_{cu})l_c \tag{a}$$

may be such that it exceeds the stretch in the steel that produced the initial stress, and complete loss of prestress force will result.

The importance of shrinkage and creep strain can be minimized by using a very high initial strain and high initial stress in the steel. This is so because the reduction in steel stress from these causes depends only on the unit strains in the concrete associated with shrinkage and creep, and the elastic modulus

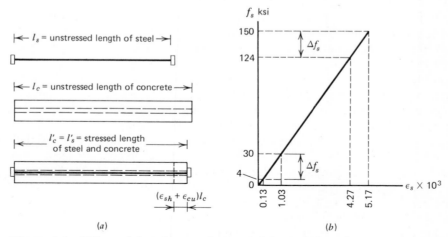

(a)   (b)

Figure 2.1 Effect of shrinkage and creep of concrete in reducing prestress force. (a) Axially prestressed concrete member. (b) Stress in steel.

E_s of the steel:

$$\Delta f_s = (\varepsilon_{sh} + \varepsilon_{cu})E_s \tag{b}$$

and is independent of the initial steel stress.

It is informative to study the results of calculations for representative values of the various parameters. Suppose first that the member is prestressed using ordinary reinforcing steel at an initial stress f_{si} of 30 ksi. The modulus of elasticity E_s for all steels is about the same and will be taken here as 29,000 ksi. The initial strain in the steel is

$$\varepsilon_{si} = \frac{f_{si}}{E_s} = \frac{30}{29,000} = 1.03 \times 10^{-3}$$

and the total steel elongation is

$$\varepsilon_s l_s = 1.03 \times 10^{-3} l_s \tag{c}$$

But a conservative estimate of the sum of shrinkage and creep strain in the concrete is about 0.90×10^{-3} and the corresponding length change is

$$(\varepsilon_{sh} + \varepsilon_{cu})l_c = 0.90 \times 10^{-3} l_c \tag{d}$$

Since l_s and l_c are nearly the same, it is clear by comparing (c) and (d) that the combined effects of shrinkage and creep of the concrete is almost a complete loss of stress in the steel. The effective steel stress remaining after time-dependent effects would be

$$f_{se} = (1.03 - 0.90) \times 10^{-3} \times 29 \times 10^3 = 4 \text{ ksi}$$

Alternatively, suppose that the prestress were applied using high strength steel at an initial stress of 150 ksi. In this case the initial strain would be

$$\varepsilon_{si} = \frac{150}{29,000} = 5.17 \times 10^{-3} \tag{e}$$

and the total elongation

$$\varepsilon_s l_s = 5.17 \times 10^{-3} l_s \tag{f}$$

The length change due to the shrinkage and creep effects would be the same as before

$$(\varepsilon_{sh} + \varepsilon_{cu})l_c = 0.90 \times 10^{-3} l_c$$

and the effective steel stress f_{se} after losses due to shrinkage and creep would be

$$f_{se} = (5.17 - 0.90) 10^{-3} \times 29 \times 10^3 = 124 \text{ ksi}$$

The loss is about 17 percent of the initial steel stress in this case, compared with 87 percent loss when mild steel was used.

The results of these calculations are shown graphically by Fig. 2.1b and illustrate clearly the need in prestressing for using steel that is capable of a very high initial stress.

2.3 TYPES OF PRESTRESSING STEEL

There are three common forms in which steel is used for prestressed concrete tendons: cold-drawn round wires, stranded cable, and alloy steel bars. Wire and strand have a tensile strength of about 250,000 psi (1720 N/mm^2), while the strength of alloy bars is between 145,000 psi and 160,000 psi (1000 N/mm^2 and 1100 N/mm^2) depending on the grade.

A. ROUND WIRES

The round wires used for post-tensioned prestressed concrete construction and occasionally for pretensioned work are manufactured to meet the requirements of ASTM Specification A 421, "Uncoated Stress-Relieved Wire for Prestressed Concrete." The individual wires are manufactured by hot-rolling steel billets into round rods. After cooling, the rods are passed through dies to reduce their diameter to the required size. In the process of this drawing operation, cold work is done on the steel, greatly modifying its mechanical properties and increasing its strength. The wires are stress-relieved after cold drawing by a continuous heat treatment to produce the prescribed mechanical properties.

Wires are available in four diameters as shown in Table 2.1 and in two types. Type BA wire is used for applications in which cold-end deformation is used for anchoring purposes (button anchorage), and type WA is used for applications in which the ends are anchored by wedges and no cold-end deformation of the wire is involved (wedge anchorage). Examples of tendons with button anchorages, more common in United States practice, are shown in Appendix B.

Low-relaxation wire, sometimes known as stabilized, is also available on special order. It is used when it is desirable to reduce loss of prestress to the minimum.

Tendons are normally composed of groups of wires, the number of wires in each group depending on the particular system used and the magnitude of

Table 2.1 Properties of Uncoated Stress-Relieved Wire (ASTM A 421)

Nominal Diameter in. (mm)	Minimum Tensile Strength psi (N/mm^2)		Minimum Stress at 1% Extension psi (N/mm^2)	
	Type BA	Type WA	Type BA	Type WA
0.192 (4.88)	[a]	250,000 (1725)	[a]	200,000 (1380)
0.196 (4.98)	240,000 (1655)	250,000 (1725)	192,000 (1325)	200,000 (1380)
0.250 (6.35)	240,000 (1655)	240,000 (1655)	192,000 (1325)	192,000 (1325)
0.276 (7.01)	[a]	235,000 (1622)	[a]	188,000 (1295)

[a] These sizes are not commonly furnished in Type BA wire.

prestress force required. Typical prefabricated post-tensioning tendons may consist of 8 to 52 individual wires. Multiple tendons, each composed of groups of wires, may be used to meet requirements.

B. STRANDED CABLE

Stranded cable is almost always used for pretensioned members, and is often used for post-tensioned construction as well. Strand is manufactured to ASTM Specification A 416, "Uncoated Seven-Wire Stress-Relieved Strand for Prestressed Concrete." It is fabricated with six wires wound tightly around a seventh of slightly larger diameter. The pitch of the spiral winding is between 12 and 16 times the nominal diameter of the strand.

The same type of cold-drawn stress-relieved wire is used in making stranded cable as is used for individual prestressing wires. However, the apparent mechanical properties are slightly different because of the tendency for the stranded wires to straighten when subjected to tension because the axis of the wires does not coincide with the direction of tension. Cable is stress-relieved by heat treatment after stranding. Low-relaxation or stabilized strand is available on special order.

Strands may be obtained in a range of sizes from 0.250 in. to 0.600 in. diameter, as shown in Table 2.2. Two grades are manufactured: Grade 250 and

Table 2.2 Properties of Uncoated Seven-Wire Stress-Relieved Strand (ASTM A 416)

Nominal Diameter in. (mm)	Breaking Strength lb (kN)	Nominal Area of Strand in.^{2} (mm^2)	Minimum Load at 1% Extension lb (kN)
Grade 250			
0.250 (6.35)	9000 (40.0)	0.036 (23.22)	7650 (34.0)
0.313 (7.94)	14,500 (64.5)	0.058 (37.42)	12,300 (54.7)
0.375 (9.53)	20,000 (89.0)	0.080 (51.61)	17,000 (75.6)
0.438 (11.11)	27,000 (120.1)	0.108 (69.68)	23,000 (102.3)
0.500 (12.70)	36,000 (160.1)	0.144 (92.90)	30,600 (136.2)
0.600 (15.24)	54,000 (240.2)	0.216 (139.35)	45,900 (204.2)
Grade 270			
0.375 (9.53)	23,000 (102.3)	0.085 (54.84)	19,550 (87.0)
0.438 (11.11)	31,000 (137.9)	0.115 (74.19)	26,350 (117.2)
0.500 (12.70)	41,300 (183.7)	0.153 (98.71)	35,100 (156.1)
0.600 (15.24)	58,600 (260.7)	0.217 (140.00)	49,800 (221.5)

Grade 270 have minimum ultimate strengths of 250,000 and 270,000 psi (1720 and 1860 N/mm²) respectively, based on the nominal area of the strand.

C. ALLOY STEEL BARS

In the case of alloy steel bars, the required high strength is obtained by introducing certain alloying elements, mainly manganese, silicon, and chromium, during the manufacture of the steel. In addition, cold work is done in making the bars, further increasing the strength. After cold-stretching, the bars are stress-relieved to obtain the required properties. Bars are manufactured to meet the requirements of ASTM Specification A 722, "Uncoated High-Strength Steel Bar for Prestressing Concrete."

Alloy steel bars are available in diameters ranging from $\frac{1}{2}$ in. to $1\frac{3}{8}$ in., as shown in Table 2.3, and in two grades, Grade 145 and Grade 160, corresponding to the minimum ultimate strengths of 145,000 and 160,000 psi (1000 and 1100 N/mm²), respectively.

Table 2.3   Properties of Alloy Steel Bars

Nominal Diameter in. (mm)	Nominal Area of Bar in.² (mm²)	Breaking Strength lb (kN)	Minimum Load at 0.7% Extension lb (kN)
		Grade 145	
$\frac{1}{2}$ (12.70)	0.196 (127)	28,000 (125)	25,000 (111)
$\frac{5}{8}$ (15.88)	0.307 (198)	45,000 (200)	40,000 (178)
$\frac{3}{4}$ (19.05)	0.442 (285)	64,000 (285)	58,000 (258)
$\frac{7}{8}$ (22.23)	0.601 (388)	87,000 (387)	78,000 (347)
1 (25.40)	0.785 (507)	114,000 (507)	102,000 (454)
$1\frac{1}{8}$ (28.58)	0.994 (642)	144,000 (641)	129,000 (574)
$1\frac{1}{4}$ (31.75)	1.227 (792)	178,000 (792)	160,000 (712)
$1\frac{3}{8}$ (34.93)	1.485 (958)	215,000 (957)	193,000 (859)
		Grade 160	
$\frac{1}{2}$ (12.70)	0.196 (127)	31,000 (138)	27,000 (120)
$\frac{5}{8}$ (15.88)	0.307 (198)	49,000 (218)	43,000 (191)
$\frac{3}{4}$ (19.05)	0.442 (285)	71,000 (316)	62,000 (276)
$\frac{7}{8}$ (22.23)	0.601 (388)	96,000 (427)	84,000 (374)
1 (25.40)	0.785 (507)	126,000 (561)	110,000 (490)
$1\frac{1}{8}$ (28.58)	0.994 (642)	159,000 (708)	139,000 (619)
$1\frac{1}{4}$ (31.75)	1.227 (792)	196,000 (872)	172,000 (765)
$1\frac{3}{8}$ (34.93)	1.485 (958)	238,000 (1059)	208,000 (926)

2.4   NON-PRESTRESSED REINFORCEMENT

Non-prestressed steel has several important applications in prestressed concrete construction. Although web reinforcement for diagonal tensile stress (see Ch. 5) may be prestressed, ordinarily it is non-prestressed bar steel. Supplementary non-prestressed reinforcement is commonly used in the region of high local compressive stress at the anchorages of post-tensioned beams. For both pre-tensioned and post-tensioned members, it is common to provide longitudinal bar steel to control shrinkage and temperature cracking. Overhanging flanges of T- and I-shaped cross sections are normally reinforced in both the transverse and longitudinal directions with nontensioned bars. Finally, it is often con-venient to increase the flexural strength of prestressed beams using supple-mentary longitudinal bar reinforcement.

Such non-prestressed reinforcing bars, which are identical to those used for ordinary reinforced concrete construction, are manufactured to meet the re-quirements of ASTM Specification A 615, "Deformed and Plain Billet-Steel Bars for Concrete Reinforcement," A 616, "Rail Steel Deformed and Plain Bars for Concrete Reinforcement, or A 617, "Axle Steel Deformed and Plain Bars for Concrete Reinforcement." Bars are available in nominal diameters from $\frac{3}{8}$ to $1\frac{3}{8}$ in., in $\frac{1}{8}$ in. increments, and also in two larger sizes of about $1\frac{3}{4}$ and $2\frac{1}{4}$ in. diameter. They are generally referred to by number, the number corresponding to the number of eighth inches in the nominal bar diameter; for example, a No. 7 bar has nominal diameter of $\frac{7}{8}$ in.

In order to identify bars that meet the requirements of the ASTM Specifica-tions, distinguishing marks are rolled into the surface of one side of the bar to denote: (a) the point of origin (the producer's mill designation), (b) the size designation by number, (c) the type of steel (N for billet steel, a rail symbol for rail steel, or A for axle steel), and (d) in the case of Grade 60 bars either the number 60 or a single continuous longitudinal line through at least five spaces offset from the center of the bar side.

In the case of bar reinforcement, it is important that steel and concrete deform together, that is, that there be a sufficiently strong bond between the two ma-terials so that little or no relative movement can occur. This bond is provided by the relatively large chemical adhesion that develops at the steel-concrete interface, by the natural roughness of the mill scale on hot-rolled reinforcement, and by closely spaced rib-shaped surface deformations with which bars are furnished in order to provide a high degree of interlocking of the two materials. Minimum requirements for these deformations have been developed in experi-mental research and are described in the ASTM specifications. Different bar producers use different patterns to satisfy these requirements.

Bars are available in different strengths. Grades 40, 50, and 60 have specified minimum yields strengths of 40,000, 50,000, and 60,000 psi, respectively (276,

345, and 414 N/mm²). The present trend is toward use of Grade 60 bars. Large diameter bars with 75,000 and 90,000 psi (517 and 621 N/mm²) yield are available on special order, although they find little application in prestressed concrete members.

Apart from single reinforcing bars, welded wire mesh is often used for reinforcing slabs, beam flanges, and other surfaces such as shells. The mesh consists of longitudinal and transverse cold-drawn steel wires, at right angles, welded at all points of intersection. Mesh is available with wire spacings from 2 to 12 in. and wire diameters from 0.080 to 0.628 in., although all combinations are not readily available. The size and spacing of the wires may be the same in both directions or may be different as needed. The steel wire and the wire mesh must meet the requirements of ASTM Specifications A 82, "Cold-Drawn Steel Wire for Concrete Reinforcement," and A 185, "Welded Steel Wire Fabric for Concrete Reinforcement."

Table 2.4 lists all commonly available reinforcing steels, including wire mesh, with information on yield stress and tensile strength. Further information pertaining to bar steel and mesh will be found in Appendix A.

Table 2.4 Non-Prestressed Reinforcement

Type	Grade or Size	Specified Minimum Yield Strength psi (N/mm²)	Tensile Strength psi (N/mm²)
Billet steel and axle steel bars	40	40,000 (276)	70,000 (483)
	60	60,000 (414)	90,000 (621)
Rail steel bars	50	50,000 (345)	80,000 (552)
	60	60,000 (414)	90,000 (621)
Cold-drawn wire		70,000 (483)	80,000 (552)
Welded wire mesh	W1.2 and larger	65,000 (448)	75,000 (517)
	Smaller than W1.2	56,000 (386)	70,000 (483)

2.5   STRESS-STRAIN PROPERTIES OF STEEL

Most of the mechanical properties for steels of interest to the design engineer can be read directly from their stress-strain curves. Such important characteristics as proportional elastic limit, yield point, strength, ductility, and strain hardening properties are immediately evident.

It is instructive to compare, in general terms, the tensile stress-strain curves for ordinary bar reinforcement and for typical prestressing steels, as in Fig. 2.2. The most striking differences are the much higher proportional elastic limit and strength available in the round wires and alloy bars used for prestressing, and the substantially lower ductility.

For ordinary reinforcing steel, typified here by Grades 40 and 60, there is an initial elastic response up to a sharply defined yield point, beyond which there is a substantial increase in strain without an accompanying increase in stress. If the load is increased, this yield plateau is followed by a region of strain hardening, during which a very nonlinear relation between stress and strain is obtained. Eventually, rupture of the material will occur, at a rather large tensile strain of about 13 percent for Grade 60 bars and 20 percent for Grade 40 bars.

The contrast provided by prestressing steels is striking. They show no well-defined yield stress. The proportional limit for round wires (and for strand made up of such wires) is about 200 ksi, five times the yield point for Grade 40 bars. With further loading, the wires show gradual yielding, but the curve continues to rise monotonically until the steel fractures. The failure stress for the wire shown is 250 ksi (1720 N/mm²), almost four times that for Grade 40 bars, but the strain at failure is only one third as great. Alloy bars have characteristics

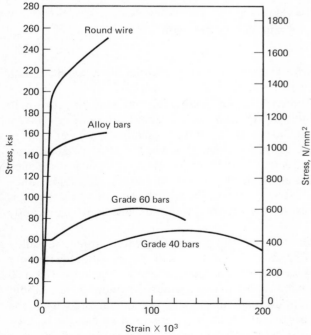

Figure 2.2   Comparative stress-strain curves for reinforcing steel and prestressing steel.

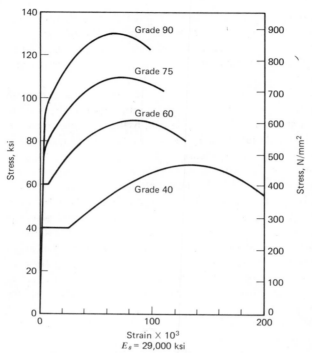

Stress, ksi

Stress, N/mm²

Strain × 10³
E_s = 29,000 ksi

Figure 2.3 Typical stress-strain curves for non-tensioned reinforcing bars.

similar to those of round wire or strand, but the proportional limit and strength are 30 to 40 percent less.

More detailed stress-strain curves for reinforcing bar steel are shown in Fig. 2.3. The elastic modulus for all such steels is about the same: 29,000 ksi (200,000 N/mm²). Although Grades 40 and 60 steels usually show a well-defined yield point, this is not so for the higher strength steels. For such cases, an equivalent yield point is defined as that stress at which the total strain is a specified amount: 0.5 percent for bars of Grades 40, 50, and 60, and 0.6 percent for Grade 75 bars. All grades show extensive strain hardening after the yield stress is reached. Ductility, as measured by the total strain at failure, is significantly less for the higher grades.

Detailed stress-strain curves for typical prestressing wires, strand, and alloy bars are given in Fig. 2.4. For smooth round wires the elastic modulus is about the same as for ordinary reinforcement, that is, about 29,000 ksi (200,000 N/mm²). For stranded cable, the apparent modulus is somewhat less, about 27,000 ksi (186,000 N/mm²), although the strand is manufactured from the same wire. This happens because the spiral-wound strand tends to straighten slightly as the cable is loaded in tension. The modulus for cables embedded in

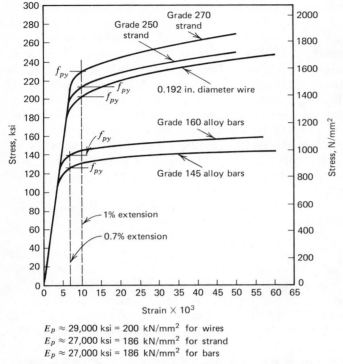

$E_p \approx$ 29,000 ksi = 200 kN/mm² for wires
$E_p \approx$ 27,000 ksi = 186 kN/mm² for strand
$E_p \approx$ 27,000 ksi = 186 kN/mm² for bars

Figure 2.4   Typical stress-strain curves for prestressing steels.

concrete may be closer to that for round wires. The elastic modulus for alloy bars is also about 27,000 ksi (186,000 N/mm²), the reduction in this case occurring because of the presence of alloying elements.

In the absence of a well-defined yield stress for prestressing steels of all types, it is necessary to adopt arbitrary definitions of yielding. For wire and strand, the yield stress is defined as the stress at which a total extension of 1 percent is attained. For alloy bars, the yield stress is taken as equal to the stress producing an extension of 0.7 percent. These values are shown in Fig. 2.4.

2.6   STEEL RELAXATION

When prestressing steel is stressed to the levels that are customary during initial tensioning and at service loads, it exhibits a property known as *relaxation*. Relaxation is defined as the loss of stress in a stressed material held at constant length. (The same basic phenomenon is known as *creep* when defined in terms of change in length of a material under constant stress.) In prestressed concrete members, creep and shrinkage of the concrete as well as fluctuations in super-imposed load cause changes in tendon length. However, in evaluating loss of steel stress as a result of relaxation, the length may be considered constant.

Relaxation is not a short-lived phenomenon. From available evidence it appears to continue almost indefinitely, although at a diminishing rate. It must be accounted for in design because it produces significant loss of prestress force.

The amount of relaxation varies depending on the type and grade of steel, but the most significant parameters are time and intensity of the initial stress. Analysis of the results of many experimental investigations, some exceeding nine years duration, has produced the information presented graphically in Fig. 2.5, in which f_p is the final stress after t hours, f_{pi} is the initial stress, and f_{py} is the yield stress. The yield stress may be taken equal to the effective yield stress as defined in Art. 2.5.

The information shown in Fig. 2.5 may be approximated with satisfactory accuracy by the following expression.

$$\frac{f_p}{f_{pi}} = 1 - \frac{\log t}{10}\left(\frac{f_{pi}}{f_{py}} - 0.55\right) \tag{2.1}$$

where $\log t$ is to the base 10, and f_{pi}/f_{py} is not less than 0.55 (Ref. 2.1).

The tests on which Fig. 2.5 and Eq. (2.1) are based were all carried out on round stress-relieved wires. The results are equally applicable to stress-relieved strand and in the absence of other information may also be applied to alloy steel bars.

In the case of pretensioned members, the relaxation loss occurring before release (transfer of force to the concrete) should be substracted from the total relaxation loss predicted for the effective stress at release. For example, if the

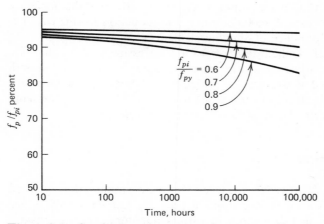

Figure 2.5   Steel relaxation curves for stress-relieved wire and strand (after Ref. 2.1).

stress is to be estimated at time t_n, the wire tensioned at time zero, and released at time t_r, then Eq. (2.1) may be modified as follows:

$$\frac{f_p}{f_{pi}} = 1 - \left(\frac{\log t_n - \log t_r}{10}\right)\left(\frac{f_{pi}}{f_{py}} - 0.55\right) \tag{2.2}$$

The term f_{pi} may be taken as the steel stress at release.

In some cases relaxation losses have been reduced by prestretching, a technique by which the stress in the steel is increased to a level higher than the intended initial stress, held at that level for a short period of time, and then reduced to the intended initial stress. However, since the practical level of initial stress is about 70 percent of the strength of the steel, it is not feasible to overstress by more than about 15 percent. On the basis of available evidence (Ref. 2.1) it appears that prestretching is of little consequence if the prestretching period is limited to only a few minutes.

Special low-relaxation wire and strand are available. According to ASTM Specifications A 416 and A 421, such steel shall exhibit relaxation after 1000 hours not more than 2.5 percent when initially loaded to 70 percent of the specified tensile strength, and not more than 3.5 percent when loaded to 80 percent of the specified tensile strength. Relaxation loss for low-relaxation wire and strand can be taken to be about 25 percent of the loss for normal wire and strand.

2.7   TYPES OF CONCRETE

For several reasons the concrete used for prestressed construction is characterized by a higher strength than that used for ordinary reinforced concrete. It is usually subjected to higher forces, and so an increase in quality generally leads to more economical results. Use of high strength concrete permits the dimensions of member cross sections to be reduced to the minimum. Significant saving in dead load results, and longer spans become technically and economically possible. Objectionable deflection and cracking, which would otherwise be associated with the use of slender members at high stress, are easily controlled by prestressing.

There are other advantages. High strength concrete has a higher elastic modulus than low strength concrete, so that any losses of prestress force due to elastic shortening of the concrete are reduced. Creep losses, which are roughly proportional to elastic losses, are lower also. High bearing stresses in the vicinity of tendon anchorages for post-tensioned members are more easily accommodated, and the size of expensive anchorage hardware can be reduced. In the case of pretensioned elements, higher bond strength results in a reduction in the development length required to transfer prestress force from the cables to the concrete. Finally, concrete of higher compressive strength also has a higher tensile strength, so that the formation of flexural and diagonal tension cracks is delayed.

The greater part of prestressed concrete construction in the United States is precast under carefully controlled plant conditions. With external form vibration as well as internal vibration of the fresh concrete, very stiff high strength mixes, with low water-cement ratios, can be placed without danger of voids. Careful control of mix proportions is more easily achieved. Steam curing is often used, providing for more complete hydration of the cement. Also, for prestressed concrete members cast on the job site, higher strength concrete is generally specified and more easily obtained, because of the more precisely engineered natured of the construction.

In the present practice, compressive strength between 4000 and 6000 psi (28 and 41 N/mm^2) is commonly specified for prestressed concrete members, although strengths as high as 10,000 psi (69 N/mm^2) have been used. It should be emphasized, however, that the concrete strength assumed in the design calculations and specified must be attained with certainty, because the calculated high stresses due to prestress force really do occur.

Special mention should be made of lightweight concrete, attained through use of lightweight aggregate in the mix. The aggregates used may be shale, clay slate, slag, or pelletized fly ash. They are light in weight because of the porous, cellular structure of the individual aggregate particles, achieved in most cases by gas or steam formation in processing the aggregates in rotary kilns at high temperatures. Concrete can be produced, using these aggregates, with careful mix design, having unit weight between 90 and 120 pcf (14 and 19 N/mm^2), compared with about 145 pcf (23 N/mm^2) for normal density concrete. The strength of lightweight concrete can be made comparable to that of stone aggregate concrete through proper selection and proportioning of components and control of the water–cement ratio.

The design and control of concrete mixes and the development of proper procedures for placing and curing are a highly specialized field of study and not within the scope of this book. Attention here will be focused on the engineering properties of the resulting material. For information on what is generally known as *concrete material technology* the reader is referred to the comprehensive treatments contained in Refs. 2.2 and 2.3. Practical information of great value is contained in publications by the Portland Cement Association (Ref. 2.4) and the American Concrete Institute (Refs. 2.5 to 2.8).

2.8 CONCRETE IN UNIAXIAL COMPRESSION

Concrete is useful mainly in compression and, at controlling sections of members, is often subject to a state of stress that is approximately uniaxial. Accordingly the uniaxial compressive stress-strain curve is of primary interest.

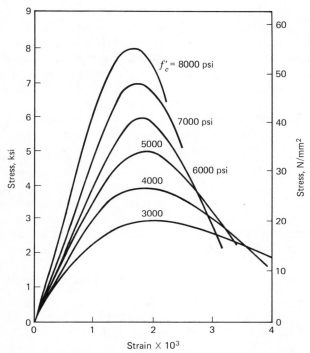

Figure 2.6   Typical uniaxial compressive stress-strain curves for concrete.

Such a curve is obtained by loading standardized cylinders parallel to their axis at prescribed rates of loading.* Figure 2.6 shows a typical set of such curves.

All of these curves have a similar character. The response is reasonably elastic for loads less than about half the maximum. Concretes of higher strength have a higher modulus of elasticity, measured by the slope of the curve at the origin. It will be noted further that the higher strength concretes are more brittle, that is, they fracture at a lower strain than do lower strength concretes. According to present design practice, the limiting strain in uniaxial compression is taken as 0.003. This is fully justifiable for concretes having strength of 6000 psi (41 N/mm²) or less, but is somewhat unconservative for materials of higher strength. All the curves reach their maximum stress at a strain of about 0.002.

Compressive stress-strain curves for lightweight concrete show the same general characteristics as those for normal density concrete, and no special distinction is made between the two types for ordinary design.

* See ASTM Specification C 192, "Standard Method of Making and Curing Concrete Test Specimens in the Laboratory" and C 39, "Standard Method of Test for Compressive Strength of Cylindrical Concrete Specimens."

It should be emphasized that the exact shape of the stress-strain curve for any given concrete is highly dependent on such variables as the rate of loading, the particular testing equipment, the method of testing, and the size and shape of the specimen. The relations shown in Fig. 2.6 are typical only of test results obtained by present standard procedures. In the actual structure, quite different results may be obtained. Fortunately, design procedures have evolved that are not particularly sensitive to the shape of the stress-strain curve.

Many expressions have been proposed relating the elastic modulus to the concrete strength. It can be computed with reasonable accuracy from an equation proposed by Pauw (Ref. 2.9) and included in the ACI Code:

$$E_c = 33w^{3/2}\sqrt{f'_c} \tag{2.3}$$

in which w is the unit weight of the hardened concrete in pcf, f'_c is its compressive cylinder strength in psi, and E_c is given in psi units.* Equation (2.3) was obtained by testing structural concretes with values of w from 90 to 155 pcf. For normal weight concrete with w of 145 pcf one obtains approximately

$$E_c = 57,000\sqrt{f'_c} \tag{2.4}$$

When compressed in one direction concrete, like all other materials, expands in the direction transverse to the direction of the applied stress. The ratio of the transverse strain to the longitudinal strain is known as *Poisson's ratio*. It is meaningful only in the elastic range, at stresses less than about half the concrete strength. In this range, Poisson's ratio for concrete varies between about 0.15 and 0.20.

The strength of concrete varies with age, the gain in strength being rapid at first, then much slower. This variation of strength is specially important in the design and fabrication of prestressed concrete members, because heavy loads may be caused at quite an early age by the tensioned steel. In prestressed construction of all types, but particularly for pretensioned plant-produced members, special methods are often followed to insure rapid development of compressive strength. These include the use in the concrete mix of high-early-strength Portland cement (Type III) rather than ordinary Portland Cement (Type I), and the use of steam curing.

A study of extensive experimental data indicates that the following expressions are suitable for predicting the strength of concrete at any time (Refs. 2.12, 2.13, and 2.14):

For moist-cured concrete using Type I cement:

$$f'_{c,t} = \frac{t}{4.00 + 0.85t} f'_{c,28} \tag{2.5a}$$

* See Appendix C for the SI equivalent of this and other dimensionally inconsistent equations.

For moist-cured concrete using Type III cement:

$$f'_{c,t} = \frac{t}{2.30 + 0.92t} f'_{c,28}$$

(2.5b)

For steam-cured concrete using Type I cement:

$$f'_{c,t} = \frac{t}{1.00 + 0.95t} f'_{c,28}$$

(2.5c)

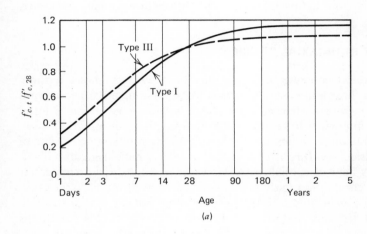

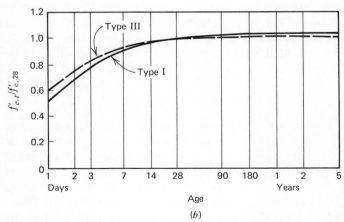

Figure 2.7 Effect of age on uniaxial compressive strength of concrete (adapted from Ref. 2.12). (*a*) Moist cured. (*b*) Steam cured.

For steam-cured concrete using Type III cement:

$$f'_{c,t} = \frac{t}{0.70 + 0.98t} f'_{c,28} \qquad (2.5d)$$

In these equations $f'_{c,t}$ is the compressive strength at time t, $f'_{c,28}$ is the compressive strength at 28 days, and t is the age of the concrete in days. Figure 2.7 presents these strength–time functions graphically, with time plotted to a logarithmic scale.

Test evidence indicates that Eqs. (2.5a) through (2.5d) are equally applicable for normal weight, sand-lightweight, and all-lightweight aggregate concretes.

2.9   CONCRETE IN UNIAXIAL TENSION

Cracks in prestressed concrete members may be caused by direct tension, flexure, combined shear and flexure in beams webs, torsion, and other actions. The behavior of members often changes abruptly when tensile cracks form. Accordingly, it is important to know the tensile strength of the material.

There are several ways to measure the tensile strength of concrete, none of them entirely satisfactory. *Direct tensile tests* have been made using dumbbell-shaped specimens held in special grips. However, results show great scatter because of the effects of minor misalignments, stress concentrations in the grips, and random effects associated with the location of aggregate, and for this reason direct tension tests are seldom used. For many years tensile strength has been measured using either the *modulus of rupture test* or the *split cylinder test*.

The modulus of rupture is the computed flexural tensile stress at which a test beam of plain concrete fractures. The test arrangement, shown in Figure 2.8a, is standardized by ASTM specifications. It employs a small block of unreinforced concrete, supported at its ends and loaded at the third points. Usually a 6×6 in. beam is used, with length between supports equal to 18 in. The modulus of rupture is

$$f'_r = \frac{PL}{bh^2} \qquad (2.5)$$

where P is the total load at fracture, L is the span, and b and h, respectively, the width and depth of the cross section. For normal density concrete the modulus of rupture is usually between $7.5\sqrt{f'_c}$ and $12\sqrt{f'_c}$, while for lightweight aggregate concrete it may range from $5\sqrt{f'_c}$ to $9\sqrt{f'_c}$. In each case the smaller values apply to higher strength concretes. Because the modulus of rupture is computed on the assumption that concrete is an elastic material, and because the critical stress occurs only at the outer surface, it is apt to be larger than the strength of concrete in uniform axial tension, which is often taken between $3\sqrt{f'_c}$ and $5\sqrt{f'_c}$ for normal density concrete and between $2\sqrt{f'_c}$ and $3.5\sqrt{f'_c}$ for lightweight material.

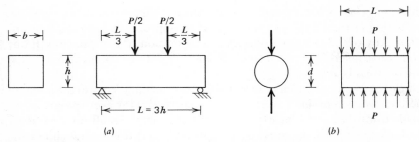

Figure 2.8 Tests to determine the uniaxial tensile strength of concrete. (*a*) Modulus of rupture test. (*b*) Split cylinder test.

In recent years the split cylinder test has come into favor because of good reproduceability of results. The standard arrangement is shown in Figure 2.8*b*. A 6 × 12 in. concrete cylinder (the same as used for the standard uniaxial compressive test) is inserted in a compression testing machine in the horizontal position, so that compression is applied along two diametrically opposite generators. It can be shown that, in an elastic cylinder loaded this way, a nearly uniform tensile stress exists at right angles to the plane of the load. The cylinder splits at a stress that is computed from the equation:

$$f'_{sp} = \frac{2P}{\pi L d} \tag{2.6}$$

where P is the rupture load, d is the diameter of the cylinder, and L is its length. For normal aggregate concrete the split cylinder strength is usually between $6\sqrt{f'_c}$ and $7\sqrt{f'_c}$, while for lightweight concrete it is generally between $4\sqrt{f'_c}$ and $5\sqrt{f'_c}$. As before, the lower values correspond to higher strength concretes.

Concrete subject to uniaxial tension responds nearly elastically up to the fracture load. The modulus of elasticity and Poisson's ratio in tension can be taken equal to the corresponding values in uniaxial compression, for design purposes.

2.10 BIAXIALLY STRESSED CONCRETE

In many locations in actual structures, concrete is subjected to a complex state of stress. For example, beam webs carry shear, combined with flexural tension or compression. Torsional shearing stresses in members generally act concurrently with transverse shears and longitudinal normal stresses. Other examples are easily found. It is clearly of some importance to be able to predict the strength, as well as the behavior before failure, of concrete subject to various states of combined stress.

Such complex stress states can always be reduced to three equivalent principal stresses, acting at right angles to each other, by appropriate coordinate transformation. Any of the principal stresses can be tension or compression. If one of them is zero, a state of *biaxial stress* is said to exist. If two of them are zero the state of stress is *uniaxial*.

In spite of extensive research in recent years, no general theory of the strength of concrete under combined stress has yet emerged. However, progress has been made toward establishing experimentally the effect of multi-axial stresses, notably for cases of biaxial stress (Refs. 2.10 and 2.11). Figure 2.9 shows the influence of the lateral principal stress f_y on the failure stress f_x in the perpendicular direction. All stresses are expressed nondimensionally in terms of the uniaxial compressive strength f'_c. It is seen that, in the biaxial compression quadrant, lateral compression in the amount of 20 percent or more of the compression in the longitudinal direction is sufficient to increase the strength in the longitudinal direction by about 20 percent. In the biaxial tension quadrant the strength is almost independent of lateral stress. In the tension-compression stress state, an approximately linear interaction is obtained. A relatively small

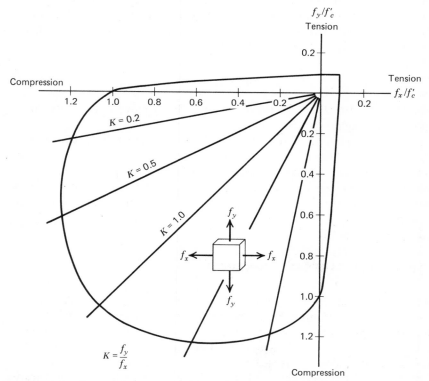

Figure 2.9   Strength envelope for concrete subject to biaxial stress.

value of lateral tension results in significant loss of longitudinal compressive strength.

It has also been found that lateral compression or tension modifies the apparent stress-strain curve obtained for a uniaxial state of stress (Refs. 2.10 and 2.11). This is due partially to the Poisson effect, but also results from the increased confinement of internal microcracks in the case of lateral compression. Such information has been useful in the refined analysis, using finite element methods, of concrete members such as deep beams and shear walls where the stress state can be considered biaxial.

While limited progress has been made in studying the behavior and strength of concrete in triaxial stress, information has not yet been developed that would be useful in design.

2.11 TIME-DEPENDENT DEFORMATION OF CONCRETE

Time-dependent deformation of concrete due to creep and shrinkage is of crucial importance in the design of prestressed concrete structures, because these volumetric changes result in a partial loss of prestress force, and because they produce significant changes in deflection. A careful estimate of the effects of creep and shrinkage requires quantitative engineering information relating such volume changes to time, stress intensity, humidity, and other factors. Because of their importance, both creep and shrinkage have been the subject of intensive research over a long period of time. The most productive studies have been experimental, and from such investigations the necessary functional relationships have been derived.

A. CREEP

Creep is the property of many materials by which they continue deforming over considerable lengths of time at constant stress or load. The rate of strain increase is rapid at first, but decreases with time until, after many months, a constant value is approached asymptotically.

Creep strain for concrete has been found experimentally to depend not only on time, but on the mix proportions, humidity, curing conditions, and the age of the concrete when it is first loaded. Creep strain is nearly linearly related to stress intensity. It is therefore possible to relate the creep strain to the initial elastic strain by means of a *creep coefficient* defined as

$$C_u = \frac{\varepsilon_{cu}}{\varepsilon_{ci}} \tag{2.7}$$

where ε_{ci} is the initial elastic strain and ε_{cu} is the *additional* strain in the concrete, after a long period of time, due to creep.

The same phenomenon is sometimes described in terms of unit creep strain, or creep per unit stress, such that

$$\varepsilon_{cu} = \delta_u f_{ci} \qquad (2.8)$$

where δ_u is the unit creep coefficient, sometimes called the specific creep, and f_{ci} is the stress intensity. Since the additional strain ε_{cu} can be written either as $C_u \varepsilon_{ci}$ or as $\delta_u f_{ci}$ it is easily seen that

$$C_u = \delta_u E_c \qquad (2.9)$$

A comprehensive study was made by Branson and Kripanarayanan of existing and original data pertaining to both shrinkage and creep (Refs. 2.12, and 2.14), Basic equations describing the functional relationships between both creep and shrinkage strains and time were recommended, together with modification factors that permit accounting for the other variables of greatest significance. These recommendations were endorsed by ACI Committee 209, charged with the study of creep and shrinkage in concrete, and provide information in a useful form for design (Ref. 2.13).

The creep coefficient at any time, C_t, can be related to the ultimate creep coefficient, C_u, by the equation:

$$C_t = \frac{t^{0.60}}{10 + t^{0.60}} C_u \qquad (2.10a)$$

or alternatively

$$\delta_t = \frac{t^{0.60}}{10 + t^{0.60}} \delta_u \qquad (2.10b)$$

where t is time in days. This relation is shown graphically in Fig. 2.10. When specific data for local aggregates and conditions are not available, an average value of C_u equal to 2.35 may be used.

Equation (2.10) applies for "standard" conditions, defined by Branson and Kripanarayanan as concrete with 4 in. slump or less, 40 percent relative

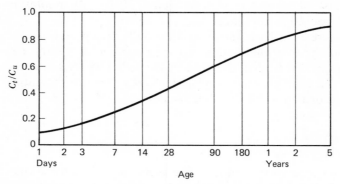

Figure 2.10 Variation of creep coefficient with time (adapted from Ref. 2.12).

humidity, minimum thickness of member of 6 in. or less, and loading age of 7 days for moist-cured concrete or loading age of 1 to 3 days for steam-cured concrete. For other than standard conditions, correction factors are recommended as follows, to be applied either to C_t or δ_t:

For loading ages later than 7 days for moist-cured concrete:

$$F_{c,la} = 1.25t_{la}^{-0.118} \tag{2.11a}$$

where t_{la} is the loading age in days.

For loading ages later than 1 to 3 days for steam-cured concrete:

$$F_{c,la} = 1.13t_{la}^{-0.095} \tag{2.11b}$$

For greater than 40 percent relative humidity:

$$F_{c,h} = 1.27 - 0.0067H \tag{2.12}$$

where H is the relative humidity in percent. Some specific values for the correction factors $F_{c,la}$ and $F_{c,h}$ are given in Tables 2.5 and 2.6, respectively. In most

Table 2.5 Creep Correction Factors for Nonstandard Loading Ages

Age at Loading t_{la} Days	Creep Correction Factor $F_{c,la}$	
	Moist Cured, Loaded Later Than 7 Days	Steam Cured, Loaded Later Than 1 to 3 Days
10	0.95	0.90
20	0.87	0.85
30	0.83	0.82
60	0.77	0.76
90	0.74	0.74

Table 2.6 Creep and Shrinkage Correction Factors for Nonstandard Relative Humidity

Relative Humidity H Percent	Creep Correction Factor $F_{c,h}$	Shrinkage Correction Factor $F_{sh,h}$
40 or less	1.00	1.00
50	0.94	0.90
60	0.87	0.80
70	0.80	0.70
80	0.73	0.60
90	0.67	0.30
100	0.60	0.00

cases corrections associated with member size, higher slump concrete, and other variables can be neglected.

B. SHRINKAGE

Normal concrete mixes contain more water than is required for hydration of the cement. This free water evaporates in time, the rate and completeness of drying depending upon the humidity, ambient temperature, and the size and shape of the concrete specimen. Drying of the concrete is accompanied by a reduction in volume, the change occurring at a higher rate initially than later, when limiting dimensions are approached asymptotically.

Branson and Kripanarayanan suggest "standard" equations relating shrinkage to time as follows:

For moist-cured concrete at any time t after age 7 days:

$$\varepsilon_{sh,t} = \frac{t}{35 + t}\, \varepsilon_{sh,u} \tag{2.13a}$$

The value of $e_{sh,u}$ may be taken as 800×10^{-6} if local data are not available. For steam-cured concrete at any time after age 1 to 3 days:

$$\varepsilon_{sh,t} = \frac{t}{55 + t}\, \varepsilon_{sh,u} \tag{2.13b}$$

An average value for $\varepsilon_{sh,u}$ of 730×10^{-6} is suggested for steam-cured concrete.

The relation between shrinkage strain and time, plotted to semilogarithmic scale, is shown in Fig. 2.11 for both moist-cured and steam-cured concrete.

For other than standard conditions of humidity, Eqs. (2.13a) and (2.13b) must be modified by a correction factor:

$$\text{For } 40 < H \le 80\% \qquad F_{sh,h} = 1.40 - 0.010H \tag{2.14a}$$

$$\text{For } 80 < H \le 100\% \qquad F_{sh,h} = 3.00 - 0.030H \tag{2.14b}$$

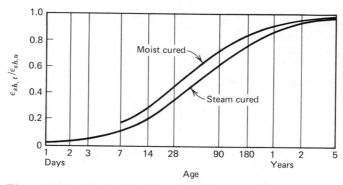

Figure 2.11 Variation of shrinkage coefficient with time (adapted from Ref. 2.12).

Representative values of the shrinkage correction for various humidity levels are presented in Table 2.6. Corrections associated with member size and slump may usually be omitted.

Test evidence shows no consistent variation between normal weight, sand-lightweight, and all-lightweight concrete, and no consistent difference between concretes using Type I or Type III cement (Refs. 2.12 and 2.13). In the absence of other information, the equations and correction factors given above may be used for all cases.

REFERENCES

2.1 Magura, D. D., Sozen, M. A., and Siess, C. P., "A Study of Stress Relaxation in Prestressing Reinforcement," *J. PCI*, Vol. 9, No. 2, April 1964, pp. 13–57.

2.2 Neville, A, M., *Properties of Concrete*, 2nd Ed., Wiley, New York, 1973, 686 pp.

2.3 Troxell, G. E., Davis, H. E., and Kelley, J. W., *Composition and Properties of Concrete*, 2nd Ed., McGraw-Hill, New York, 1968.

2.4 *Design and Control of Concrete Mixtures*, 11th Ed., Portland Cement Association, Old Orchard Rd; Skokie, Illinois, 1968, 124 pp.

2.5 *Recommended Practice for Selecting Proportions for Normal Weight Concrete*, ACI Standard 211.1–70, 16 pp.

2.6 *Recommended Practice for Measuring, Mixing, Transporting, and Placing Concrete*, ACI Standard 304–73, 40 pp.

2.7 "Guide for Structural Lightweight Aggregate Concrete," reported by ACI Committee 213, *J. ACI*, Vol. 64, No. 8, August 1967, pp. 433–469.

2.8 *Recommended Practice for Selecting Proportions for Structural Lightweight Concrete*, ACI Standard 211.2–69, 20 pp.

2.9 Pauw, A., "Static Modulus of Elasticity of Concrete as Affected by Density," *J. ACI*, Vol. 32, No. 6, December 1960, pp. 679–687.

2.10 Liu, T. C. Y., Nilson, A. H., and Slate, F. O., "Stress-Strain Response and Fracture of Concrete in Uniaxial and Biaxial Compression," *J. ACI*, Vol. 69, No. 5, May 1972, pp. 291–295.

2.11 Tasuji, M. E., Slate, F. O., and Nilson, A. H., *The Behavior of Plain Concrete Subject to Biaxial Stress*, Research Report No. 360, Department of Structural Engineering, Cornell University, May 1976, 180 pp.

2.12 Branson, D. E. and Kripanarayanan, K. M., "Loss of Prestress, Camber and Deflection of Non-Composite and Composite Prestressed Concrete Structures," *J. PCI*, Vol. 16, No. 5, September 1971, pp. 22–52.

2.13 "Prediction of Creep, Shrinkage, and Temperature Effects in Concrete Structures," Report by ACI Committee 209, *Designing for Effects of Creep, Shrinkage, Temperature in Concrete Structures*, ACI Special Publication SP–27, 1971, pp. 51–93.

2.14 Branson, D. E., *Deformation of Concrete Structures*, McGraw-Hill, New York, 1977, 546 pp.

CHAPTER 3
FLEXURAL ANALYSIS

3.1 INTRODUCTION

Consideration of beams may require analysis or design.

In the case of *flexural analysis,* the concrete and steel dimensions, as well as the magnitude and line of action of the effective prestress force, are usually known. If the loads are given, one may wish to find the resulting stresses and compare these against a set of permissible values. Alternately, if permissible stresses are known, then one may calculate maximum loads that could be carried without exceeding those stresses. For given material strengths, the member capacity can be calculated, and safety against collapse determined for any loading.

In contrast, in *flexural design,* permissible stresses and material strengths are known, the loads to be resisted are given, and the engineer must determine concrete and steel dimensions as well as the magnitude and line of action of the prestressing force.

The analysis of prestressed flexural members is by far the simpler task. Design is complicated by the interdependence of the many variables. Changes in one variable generally will affect many, if not all, of the others, and often the best path to the final design is an iterative one. A trial member chosen on the basis of approximate calculation is analyzed to check its adequacy, then refined. In this way, the designer converges on the solution that is "best" in some sense.

Both analysis and design of prestressed concrete may require the consideration of several load stages as follows:

1. Initial prestress, immediately after transfer, when P_i alone may act on the concrete.
2. Initial prestress plus self-weight of the member.
3. Initial prestress plus full dead load.
4. Effective prestress, P_e, after losses plus service loads consisting of full dead and expected live loads.
5. Ultimate load, when the expected service loads are increased by load factors, and the member is at incipient failure.

At and below the service load level, both concrete and steel stresses are usually within the elastic range. Should the member be overloaded, however, one or

57

both materials are likely to be stressed into the inelastic range, in which case predictions of ultimate strength must be based on actual, nonlinear stress-strain relations.

Only simple-span, statically determinate beams will be treated in this chapter. Study of such members permits the establishment of basic principles in the clearest possible way. In addition, these members are of great practical importance, because a large percentage of prestressed concrete construction in the United States is presently precast and erected in the form of simple spans.

The study of indeterminate beams, used increasingly for buildings as well as bridges and other structures, will be deferred until Ch. 8.

3.2   NOTATION

The study and design of prestressed concrete structures is greatly facilitated by adoption of a logical and self-consistent set of symbols to describe dimensions, stresses, forces, loads, and other important quantities. Unfortunately, there is no general agreement as to what these symbols should be, and most authors proceed in independent directions.

The ACI Code notation provides the basis for the notation used in this text. A few minor changes have been made, in the interests of clarity or consistency. The reader should have little difficulty adapting to Code notation, if he prefers, in these instances. All symbols are defined where they first appear.

Consistent with the general practice in structural engineering, tensile strains and stresses are taken to be positive (since they are associated with length increase) and compressive strains and stresses as negative. Strains or stresses referring to the top surface of a flexural member are given the subscript 1 and those referring to the bottom the subscript 2.

3.3   PARTIAL LOSS OF PRESTRESS FORCE

It is not possible to proceed very far with the analysis or design of prestressed concrete members without considering that the prestressing force is not constant. As already discussed briefly in Ch. 1, the jacking tension P_j, initially applied to the tendon, is reduced at once to what is termed the initial prestress force P_i. A part of this loss in jacking tension, that due to friction between a post-tensioned tendon and its encasing duct, actually occurs before transfer of prestress force to the concrete. The remainder due to elastic shortening of the concrete and due to slip at post-tensioning anchorages as the wedges take hold, occurs immediately upon transfer.

Additional losses occur over an extended period, because of concrete shrinkage and creep, and because of relaxation of stress in the steel tendon. As a result the prestress force is reduced from P_i to its final or effective value, P_e, after all significant time-dependent losses have taken place.

The values of greatest interest in calculating stresses in the concrete are the initial prestress P_i and the effective prestress P_e. It is convenient to express the relation between these in terms of an *effectiveness ratio R*, defined such that

$$P_e = RP_i \qquad (3.1)$$

Put another way, the ratio of time-dependent losses to initial prestress force is

$$\frac{P_i - P_e}{P_i} = 1 - R \qquad (3.2)$$

In works of major importance it is always advisable to make a careful estimate of each component of loss of prestress force, making use of the best available knowledge of the material properties and the construction sequence. In routine design or in cases of lesser importance, it is adequate to assume a value for the effectiveness ratio R, based on published information or past experience with similar construction. Detailed information to assist in the calculation of individual loss components will be presented in Ch. 6. In the present chapter, in all examples, in order not to obscure fundamental principles, a reasonable value for losses will be assumed.

3.4   ELASTIC FLEXURAL STRESSES IN UNCRACKED BEAMS

A.   BEHAVIOR OF PRESTRESSED BEAMS IN THE ELASTIC RANGE

A simple span prestressed beam with a curved tendon is shown in Fig. 3.1a. The concrete centroid is that of the entire, uncracked cross section, and the steel will be represented by its centroidal axis, whether there is one tendon or many. The eccentricity of the steel centroid, positive if measured downward from the concrete centroid, is e. The distances from the concrete centroid to the top and bottom surfaces of the member are c_1 and c_2, respectively.

Figure 3.1b shows the force resultants acting on the concrete after the steel is tensioned. The force F acts on the concrete at the tendon anchorages near the ends of the member. The force P at midspan is the resultant of all the normal compressive stresses in the concrete at that section. These normal stresses vary from a value f_1 at the top surface to f_2 at the bottom surface. The forces N are exerted on the concrete by the tendon because of its curvature, and the exact distribution of these forces depends on the particular tendon profile used.

The three forces F, N, and P form a self-equilibrating system, as illustrated by the closing force polygon of Fig. 3.1c. Note that when prestress forces act alone on a statically determinate beam, the external reactions on the beam are zero.

Figure 3.1d shows an alternative representation of the forces of Fig. 3.1b, in which the forces F and N are replaced by their vector sum T. The compressive resultant P acts as before. Note that P and T are equal and opposite forces,

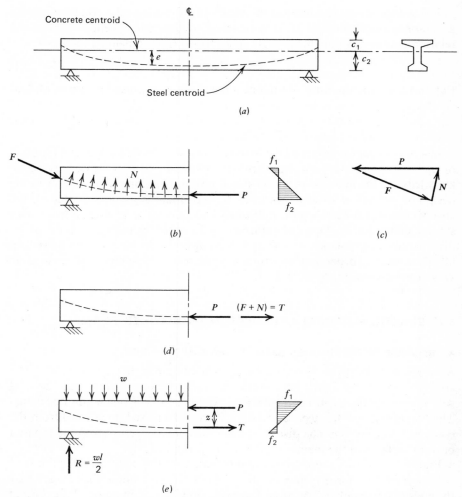

Figure 3.1 Forces acting on typical prestressed beam. (*a*) Beam profile and section. (*b*) Forces acting on concrete. (*c*) Force equilibrium polygon. (*d*) Anchorage and curvature forces replaced by resultant. (*e*) Beam with transverse loads.

acting at the same point on the cross section. It is concluded that, for a statically determinate beam, the consequence of prestressing is a compressive resultant force that acts at the location of the steel centroid at any section.

The direction of the compressive resultant is always tangent to the tendon profile at any section. For the midspan section of the symmetrical beam just considered, the compressive resultant was horizontal. If the section had been taken at another location, say at the quarter point of the span, the compressive resultant would have both a horizontal and vertical component. In such case, the horizontal component would represent the summation of all the normal forces acting on the concrete, and the vertical component the summation of all the shearing forces.

Next a uniformly distributed load of intensity w is caused to act, as shown in Fig. 3.1e. There is an associated reaction force $R = wl/2$ at each support. As the load w is gradually applied, the magnitude of the prestressing force stays essentially constant (the actual, slight increase will be discussed in Art. 3.6), and T maintains both its magnitude and position. However, as flexural stresses due to the applied load are superimposed on axial and flexural stresses due to prestressing, the compressive resultant P moves upward. An internal resisting couple is generated, with equal forces P and T and lever arm z. This couple exactly equilibrates the external moment.

The difference between the behavior of a prestressed concrete beam and a reinforced concrete beam should be noted carefully. In the case of the reinforced concrete beam, the internal lever arm remains essentially constant as the load is increased, and the increasing moment is accompanied by an almost proportionate increase in the internal forces. For the prestressed beam, the forces stay essentially constant as the load is increased, and the increasing moment is accompanied by an increase in the internal lever arm.

B. ELASTIC STRESSES

As long as the beam remains uncracked, and both steel and concrete are stressed only within their elastic ranges, then concrete stresses can be found using the familiar equations of mechanics, based on linear elastic behavior. In present practice, these conditions are often satisfied up to, and including, the level of service loading.

According to the ACI Code, stresses may be found using linear elastic methods even though the *nominal* tension is somewhat in excess of the probable value of the modulus of rupture. The rationale for this is that a certain amount of bonded reinforcement, prestressed or otherwise, must be provided in the tension zone. This serves the purpose of controlling both cracking and deflection, and permits the member to respond essentially as if it were uncracked.

If the member is subjected only to the initial prestressing force P_i, it has just been shown that the compressive resultant acts at the steel centroid. The concrete stress f_1 at the top face of the member, and f_2 at the bottom face, can be found by superimposing axial and bending effects:

$$f_1 = -\frac{P_i}{A_c} + \frac{P_i e c_1}{I_c} \tag{3.3a}$$

$$f_2 = -\frac{P_i}{A_c} - \frac{P_i e c_2}{I_c} \tag{3.3b}$$

where e is the tendon eccentricity measured downward from the concrete centroid, A_c is the area of the concrete cross section, and I_c is the moment of inertia of the concrete cross section. Other terms are as already defined. Substituting the radius of gyration $r^2 = I_c/A_c$ these equations can be written in the more convenient form:

$$f_1 = -\frac{P_i}{A_c}\left(1 - \frac{ec_1}{r^2}\right) \tag{3.4a}$$

$$f_2 = -\frac{P_i}{A_c}\left(1 + \frac{ec_2}{r^2}\right) \tag{3.4b}$$

The resulting stress distribution is shown in Fig. 3.2a.

Almost never would the initial prestress P_i act alone. In most practical cases, with the tendon below the concrete centroid, the beam will deflect upward because of the bending moment caused by prestressing. It will then be supported by the formwork or casting bed essentially at its ends, and the dead load of the beam itself will cause moments M_o to be superimposed immediately. Consequently, at the initial stage, immediately after transfer of prestress force, the stresses in the concrete at the top and bottom surfaces are

$$f_1 = -\frac{P_i}{A_c}\left(1 - \frac{ec_1}{r^2}\right) - \frac{M_o}{S_1} \tag{3.5a}$$

$$f_2 = -\frac{P_i}{A_c}\left(1 + \frac{ec_2}{r^2}\right) + \frac{M_o}{S_2} \tag{3.5b}$$

where M_o is the bending moment due to the self-weight of the member, and $S_1 = I_c/c_1$ and $S_2 = I_c/c_2$ are the section moduli with respect to the top and bottom surfaces of the beam. The stress distribution at this load stage is shown in Fig. 3.2b.

Superimposed dead loads (additional to the self-weight) may be placed when the prestress force is still close to its initial value, that is, before time-dependent losses have occurred. However, this load stage would seldom if ever control the design, as can be confirmed by study of Fig. 3.2.

Superimposed live loads are generally applied sufficiently late for the greatest part of the loss of prestress to have occurred. Consequently, the next load stage of interest is the full service load stage, when the effective prestress P_e acts with the moments due to self-weight (M_o), superimposed dead load (M_d), and superimposed live load (M_l). The resulting stresses are

$$f_1 = -\frac{P_e}{A_c}\left(1 - \frac{ec_1}{r^2}\right) - \frac{M_t}{S_1} \tag{3.6a}$$

$$f_2 = -\frac{P_e}{A_c}\left(1 + \frac{ec_2}{r^2}\right) + \frac{M_t}{S_2} \tag{3.6b}$$

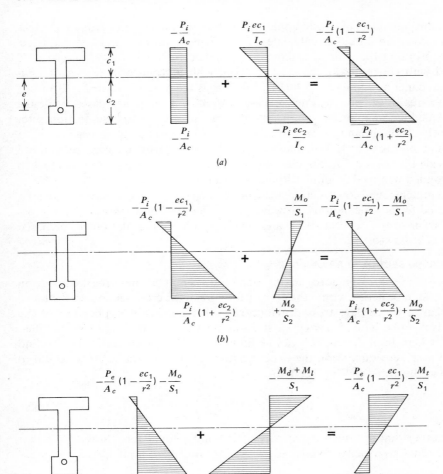

$$(a)$$

$$(b)$$

$$(c)$$

Figure 3.2   Elastic stresses in an uncracked prestressed beam. (a) Effect of initial prestress. (b) Effect of initial prestress plus self-weight. (c) Effect of final prestress plus full service load.

where the total moment M_t is

$$M_t = M_o + M_d + M_l \qquad (3.7)$$

These *service load stresses* are shown in Fig. 3.2c.

C.   CALCULATION OF SECTION PROPERTIES

In calculating the properties of the concrete cross section to be used in the above equations, it should be noted that in post-tensioned construction tendons may

pass through ducts of considerable size. Before the tendons are grouted stresses
in the concrete should be calculated using the net section, with holes deducted.
After grouting, the transformed section should be used. Holes may be considered
filled with concrete and the steel replaced with its transformed area of equivalent concrete equal to $(n_p - 1)A_p$, where n_p is the modular ratio E_p/E_c and A_p
is the area of the prestressing steel (see Ref. 3.14). In practical cases, while the
hole deduction may be significant, use of the gross concrete section after
grouting rather than the transformed section will normally be satisfactory.

In many cases the hole deduction is small and the gross concrete section can
provide the basis for all calculations. This will almost always be the case when
unbonded wrapped tendons without ducts are used.

In pretensioned construction, the transformed cross section should, in theory,
be used for all calculations. However, the difference in properties of the gross
and transformed sections is usually small, permitting calculations to be based
on the gross cross section.

D. CROSS SECTION KERN OR CORE

When the prestressing force, acting alone, causes no tension in the cross section
it is said to be acting within the *kern* or the *core* of the cross section. In the limiting cases, triangular stress distributions will result from application of the
prestress force, with zero concrete stress at the top or the bottom of the member.

The kern limit dimensions can be found from Eqs. (3.4a) and (3.4b). To find
the lower kern dimension the concrete stress at the top surface is set equal to
zero as illustrated in Fig. 3.3. Thus

$$f_1 = -\frac{P_i}{A_c}\left(1 - \frac{ec_1}{r^2}\right) = 0$$

indicating that the quantity in parentheses must equal zero. Solving for that
particular eccentricity, defined as $e = k_2$ the lower kern limit is

$$1 - \frac{k_2 c_1}{r^2} = 0$$

$$k_2 = \frac{r^2}{c_1} \tag{3.8a}$$

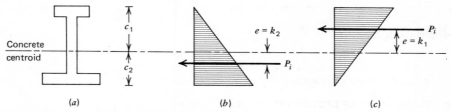

(a)   (b)   (c)

Figure 3.3 Stress distributions for prestress force applied at kern limits.
(*a*) Cross section. (*b*) Lower kern limit. (*c*) Upper kern limit.

Similarly the upper kern limit is found by setting the expression for the concrete stress at the bottom surface equal to zero, from which

$$k_1 = -\frac{r^2}{c_2} \qquad (3.8b)$$

the minus sign confirming that the limit dimension is measured upward from the concrete centroid.

It would be unwise to place great emphasis on these limit dimensions. It should not be implied that the steel centroid must remain within the kern. However, the kern limits often serve as convenient reference points in the design of beams.

EXAMPLE   Flexural Stresses for Given Beam and Loads

The simply supported I beam shown in cross section and elevation in Fig. 3.4 is to carry a uniformly distributed service dead and live load totaling 0.55 kips per ft over the 40 ft span, in addition to its own weight. Normal concrete having density of 150 lb/ft³ will be used. The beam will be pretensioned using multiple seven-wire strands; eccentricity is constant and equal to 5.19 in. The prestress force P_i immediately after transfer (after elastic shortening loss) is 169 kips. Time-dependent losses due to shrinkage, creep, and relaxation total 15 percent of the initial prestress force. Find the concrete flexural stresses at midspan and support sections under initial and final conditions. (Load 8.02 kN/m, span 12.19 m, density 24 kN/m³, $e = 132$ mm, $P_i = 752$ kN.)

For pretensioned beams using stranded cables, the difference between section properties based on the gross and transformed section is usually small. Accordingly, all calculations will be based on properties of the gross concrete section. Average flange thickness will be used, as shown in Fig. 3.4b. For that section

$$\text{Moment of inertia } I_c = 12{,}000 \text{ in.}^4 \ (4.99 \times 10^9 \text{ mm}^4)$$

$$\text{Concrete area } \quad A_c = 176 \text{ in.}^2 \ (114 \times 10^3 \text{ mm}^2)$$

$$\text{Section modulus } \quad S_1 = S_2 = 1000 \text{ in.}^3 \ (16.4 \times 10^6 \text{ mm}^3)$$

$$\text{Radius of gyration } r^2 = I_c/A_c = 68.2 \text{ in.}^2 \ (44 \times 10^3 \text{ mm}^3)$$

Stresses in the concrete resulting from the initial prestress force of 169 kips may be found by Eq. (3.4). At the top and bottom surfaces, respectively, these stresses are

$$f_1 = -\frac{P_i}{A_c}\left(1 - \frac{ec_1}{r^2}\right) = -\frac{169{,}000}{176}\left(1 - \frac{5.19 \times 12}{68.2}\right) = -83 \text{ psi}$$

$$f_2 = -\frac{P_i}{A_c}\left(1 + \frac{ec_2}{r^2}\right) = -\frac{169{,}000}{176}\left(1 + \frac{5.19 \times 12}{68.2}\right) = -1837 \text{ psi}$$

as shown by distribution (1) in Fig. 3.4c. These stresses exist throughout the length of the member. However, as the prestress force is applied, the beam will camber off the casting bed, and stresses due to the beam-load bending moment will act. The member dead load is

$$w_o = \frac{176}{144} \times 0.150 = 0.183 \text{ kips/ft}$$

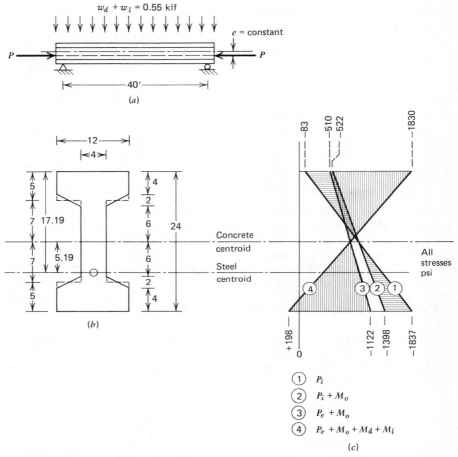

Figure 3.4 I beam with constant eccentricity. (*a*) Elevation. (*b*) Cross section. (*c*) Concrete stresses at midspan.

At midspan the corresponding moment is

$$M_o = \frac{1}{8} \times 0.183 \times 40^2 = 36.6 \text{ ft-kips}$$

This moment produces top and bottom concrete stresses at midspan of

$$f_1 = -\frac{M_o}{S_1} = -\frac{36.6 \times 12{,}000}{1000} = -439 \text{ psi}$$

$$f_2 = +\frac{M_o}{S_2} = +\frac{36.6 \times 12{,}000}{1000} = +439 \text{ psi}$$

The combined effect of initial prestress and self-weight is found by superposition.

$$f_1 = -83 \quad - 439 = -522 \text{ psi} \ (-3.6 \text{ N/mm}^2)$$
$$f_2 = -1837 + 439 = -1398 \text{ psi} \ (-9.6 \text{ N/mm}^2)$$

as shown by distribution (2).

Time-dependent losses are 15 percent of P_i. Accordingly, the effectiveness ratio

$$R = \frac{P_e}{P_i} = 0.85$$

and the effective prestress force after all losses is

$$P_e = 0.85 \times 169 = 144 \text{ kips}$$

Top and bottom concrete stresses due to P_e are

$$f_1 = 0.85 \times (-83) \quad = -71 \text{ psi}$$
$$f_2 = 0.85 \times (-1837) = -1561 \text{ psi}$$

Flexural stresses due to self-weight must be superimposed as before. The resulting midspan stresses due to P_e and self-weight are

$$f_1 = -71 \quad - 439 = -510 \text{ psi} \ (-3.5 \text{ N/mm}^2)$$
$$f_2 = -1561 + 439 = -1122 \text{ psi} \ (-7.7 \text{ N/mm}^2)$$

as given by distribution (3) in Fig. 3.4c.

The midspan moment due to superimposed dead and live load is

$$M_d + M_l = \frac{1}{8} \times 0.55 \times 40^2 = 110 \text{ ft-kips}$$

and the corresponding concrete stresses are

$$f_1 = -\frac{110 \times 12{,}000}{1000} = -1320 \text{ psi}$$

$$f_2 = +\frac{110 \times 12{,}000}{1000} = +1320 \text{ psi}$$

Then, combining effective prestress force with moments due to self-weight and superimposed load, the stresses produced are

$$f_1 = -510 \ - 1320 = -1830 \text{ psi} \ (-12.6 \text{ N/mm}^2)$$
$$f_2 = -1122 + 1320 = +198 \text{ psi} \ (+1.4 \text{ N/mm}^2)$$

as shown by distribution (4). In Fig. 3.4c the stress change resulting from the member self-weight is shown by horizontal shading, while that resulting from superimposed dead and live loads is shown by vertical shading.

At the support sections, the transverse loads cause no flexural stresses, and concrete stresses are those resulting from prestress alone. The initial values of -83 and -1837 psi at the top and bottom surfaces gradually reduce to -71 and -1561 psi, respectively, as time-dependent losses occur.

Additional Comments

1. The stress at the concrete centroid due to initial prestress is

$$f_{cc} = -\frac{169{,}000}{176} = -960 \text{ psi}$$

and this stress does not change as the member self-weight is introduced. Nor does the concrete centroidal stress, after losses, of $0.85 \times (-960) = -816$ psi change as the superimposed dead and live loads are applied.

2. The stress change in the prestressing steel resulting from application of loads can easily be calculated. Assuming that the bond between concrete and steel remains intact, the change in steel stress will be n_p times the change in concrete stress at that level in the member, where $n_p = E_p/E_c$. A value of $n_p = 8$ will be assumed here. Referring to Fig. 3.4c, as the self-weight is applied the stress increase in the steel is

$$\Delta f_p = 8(-1398 + 1837) \times \frac{5.19}{12} = 1519 \text{ psi}$$

while the further increase associated with the superimposed dead and live load is

$$\Delta f_p = 8(198 + 1122) \times \frac{5.19}{12} = 4567 \text{ psi}$$

The total increase is about 3 percent of the probable initial stress in the steel. This change is generally disregarded.

3. The magnitude of tensile stress at the bottom concrete surface of 198 psi tension is well below the probable modulus of rupture of the concrete, confirming that the concrete has not cracked and that the stress calculations based on the entire cross section are valid.

4. Note that in the unloaded stage, represented by stress distribution (2), substantial precompression exists in the upper part of the beam, which will later be further compressed by application of a superimposed load. This suggests that a more efficient design would result from the use of increased tendon eccentricity or reduced prestress force or both. However, for a member with straight tendons, such changes may result in undesirably large tensile stresses at the top of the member at the supports, where beam dead load causes no flexural stress. For this and other reasons, tendon eccentricity is often reduced toward the supports.

3.5 ALLOWABLE FLEXURAL STRESSES

Most specifications for prestressed concrete construction impose certain limitations on stresses in the concrete and steel at particular stages, such as while tensioning the steel, immediately after transfer of prestress force to the concrete, and at full service load. These stress limits are intended to avoid damage to the member during construction, and to insure serviceability by indirectly limiting crack width and deflection. In present practice, stress limit specifications often provide the starting point in selecting the dimensions for prestressed concrete members. The resulting design must, of course, be checked for strength to insure adequate safety against failure. Often deflections must also be calculated explicitly at particular load stages of importance.

A. CONCRETE

Concrete stress limits imposed by the ACI Code are summarized in Table 3.1. Here f'_{ci} is the compressive strength of the concrete at the time of initial prestress, and f'_c is the specified compressive strength of the concrete. Both are expressed in psi units, as are the resulting stresses.

The allowable stresses of part 1 of Table 3.1 apply immediately after transfer of prestress force to the concrete, after losses due to friction, anchorage slip, and elastic shortening of the concrete have been deducted, but before time-dependent losses due to shrinkage, creep, and relaxation are taken into account.

Table 3.1   Permissible Stresses in Concrete in Prestressed Flexural Members[a]

1. Stresses immediately after prestress transfer (before prestress losses) shall not exceed the following:
    a. Extreme fiber stress in compression — $0.60f'_{ci}$
    b. Extreme fiber stress in tension except as permitted in c — $3\sqrt{f'_{ci}}$
    c. Extreme fiber stress in tension at ends of simply-supported members — $6\sqrt{f'_{ci}}$
        Where computed tensile stresses exceed these values, bonded auxiliary reinforcement (non-prestressed or prestressed) shall be provided in the tensile zone to resist the total tensile force in the concrete computed with the assumption of an uncracked section.

2. Stresses at service loads (after allowance for all prestress losses) shall not exceed the following:
    a. Extreme fiber stress in compression — $0.45f'_c$
    b. Extreme fiber stress in tension in precompressed tensile zone — $6\sqrt{f'_c}$
    c. Extreme fiber stress in tension in precompressed tensile zone of members (except two-way slab systems) where analysis based on transformed cracked sections and on bilinear moment-deflection relationships shows that immediate and long-time deflections comply with requirements stated elsewhere in the Code — $12\sqrt{f'_c}$

3. The permissible stresses of sections 1 and 2 may be exceeded if shown by test or analysis that performance will not be impaired.

[a] Adapted with permission of the American Concrete Institute from ACI Building Code 318–77.

The tension stress limits of $3\sqrt{f'_{ci}}$ and $6\sqrt{f'_{ci}}$ refer to tensile stress at locations other than the precompressed tensile zone.* If the tensile stress exceeds the applicable limiting value, the total force in the tension zone should be calculated, and bonded auxiliary reinforcement provided to resist this force. For design purposes, such steel is assumed to act at a stress of 60 percent of its yield stress, but not at a stress greater than 30 ksi.

The service load stress limits of part 2 of Table 3.1, apply after all losses have occurred, and when the full service load acts. The allowable concrete tensile stress of $6\sqrt{f'_c}$ has been established mostly on the basis of experience with test members and actual structures. Use of this stress limit, rather than a lower value or zero, requires that there be a sufficient amount of bonded reinforcement in the precompressed tension zone to control cracking, that the amount of concrete cover for the reinforcement is sufficient to avoid corrosion, and that unusually corrosive conditions will not be encountered. Bonded reinforcement may consist of bonded prestressed or non-prestressed tendons, or of bonded reinforcing bars, well distributed over the tension zone.

The use of a tensile stress limit of $12\sqrt{f'_c}$ is permitted to obtain improved service load deflection characteristics, particularly when a substantial part of the live load is of a transient nature. It should be emphasized that an allowable tensile stress of $12\sqrt{f'_c}$, calculated on the basis of an uncracked cross section is a nominal stress only, since its value is well above any reasonable estimate of the modulus of rupture of the concrete. If this stress limit is used, the concrete protection for the reinforcement must be increased 50 percent above its usual value, according to the Code, and an explicit check made of service load deflection.

The "escape clause" of Part 3, Table 3.1, permits higher stress limits to be used when tests or analysis indicate that satisfactory performance can be expected.

B. STEEL

The permissible tensile stresses in prestressing steel given in Table 3.2 are expressed in terms of f_{pu}, the ultimate strength of the steel, and f_{py}, the specified yield strength. It is seen that the stress permitted by the Code depends on the stage of loading. When the jacking force is first applied, a stress of $0.80f_{pu}$ or $0.94f_{py}$ is allowed, whichever is lower. The justification for these high stress limits is that the steel stress is known rather precisely during the stretching operation, since hydraulic pressure and total steel strain can easily be measured. In addition, if a deficient tendon should break accidentally, it could easily be replaced.

The value of $0.70f_{pu}$ applies after elastic shortening and anchorage slip losses have taken place, but before time-dependent losses due to shrinkage, creep,

---

* The precompressed tension zone is defined in the ACI Code Commentary as that portion of the member in which flexural tension occurs under dead and live loads.

Table 3.2   Permissible Stresses in Prestressing Steel[a]

Tensile stress in prestressing tendons shall not exceed the following:	
1. Due to tendon jacking force	$0.80f_{pu}$
	or
	$0.94f_{py}$
whichever is smaller, but not greater than the maximum value recommended by the manufacturer of the prestressing tendons or anchorages.	
2. Pretensioning tendons immediately after prestress transfer	$0.70f_{pu}$
3. Post-tensioning tendons immediately after tendon anchorage	$0.70f_{pu}$

[a] Adapted with permission of the American Concrete Institute from ACI Building Code 318–77.

and relaxation. No limit need be placed on steel stress after all losses, because that stress will always be less than the steel stress under initial conditions, when an adequate factor of safety must be obtained.

3.6   CRACKING LOAD

The relation between applied load and steel stress in a typical well-bonded pretensioned beam is shown in a quantitative way in Fig. 3.5. Performance of a grouted post-tensioned beam is similar. When the jacking force is first applied and the strand is stretched between abutments, the steel stress is f_{pj}. Upon transfer of force to the concrete member, there is an immediate reduction of stress to the initial stress level f_{pi}, due to elastic shortening of the concrete. At the same time the self-weight of the member is caused to act as the beam cambers upward. It will be assumed here that all time-dependent losses occur prior to superimposed loading, so that the stress is further reduced to the effective prestress level, f_{pe}, as shown in Fig. 3.5.

As the superimposed dead and live loads are added, there is a slight increase in steel stress. Assuming that perfect bond is maintained between steel and concrete, this increase must be n_p times the increase in stress in the concrete at the level of the steel. The change is no more than about 3 or 4 percent of the initial stress, and is usually ignored in the calculations.

Unless the beam has cracked prior to loading due to shrinkage or other causes, there is no significant modification in behavior at the *decompression load*, when the compression at the bottom of the member is reduced to zero. The steel stress continues to increase only slightly and linearly, until the cracking load is reached. At that load, there is a sudden increase in steel stress, as the tension that was formerly carried by the concrete is transferred to the steel.

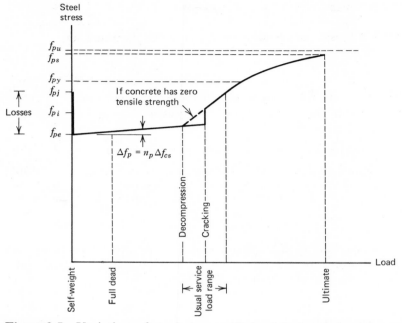

Figure 3.5 Variation of steel stress with load in bonded preten-sioned beam.

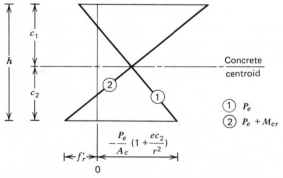

Figure 3.6 Change in concrete stresses as cracking moment is applied.

In a beam with prior cracks, or in a segmentally cast beam, the curve changes slope at the decompression load as shown.

After cracking, the steel stress increases much more rapidly than before. After the yield stress f_{py} is reached, the steel elongates disproportionately, but carries increasing stress due to the shape of its stress-strain curve, and the stress vs. load curve continues upward at a gradually reducing slope. The steel stress at failure, f_{ps}, may be equal to the tensile strength, f_{pu}, but is usually somewhat below it, depending on the geometry of the beam, the steel ratio, and the properties of the materials.

The cracking load represents the limit of validity of those equations for elastic stresses in the concrete that are based on the homogeneous cross section (although that section may provide the basis of *nominal* stress calculations above that load, as indicated in Art. 3.5). Although the importance of cracking has been overemphasized in the past, it may be necessary to predict the cracking load for any of the following reasons:

1. Deflection is influenced by the reduction in flexural rigidity that accompanies cracking.
2. After the beam cracks, the prestressing steel is more vulnerable to corrosion.
3. The fatigue resistance of beams is reduced by cracking because of the greater stress range experienced by the prestressing steel near the cracks.
4. Cracks may be visually objectionable in some cases.
5. In the case of liquid containment vessels, leaks are more likely after cracking.

The moment causing cracking may easily be found for a typical beam by writing the equation for the concrete stress at the bottom face, based on the homogeneous section, and setting it equal to the modulus of rupture:

$$f_2 = -\frac{P_e}{A_c}\left(1 + \frac{ec_2}{r^2}\right) + \frac{M_{cr}}{S_2} = f_r' \tag{a}$$

in which M_{cr} is the total moment at cracking (including moment due to self-weight and superimposed dead and partial live loads) and f_r' is the modulus of rupture (see Art. 2.9). Rearranging, we obtain

$$\frac{M_{cr}}{S_2} = f_r' + \frac{P_e}{A_c}\left(1 + \frac{ec_2}{r^2}\right) \tag{b}$$

which simply states that the change in bottom face stress as the full cracking moment is applied must be such as to overcome the initial precompression due to prestress, and to introduce a tensile stress just equal to the modulus of rupture. This is shown in Fig. 3.6. If we rearrange terms and note that $S_2 = I_c/c_2$, the equation for cracking moment is

$$M_{cr} = f_r'S_2 + P_e\left(\frac{r^2}{c_2} + e\right) \tag{3.9}$$

It may be observed that the first term in the parentheses in Eq. (3.9) is the dimension to the upper kern limit and, consequently, the entire second term represents the moment necessary to move the compressive resultant from the level of the steel centroid to the upper kern where, by definition, it will produce

zero stress at the bottom of the beam. The additional moment corresponding
to the first term, when superimposed, results in flexural cracking.

It is sometimes useful to state the safety factor relative to cracking. This
may be defined in several ways but is usually stated with respect to the live
load bending moment such that

$$M_o + M_d + F_{cr}M_l = M_{cr} \tag{c}$$

in which the factor F_{cr} may be less than, equal to, or larger than unity. Then

$$F_{cr} = \frac{M_{cr} - M_o - M_d}{M_l} \tag{3.10}$$

EXAMPLE   Calculation of Cracking Moment for
Given Beam and Loads

Calculate the cracking moment and find the factor of safety against cracking for the I beam
considered in the example of Art. 3.4 and shown in Fig. 3.4. The modulus of rupture of
the concrete is $f'_r = 350$ psi (2.4 N/mm^2).

The cracking moment can be found by direct substitution into Eq. (3.9):

$$M_{cr} = f'_r S_2 + P_e \left(\frac{r^2}{c_2} + e\right)$$

$$= 350 \times 1000 + 144{,}000 \left(\frac{68.2}{12} + 5.19\right)$$

$$= 1{,}916{,}000 \text{ in.-lb}$$

$$= 160 \text{ ft-kips (217 kN-m)}$$

Assuming for present purposes that the entire superimposed load is a live load, then the
safety factor against cracking, expressed with respect to an increase in the live load is,
from Eq. (3.10):

$$F_{cr} = \frac{M_{cr} - M_o - M_d}{M_l}$$

$$= \frac{160 - 37 - 0}{110} = 1.12$$

3.7 FLEXURAL STRENGTH

The most important single property of a structure is its strength, because a
member's strength relates directly to its safety. Adequate strength of a prestressed concrete member is *not* automatically insured by limiting stresses at
service load. Should the member be overloaded, significant changes in behavior
result from cracking, and because one or both of the materials will be stressed
into the inelastic range before failure. The true factor of safety can be established
only by calculating the strength of the member, with full recognition of these

effects, and comparing the load that would cause the member to fail with the load that is actually expected to act.

It has already been shown that prestressed concrete beams differ in their behavior from reinforced concrete beams. As the load is increased up to about the service load stage, the forces composing the internal resisting couple stay nearly constant, the increase in applied moment being resisted through an increase in the internal lever arm.

Obviously this cannot continue indefinitely. Upon cracking, there is a sudden increase in the steel stress, accompanied by an increase in the concrete compressive stress resultant. As the load is further increased, a prestressed beam behaves more like an ordinary reinforced concrete beam. The internal lever arm remains about constant, and both concrete and steel stresses increase with load. As for a reinforced concrete beam, the flexural capacity is reached when the steel is stressed to its ultimate strength, or when the compressive strain capacity of the concrete is reached.

Even at loads near the ultimate, however, there are important differences between prestressed and reinforced concrete beams, as a result of the following: (1) In reinforced concrete, under zero load, the strain in the reinforcement is zero. In prestressed concrete, the strain in the tendons at zero load is not zero, but corresponds to the effective prestress after losses. Any further strain in the steel caused by applied loads adds to this preexisting strain. (2) The stress-strain characteristics of prestressing steel are quite different from those of reinforcing bars, as shown by Fig. 2.2. Prestressing steels do not show a definite yield plateau. Yielding develops gradually and, in the inelastic range, the stress-strain curve continues to rise smoothly until the tensile strength is reached. The spread between the nominal yield strength f_{py} and the ultimate tensile strength f_{pu} is much smaller for prestressing steels than is the spread between the corresponding values for reinforcing steel. Also, the total elongation ε_{pu} at rupture is much smaller.

A. STRESS-STRAIN CURVES

Representative stress-strain curves for prestressing steel and concrete are shown in Fig. 3.7 for reference. For the steel, Fig. 3.7a, a convenient and easily remembered notation is as follows:

f_{pe}, ε_{pe} = stress and strain in the steel due to effective prestress force P_e after all losses*

f_{py}, ε_{py} = yield stress and yield strain for the steel, defined as in Art. 2.5, pg 41

f_{pu}, ε_{pu} = ultimate tensile strength and ultimate strain of the steel

f_{ps}, ε_{ps} = stress and strain in the steel when the beam fails

* This stress is termed f_{se} in the ACI Code.

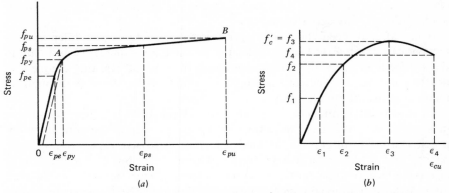

Figure 3.7   Representative stress-strain curves. (*a*) Prestressing steel.
(*b*) Concrete.

For the concrete, the ultimate compressive strength is termed f'_c as usual, and the failure strain is ε_{cu}, shown in Fig. 3.7*b*. Measurements of concrete strain at failure in beam tests indicate that values of ε_{cu} between 0.003 and 0.004 are attained. Consistent with the ACI Code, a limiting strain of 0.003 for the concrete will be assumed.

B. SUCCESSIVE CONCRETE STRESS DISTRIBUTIONS AS BEAM IS OVERLOADED

As for ordinary reinforced concrete beams, prestressed beams may be divided into two types, based on mode of flexural failure. For under-reinforced beams, failure is initiated by yielding of the tensile steel. The associated large tensile strains permit widening of flexural cracks and upward migration of the neutral axis. The increased concrete stresses acting on the reduced compressive area result in a "secondary" compression failure of the concrete, even though the failure is initiated by yielding. The stress in the steel at failure will be between points *A* and *B* of Fig. 3.7*a*. The large steel strains produce visible cracking and considerable deflection of the member before the failure load is reached, as illustrated by the test beam of Fig. 3.8. This is an important safety consideration.

Over-reinforced beams, on the other hand, fail when the compressive strain limit of the concrete is reached, at a load when the steel is still below its yield stress, between points *O* and *A* of Fig. 3.7*a*. This second type of failure is accompanied by a *downward* movement of the neutral axis, because the concrete is stressed into its nonlinear range while the steel response is still linear. This type of failure occurs suddenly, with little warning.

The concrete compressive stress distributions in under- and over-reinforced prestressed beams, at successive loading stages, are shown in Fig. 3.9. For either under- or over-reinforced members, the stress distribution at any stage can be found from the concrete stress-strain curve as follows.

Figure 3.8 Flexural failure of bonded pretensioned beam (courtesy Portland Cement Association).

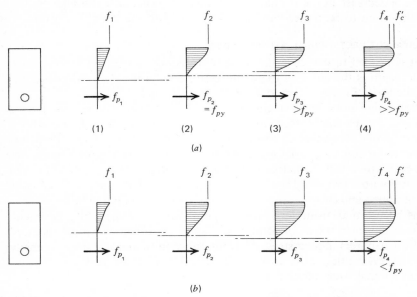

Figure 3.9 Successive flexural stress distributions as load is increased from cracking to ultimate loads. (*a*) Underreinforced prestressed beam. (*b*) Overreinforced prestressed beam.

Based on the usual assumption that plane cross sections of a beam remain plane as bending moment is applied, the concrete strains at any load stage vary linearly from zero at the neutral axis to a maximum at the top face. Consequently, the variation of compressive stress with distance from the neutral axis is identically the same as the variation of stress with strain indicated by the stress-strain curve, up to that strain corresponding to the maximum value, at the top face of the beam.

Accordingly, the stress distribution at stage (1) (Figs. 3.9a or 3.9b), is approximately linear, while that at stage (2) shows a slight curvature near the top of the beam. At stage (3) the stress-strain curve up to the maximum stress f'_c is reproduced, but failure is not obtained until stage (4) when the maximum strain is equal to ε_{cu}, and the entire stress-strain curve is reproduced.

Except in unusual cases, prestressed concrete beams are underreinforced. When the concrete reaches its limiting strain, the steel stress f_{ps} will be between f_{py} and f_{pu} as shown in Fig. 3.7a.

It is interesting to observe that an over-reinforced prestressed beam, in which the steel stress is below yield at failure, can be transformed into an under-reinforced prestressed beam by increasing the intensity of prestress in the steel. Thus it is evident that the distinction between an under- and over-reinforced prestressed beam depends, not only on the steel ratio and properties of the materials, as for a reinforced concrete beam, but on the intensity of prestress in the steel as well. But it must also be noted that, if the intensity of stress in the steel is to be increased, yet the same prestress force applied to the beam as before, a decrease in the steel area is required. It is actually this change that causes the beam to be under-reinforced, according to the definition given.

C. EQUIVALENT RECTANGULAR STRESS BLOCK

All that is needed to calculate the ultimate resisting moment of a prestressed concrete beam is the value of the compressive resultant C (which must equal the tensile force T) and the internal lever arm at failure.

If the concrete had a stress-strain curve that could be defined mathematically, it would be a simple matter to establish explicit relations for both the magnitude and location of C. However, as was discussed in Art. 2.8, the shape of the stress-strain curve for concrete varies greatly. For this reason, such explicit equations cannot be written. But the actual unknown distribution of concrete stress can be replaced with a simplified representation chosen so that (a) the correct value of C is obtained and (b) the force C acts at the correct level in the beam.

It has been found, using an approach combining analysis and experiment, that the actual distribution of compressive stress in the beam can be replaced by an equivalent rectangular stress distribution having a uniform stress intensity of $0.85f'_c$ and a depth a, as shown in Fig. 3.10. The relation between the equivalent and actual stress block depths is

$$a = \beta_1 c \qquad\qquad (3.11)$$

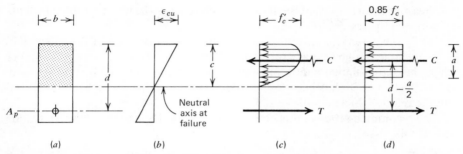

Figure 3.10 Strain and stress distributions at failure load. (*a*) Cross section. (*b*) Strains. (*c*) Actual stress distribution. (*d*) Equivalent rectangular distribution.

The value of β_1 has been established experimentally as given by the relation $\beta_1 = 0.85 - 0.05(f'_c - 4000)/1000$, where β_1 is not to exceed 0.85 and is not to be less than 0.65. Values for common concrete strengths are shown in Table 3.3.

Table 3.3 Values of β_1 = Stress Block Depth/Neutral Axis Depth

Concrete Compressive Strength f'_c	psi	3000	4000	5000	6000	7000	≥ 8000
	N/mm²	21	28	34	41	48	≥ 55
$\beta_1 = a/c$		0.85	0.85	0.80	0.75	0.70	0.65

A complete explanation of the equivalent rectangular stress block and its development is to be found in Ref. 3.14. It must be emphasized that the depth *a* is *not* the distance to the true neutral axis, nor are the concrete stresses actually distributed in the highly unlikely way suggested by Fig. 3.10*d*. The rectangular stress block is merely a computational device invented to give the correct answers, even though the actual distribution of concrete stress is not known in a particular case.

D. EFFECTIVE FLANGE WIDTH

If the compression flange of a prestressed concrete beam is but little wider than the web, the entire flange can be considered effective in resisting the compressive force. However, for very wide flanges, the compressive stress in the flange is not uniform, but decreases with lateral distance from the web. This is so because of shearing deformation of the flange, which relieves the more remote elements of some compressive stress.

While the actual longitudinal compression varies because of this effect, it is convenient in design to make use of an *effective flange width* that may be smaller than the actual flange width, but that is considered to be uniformly stressed. This effective width has been found to depend primarily on the beam span and on the relative thickness of the slab.

The recommendations for effective flange width that appear in the ACI Code are as follows:

1. For symmetrical T beams the effective width b shall not exceed one-fourth the span length of the beam. The overhanging width $(b - b_w)/2$ on either side of the beam web shall not exceed 8 times the thickness of the slab nor one-half the clear distance to the next beam.
2. For beams having a flange on one side only, the effective overhanging flange width shall not exceed one-twelfth the span length of the beam, nor 6 times the slab thickness, nor one-half the clear distance to the next beam.
3. For isolated beams in which the T form is used only for the purpose of providing additional compressive area, the flange thickness shall not be less than one-half the width of the web, and the total flange width shall not be more than 4 times the web width.

E. FLEXURAL STRENGTH BY STRAIN-COMPATIBILITY ANALYSIS

Strains and stresses in the concrete and steel at loading stages presently of interest are shown in Fig. 3.11. Strain distribution (1) of Fig. 3.11a results from application of effective prestress force P_e, acting alone, after all losses. At this stage the stress in the steel and the associated strain are, respectively,

$$f_{pe} = \frac{P_e}{A_p} \tag{3.12}$$

$$\varepsilon_1 = \varepsilon_{pe} = \frac{f_{pe}}{E_p} \tag{3.13}$$

Steel strain, in Fig. 3.11a, is shown with respect to its own separate origin.

Next, it is useful to consider an intermediate load stage (2) corresponding to decompression of the concrete at the level of the steel centroid. Assuming that bond remains intact between the concrete and steel, the increase in steel strain produced as loads pass from stage (1) to stage (2) is the same as the decrease in concrete strain at that level in the beam. It is given by the expression

$$\varepsilon_2 = \frac{P_e}{A_c E_c} \left(1 + \frac{e^2}{r^2} \right) \tag{3.14}$$

All terms are as defined earlier in this chapter.

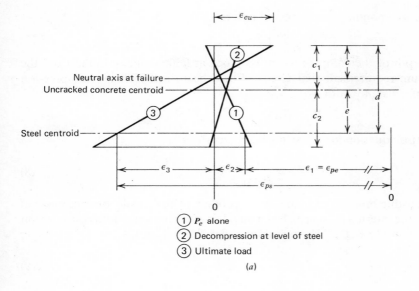

(1) P_e alone
(2) Decompression at level of steel
(3) Ultimate load

(a)

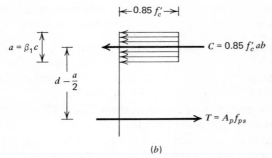

(b)

Figure 3.11 Strains and stresses as beam load is increased to failure. (a) Strains in concrete and steel. (b) Equivalent concrete stress distribution at failure.

When the member is overloaded to the failure stage (3), the neutral axis is at a distance c below the top of the beam. The increment of strain is

$$\varepsilon_3 = \varepsilon_{cu} \left(\frac{d - c}{c} \right) \tag{3.15}$$

The total steel strain at failure ε_{ps} is the sum of the three components just found from Eqs. (3.13), (3.14), and (3.15):

$$\varepsilon_{ps} = \varepsilon_1 + \varepsilon_2 + \varepsilon_3 \tag{3.16}$$

and the corresponding steel stress at failure f_{ps} is

$$f_{ps} = E_p \varepsilon_{ps} \tag{3.17}$$

The depth of the compressive stress block at failure can be found from the equilibrium requirement that $C = T$. For a beam in which the compression zone is of constant width b

$$0.85 f_c' ab = A_p f_{ps}$$

Solving this equation for the stress block depth

$$a = \frac{A_p f_{ps}}{0.85 f_c' b} = \beta_1 c \tag{3.18}$$

The resisting moment at failure is the product of the tensile (or compressive) force and the internal lever arm. For a member with constant width compression zone, referring to Fig. 3.11b, the nominal flexural strength is

$$M_n = A_p f_{ps} \left(d - \frac{a}{2} \right) \tag{3.19}$$

Equations (3.18) and (3.19) cannot be used directly to calculate the failure moment for a beam, because the steel stress f_{ps} at failure is not known. However an iterative solution can be devised, along the following lines:

1. Assume a reasonable value for the steel stress f_{ps} at failure, and note from the steel stress-strain curve the corresponding failure strain ε_{ps}.
2. Calculate the depth c to the actual neutral axis, based on that steel stress, using Eq. (3.18) based on horizontal equilibrium.
3. Calculate the incremental strain ε_3 from Eq. (3.15) and add this to the prior strains as indicated by Eq. (3.16).
4. If the failure strain ε_{ps} so obtained differs significantly from that assumed in step (1), revise that assumption and repeat steps (1) through (3) until satisfactory agreement is obtained.
5. With both $a = \beta_1 c$ and f_{ps} now known, calculate the ultimate flexural moment using Eq. (3.19).

It will be found that in most cases the iterative solution proposed converges quite rapidly and that often only two cycles are sufficient.

The method just described pertains to beams for which the width of the compression zone at failure is constant. Thus it applies to rectangular section beams, and also to T and I section beams for which the stress block depth a is less than, or at the most equal to, the compression flange thickness. This is often the case.

For beams having a T or I section, for which the stress block depth is greater than the flange thickness, Eqs. (3.18) and (3.19) are not correct because of the irregular shape of the compression zone. However, the depth a can easily be found on the basis that the compression zone, when stressed uniformly to $0.85f'_c$, must provide a force equal to the tensile force $A_p f_{ps}$. The ultimate resisting moment is found taking the internal lever arm equal to the distance from the steel centroid to the centroid of the irregularly shaped compression zone.

The suitability of the equivalent rectangular stress block, with uniform stress of $0.85f'_c$, for determining the resisting moment of I and T sections may reasonably be questioned. Its experimental basis was developed with reference to rectangular section beams. However, comparison with results of extensive calculations based on stress distributions from actual compressive stress-strain curves (Ref. 3.16) indicates that use of the rectangular stress block for T and I section beams, as well as for beams of circular or triangular section, introduces only minor error and is fully justified.

F. FLEXURAL STRENGTH OF MEMBERS WITH UNBONDED TENDONS

The preceding analysis is applicable if the steel tendons are bonded to the concrete, so that no relative movement (slip) occurs between the two components. This is naturally the case for pretensioned beams, and is normally true for post-tensioned members in which the tendons are grouted after they are tensioned.

However, with some types of post-tensioned construction, such as when asphalt-coated paper-wrapped tendons are used, or when tendons are located in the hollow cells of box girders, grouting is not possible. In the resulting members, where the steel is not bonded to the concrete, slip can occur between the two as flexural loading is applied.

The result is that the elongation of the steel is distributed over the entire length of the tendon, rather than being concentrated at the cracks as for bonded construction. The increase in steel strain and stress at the critical moment section is less than for a bonded beam, and the stress may be only slightly more than the effective prestress f_{pe} when the member fails. Failure in such case is characterized by a small number of rather wide cracks. The growth of such cracks causes a concentration of compression in the reduced area of concrete above the cracks, exceeding the capacity of the concrete to resist.

Test indicate that the failure load of an unbonded beam may be only 75 to 80 percent of that for an otherwise identical bonded member (Refs. 3.6, 3.7).

G. CONTRIBUTION OF NONPRESTRESSED REINFORCEMENT

Prestressed concrete beams almost always contain a significant amount of non-prestressed reinforcing bars, as indicated in Fig. 3.12. Stirrups (*a*) are provided to resist shear and diagonal tensile stresses, as in ordinary reinforced concrete construction. Transverse bars (*b*) insure the integrity of thin projecting flanges or may be included (*c*) as an aid in positioning other steel during construction. Small diameter longitudinal bars (*d*) and (*e*) are included in post-tensioned members to control shrinkage cracking prior to tensioning the main steel and to aid in crack control in partially prestressed beams; the contribution to flexural resistance of these small longitudinal bars is usually not significant.

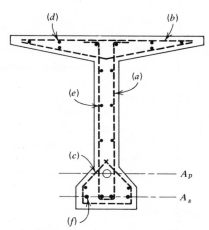

Figure 3.12 Cross section of post-tensioned beam.

However, other non-prestressed bars (f) of larger diameter may be included, not only to limit the width of flexural cracks, and to aid in controlling deflection, but also, in many situations, specifically to increase the ultimate flexural strength of the beam. Unstressed high strength tendons may be incorporated for the same purpose.

While the eccentricity of the prestressing tendon must normally be limited, in order to avoid excessive tensile stresses at the top of the unloaded member, unstressed bars (f) may be placed as close to the tension face of the beam as permitted by requirements of concrete protection for the bars. In this way their contribution to flexural strength is maximized.

Members in which substantial amounts of nonprestressed flexural reinforcement are present are sometimes referred to as *prestressed reinforced concrete beams* (Ref. 3.8) and may combine the advantages of each type of construction.

The non-prestressed bars of area A_s (Fig. 3.12) will almost always be stressed at or above their yield strength when the member is loaded to failure. The reason for this is evident from Fig. 3.13, in which the stress-strain curves for the non-prestressed and prestressed reinforcement are superimposed. When the tendon is at its effective stress f_{pe}, the reinforcing bars carry a compressive stress equal to n_s times the concrete compressive stress at the level of the steel, where $n_s = E_s/E_c$. (Effects of concrete shrinkage and creep are neglected here.) As the beam is overloaded to failure, both the tendon and the bar reinforcement experience the same strain increment $\Delta\varepsilon$ if they are at the same level in the member. If, as is often the case, the bars are at a greater depth than the tendon, they will experience a strain increment greater than that of the tendon. In either case, the strain increment $\Delta\varepsilon$ is sufficient to stress the bars past the tensile yield point except in very unusual cases.

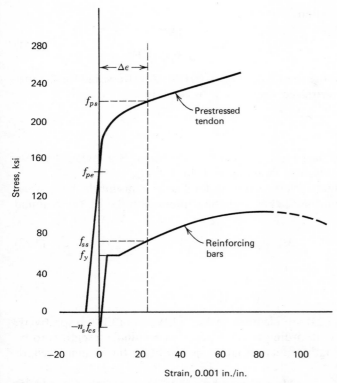

Figure 3.13 Superimposed stress-strain curves for reinforcing bars and tendons.

The inclusion of non-prestressed bars in a strain-compatibility analysis presents no serious complication, and the modifications to be made are obvious, as illustrated by an example in Art. 3.9. In most cases, it is sufficient to assume that they act at their yield stress.

H. ACI EQUATIONS FOR FLEXURAL STRENGTH

According to the ACI Code, the flexural strength of prestressed concrete beams can be calculated using a strain-compatibility analysis such as described in Art. 3.7(E). Alternatively, within certain limitations, an approximate determination may be made. Provided the effective prestress in the steel f_{pe} is not less than $0.5f_{pu}$, the steel stress at failure may be taken equal to the following, according to the Code:

a. For bonded tendons

$$f_{ps} = f_{pu}\left(1 - 0.5\rho_p \frac{f_{pu}}{f'_c}\right) \qquad (3.20)$$

b.   For unbonded tendons

$$f_{ps} = f_{pe} + 10,000 + \frac{f_c'}{100\rho_p} \qquad (3.21)$$

but in either case not more than f_{py} or (f_{pe} + 60,000). All stresses in these equations are in psi. The prestressed steel ratio ρ_p is equal to

$$\rho_p = \frac{A_p}{bd} \qquad (3.22)$$

where b is the width of the compression face of the beam. Non-prestressed bar reinforcement may be assumed to act at its yield stress.

For beams of rectangular cross section, or for T or I beams in which the stress block depth falls within the thickness of the compression flange, the nominal flexural strength is

$$M_n = A_p f_{ps}\left(d - \frac{a}{2}\right) \qquad (3.23)$$

and

$$a = \frac{A_p f_{ps}}{0.85 f_c' b} \qquad (3.24)$$

Equations (3.23) and (3.24) are identical to Eqs. (3.19) and (3.18), respectively.

For design purposes, according to the Code, this nominal strength is to be multiplied by the strength reduction factor ϕ to obtain the design strength

$$\phi M_n = \phi A_p f_{ps}\left(d - \frac{a}{2}\right) \qquad (3.25)$$

where $\phi = 0.90$ for flexure.

For flanged members such as T and I beams in which the stress block depth is greater than the flange thickness,* the total steel area is divided for computational purposes into two parts. The first part, of area A_{pf} acting at stress f_{ps}, exactly balances the compression in the overhanging portion of the flange:

$$A_{pf} = 0.85 \frac{f_c'}{f_{ps}} (b - b_w)h_f \qquad (3.26)$$

and acts with an internal lever arm $[d - (h_f/2)]$. All geometric terms are defined in Fig. 3.14.

The remaining part of the steel area A_{pw} is paired with the compression in the web. Accordingly,

$$A_{pw} = A_p - A_{pf} \qquad (3.27)$$

---

* According to the Code Commentary, this is usually the case where the flange thickness is less than $1.4d\rho_p f_{ps}/f_c'$.

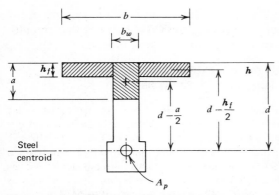

Figure 3.14   Division of compression zone
of flanged beam for computation of ultimate
resisting moment.

and the depth of the stress block is

$$a = \frac{A_{pw}f_{ps}}{0.85f'_c b_w}$$

(3.28)

The internal lever arm for this part of the resisting moment is $[d - (a/2)]$.
  The total resisting moment at failure is found by summing the two parts:

$$M_n = A_{pw}f_{ps}\left(d - \frac{a}{2}\right) + A_{pf}f_{ps}\left(d - \frac{h_f}{2}\right)$$

(3.29)

and for design purposes, as usual the flexural resistance is assumed equal to
ϕM_n.
  If the reinforcement index

$$\rho_p \frac{f_{ps}}{f'_c}$$

(3.30)

exceeds 0.30, it has been found that Eqs. (3.23) and (3.29) do not correlate well
with tests. Consequently alternate expressions are given in the Code for ultimate
moment in such cases. For rectangular beams, or beams in which the stress
block depth is equal to or less than the flange thickness,

$$M_n = 0.25f'_c bd^2$$

(3.31)

and for flanged sections in which the stress block depth is greater than the
flange thickness:

$$M_n = 0.25f'_c b_w d^2 + 0.85f'_c (b - b_w)h_f\left(d - \frac{h_f}{2}\right)$$

(3.32)

In either case, the design strength is to be taken equal to ϕM_n.

As a precaution against abrupt flexural failure resulting from rupture of the prestressing steel immediately upon cracking, the Code requires that the ultimate resisting moment be at least 1.2 times the cracking moment.

EXAMPLE   Ultimate Flexural Capacity by Strain Compatibility Analysis

Using the strain compatibility method of Art. 3.7E, find the ultimate moment capacity for the I beam example of Art. 3.4, shown in Figs. 3.4 and 3.15. Normal density concrete is to be used, with compressive strength $f'_c = 4000$ psi and elastic modulus $E_c = 3.61 \times 10^6$ psi. The ultimate strain capacity of the concrete is $\varepsilon_{cu} = 0.0030$, and $\beta_1 = 0.85$. The beam is pretensioned, using seven Grade 250 1/2 in. diameter seven wire strands, for which the stress-strain curve is as shown in Fig. 2.4. The effective prestress force $P_e = 144$ kips as for the previous example ($f'_c = 28$ N/mm², $E_c = 24,890$ N/mm², and $P_e = 641$ kN).

From Table 2.2 the cross-sectional area of one 1/2 in. strand is 0.144 in.²; hence

$$A_p = 7 \times 0.144 = 1.008 \text{ in.}^2$$

The stress and strain in the tendons due to the effective prestress force are, respectively,

$$f_{pe} = \frac{P_e}{A_p} = \frac{144}{1.008} = 143 \text{ ksi}$$

$$\varepsilon_{pe} = \frac{f_{pe}}{E_p} = \frac{143}{27000} = 0.0053 = \varepsilon_1$$

The increase in steel strain as the concrete at its level is decompressed is found from Eq. (3.14)

$$\varepsilon_2 = \frac{P_e}{A_c E_c}\left(1 + \frac{e^2}{r^2}\right) = \frac{144}{176 \times 3.61 \times 10^3}\left(1 + \frac{5.19^2}{68.2}\right) = 0.0003$$

The steel stress at failure will initially be assumed to be 200 ksi. From Fig. 2.4 the corresponding strain is $\varepsilon_{ps} = 0.0070$. Assuming that the stress block depth is less than the average flange thickness of 5 in.; its depth is calculated using Eq. (3.18):

$$a = \frac{A_p f_{ps}}{0.85 f'_c b} = \frac{1.008 \times 200}{0.85 \times 4 \times 12} = 4.94 \text{ in.}$$

and the actual neutral axis location is

$$c = \frac{4.94}{0.85} = 5.81$$

below the top surface. Next the increment of steel strain as the beam passes from the decompression stage to failure is found, using Eq. (3.15):

$$\varepsilon_3 = \varepsilon_{cu} \frac{d - c}{c} = 0.0030 \times \frac{17.19 - 5.81}{5.81} = 0.0059$$

and the total steel strain at failure, found from the sum of the three parts, as indicated by Eq. (3.16) is

$$\varepsilon_{ps} = \varepsilon_1 + \varepsilon_2 + \varepsilon_3$$
$$= 0.0053 + 0.0003 + 0.0059$$
$$= 0.0115$$

which must be compared with the strain of 0.0070 assumed at the start. Clearly a revised estimate is required.

For the second trial, a steel failure stress of 210 ksi is assumed, with corresponding strain of 0.0095. The stress block depth in this case is

$$a = 4.94 \times \frac{210}{200} = 5.19$$

$$c = \frac{5.19}{0.85} = 6.10$$

and the incremental strain in the tendon

$$\varepsilon_3 = 0.0030 \times \frac{17.19 - 6.10}{6.10} = 0.0055$$

as shown in Fig. 3.15b. The total steel strain at failure is thus

$$\varepsilon_{ps} = 0.0053 + 0.0003 + 0.0055$$
$$= 0.0111$$

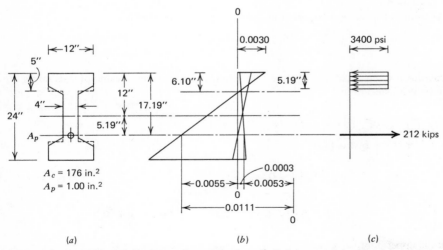

(a)   (b)   (c)

Figure 3.15 Flexural strength analysis of I beam. (a) Cross section. (b) Strains in concrete and steel. (c) Stress and steel force.

compared with the assumed value of 0.0095. It is clear from inspection of the stress–strain curve that further refinement would result in negligible change in the failure stress in the steel. The steel stress at failure is very close to 210 ksi (1450 N/mm^2) and the nominal strength, from Eq. (3.19) is

$$M_n = A_p f_{ps}\left(d - \frac{a}{2}\right)$$

$$= 1.008 \times 210 \left(17.19 - \frac{5.19}{2}\right)$$

$$= 3089 \text{ in.-kips}$$

$$= 257 \text{ ft-kips } (348 \text{ kN-m})$$

Additional Comments

1.   Although the stress block depth exceeds the thickness of the outer portions of the flange, it is about equal to the average thickness; refinement to account for the actual shape of the compression zone would have little effect on results in this case.
2.   The steel strain increment ε_2 caused by decompression of the concrete is very small compared with ε_1 and ε_3. Neglect of this quantity would have little influence on results.
3.   The steel strain at failure is close to that corresponding to the yield stress. Consequently, very little elongation of the steel would occur, should the beam be overloaded, prior to abrupt crushing of the concrete. From the viewpoint of safety, the design could be improved if a more ductile failure mode could be insured. Such modifications will be explored in Ch. 4.

EXAMPLE   Ultimate Flexural Capacity by ACI Equations

Find the ultimate moment capacity of the beam just considered by using the approximate ACI equations.
  The ratio of effective prestress to ultimate strength of the steel is

$$\frac{f_{pe}}{f_{pu}} = \frac{143}{250} = 0.57 > 0.50$$

Consequently, Eq. (3.20) may be used to obtain the approximate value of steel stress at failure. With steel ratio

$$\rho_p = \frac{A_p}{bd} = \frac{1.008}{12 \times 17.19} = 0.0049$$

the failure stress, by Eq. (3.20) is

$$f_{ps} = f_{pu}\left(1 - 0.5\rho_p \frac{f_{pu}}{f_c'}\right)$$

$$= 250\left(1 - 0.5 \times 0.0049 \times \frac{250}{4}\right) = 212 \text{ ksi}$$

But the upper limit values are

$$f_{se} + 60,000 = 203,000 \text{ psi} = 203 \text{ ksi}$$

$$f_{py} = 210 \text{ ksi (from Fig. 2.4)}$$

The first of these limits is seen to control in this case and $f_{ps} = 203$ ksi (1400 N/mm²), according to the Code. From Eq. (3.30) the reinforcement index is

$$\rho_p \frac{f_{ps}}{f_c'} = 0.0049 \times \frac{203}{4} = 0.25$$

Since this is less than 0.30 the beam is classed as underreinforced, according to the Code, and either Eq. (3.23) or (3.29) is applicable. To determine which equation to use, one compares the parameter

$$1.4 \, d\rho_p \frac{f_{ps}}{f_c'} = 1.4 \times 17.19 \times 0.0049 \times \frac{203}{4} = 5.99$$

with the 5 in. average flange thickness. It is clear that Eq. (3.29) for flanged sections is applicable. From Eq. (3.26) the flange steel area is

$$A_{pf} = 0.85 \times \frac{f_c'}{f_{ps}} (b - b_w) h_f$$

$$= 0.85 \times \frac{4}{203} \times 8 \times 5 = 0.670 \text{ in.}^2$$

while from Eq. (3.27) the web steel area is

$$A_{pw} = A_p - A_{pf} = 1.008 - 0.670 = 0.338 \text{ in.}^2$$

The depth of the stress block within the beam web is found from Eq. (3.28) to be

$$a = \frac{A_{pw} f_{ps}}{0.85 f_c' b_w} = \frac{0.338 \times 203}{0.85 \times 4 \times 4} = 5.05 \text{ in.}$$

Finally, using Eq. (3.29) the nominal flexural strength is

$$M_n = A_{pw} f_{ps} \left(d - \frac{a}{2} \right) + A_{pf} f_{ps} \left(d - \frac{h_f}{2} \right)$$

$$= 0.338 \times 203 \left(17.19 - \frac{5.05}{2} \right) + 0.670 \times 203 \left(17.19 - \frac{5}{2} \right)$$

$$= 3004 \text{ in.-kips}$$

$$= 250 \text{ ft-kips (339 kN-m)}$$

Additional Comments

1.   The predicted failure moment of 250 ft-kips according to the ACI approximate method is very close to the value of 257 ft-kips obtained by the more exact strain-compatibility analysis. Agreement will not always be so good, particularly for beams with high steel ratios.

2.   Although a flanged-beam analysis is indicated by the Code equation, the depth of the stress block in the web, when calculated, is actually nearly equal to the flange thickness of 5 in. This indicates that an analysis based on a constant width compression zone would have been suitable, as was found by the more exact analysis.

3.   Whichever method is used to calculate the nominal flexural strength, M_n, that value must be reduced by the factor ϕ to obtain the design strength ϕM_n.

3.8 FULL VERSUS PARTIAL PRESTRESSING

Early in the development of prestressed concrete, the goal of prestressing was the complete elimination of concrete tensile stress at service loads. The concept was that of an entirely new, homogeneous material that would remain uncracked and respond elastically up to the maximum anticipated loading. This kind of design, where the limiting tensile stress in the concrete at full service load is zero, is generally known as *full prestressing*, while an alternative approach, in which a certain amount of tensile stress is permitted in the concrete at full service load, is called *partial prestressing*.*

There are cases in which it is necessary to avoid all risk of cracking and in which full prestressing is required. Such cases include tanks or reservoirs where leaks must be avoided, submerged structures or those subject to a highly corrosive environment where maximum protection of reinforcement must be insured, and structures subject to high frequency repetition of load where fatigue of the reinforcement may be a consideration.

However, there are many cases where substantially improved performance, reduced cost, or both may be obtained through the use of a lesser amount of prestress. Fully prestressed beams may exhibit an undesirable amount of upward camber because of the eccentric prestressing force, a displacement that is only partially counteracted by the gravity loads producing downward deflection. This tendency is aggravated by creep in the concrete, which magnifies the upward displacement due to the prestress force, but has little influence on the downward deflection due to live loads, which may be only intermittently applied. Also, should heavily prestressed members be overloaded and fail, they may do so in a brittle way, rather than gradually as do beams with a smaller amount of prestress. This is important from the point of view of safety, because sudden failure without warning is dangerous, and gives no opportunity for corrective measures to be taken. Furthermore, experience indicates that in many cases improved economy results from the use of a combination of unstressed bar steel and high strength prestressed steel tendons.

While tensile stress and possible cracking may be allowed at full service load, it is also recognized that such full service load may be infrequently applied. The typical, or characteristic, load acting is likely to be the dead load plus a small fraction of the specified live load. Thus a partially prestressed beam may not be subject to tensile stress under the usual conditions of loading. Cracks may form occasionally, when the maximum load is applied, but these will close completely when that load is removed. They may be no more objectionable

---

* The pioneer designer Freyssinet was originally a strong advocate of full prestressing, although in later years he modified his position, indicating that concrete tensile stress somewhat in excess of the modulus of rupture was quite appropriate for bridge structures, for example, where the maximum load occurred only rarely. The advantages of partial prestressing were presented convincingly by Abeles as early as 1951 (Ref. 3.10).

in prestressed structures than in ordinary reinforced concrete, in which flexural cracks always form. They may be considered a small price to pay for the improvements in performance and economy that are obtained.

It has been observed that reinforced concrete is but a special case of prestressed concrete in which the prestressing force is zero. The behavior of reinforced and prestressed concrete beams, as the failure load is approached, is essentially the same.

Load-deflection relations for beams with a varying amount of prestress force are presented in a qualitative way in Fig. 3.16. Both reinforced concrete and prestressed concrete beams may be *under-reinforced*, with a relatively small steel area such that failure is triggered by yielding or rupture of the steel, or

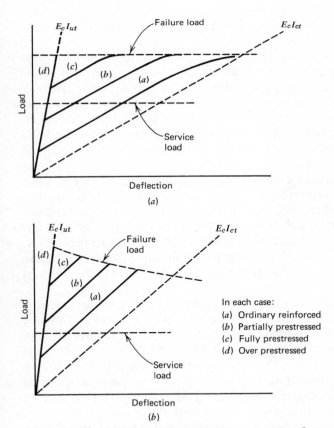

In each case:

(a) Ordinary reinforced
(b) Partially prestressed
(c) Fully prestressed
(d) Over prestressed

Figure 3.16   Idealized load-deflection curves for beams with varying amount of prestress force (adapted from Ref. 3.5). (a) Under-reinforced beams. (b) Over-reinforced beams.

over-reinforced, with a relatively large steel area so that failure is initiated by crushing of the concrete on the compression side of the member before the steel reaches its yield stress. In each case, the amount of prestress force introduced by the given steel area may vary from zero (reinforced concrete) to a very large value (over-prestressing).

Figure 3.16a shows load-deflection curves for under-reinforced beams, all having the same steel area and concrete dimensions but with varying amounts of prestress. The dotted lines represent load-deflection curves calculated using the flexural rigidity of the uncracked transformed cross section ($E_c I_{ut}$) and that of the cracked transformed cross section ($E_c I_{ct}$). The load causing failure is about the same in all cases. Beam (a), with zero prestress, responds linearly up to its cracking load, after which its load-deflection curve is approximately linear and parallel to the $E_c I_{ct}$ line. Obviously for the beams (b), (c), and (d) that are prestressed, the load causing cracking is higher because initial compression stresses are superimposed in the tension zone. The location of the point of departure from the line $E_c I_{ut}$ depends on the degree of prestress. Beam (b) represents a partially prestressed beam, in which cracking may occur below full service load, while beam (c) is fully prestressed, with zero tensile stress at service load, cracking only when a higher load is reached. Beam (d) is over-prestressed, and will fail suddenly in a brittle fashion. As shown in the figure, for under-reinforced beams there is normally a further change in slope of the load-deflection curve before failure, as the steel is stressed to its inelastic range, and as extensive cracking occurs.

The corresponding curves for over-reinforced beams are given by Fig. 3.16b. Such beams may also have zero prestress or may be partially, fully, or over-prestressed, the degree of prestressing determining the cracking load as before. However, after cracking, the curves follow more or less parallel to the $E_c I_{ct}$ line all the way to failure. They fail suddenly and with much less warning than before. The effect of varying the prestress is similar to that for under-reinforced beams, except that the load that causes failure increases to some extent as the prestress force is increased (Ref. 3.5).

One may speak of the *ductility* of a prestressed concrete beam when referring to its capacity to deflect extensively before failure. It is clear from Fig. 3.16 that, as a class, under-reinforced beams are more ductile than over-reinforced beams, and that in either case partially prestressed beams exhibit more ductility than fully or over-prestressed beams. The capacity of flexural members to absorb the energy of impact is directly related to the area under its load-deflection diagram. The advantage of partial prestressing, in this respect, is also clear.

Regardless of the amount of prestress force used, the amount of steel must be such as to provide adequate flexural strength when the beam is overloaded, so that the desired factor of safety is obtained. This requirement may determine the total steel area to be used. The amount of prestress force may then be controlled (a) by stressing all tendons to less than the full permitted value, (b) by stressing some tendons fully, leaving others free of prestress, or (c) by providing the desired steel area partially by fully stressed tendons and partially by ordinary unstressed reinforcing bars. It will be shown in Art. 3.9 that, in the last case, both the tendons and the bar reinforcement act together at or near their respective ultimate strength before the member fails.

The choice of a suitable amount of prestress, as Abeles has observed, is governed by a variety of factors. These include the nature of the loading (for example, highway or railroad bridges, storage, etc.), the ratio of live to dead load, the frequency of occurrence of the full load, and the presence of corrosive agents. With structures in which the direction of loading may be reversed, such as in transmission poles (see Ch. 13), a high uniform prestress would result in reduced ultimate strength and in brittle failure. In such a case, partial prestressing provides the only satisfactory solution.

The Joint European Committee on Concrete (Ref. 3.11) establishes three classes of prestressed beams:

Class 1:   *Fully prestressed*, in which no tensile stress is allowed in the concrete at service load.

Class 2:   *Partially prestressed*, in which occasional temporary cracking is permitted under infrequent high loads.

Class 3:   *Partially prestressed*, in which there may be permanent cracks provided that their width is suitably limited.

The British Standard Code (Ref. 3.12) includes similar categories.

The ACI Code permits concrete tension of $6\sqrt{f'_c}$ at full service load, slightly less than the usual modulus of rupture, and requires the inclusion of sufficient bonded reinforcement in the tension zone to control cracking. If explicit calculation of deflection due to immediate and sustained loads indicates that those deflections are within allowable limits, and if the concrete protection for the reinforcement is increased above the usual limit, the Code permits an allowable tensile stress of $12\sqrt{f'_c}$ (see Table 3.1). Both stresses are equivalent to partial prestressing, according to the definition given earlier.

In each case, according to present United States practice, the stresses are calculated on the basis of properties of the uncracked cross section. It is clear, then, that the higher stress limit represents only a *nominal stress*, since it is well above the modulus of rupture. The justification for basing calculations on the uncracked section, in such case, is that sufficient bonded steel is present to confine and control cracking, and that the overall performance of the member at that load is approximately what it would be if the concrete could, in fact, develop the nominal tensile stress.

After the member has cracked, if both concrete and steel stresses remain in the elastic range, stresses may be computed using properties of the cracked transformed cross section (Ref. 3.17). Such calculations are described in the following article.

3.9 FLEXURAL STRESSES AFTER CRACKING AND STRENGTH OF PARTIALLY PRESTRESSED BEAMS

At the full service load stage, partially prestressed beams are cracked, although generally both concrete and steel stresses remain within the elastic range. While service load stresses at a cracked cross section may properly be considered of secondary importance, compared with the strength and safety of the member should it be overloaded, calculation of stresses may be required for several reasons:

1. For prestressed members, crack widths at service load are related to the increase in steel stress past the stage of concrete decompression; consequently, the service load steel stress must be known as well as the stress at decompression.
2. An accurate calculation of both elastic and creep deflection at service load requires that curvatures be based on actual, not nominal, stress and strain distributions.
3. If fatigue is a factor in design, it is necessary to determine actual stress ranges in both concrete and steel.
4. It may be necessary to compute stresses in the cracked section to demonstrate compliance with design codes.

For an ordinary reinforced concrete beam, calculation of stresses at a cracked section is a simple matter. The transformed section concept permits use of the familiar equations of mechanics for homogeneous elastic beams to locate neutral axis, determine section properties, and calculate stresses. Alternately, explicit equations may be derived for nonhomogeneous reinforced concrete sections (Ref. 3.14).

For cracked prestressed concrete beams, matters are more complicated. The neutral axis location and effective section properties depend not only on the geometry of the cross section and the material properties, as for reinforced concrete beams, but also on the axial prestressing force and the loading. The axial force is not constant after cracking, but depends on the loading and on the section properties.

The effective cross section of a typical partially prestressed beam at service load is shown in Fig. 3.17a. The member shown includes both prestressed steel of area A_p and non-prestressed bar reinforcement of area A_s, as is commonly the case. It is assumed that the member has cracked, that both concrete and steel are stressed only within their elastic ranges, and that the contribution of the tensile concrete can be disregarded.

The strains and stresses in the concrete and steel will be considered at several load stages, certain of which are not actually experienced by the member, but are considered only as a computational convenience (Ref. 3.15).

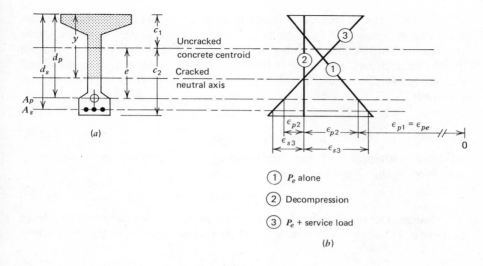

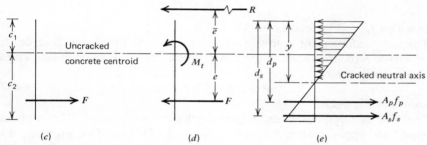

Figure 3.17 Basis for analysis of cracked cross section.
(*a*) Cracked cross section. (*b*) Concrete and steel strains.
(*c*) Decompression force. (*d*) Forces on cracked section.
(*e*) Resulting stresses.

Load stage (1) (Fig. 3.17*b*) corresponds to application of effective prestress P_e alone. At this stage, the stress in the tendon is

$$f_{p1} = f_{pe} = \frac{P_e}{A_p} \tag{3.33}$$

The compressive strain in the bar reinforcement at this stage, assuming perfect bond between the two materials, is the same as that in the concrete at the same level. Consequently the bar reinforcement is initially subjected to a compressive stress

$$f_{s1} = -E_s \varepsilon_{s2} \tag{3.34}$$

Next it is useful to consider a fictitious load stage (2) corresponding to complete decompression of the concrete, at which there is zero concrete strain through the entire depth as shown in Fig. 3.17b. Compatibility of deformation of the concrete and steel requires that the changes of stress in the tendon and the bar reinforcement as the beam passes from stage (1) to stage (2) are, respectively,

$$f_{p2} = E_p \varepsilon_{p2} \tag{3.35}$$

$$f_{s2} = E_s \varepsilon_{s2} \tag{3.36}$$

At this hypothetical load stage, the stress in the bar reinforcement, neglecting the effects of shrinkage and creep, is

$$f_s = E_s(-\varepsilon_{s2} + \varepsilon_{s2}) = 0 \tag{3.37}$$

The change in strain in the tendon is the same as that in the concrete at that level, and can be calculated on the basis of the uncracked concrete section properties:

$$\varepsilon_{p2} = \frac{P_e}{A_c E_c}\left(1 + \frac{e^2}{r^2}\right) \tag{3.38}$$

after which f_{p2} can be found from Eq. (3.35).

The bar reinforcement is unstressed at stage (2), as noted, but in order to produce the zero stress state in the concrete, the tendon must be pulled with a *fictitious external force*

$$F = A_p(f_{p1} + f_{p2}) \tag{3.39}$$

as shown in Fig. 3.17c.

The effect of this fictitious decompressing force is now cancelled by applying an equal and opposite force F as shown in Fig. 3.17d. This force, together with the external moment M_t due to self-weight and superimposed loads, can be represented by a resultant force R applied with eccentricity $\bar{e}$ above the uncracked concrete centroid, where $R = F$ and

$$\bar{e} = \frac{M_t - Fe}{R} \tag{3.40}$$

The beam can now be analyzed as an ordinary reinforced concrete member subjected to an eccentric compression force. The resultant strain distribution (3) in the concrete is shown in Fig. 3.17b. The incremental strains in the tendon and bar reinforcement, ε_{p3}, and ε_{s3}, respectively, together with their corresponding stresses f_{p3} and f_{s3}, are superimposed on the strains and stresses already present in the tendon and bar.

These incremental steel stresses, as well as the stress in the concrete, can be found using the transformed section concept (Ref. 3.14). The tendon is replaced by an equivalent area of tensile concrete $n_p A_p$ and the bar reinforcement is replaced by the area $n_s A_s$, where $n_p = E_p/E_c$ and $n_s = E_s/E_c$, as shown in Fig. 3.18a.

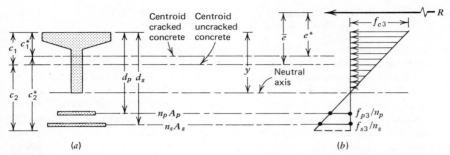

Figure 3.18 Transformed cracked cross section of partially prestressed beam. (*a*) Transformed cracked cross section. (*b*) Stresses.

The neutral axis for the equivalent homogeneous transformed section, a distance y from the top surface, can be found from the equilibrium condition that the moment of all internal forces about the line of action of R must be zero. These internal forces are based on the concrete stresses and the stresses acting on the transformed steel areas, as shown in Fig. 3.18b.

The moment equation for the internal forces about the external resultant R results in a cubic equation for y that can be solved by successive trials. Once y is known, the effective transformed area A_{ct} and moment of inertia I_{ct} of the cracked section, *about its own centroid* c_1^* from the top surface, can be found. The incremental stresses sought, as loading passes from stage (2) to stage (3), are

$$f_{c3} = -\frac{R}{A_{ct}} - \frac{Re^* c_1^*}{I_{ct}} \tag{3.41}$$

$$f_{p3} = n_p \left[-\frac{R}{A_{ct}} + \frac{Re^*(d_p - c_1^*)}{I_{ct}} \right] \tag{3.42}$$

$$f_{s3} = n_s \left[-\frac{R}{A_{ct}} + \frac{Re^*(d_s - c_1^*)}{I_{ct}} \right] \tag{3.43}$$

where geometric terms are as defined in Fig. 3.18.

The final stress in the tendon is now found by superimposing the stresses of Eqs. (3.33), (3.35), and (3.42). The stress in the bar reinforcement is given by Eq. (3.43). The concrete stress at the top surface of the beam is given by Eq. (3.41). Specifically,

$$f_p = f_{p1} + f_{p2} + f_{p3} \tag{3.44}$$

$$f_s = f_{s3} \tag{3.45}$$

$$f_c = f_{c3} \tag{3.46}$$

EXAMPLE   Elastic Flexural Stresses in Partially
Prestressed Beam after Cracking

The partially prestressed T beam shown in cross section in Fig. 3.19a is subjected to superimposed dead and service live load moments of 38 and 191 ft-kips, in addition to a moment
of 83 ft-kips due to its own weight. An effective prestress force of 123 kips is applied using
six Grade 250 1/2 in. diameter strands. Two non-prestressed Grade 60 no. 8 bars are
located close to the tension face of the beam. The elastic moduli for the concrete, tendon
steel, and bar steel are, respectively, 3.61×10^6 psi, 27×10^6 psi, and 29×10^6 psi. The
modulus of rupture of the concrete is 500 psi. Find the stresses in the concrete, prestressed
steel, and bar reinforcement at the full service load. ($M_o = 113$ kN–m, $M_d = 52$ kN-m,
$M_l = 259$ kN-m, $P_e = 547$ kN, $E_c = 24.9$ kN/mm^2, $E_p = 186$ kN/mm^2, $E_s = 200$ kN/mm^2,
and $f'_r = 3.4$ N/mm^2.)

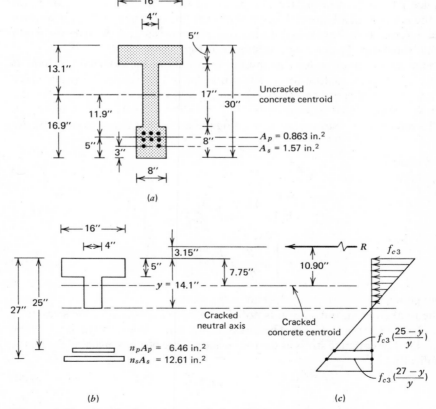

Figure 3.19   Cracked section analysis of T beam. (a) Member cross section. (b) Transformed cracked cross section. (c) Concrete stresses.

First the tensile stress in the concrete at the bottom of the beam will be checked, assuming the member is uncracked. Properties of the uncracked cross section are

$$A_c = 212 \text{ in.}^2 \ (137 \times 10^3 \text{ mm}^2)$$
$$S_1 = 1664 \text{ in.}^3 \ (27.3 \times 10^6 \text{ mm}^3)$$
$$S_2 = 1290 \text{ in.}^3 \ (21.1 \times 10^6 \text{ mm}^3)$$
$$c_1 = 13.1 \text{ in. (333 mm)}$$
$$c_2 = 16.9 \text{ in. (429 mm)}$$
$$r^2 = 103 \text{ in.}^2 \ (66.5 \times 10^3 \text{ mm}^3)$$

Then using Eq. (3.6):

$$f_2 = -\frac{P_e}{A_c}\left(1 + \frac{ec_2}{r^2}\right) + \frac{M_t}{S_2}$$

$$= -\frac{123{,}000}{212}\left(1 + \frac{11.9 \times 16.9}{103}\right) + \frac{312{,}000 \times 12}{1290}$$

$$= +1186 \text{ psi } (8.2 \text{ N/mm}^2)$$

This stress greatly exceeds the modulus of rupture, indicating that the section has, in fact, cracked. Analysis will proceed according to the method described above.

From Eq. (3.33), the effective stress in the tendon when P_e acts alone is

$$f_{p1} = f_{pe} = \frac{P_e}{A_p} = \frac{123{,}000}{0.863} = 143{,}000 \text{ psi } (986 \text{ N/mm}^2)$$

Then, with reference to Fig. 3.17b and using Eq. (3.38) the change in strain in the tendon as the section is decompressed is

$$\varepsilon_{p2} = \frac{P_e}{A_c E_c}\left(1 + \frac{e^2}{r^2}\right) = \frac{123{,}000}{212 \times 3.61 \times 10^6}\left(1 + \frac{11.9^2}{103}\right) = 0.0004$$

Thus, the corresponding increase in stress in the tendon is found from Eq. (3.35) to be

$$f_{p2} = E_p \varepsilon_{p2} = 27 \times 10^6 \times 0.0004 = 10{,}800 \text{ psi } (74 \text{ N/mm}^2)$$

In order to obtain decompression of the concrete, the fictitious external tension

$$F = A_p(f_{p1} + f_{p2}) = 0.863(143 + 10.8) = 133 \text{ kips}$$

must have been applied to the tendon. This is now cancelled by applying an equal and opposite force F. This force, acting together with the total moment of 312 ft-kips, is equivalent to a compressive force $R = 133$ kips applied with eccentricity

$$\bar{e} = \frac{M_t - Fe}{R} = \frac{312 \times 12 - 133 \times 11.9}{133} = 16.25 \text{ in.}$$

above the centroid of the uncracked concrete, or 3.15 in. above the top surface of the member as shown in Fig. 3.19. With $n_p = 27/3.61 = 7.48$ and $n_s = 29/3.61 = 8.03$ the transformed areas of the tendon and the bars are, respectively, 6.46 in.^{2} and 12.61 in.^{2} The effective cross section of the cracked beam, with neutral axis dimension y still unknown, is shown in Fig. 3.19b.

The stresses in the concrete and transformed steel, as the loads pass from stage (2) to stage (3), are shown in Fig. 3.19c. Taking moments of the resulting forces about the force R gives a cubic equation in y that is solved by successive trial to obtain $y = 14.1$ in. as shown.

With y known, the location of the centroid of the cracked transformed section is a routine matter. Taking moments of the partial areas about the top surface locates the centroid $c_1^* = 7.75$ in. from the top of the section. Section properties are

$$A_{ct} = 135 \text{ in.}^2$$
$$I_{ct} = 9347 \text{ in.}^4$$

The eccentricity of the force R with respect to the centroid of the cracked transformed section is

$$e^* = 16.25 - 13.1 + 7.75 = 10.90 \text{ in.}$$

Now the incremental stresses in the concrete and steel can be found from Eqs. (3.41), (3.42), and (3.43):

$$f_{c3} = -\frac{R}{A_{ct}} - \frac{Re^*c_1^*}{I_{ct}}$$

$$= -\frac{133,000}{135} - \frac{133,000 \times 10.90 \times 7.75}{9347} = -2,190 \text{ psi } (-15.1 \text{ N/mm}^2)$$

$$f_{p3} = n_p \left[-\frac{R}{A_{ct}} + \frac{Re^*(d_p - c_1^*)}{I_{ct}} \right]$$

$$= 7.48 \left[-\frac{133,000}{135} + \frac{133,000 \times 10.90 \times 17.25}{9347} \right] = 12,600 \text{ psi } (87 \text{ N/mm}^2)$$

$$f_{s3} = n_s \left[-\frac{R}{A_{ct}} + \frac{Re^*(d_s - c_1^*)}{I_{ct}} \right]$$

$$= 8.03 \left[-\frac{133,000}{135} + \frac{133,000 \times 10.90 \times 19.25}{9347} \right] = 16,100 \text{ psi } (111 \text{ N/mm}^2)$$

The final stress in the tendon at full service load is found by summing the three parts:

$$f_p = f_{p1} + f_{p2} + f_{p3}$$
$$= 143,000 + 10,800 + 12,600 = 166,400 \text{ psi } (1147 \text{ N/mm}^2)$$

while the stress in the bar reinforcement is

$$f_s = f_{s3} = 16,100 \text{ psi } (111 \text{ N/mm}^2)$$

and that the top surface of the concrete is

$$f_c = f_{c3} = -2190 \text{ psi } (-15.1 \text{ N/mm}^2)$$

Additional Comments

1.   The stress increase in the tendon as the beam is brought to full service load is about 17 percent of the effective prestress. In calculating service load stresses in partially prestressed beams, such increase clearly cannot be neglected.

2. The service load stress of only 16,100 psi in the bar reinforcement indicates that requirements of strength, not service load stress, probably controlled the choice of bar area.

3. Although the allowable concrete stress was not given, the stress of 2190 psi appears reasonable for concrete having a compressive strength of about 5 ksi.

4. The strain and stress information developed provides a rational basis for judging the serviceability of the beam. For example, an estimate of crack width could be made based on the stress in the bar reinforcement, using standard methods, or could be based on the increase in stress in the tendon as the member passes from the decompression stage to the full service load stage.

EXAMPLE   Ultimate Flexural Strength of Beam with Prestressed and Nontensioned Reinforcement

Using the strain compatibility method, find the ultimate moment capacity of the T beam of the preceding example. Normal density concrete having strength $f'_c = 4000$ psi is to be used; its elastic modulus is $57,000\sqrt{4000} = 3.61 \times 10^6$ psi, and its strain limit $\varepsilon_{cu} = 0.003$. It may be assumed that the stress-strain curve for the strands is as shown by Fig. 2.4, and that for the bars is as shown by Fig. 2.3. ($f'_c = 28$ N/mm^2 and $E_c = 24.9$ kN/mm^2.)

The strain in the tendon at effective prestress is

$$\varepsilon_{p1} = \varepsilon_{pe} = \frac{f_{pe}}{E_p} = \frac{143,000}{27 \times 10^6} = 0.0053$$

and the increment of strain as the concrete at the level of the tendon is decompressed is $\varepsilon_{p2} = 0.0004$ as before. (see Fig. 3.20)

The stress in the tendon will first be assumed at 200,000 psi at failure, and from the stress–strain curve the corresponding strain is $\varepsilon_{ps} = 0.0070$. The non-prestressed bars are assumed to act at their yield stress of 60,000 psi. In this case, the stress block depth at

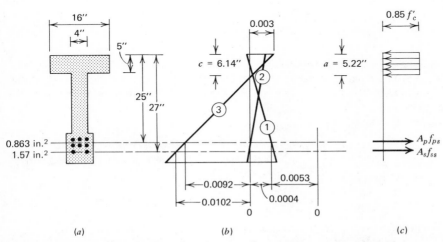

(a)   (b)   (c)

Figure 3.20 Flexural strength analysis of partially prestressed T beam. (a) Cross section. (b) Concrete and steel strains. (c) Stresses at failure.

failure is

$$a = \frac{A_p f_{ps} + A_s f_y}{0.85 f'_c b}$$

$$= \frac{0.863 \times 200 + 1.57 \times 60}{0.85 \times 4 \times 16} = 4.90 \text{ in.}$$

and $c = 4.90/0.85 = 5.77$ in. Then the increment of strain in the tendon as the loads pass from stage (2) to stage (3) is

$$\varepsilon_{p3} = \varepsilon_{cu} \frac{d - c}{c} = 0.003 \left(\frac{25 - 5.77}{5.77} \right) = 0.0100$$

and the total steel strain at failure is

$$\varepsilon_{ps} = 0.0053 + 0.0004 + 0.0100 = 0.0157$$

rather than 0.0070 as assumed.

Revised calculations for an assumed stress at failure of 220,000 psi and attendant strain of 0.0130 give

$$a = 5.22 \text{ in. (133 mm) (essentially equal to the flange thickness)}$$
$$c = 6.14 \text{ in. (156 mm)}$$
$$\varepsilon_{p3} = 0.0092$$
$$\varepsilon_{ps} = 0.0149$$

as shown in Fig. 3.20b. It is clear from the stress–strain curve for the strand that no further refinement is necessary.

The strain in the bar reinforcement at failure is

$$\varepsilon_{s3} = 0.003 \left(\frac{27 - 6.14}{6.14} \right) = 0.0102 > \varepsilon_y$$

confirming that the bars have yielded as assumed previously.

The resisting moment at failure is found taking moments of the steel forces about the compressive resultant (which may be assumed to act at the middepth of the flange in the present case):

$$M_n = A_p f_{ps} \left(d_p - \frac{a}{2} \right) + A_s f_y \left(d_s - \frac{a}{2} \right)$$

$$= 0.863 \times 220 \left(25 - \frac{5}{2} \right) + 1.57 \times 60 \left(27 - \frac{5}{2} \right)$$

$$= 6580 \text{ in.-kips} = 548 \text{ ft-kips (743 kN-m)}$$

If we apply the usual strength reduction factor, the design strength of the beam is

$$\phi M_n = 0.90 \times 548 = 493 \text{ ft-kips (669 kN-m)}$$

REFERENCES

3.1 Parme, A. L. and Paris, G. H., "Designing for Continuity in Prestressed Concrete Structures," *J. ACI*, Vol. 48, No. 1, September 1951, pp. 45–64.

3.2 Lin, T. Y., "Load-Balancing Method for Design and Analysis of Prestressed Concrete Structures," *J. ACI*, Vol. 60, No. 6, June 1963, pp. 719–742.

3.3 Leonhardt, F., discussion of Ref. 3.2, *J. ACI*, Vol. 60, No. 12, December 1963, pp. 1859–1862.

3.4 Nilson, A. H., "Flexural Design Equations for Prestressed Concrete Members," *J. PCI*, Vol. 14, No. 1, February 1969, pp. 62–71.

3.5 Abeles, P. W., *Introduction to Prestressed Concrete*, Vol. 1, Concrete Publications, Ltd., London, 1964.

3.6 Abeles, P. W., *Introduction to Prestressed Concrete*, Vol. 2, Concrete Publications, Ltd., London, 1966.

3.7 Leonhardt, F., *Prestressed Concrete Design and Construction*, Wilhelm Ernst and Son, Berlin, 1964, 676 pp.

3.8 Guyon, Y., *Limit State Design of Prestressed Concrete*, Vol. 1, Applied Science Publishers, London, 1972.

3.9 Guyon, Y., *Limit State Design of Prestressed Concrete*, Vol. 2, Applied Science Publishers, London, 1975.

3.10 Abeles, P. W., "How Much Prestress?," *Engineering News-Record*, July 5, 1951, pp. 32–33.

3.11 CEB-FIP Joint Committee, *International Recommendations for the Design and Construction of Prestressed Concrete Structures*, Cement and Concrete Association, London, June 1970.

3.12 British Standards Institution, *Draft British Standard Code of Practice for the Structural Use of Concrete*, London, 1969.

3.13 Abeles, P. W., "Design of Partially-Prestressed Concrete Beams," *J. ACI*, Vol. 64, No. 10, October 1967, pp. 669–677.

3.14 Winter, G. and Nilson, A. H., *Design of Concrete Structures*, 8th Ed., McGraw-Hill, New York, 1972, 615 pp.

3.15 Thurlimann, B., "A Case for Partial Prestressing," *Structural Concrete Symposium Proceedings*, University of Toronto, May 1971, pp. 253–301.

3.16 Dolan, C. W., Ultimate Capacity of Reinforced Concrete Sections Using a Continuous Stress-Strain Function, M. S. thesis, Cornell University, Ithaca, N.Y., June 1967.

3.17 Nilson, A. H., "Flexural Stresses After Cracking in Partially Prestressed Beams," *J. PCI*, Vol. 21, No. 4, July–August 1976, pp. 72–81.

PROBLEMS

3.1 A rectangular concrete beam of width $b = 11$ in. and total depth $h = 28$ in. is post-tensioned using a single parabolic tendon having eccentricity 7.8 in. at midspan and 0 in. at the simple supports. The initial prestress force $P_i = 334$ kips and the effectiveness ratio $R = 0.84$. The member is to carry superimposed dead and live loads of 300 plf and 1000 plf, respectively, uniformly distributed over the 40 ft span. Specified concrete strength $f'_c = 5000$ psi, and at the time of transfer $f'_{ci} = 4000$ psi. Determine the flexural stress distributions in the concrete at midspan (a) for initial conditions before application of superimposed load, and (b) at full service load. Compare with ACI limit stresses.

3.2   The concrete I beam of Fig. P3.2a is prestressed with four stranded cables having total area $A_p = 0.575$ in.[2] Eccentricity of the steel varies parabolically from 0 at the supports to 7.58 in. at the center of the 30 ft. span. The effective stress in the steel after losses is 132,000 psi. (a) What superimposed load, uniformly distributed, will produce cracking of the beam, given that the modulus of rupture $f'_r = 475$ psi? (b) What superimposed load will produce a balanced condition of external and equivalent prestress load, such that uniform axial compression will be obtained in the concrete? (c) For the balanced load just computed, would the midspan deflection be downward, upward, or zero? Explain.

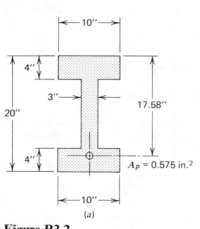
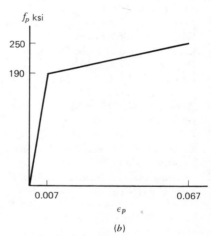

(a)   (b)

Figure P3.2

3.3   Given that the prestressing steel for the beam of problem 3.2 has a stress–strain curve as idealized in Fig. P3.2b, and that the concrete has ultimate strain capacity of 0.003, determine the nominal flexural strength M_n of the member, based on a strain compatibility analysis. Compare with the strength predicted by the ACI approximate method. Concrete strength $f'_c = 4000$ psi.

3.4   An AASHTO Type II bridge girder (see Appendix A, Table A11) is used on a 50 ft. simple span. The beam is pretensioned using stranded cables that apply a compressive force P_i of 432 kips at transfer. After all time-dependent losses, an effective prestress P_e of 367 kips is attained. The steel consists of 29 3/8 in. diameter Grade 270 strands and the centroid has a constant eccentricity of 12.5 in. (a) Given that the girder cambers upward immediately upon release of prestress force to the beam, what concrete stresses are obtained at the midspan section at that loading stage? (b) What stresses are obtained for the unloaded member (prestress plus self-weight only) after all important losses have occurred? (c) What stresses result upon application of full service load (sum of superimposed dead and live load) of 1.630 kips per ft? (d) What is the safety factor against cracking (defined with respect to the superimposed load increase) given that the modulus of rupture is 530 psi? (e) If the concrete strength $f'_c = 5000$ psi, and the steel has a stress–strain curve as shown by Fig. 2.4, what total load will produce failure of the member? (Use the ACI approximate equation for steel stress and apply the usual strength reduction factor to the nominal member strength.)

3.5 Recalculate the nominal flexural strength for the AASHTO girder of Problem 3.4, based on a strain compatibility analysis.

CHAPTER 4
BEAM DESIGN

4.1 BASIS OF DESIGN

It is useful to summarize the performance of a typical prestressed concrete beam in terms of its load-deflection curve, shown in Fig. 4.1.

When the initial prestress force is applied, there will be an immediate upward camber δ_{pi} due to the bending moment associated with prestress eccentricity. With the beam supported mainly at its ends, the self-weight is immediately

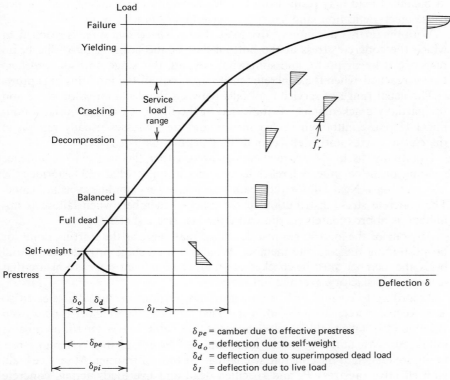

δ_{pe} = camber due to effective prestress
δ_{d_o} = deflection due to self-weight
δ_d = deflection due to superimposed dead load
δ_l = deflection due to live load

Figure 4.1 Load-deflection curve for typical beam.

109

brought into effect, superimposing a downward component of deflection δ_o on the upward camber due to prestressing. This is referred to as the *unloaded stage*, with initial prestress and self-weight acting.

It will be assumed here, for simplicity, that all losses occur at once, such that the net deflection at the start is $\delta_{pe} - \delta_o$ due to the combination of effective prestress force P_e and self-weight w_o. At this stage, the concrete flexural stress distribution at midspan is generally as shown by the small shaded sketch superimposed on the load-deflection curve, varying linearly from a low value of tensile stress at the top face of the beam to maximum compression at the bottom.

When the superimposed dead load is added, the deflection increases in the positive, downward sense, by the amount δ_d. The net deflection is often upward at this stage, as suggested by Fig. 4.1, but not always so.

With the addition of a portion of the live load, a *balanced load stage* may be reached, such that the upward equivalent load from prestressing is exactly equal to the downward external load. The result is a uniform compressive stress in the member, as shown. While zero deflection is indicated in Fig. 4.1, this would not necessarily be obtained, because the uniform compressive stress distribution at balanced load may result from the superposition of sustained loads, which cause creep deflection, and short term live loads, which do not.

With the further addition of live load, the *decompression stage* is reached, at which the concrete stress at the bottom face of the beam is zero. The beam response is linear up to, and somewhat beyond, this stage until the *cracking load* is reached, when the concrete tensile stress equals the modulus of rupture.

The usual range of service load falls between the decompression stage and the partially cracked stage, as indicated in the figure. Cracking initiates non-linear response, although both concrete and steel stresses usually remain in the elastic ranges until well beyond the cracking load.

Eventually, as loads are further increased, either the steel will commence yielding, or the concrete will reach its crushing strain, at what will be termed the *overload stage*. Near failure, the beam response is very nonlinear, as indicated. The concrete stress distribution in the cracked member, when failure is imminent, is approximately as shown by the last stress sketch.

Any one of the load stages just described may serve as the starting point for proportioning the concrete member. Whatever load stage provides the initial basis, the member must be checked at all other significant stages to insure that it will be satisfactory over the full range.

According to current practice, member proportions are usually selected so as to keep concrete stresses within specified limits as the member ranges from the unloaded stage to the service load stage (see Table 3.1). When the member is unloaded, with initial prestress force and self-weight acting, concrete stress limits are related to the concrete strength at the time of transfer. At service load, with effective prestress P_e and specified dead and live loads acting, concrete stress limits are generally not the same as for the unloaded stage. In addition they are related to the full specified design strength of the concrete.

Beams proportioned on a stress basis must also satisfy all other requirements. Beam deflections at full service load and often at a partial loading are an important design consideration and must be checked. For partially prestressed beams, an explicit check of crack widths may be required, but more often cracking is controlled indirectly by limiting the nominal concrete tensile stress. Member strength should always be calculated to insure an adequate margin of safety against collapse.

Member dimensions may also be selected, based on providing exactly the required strength should the expected loads be increased by specified load factors. In this case, the prestress force may be selected to provide the desired deflection characteristics or crack control. Stresses in both the unloaded stage and full service load stage must be investigated as well, even though initial design is based on strength.

Another alternative is to select member proportions, prestress force, and steel profile based on load balancing for controlled deflections. With this design basis, too, other significant load stages must be investigated. Stresses in the beam when unloaded, and when subjected to full service load, must be within accepted limits, and adequate strength must be provided.

The resulting design in any given case is, to some extent, dependent upon the design basis selected, even though the same criteria must be satisfied at the several load stages.

4.2   SAFETY AND SERVICEABILITY CRITERIA

The approach to structural safety that is incorporated in the ACI Code, which provides the basis for most concrete building design and construction in the United States, has been described in Art. 1.8. (The provisions of the AASHTO Specification, which pertains to highway structures, are similar and in many cases identical.) Load factors are established, as summarized in Table 1.2. These factors are to be applied to the calculated dead loads, and calculated or specified live loads, to obtain the minimum required strength that the member must possess. This required strength must not exceed the design strength, obtained by applying a *strength reduction factor* to the *nominal strength* calculated according to the best current knowledge of structural behavior and material characteristics. ACI strength reduction factors are given in Table 1.3.

The same specifications establish certain *allowable stresses* for the concrete and the prestressing steel. These pertain to loadings in the elastic range, from the unloaded stage to full service load stage. Allowable stresses are different for different loadings, and for different regions of beams. ACI Code allowable stresses for concrete are summarized in Table 3.1, and allowable stresses in the prestressed reinforcing steel are given in Table 3.2. No restrictions are placed on service load stresses in non-prestressed bar reinforcement, should it be present in prestressed concrete members, in either the ACI Code or the AASHTO Specification.

Deflections may be limited indirectly by placing limits on stresses or on the maximum span-depth ratio for beams, or directly by requiring that deflections be calculated and placing upper limits on values found. According to the ACI Code, deflections must be calculated for all prestressed concrete flexural members. A table of maximum allowable computed deflections is included in the Code.

No specific provisions relating to the deflection of prestressed concrete members are found in the AASHTO Specification. Even so, the prudent engineer would calculate deflections at all load stages of importance.

4.3 FLEXURAL DESIGN BASED ON ALLOWABLE STRESSES

Usually, in present practice, the concrete dimensions and prestress force for beams are selected to insure that specified limiting stresses are not exceeded as the beam passes from the unloaded stage to the service load stage. Both concrete and steel may be considered elastic in this range. After member proportions have been tentatively selected on this basis, the deflections at load stages of interest, and the ultimate strength of the member, are checked and dimensions are revised if necessary.

This approach is reasonable, considering that one of the most important objectives of prestressing is to improve service load performance. Furthermore, it is usually the performance criteria at service loads that determine the amount of prestress force used, although requirements of strength may determine the total tensile steel area.

Many designers adopt a trial-and-error approach. A cross section is assumed, and the prestress force and profile determined. The trial member is then checked to insure that stresses are within allowable limits, deflections are satisfactory, and the required strength is available. A more systematic approach is possible, however, based on attaining limit stresses, as nearly as possible, at the controlling load stages (Ref. 4.1). This approach will be followed here.

Notation is established pertaining to the concrete stresses at limiting stages as follows:

f_{ci} = allowable compressive stress immediately after transfer

f_{ti} = allowable tensile stress immediately after transfer

f_{cs} = allowable compressive stress at service load, after all losses

f_{ts} = allowable tensile stress at service load, after all losses

The values of these limit stresses are normally set by specification (see Table 3.1).

A. BEAMS IN WHICH PRESTRESS ECCENTRICITY VARIES ALONG THE SPAN

For a typical beam in which the tendon eccentricity is permitted to vary along the span, flexural stress distributions in the concrete at the maximum moment section are shown in Fig. 4.2a. The eccentric prestress force, having an initial value of P_i, produces the linear distribution (1). However, because of the upward camber of the beam as that force is applied, the self-weight of the member is immediately introduced, the flexural stresses resulting from the moment M_o are superimposed, and the distribution (2) is the first that is actually attained. At this stage, the tension at the top surface is not to exceed f_{ti} and the compression at the bottom surface is not to exceed f_{ci}, as suggested by Fig. 4.2a.

It will be assumed that all the losses occur at this stage, and that the stress distribution gradually changes to distribution (3). The losses produce a reduction of tension in the amount Δf_1 at the top surface, and a reduction of compression in the amount Δf_2 at the bottom surface.

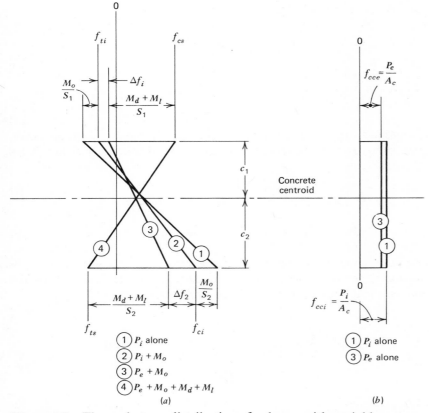

(a)

(b)

Figure 4.2 Flexural stress distributions for beam with variable eccentricity. (a) Maximum moment section. (b) Support section.

As the superimposed dead load moment M_d and the service live load moment M_l are now introduced, the associated flexural stresses, when superimposed on stresses already present, produce distribution (4). At this stage the tension at the bottom surface must not be greater than f_{ts} and the compression at the top of the section must not exceed f_{cs} as shown.

The requirements for the sections moduli S_1 and S_2 with respect to the top and bottom surfaces, respectively, are

$$S_1 \geq \frac{M_d + M_l}{f_{1r}} \tag{a}$$

$$S_2 \geq \frac{M_d + M_l}{f_{2r}} \tag{b}$$

where the available stress ranges f_{1r} and f_{2r} at the top and bottom face can be calculated from the specified stress limits f_{ti}, f_{cs}, f_{ts}, and f_{ci} once the stress changes Δf_1 and Δf_2, associated with prestress loss, are known.

The effectiveness ratio R has been defined in Art. 3.3 as

$$R = \frac{P_e}{P_i} \tag{3.1}$$

Thus the loss in prestress force is

$$P_i - P_e = (1 - R)P_i \tag{3.2}$$

The changes in stress at the top and bottom faces, Δf_1 and Δf_2, as losses occur, are equal to $(1 - R)$ times the corresponding stresses due to the initial prestress force P_i acting alone:

$$\Delta f_1 = (1 - R)\left(f_{ti} + \frac{M_o}{S_1} \right) \tag{c}$$

$$\Delta f_2 = (1 - R)\left(-f_{ci} + \frac{M_o}{S_2} \right) \tag{d}$$

where Δf_1 is a reduction of tension at the top surface and Δf_2 is a reduction of compression at the bottom surface.* Thus the stress ranges available as the superimposed load moments $M_d + M_l$ are applied are

$$f_{1r} = f_{ti} - \Delta f_1 - f_{cs}$$

$$= Rf_{ti} - (1 - R)\frac{M_o}{S_1} - f_{cs} \tag{e}$$

---

* Note that the stress limits such as f_{ti} and other specific points along the stress axis are considered as signed quantities, while stress changes such as M_o/S_1 and Δf_2 are taken as absolute values.

and

$$f_{2r} = f_{ts} - f_{ci} - \Delta f_2$$

$$= f_{ts} - R f_{ci} - (1 - R) \frac{M_o}{S_2} \tag{f}$$

The minimum acceptable value of S_1 is thus established:

$$S_1 \geq \frac{M_d + M_l}{R f_{ti} - (1 - R) \dfrac{M_o}{S_1} - f_{cs}}$$

or

$$S_1 \geq \frac{(1 - R)M_o + M_d + M_l}{R f_{ti} - f_{cs}} \tag{4.1}$$

Similarly the minimum value of S_2 is

$$S_2 \geq \frac{(1 - R)M_o + M_d + M_l}{f_{ts} - R f_{ci}} \tag{4.2}$$

The cross section must be selected so as to provide at least these values of S_1 and S_2. Furthermore, since $I_c = S_1 c_1 = S_2 c_2$ the centroidal axis must be located such that

$$\frac{c_1}{c_2} = \frac{S_2}{S_1} \tag{g}$$

or in terms of the total section depth $h = c_1 + c_2$

$$\frac{c_1}{h} = \frac{S_2}{S_1 + S_2} \tag{4.3}$$

From Fig. 4.2a, the concrete centroidal stress under initial conditions is given by

$$f_{cci} = f_{ti} - \frac{c_1}{h}(f_{ti} - f_{ci}) \tag{4.4}$$

The initial prestress force is easily obtained by multiplying the value of the concrete centroidal stress by the concrete cross sectional area A_c:

$$P_i = A_c f_{cci} \tag{4.5}$$

The eccentricity of the prestress force may be found by considering the flexural stresses that must be imparted by the bending moment $P_i e$. With reference to Fig. 4.2, the flexural stress at the top surface of the beam resulting from the eccentric prestress force alone is

$$\frac{P_i e}{S_1} = (f_{ti} - f_{cci}) + \frac{M_o}{S_1} \tag{h}$$

from which the required eccentricity is

$$e = (f_{ti} - f_{cci})\frac{S_1}{P_i} + \frac{M_o}{P_i} \tag{4.6}$$

To summarize the design process in determining the best cross section, and the required prestress force and eccentricity based on stress limitations: the required section moduli with respect to the top and bottom surfaces of the member are found from Eqs. (4.1) and (4.2), with centroidal axis located by Eq. (4.3). Concrete dimensions are chosen so as to satisfy these requirements as nearly as possible. The concrete centroidal stress for this ideal section is given by Eq. (4.4), the desired initial prestress force is found by Eq. (4.5) and its eccentricity by Eq. (4.6).

In practical cases, although the inequalities of Eqs. (4.1) and (4.2) will be satisfied, concrete dimensions will exceed those producing the minimum acceptable values of S_1 and S_2. The concrete centroidal stress may still be found by Eq. (4.4) by using the actual value of c_1/h, and Eqs. (4.5) and (4.6) applied without change. Further discussion of this situation, where the concrete section is larger than the minimum, will be found in Art. 4.9.

It will be observed that an estimate of the dead weight of the member must be made at the outset of the calculations since M_o is required. This estimate may be made on the basis of typical span–depth ratios or past experience. If the estimate of member self-weight is substantially in error, the calculations should be revised.

The stress distributions of Fig. 4.2a, on which the design equations are based, apply at the maximum moment section of the member. Elsewhere M_o is less and, consequently, the prestress eccentricity must be reduced if the stress limits f_{ti} and f_{ci} are not to be exceeded. In Art. 4.4 expressions are developed that establish the limits of tendon eccentricity elsewhere in the span. In many cases, tendon eccentricity is reduced to zero at the support sections, where all moments due to transverse load are zero. In this case, the stress distributions of Fig. 4.2b are obtained. The stress in the concrete is uniformly equal to the centroidal value, f_{cci} under conditions of initial prestress and f_{cce} after losses.

B. BEAMS WITH CONSTANT ECCENTRICITY

The design method presented in the previous section was based on stress conditions at the maximum moment section of a beam, with the maximum value of moment M_o due to self-weight immediately superimposed. If P_i and e were to be held constant along the span, as if often convenient in pretensioned prestressed construction, then the stress limits f_{ti} and f_{ci} would be exceeded elsewhere along the span, where M_o is less than its maximum value. In order to avoid this condition, the constant eccentricity must be less than that given by

Eq. (4.6). Its maximum value is given by conditions at the support of a simple span, where M_o is zero.

Figure 4.3 shows the flexural stress distributions at the support and midspan sections for a beam with constant eccentricity. In this case, the stress limits f_{ti} and f_{ci} are not to be violated when the eccentric prestress moment acts alone, as at the supports. The stress changes Δf_1 and Δf_2 as losses occur are equal to $(1 - R)$ times the top and bottom surface stresses, respectively, due to initial prestress alone:

$$\Delta f_1 = (1 - R)(f_{ti}) \tag{a}$$

$$\Delta f_2 = (1 - R)(-f_{ci}) \tag{b}$$

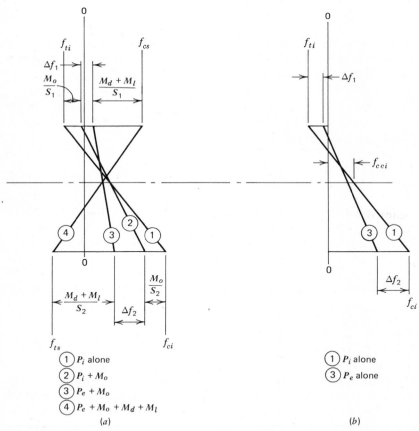

① P_i alone
② $P_i + M_o$
③ $P_e + M_o$
④ $P_e + M_o + M_d + M_l$

(a)

① P_i alone
③ P_e alone

(b)

Figure 4.3 Flexural stress distributions for beam with constant eccentricity. (*a*) Maximum moment section. (*b*) Support section.

In this case the available stress ranges between limit stresses must provide for
the effect of M_o as well as M_d and M_l, as seen from Fig. 4.3a, and are

$$f_{1r} = f_{ti} - \Delta f_1 - f_{cs}$$
$$= Rf_{ti} - f_{cs} \tag{c}$$

$$f_{2r} = f_{ts} - f_{ci} - \Delta f_2$$
$$= f_{ts} - Rf_{ci} \tag{d}$$

and the requirements on the section moduli are that

$$S_1 \geq \frac{M_o + M_d + M_l}{Rf_{ti} - f_{cs}} \tag{4.7}$$

$$S_2 \geq \frac{M_o + M_d + M_l}{f_{ts} - Rf_{ci}} \tag{4.8}$$

The concrete centroidal stress may be found by Eq. (4.4) and the initial prestress
force by Eq. (4.5) as before. However, the expression for required eccentricity
differs. In this case, referring to Fig. 4.3b,

$$\frac{P_i e}{S_1} = f_{ti} - f_{cci} \tag{e}$$

from which the required eccentricity is

$$e = (f_{ti} - f_{cci}) \frac{S_1}{P_i} \tag{4.9}$$

A significant difference between beams with variable eccentricity and those
with constant eccentricity will be noted by comparing Eqs. (4.1) and (4.2) with
the corresponding Eqs. (4.7) and (4.8). In the first case, the section modulus
requirement is governed mainly by the superimposed load moments M_d and
M_l. Almost all of the self-weight is carried "free," that is, without increasing
section modulus or prestress force, by the simple expedient of increasing the
eccentricity along the span by the amount M_o/P_i. In the second case the eccentricity is controlled by conditions at the supports, where M_o is zero, and the
full moment M_o due to self-weight must be included in determining section
moduli. Nevertheless beams with constant eccentricity are often used for practical reasons.

Certain alternative means are available for coping with the problem of excessive concrete stresses due to prestress at the ends of members with constant
eccentricity. The prestress force may be reduced near the ends of the span by
encasing some of the tendons in plastic sheathing, effectively moving the point
of application of prestress force inward toward midspan for a part of the strands.
Or supplementary non-prestressed bar reinforcement may be used in the end
regions to accommodate the local high stresses.

The ACI Code includes a special provision that the concrete tensile stress immediately after transfer, before time-dependent losses, at the ends of simply supported members may be as high as $6\sqrt{f'_{ci}}$, twice the limit of $3\sqrt{f'_{ci}}$ that applies elsewhere (see Table 3.1). Conditions at the supports will generally control for beams with constant eccentricity, and f_{ti} may be taken equal to $6\sqrt{f'_{ci}}$ in the preceding equations.

C. EXAMPLE: DESIGN OF BEAM WITH VARIABLE ECCENTRICITY TENDONS

A post-tensioned prestressed concrete beam is to carry a live load of 1000 plf and super-imposed dead load of 500 plf, in addition to its own weight, on a 40 ft simple span. Normal density concrete will be used with design strength $f'_c = 6000$ psi. It is estimated that, at the time of transfer, the concrete will have attained 70 percent of its ultimate strength, or 4200 psi. Time-dependent losses may be assumed at 15 percent of the initial prestress, giving an effectiveness ratio of 0.85. Determine the required concrete dimensions, magnitude of prestress force, and eccentricity of the steel centroid based on ACI stress limitations as given in Tables 3.1 and 3.2. ($w_l = 14.6$ kN/m, $w_d = 7.3$ kN/m, span $= 12.2$ m, $f'_c = 41$ N/mm^2, and $f'_{ci} = 29$ N/mm^2.)

Referring to Table 3.1 we obtain the following stress limits:

$$f_{ci} = -0.60 \times 4200 = -2520 \text{ psi}$$
$$f_{ti} = 3\sqrt{4200} = +195 \text{ psi}$$
$$f_{cs} = -0.45 \times 6000 = -2700 \text{ psi}$$
$$f_{ts} = 6\sqrt{6000} = +465 \text{ psi}$$

The self-weight of the girder will be estimated at 250 plf. The moments due to transverse loading are

$$M_o = \frac{1}{8} \times 0.250 \times 40^2 = 50 \text{ ft-kips}$$

$$M_d + M_l = \frac{1}{8} \times 1.500 \times 40^2 = 300 \text{ ft-kips}$$

The required section moduli with respect to the top and bottom surfaces of the concrete beam are found from Eqs. (4.1) and (4.2):

$$S_1 \geq \frac{(1-R)M_o + M_d + M_l}{Rf_{ti} - f_{cs}} = \frac{(0.15 \times 50 + 300)12{,}000}{0.85 \times 195 + 2700} = 1288 \text{ in.}^3$$

$$S_2 \geq \frac{(1-R)M_o + M_d + M_l}{f_{ts} - Rf_{ci}} = \frac{(0.15 \times 50 + 300)12{,}000}{465 + 0.85 \times 2520} = 1415 \text{ in.}^3$$

These values are so nearly the same that a symmetrical beam will be adopted. The 28 in. depth I section shown in Fig. 4.4a will meet the requirements, and has the following properties:

$$I_c = 19{,}904 \text{ in.}^4 \ (8.28 \times 10^9 \text{ mm}^4)$$
$$S = 1422 \text{ in.}^3 \ (23.3 \times 10^6 \text{ mm}^3)$$
$$A_c = 240 \text{ in.}^2 \ (155 \times 10^3 \text{ mm}^2)$$
$$r^2 = 82.9 \text{ in.}^2$$
$$w_o = 250 \text{ plf (as assumed)}$$

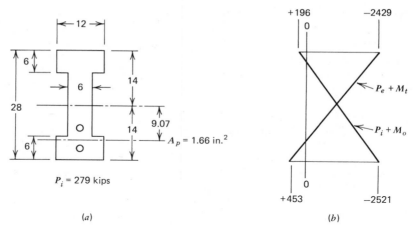

Figure 4.4 Beam with variable-eccentricity tendons. (*a*) Cross section dimensions. (*b*) Stresses at midspan.

Next the concrete centroidal stress is found from Eq. (4.4):

$$f_{cci} = f_{ti} - \frac{c_1}{h}(f_{ti} - f_{ci}) = 195 - \frac{1}{2}(195 + 2520) = -1163 \text{ psi}$$

and from Eq. (4.5) the initial prestress force is

$$P_i = A_c f_{cci} = 240 \times 1.163 = 279 \text{ kips (1241 kN)}$$

From Eq. (4.6) the required tendon eccentricity at the maximum moment section of the beam is

$$e = (f_{ti} - f_{cci})\frac{S_1}{P_i} + \frac{M_o}{P_i} = (195 + 1163)\frac{1422}{279,000} + \frac{50 \times 12,000}{279,000} = 9.07 \text{ in. (230 mm)}$$

Elsewhere along the span the eccentricity will be reduced in order that the concrete stress limits not be violated.

The required initial prestress force of 279 kips will be provided using tendons consisting of 1/4 in. diameter stress-relieved wires. The minimum tensile strength, according to Table 2.1, is 240 ksi and, according to the ACI requirements, they will be used at an initial stress of $0.70 \times 240 = 168$ ksi. The required prestressing steel area is thus

$$A_p = \frac{279}{168} = 1.66 \text{ in.}^2 \text{ (1071 mm}^2\text{)}$$

The cross-sectional area of one 1/4 in. diameter wire is 0.0491 in.²; hence the number of wires required is

$$\text{No. of wires} = \frac{1.66}{0.0491} = 34$$

Two 17 wire tendons will be used, as shown in Fig. 4.4*a*.

It is good practice to check the calculations by confirming that stress limits are not exceeded at critical load stages. The top and bottom surface concrete stresses produced, in this case, by the separate loadings are:

$$P_i: \quad f_1 = -\frac{279,000}{240}\left(1 - \frac{9.07 \times 14}{82.9}\right) = +618 \text{ psi}$$

$$f_2 = -\frac{279,000}{240}\left(1 + \frac{9.07 \times 14}{82.9}\right) = -2943 \text{ psi}$$

$$P_e: \quad f_1 = 0.85 \times 618 = 525 \text{ psi}$$

$$f_2 = 0.85(-2943) = -2501 \text{ psi}$$

$$M_o: \quad f_1 = -\frac{50 \times 12,000}{1422} = -422 \text{ psi}$$

$$f_2 = +422 \text{ psi}$$

$$M_d + M_l: \quad f_1 = -\frac{300 \times 12,000}{1422} = -2532 \text{ psi}$$

$$f_2 = +2532 \text{ psi}$$

Thus, when the initial prestress force of 279 kips is applied and the beam self-weight acts, the top and bottom stresses in the concrete at midspan are, respectively:

$$f_1 = +618 - 422 = +196 \text{ psi}$$
$$f_2 = -2943 + 422 = -2521 \text{ psi}$$

When the prestress force has reduced to its effective value of 237 kips and the full service load is applied, the concrete stresses are:

$$f_1 = +525 - 422 - 2532 = -2429 \text{ psi}$$
$$f_2 = -2501 + 422 + 2532 = +453 \text{ psi}$$

These limiting stress distributions are shown in Fig. 4.4b. Comparison with the specified limit stresses confirms that the design is satisfactory.

Additional Comments

1.   From the resulting stresses shown in Fig. 4.4b it is clear that the specified stress limits are satisfied almost exactly at the top and bottom surface for the initial condition (slight differences appear because of rounding errors and selecting practical dimensions). In the fully loaded condition, the tension at the bottom surface of 453 psi is close to the limit of 465 psi; however, the compression at the top of the beam, 2429 psi, is well below the allowable 2700 psi. This result is due to the use of a symmetrical member, the section modulus of which is larger than the required S_1.

2.   For cases such as this, in which one or both of the section moduli exceed the minimum requirement, some flexibility exists regarding the selection of prestress force and eccentricity. This point will be developed in Art. 4.9.

3.   The cross section shown in Fig. 4.4a is idealized for computational purposes. The member actually used would probably have tapered inner flange surfaces, filets, and other features to facilitate construction.

4.   The final design should also include non-prestressed longitudinal reinforcement to control possible cracking due to shrinkage before the beam is posttensioned, and would undoubtedly include web reinforcement to provide the required resistance to shear forces.

D. EXAMPLE: DESIGN OF BEAM WITH CONSTANT ECCENTRICITY TENDONS

The beam of the preceding example is to be redesigned using straight tendons with constant eccentricity. All other design criteria are the same as before. At the supports, a temporary concrete tensile stress of $6\sqrt{f'_{ci}} = 390$ psi is permitted.

Anticipating a somewhat less efficient beam, the dead load estimate will be increased to 270 plf in this case. The resulting moment M_o is 54 ft-kips. The moment due to superimposed dead load and live load is 300 ft-kips as before.

Using Eqs. (4.7) and (4.8) the requirements for section moduli are

$$S_1 \geq \frac{M_o + M_d + M_l}{Rf_{ti} - f_{cs}} = \frac{(54 + 300)12,000}{0.85 \times 390 + 2700} = 1401 \text{ in.}^3$$

$$S_2 \geq \frac{M_o + M_d + M_l}{f_{ts} - Rf_{ci}} = \frac{(54 + 300)12,000}{465 + 0.85 \times 2520} = 1629 \text{ in.}^3$$

Once again a symmetrical section will be chosen. Flange dimensions and web width will be kept unchanged, as compared with the previous example, but in this case a beam depth of 30.5 in. is required. The dimensions of the cross section are shown in Fig. 4.5a. The following properties are obtained:

$$I_c = 25,207 \text{ in.}^4 \ (10.49 \times 10^9 \text{ mm}^4)$$
$$S = 1653 \text{ in.}^3 \ (27.1 \times 10^6 \text{ mm}^3)$$
$$A_c = 255 \text{ in.}^2 \ (165 \times 10^3 \text{ mm}^2)$$
$$r^2 = 98.9 \text{ in.}^2$$
$$w_o = 266 \text{ plf (close to the assumed value)}$$

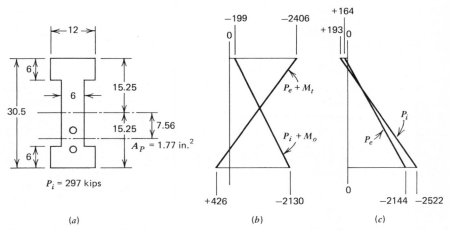

Figure 4.5 Beam with constant-eccentricity tendons. (*a*) Cross section dimensions. (*b*) Stresses at midspan. (*c*) Stresses at supports.

The concrete centroidal stress, from Eq. (4.4), is

$$f_{cci} = f_{ti} - \frac{c_1}{h}(f_{ti} - f_{ci}) = 390 - \frac{1}{2}(390 + 2520) = -1065 \text{ psi}$$

and from Eq. (4.5) the initial prestress force is

$$P_i = A_c f_{cci} = 255 \times 1.065 = 272 \text{ kips (1210 kN)}$$

From Eq. (4.9) the required constant eccentricity is

$$e = (f_{ti} - f_{cci})\frac{S_1}{P_i} = (390 + 1065)\frac{1653}{272,000} = 8.84 \text{ in. (224 mm)}$$

Again two tendons will be used to provide the required force P_i, each composed of multiple 1/4 in. diameter wires. With the maximum permissible stress in the wires of 168 ksi the total required steel area is

$$A_p = \frac{272}{168} = 1.62 \text{ in.}^2 \text{ (1045 mm}^2\text{)}$$

A total of 34 wires is required as before, 17 in each tendon.

The calculations will be checked by verifying concrete stresses at the top and bottom of the beam for the critical load stages. The component stress contributions are

$$P_i: \quad f_1 = -\frac{272,000}{255}\left(1 - \frac{8.84 \times 15.25}{98.9}\right) = +387 \text{ psi}$$

$$f_2 = -\frac{272,000}{255}\left(1 + \frac{8.84 \times 15.25}{98.9}\right) = -2522 \text{ psi}$$

$$P_e: \quad f_1 = 0.85 \times 387 = +328 \text{ psi}$$

$$f_2 = 0.85(-2522) = -2144 \text{ psi}$$

$$M_o: \quad f_1 = -\frac{54 \times 12,000}{1653} = -392 \text{ psi}$$

$$f_2 = +392 \text{ psi}$$

$$M_d + M_l: \quad f_1 = -\frac{300 \times 12,000}{1653} = -2178 \text{ psi}$$

$$f_2 = +2178 \text{ psi}$$

Superimposing the appropriate stress contributions, the stress distributions in the concrete at midspan and at the supports are obtained, as shown in Figs. 4.5b and 4.5c, respectively. When the initial prestress force of 272 kips acts alone, as at the supports, the stresses at the top and bottom surfaces are

$$f_1 = +387 \text{ psi}$$
$$f_2 = -2522 \text{ psi}$$

After losses, the prestress force is reduced to 231 kips and the support stresses are reduced accordingly. At midspan the beam weight is immediately superimposed, and stresses due to P_i plus M_o are

$$f_1 = +387 - 392 = -5 \text{ psi}$$
$$f_2 = -2522 + 392 = -2130 \text{ psi}$$

When the full service load acts, together with P_e, the midspan stresses are

$$f_1 = +328 - 392 - 2178 = -2242 \text{ psi}$$
$$f_2 = -2144 + 392 + 2178 = +426 \text{ psi}$$

If we check against the specified limiting stresses, it is evident that the design is satisfactory in this respect at the critical load stages and locations.

Additional Comments

1. Once again it is found that the stress specification is satisfied almost exactly at the supports under conditions of initial prestress, and closely satisfied at midspan at the bottom surface for the loaded condition. Because of the choice of a symmetrical section, the compressive stress at the top of the member at midspan in the fully loaded stage is well below the permitted value.

2. At midspan in the unloaded stage, with only P_i and self-weight acting, compressive stresses of 5 psi and 2130 psi are present at the top and bottom surfaces, respectively. The stress ranges that were available in the previous example to resist superimposed dead and live loads are reduced. This may be thought of as a penalty that is often paid in the case of pretensioned members to obtain the practical advantages of straight tendons. In posttensioned members it is easy to provide for variable eccentricity, and it is likely that the design of the previous example would be chosen.

3. Comparing the designs with variable and constant eccentricity, the increase in concrete section in the second case is about 6 percent. For longer span beams, in which the self-weight is proportionately larger, the penalty would be larger than this.

4.4   VARIATION OF ECCENTRICITY ALONG THE SPAN

The equations developed in Art. 4.3 for members with variable tendon eccentricity establish the requirements for beam section modulus, prestress force, and tendon eccentricity at the maximum moment section of the member. Elsewhere along the span, where moments are smaller, the eccentricity of the steel must be reduced in order to avoid exceeding the limiting stresses in the concrete when the beam is in the unloaded stage. Conversely, there is a minimum eccentricity, or upper limit for the steel centroid, such that the limiting concrete stresses are not exceeded when the beam is in the fully loaded stage.

Limiting locations for the prestress steel centroid at any point along the span can be established using Eqs. (3.5) and (3.6), which give the values of concrete stress at the top and bottom of the beam in the unload and loaded stages, respectively. The stresses produced for those load stages are to be compared with the limiting stresses applicable in a particular case, such as the ACI stress limits of Table 3.1. This permits solution for tendon eccentricity e as a function of distance x along the span.

To indicate that both eccentricity e and moments M_o or M_t are functions of distance x from the support, they will be written as $e(x)$ and $M_o(x)$ or $M_t(x)$, respectively. In writing statements of inequality it is convenient to designate tensile stress as larger than zero and compressive stress as smaller than zero. Thus $+450 > -1350$, and $-600 > -1140$, for example.

Considering first the unloaded stage, we find the tensile stress at the top of the beam must not exceed f_{ti}. From Eq. (3.5a)

$$f_{ti} \geq -\frac{P_i}{A_c}\left(1 - \frac{e(x)c_1}{r^2}\right) - \frac{M_o(x)}{S_1} \tag{a}$$

Solving for the maximum eccentricity we obtain

$$e(x) \leq \frac{f_{ti}S_1}{P_i} + \frac{S_1}{A_c} + \frac{M_o(x)}{P_i} \tag{4.10}$$

At the bottom of the unloaded beam the stress must not exceed the limiting initial compression. From Eq. (3.5b)

$$f_{ci} \leq -\frac{P_i}{A_c}\left(1 + \frac{e(x)c_2}{r^2}\right) + \frac{M_o(x)}{S_2} \tag{b}$$

hence the second lower limit for the steel centroid is

$$e(x) \leq -\frac{f_{ci}S_2}{P_i} - \frac{S_2}{A_c} + \frac{M_o(x)}{P_i} \tag{4.11}$$

Now considering the member in the fully loaded stage, the upper limit values for the eccentricity may be found. From Eq. (3.6a)

$$f_{cs} \leq -\frac{P_e}{A_c}\left(1 - \frac{e(x)c_1}{r^2}\right) - \frac{M_t(x)}{S_1} \tag{c}$$

from which

$$e(x) \geq \frac{f_{cs}S_1}{P_e} + \frac{S_1}{A_c} + \frac{M_t(x)}{P_e} \tag{4.12}$$

and using Eq. (3.6b)

$$f_{ts} \geq -\frac{P_e}{A_c}\left(1 + \frac{e(x)c_2}{r^2}\right) + \frac{M_t(x)}{S_2} \tag{d}$$

from which

$$e(x) \geq -\frac{f_{ts}S_2}{P_e} - \frac{S_2}{A_c} + \frac{M_t(x)}{P_e} \tag{4.13}$$

Using Eqs. (4.10) and (4.11) the lower limit of tendon eccentricity is established at successive points along the span. Then using Eqs. (4.12) and (4.13) the corresponding upper limit is established. This upper limit may well be negative, indicating that the tendon centroid may be above the concrete centroid at that location.

It is often convenient to plot the envelope of acceptable tendon profiles, as has been done in Fig. 4.6 for a typical case, in which both dead and live loads are uniformly distributed. Any tendon centroid falling completely within the shaded zone would be satisfactory, from the point of view of concrete stress limits. It should be emphasized that it is only the tendon centroid that must be within the shaded zone; individual cables are often outside of it.

The tendon profile actually used is often a parbolic curve or a catenary in the case of post-tensioned beams. The duct containing the prestressing steel · is draped to the desired shape and held in that position by wiring it to the transverse web reinforcement, after which the concrete may be poured. In pretensioned beams, often *harped tendons* are used. The cables are held down at midspan, at the third points, or at the quarter points of the span and held up at the ends, so that a smooth curve is approximated to a greater or lesser degree.

For simple spans designed by load-balancing methods (see Art. 4.10) the tendon centroid must pass through the concrete centroid at the supports, because the moments due to external loads are zero at the supports. It is seen from Fig. 4.6 that this special case is included in the range of acceptable tendon profiles.

In practical cases, it is often not necessary to make a centroid zone diagram such as is shown in Fig. 4.6. By placing the centroid at its known location at midspan, at or close to the concrete centroid at the supports, and with a near-parabolic shape between those control points, satisfaction of the limiting stress requirements is assured. With nonprismatic beams, beams in which a curved concrete centroidal axis is employed, or with continuous beams, diagrams such as Fig. 4.6 are a great aid.

EXAMPLE   Determination of Tendon Centroid Limit Zone

Determine the limiting tendon zone for the 40 ft span post-tensioned beam of 28 in. depth designed in the example of Art. 4.3C. (Span is 12.2 m and depth 711 mm). Results of that

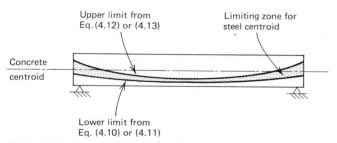

Figure 4.6 Typical limiting zone for centroid of prestressing steel.

design are summarized as follows:

$$f_{ci} = -2520 \text{ psi} \qquad\qquad M_o = 50 \text{ ft-kips} \qquad\qquad S_1 = 1422 \text{ in.}^3$$
$$(-17.4 \text{ N/mm}^2) \qquad\qquad (68 \text{ kN-m}) \qquad\qquad (23.3 \times 10^6 \text{ mm}^3)$$

$$f_{ti} = +195 \text{ psi} \qquad\qquad M_t = 350 \text{ ft-kips} \qquad\qquad S_2 = 1422 \text{ in.}^3$$
$$(+1.3 \text{ N/mm}^2) \qquad\qquad (475 \text{ kN-m}) \qquad\qquad (23.3 \times 10^6 \text{ mm}^3)$$

$$f_{cs} = -2700 \text{ psi} \qquad\qquad P_i = 279 \text{ kips} \qquad\qquad A_c = 240 \text{ in.}^2$$
$$(-18.6 \text{ N/mm}^2) \qquad\qquad (1241 \text{ kN}) \qquad\qquad (155 \times 10^3 \text{ mm}^2)$$

$$f_{ts} = +465 \text{ psi} \qquad\qquad P_e = 237 \text{ kips} \qquad\qquad r^2 = 82.9 \text{ in.}^2$$
$$(+3.2 \text{ N/mm}^2) \qquad\qquad (1054 \text{ kN}) \qquad\qquad (53.5 \times 10^3 \text{ mm}^2)$$

Since the member self-weight and all superimposed loads are uniformly distributed, the variation of all moments is parabolic, from maximum at midspan to zero at the supports. Accordingly the moment ordinates may be established:

	Midspan	Quarter Span	Support
M_o	50 ft-kips	37.5 ft-kips	0
M_t	350 ft-kips	262.5 ft-kips	0

The lower limit of the steel centroid will be found first from Eq. (4.10):

At support: $\qquad e(x) = \dfrac{195 \times 1422}{279,000} + \dfrac{1422}{240} = 6.92 \text{ in. (176 mm)}$

At quarter span: $\quad e(x) = 6.92 + \dfrac{37.5 \times 12,000}{279,000} = 8.53 \text{ in. (217 mm)}$

At midspan: $\qquad e(x) = 6.92 + \dfrac{50 \times 12,000}{279,000} = 9.07 \text{ in. (230 mm)}$

while the lower limits from Eq. (4.11) are:

At support: $\qquad e(x) = \dfrac{2520 \times 1422}{279,000} - \dfrac{1422}{240} = 6.92 \text{ in. (176 mm)}$

At quarter point: $\quad e(x) = 8.53 \text{ in. (217 mm)}$

At midspan: $\qquad e(x) = 9.07 \text{ in. (230 mm)}$

That identical results are obtained from Eqs. (4.10) and (4.11) simply confirms that the prestress force has been chosen so as to exactly satisfy the stress limits f_{ti} and f_{ci}.

Next the upper limit curve will be established using Eqs. (4.12) and (4.13). From Eq. (4.12):

At support: $\qquad e(x) = -\dfrac{-2700 \times 1422}{237,000} + \dfrac{1422}{240} = -10.28 \text{ in. (261 mm)}$

At quarter point: $\quad e(x) = -10.28 + \dfrac{263 \times 12,000}{237,000} = 3.04 \text{ in. (77 mm)}$

At midspan: $\qquad e(x) = -10.28 + \dfrac{350 \times 12,000}{237,000} = 7.44 \text{ in. (189 mm)}$

while from Eq. (4.13):

At support: $\quad e(x) = \dfrac{-465 \times 1422}{237,000} - \dfrac{1422}{240} = -8.72$ in. (-221 mm)

At quarter span: $\quad e(x) = -8.72 + \dfrac{263 \times 12,000}{237,000} = 4.60$ in. (117 mm)

At midspan: $\quad e(x) = -8.72 + \dfrac{350 \times 12,000}{237,000} = 9.00$ in. (229 mm)

It is clear that Eq. (4.13), based on limiting tension, controls in the loaded stage. This could be anticipated by the study of Fig. 4.4b, which indicates that in the loaded stage, for the value of effective prestress used, top surface compression is well below the allowed value.

The results of the calculations are summarized in Fig. 4.7a, which shows the upper and lower limit curves for the tendon centroid. The small range between the upper and lower

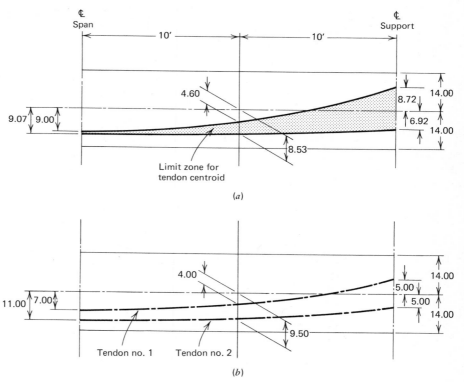

Figure 4.7 Location of tendons for example. (a) Upper and lower steel centroid limits (b) Actual tendon locations.

limits of the prestress force at midspan is typical of closely designed beams in which the concrete cross section meets but does not greatly exceed the requirements of flexure. The actual centerline profiles of the two tendons is shown in Fig. 4.7*b*. The ducts are spaced 4 in. apart at midspan with the steel centroid 9 in. below the concrete centroid. Steel and concrete centroids are made to coincide at the supports, but the individual tendons are flared apart to provide clearance for the end anchorage hardware. A parabolic variation of eccentricity along the span is used for each tendon.

4.5   VARIATION OF PRESTRESS FORCE ALONG THE SPAN

It has already been shown that a particular combination of prestress force and eccentricity that may prove satisfactory at the maximum moment section of a beam may result in excessive stresses elsewhere, where the moment due to self-weight is less. A common example is the case of beams pretensioned with straight cables. Near the supports, where moment due to self-weight reduces to zero, excessively high tension would often result in the concrete at the top of the beam. This can be avoided by reducing the eccentricity of the steel near the supports. An alternative with distinct practical advantages is to keep the eccentricity constant or nearly so, but to reduce the magnitude of the prestress force.

This is easily achieved by preventing certain of the cables from bonding to the concrete near the ends of the span. The most common way to accomplish this is to enclose those cables in tightly fitting split plastic tubes, as suggested by Fig. 4.8, or by wrapping with heavy paper or cloth tape through the desired length. In such case, there is no prestress force transmitted to the concrete from the sheathed strands near the ends of the span, and the effective prestress force is provided by the remainder of the steel area. It may be evident that there will usually be some reduction in the effective eccentricity as well, even if straight

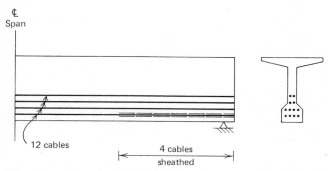

Fig. 4.8   Use of sheathed cables to reduce prestress force near supports.

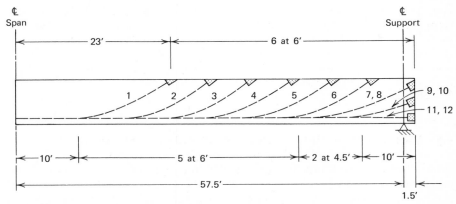

Figure 4.9   Bridge girder with raised cables (adapted from Ref. 4.2).

cables are used, because of the upward shift of the steel centroid when a part of the steel area becomes ineffective.

With such an arrangement consideration should be given to the required transfer length for the sheathed tendons, measured toward the center of the span from the end of the sheathing, to insure that the total prestress force is developed where needed (See Art. 4.12.)

In post-tensioned beams of long span, particularly in bridges, it is often advantageous to stop off certain of the tendons where they are no longer needed to resist flexural stress. Normally, they are swept upward and anchored at the top face of the beam, as shown in Fig. 4.9. Apart from an appreciable saving in the quantity of high tensile steel, the main advantage of this arrangement is that it is usually possible to raise the tendons one by one without thickening the web, as will often prove necessary if several tendons are raised at one location. In addition, anchoring part of the tendons in the top face of the beam reduces the number of anchorages that must be accommodated in the end sections and avoids excessive stresses there. Furthermore, the inclined component of compression due to prestress produces a shear of sign opposite to that resulting from applied loads, reducing the net shear force acting.

Frictional losses may be large for cables that are stopped short of the supports because of the curvature of the ducts. Such losses can be minimized by keeping the inclination of the raised ends as small as possible and by using a large radius of curvature. If the number of through cables is equal to or greater than the number of raised cables, it is possible to raise only one end of each tendon, and to have the other half of the same cable run straight through to the far end of the beam. In this case the cables are arranged in pairs so that there are two symmetrically placed raised anchorages for each pair (Ref. 4.2).

In post-tensioned continuous beams, an arrangement similar to that of Fig. 4.9 is used, except that in this case it is usually the cables needed for negative bending at the supports that are swept down and anchored at the bottom face of the member.

4.6 BEAMS OF LIMITED DEPTH

In deriving Eqs. (4.1) and (4.2) for required section moduli for beams, the stress limits f_{ti} and f_{ci} were matched aganist the stresses at the top and bottom faces of the beam that resulted from the combined effects of the eccentric prestress force P_i and the full moment M_o due to self-weight, as shown by Fig. 4.2a. The moment due to the beam's own weight was compensated by increasing the tendon eccentricity along the span by the amount M_o/P_i below the eccentricity that would produce the limiting stresses, were P_i to be acting alone. The entire stress range $f_{ti} - f_{cs}$ at the top surface, and the full stress range $f_{ts} - f_{ci}$ at the bottom surface, reduced only by the effect of loss of prestress force, were available to resist the superimposed load moment $M_d + M_l$.

Full compensation for member self-weight may not be possible if the beam depth is limited for architectural or other reasons, or if there is a high ratio of self-weight to superimposed loads, as would be the case for long spans. The problem will become evident when the required tendon eccentricity is calculated from Eq. (4.6). The calculated eccentricity may provide insufficient concrete cover for the tendon, and in extreme cases may require that the tendon be placed outside of the concrete section, obviously not a practical arrangement. It is possible to calculate the "critical span" for a member of given cross section, up to which the self-weight can be compensated by tendon eccentricity, and beyond which it cannot (Ref. 4.2).

If the calculations indicate that, for the concrete section chosen, the desired tendon eccentricity cannot be achieved, the section proportions should be modified if possible, providing the same section moduli with a section that is deeper and narrower and that can accommodate the desired tendons. If it is not possible to make the section deeper, then the section moduli must be increased for the member of restricted depth, since the stress ranges available to accommodate the superimposed loads are reduced.

The modified equations for required section moduli are developed with reference to Fig. 4.10. If the eccentric prestress force P_i were acting alone, distribution (1) would result. The moment M_o due to self-weight is immediately superimposed, however, and distribution (2) is obtained. It is noted that the stress limits f_{ti} and f_{ci} are satisfied but not equaled. Since the bending moment due to prestress force P_i cannot be increased because of the restriction on depth and eccentricity, this condition must be accepted.

The effect of this is that the partial stress distribution shown shaded must be accounted for in writing the equations for the required section moduli. At

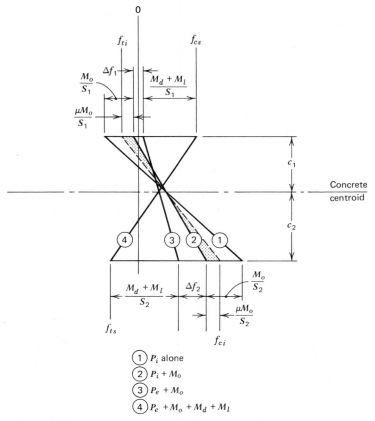

Figure 4.10 Flexural stress distributions when member self-weight cannot be fully compensated.

the top surface, the additional compressive stress to be included within the available stress range between f_{ti} and f_{cs} is $\mu M_o / S_1$, and at the bottom the tensile stress to be included between f_{ts} and f_{ci} is $\mu M_o / S_2$, where μ is a number, less than unity, defining the fractional part of the stresses due to the self-weight to be accounted for in this way. Thus

$$S_1 \geq \frac{\mu M_o + M_d + M_l}{f_{1r}} \tag{a}$$

$$S_2 \geq \frac{\mu M_o + M_d + M_l}{f_{2r}} \tag{b}$$

The change in top and bottom surface stresses as losses in prestress force take place are, respectively,

$$\Delta f_1 = (1 - R)\left(f_{ti} + \frac{(1 - \mu)M_o}{S_1}\right) \tag{c}$$

$$\Delta f_2 = (1 - R)\left(-f_{ci} + \frac{(1 - \mu)M_o}{S_2}\right) \tag{d}$$

Then the stress ranges available to carry the moments included in Eqs. (a) and (b) are:

$$f_{1r} = f_{ti} - \Delta f_1 - f_{cs}$$

$$= R f_{ti} - (1 - R)\frac{(1 - \mu)M_o}{S_1} - f_{cs} \tag{e}$$

$$f_{2r} = f_{ts} - f_{ci} - \Delta f_2$$

$$= f_{ts} - R f_{ci} - (1 - R)\frac{(1 - \mu)M_o}{S_2} \tag{f}$$

The equations for required section moduli are found by substituting the stress ranges of Eqs. (e) and (f) into Eqs. (a) and (b). The results are as follows:

$$S_1 \geq \frac{(1 - R + \mu R)M_o + M_d + M_l}{R f_{ti} - f_{cs}} \tag{4.14}$$

$$S_2 \geq \frac{(1 - R + \mu R)M_o + M_d + M_l}{f_{ts} - R f_{ci}} \tag{4.15}$$

Comparing Eqs. (4.1) and (4.2) with Eqs. (4.14) and (4.15), it is seen that they differ only by the inclusion of the factor μR in the last two equations. Since μ is not known at the outset of a design it must be assumed; a good initial guess is zero.

The concrete centroidal stress and the initial prestress force can be found by using the equations of Art. 4.3(a) without change:

$$f_{cci} = f_{ti} - \frac{c_1}{h}(f_{ti} - f_{ci}) \tag{4.4}$$

$$P_i = A_c f_{cci} \tag{4.5}$$

as is easily confirm by Fig. 4.10.

For the beam of limited depth, the maximum eccentricity e_{max} is determined on the basis of the minimum distance from the steel centroid to the bottom face of the beam, based on requirements of tendon spacing and concrete cover (see Art. 4.16). With e_{max} known, the ratio μ can be determined for the beam chosen, and this value compared with that originally assumed. With reference to Fig. 4.10:

$$\frac{P_i e}{S_1} = (f_{ti} - f_{cci}) + (1 - \mu)\frac{M_o}{S_1} \tag{g}$$

from which

$$e = (f_{ti} - f_{cci})\frac{S_1}{P_i} + (1 - \mu)\frac{M_o}{P_i} \tag{4.16}$$

This eccentricity is now set equal to the available e_{max} and Eq. (4.16) is solved for μ, the only unknown. If this value differs appreciably from that assumed in calculating the section moduli, a revised value of μ is adopted and the calculations repeated.

It is clear from Eqs. (4.14) and (4.15) that the calculations are not sensitive to changes in μ, and as a result the iterative design process converges to a satisfactory degree very quickly, often in only one cycle.

4.7 SHAPE SELECTION AND FLEXURAL EFFICIENCY

One of the unique features of prestressed concrete design is the freedom to select cross section proportions and dimensions to suit the special requirements of the job at hand. The steel designer is limited to choosing from a number of readily available, usually symmetrical, cross section shapes. In timber design, rectangular sections are used almost without exception. But in the case of prestressed concrete, not only can the member depth be changed, but the web thickness modified and the flange widths and thicknesses varied independently to produce a beam with nearly ideal proportions for a given case. Particularly for post-tensioned beams of medium or long span but for other cases as well, the careful design of the cross section is an important part of the total design process.

For short span beams, in which the dead load of the beam is likely to be only a small fraction of the total load to be carried, rectangular members such as in Fig. 4.11a may provide the most economical solution, because forming costs are minimized. But for rectangular sections the kern distances are small, and the distance through which the compressive resultant may pass as load is applied is limited. For medium and long spans, the more efficient flanged shapes of Figs. 4.11b through 4.11e are preferred. The steel centroid may be kept lower, for such sections, without exceeding stress limits in the unloaded stage. The internal lever arm between tension and compression resultant forces at the service load and ultimate load stages is maximized.

In choosing a section, often the most expedient procedure is to start with a trial section, the properties of which match very closely the desired values of S_1 and S_2. The tabulated section constants of Appendix A will prove helpful in this connection. The trial section is then modified as required, With only two conditions to be satisfied (provision of the required S_1 and S_2) and six inde-

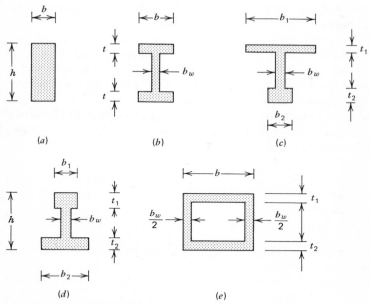

Figure 4.11   Idealized beam cross sections.

pendent section dimensions to be chosen in general (Fig. 4.11), it is clear that there are many possible solutions. The designer must choose the best.

It is not always necessary or desirable to satisfy requirements for S_1 and S_2 exactly. In some cases a broad top flange is desired to provide a useful surface, as for bridge decks or building floors. Considering the ultimate flexural strength of a member, it is often desirable to provide a generous top flange so that, should the beam be overloaded, the concrete stresses will remain low, and a ductile failure insured through yielding of the tensile steel. In such cases, the compressive stress at the top face of the beam at full service load will be well below the allowed value. For long span girders with a high ratio of self-weight to superimposed load, there is little danger of overstressing the bottom flange in compression at transfer, and the bottom flange may in some cases be eliminated altogether, resulting in a T section.

In practice the beam depth may be selected first, on the basis of a desirable span-to-depth ratio, or from requirements of headroom and clearance. The ratio of span to total depth for typical simple span beams varies from about 16 to 22 depending on loading conditions and design criteria. For lightly loaded double T floor or roof deck, L/h may be as high as 30 to 40. Hollow core flat deck planks may have L/h in excess of 40 yet give good performance (Ref. 4.7). For simply supported bridge beams between 60 and 120 ft long, Guyon suggests that the depth not be less than $L/25$ plus 4 in., but for longer spans this depth must be increased (Ref. 4.2). In all cases, continuity will permit larger span-to-depth ratios.

Once the depth of a beam is chosen, it is desirable to have a measure of the relative flexural efficiency of the cross sections being compared. In general terms, the ratio of section modulus to concrete area, S/A_c, will serve as such a measure. A beam characterized by a high ratio of S/A_c would represent a more efficient use of the material than one with a low ratio.

For the general case of nonsymmetrical cross sections, one would like simultaneously to maximize the ratios S_1/A_c and S_2/A_c. Since $S_1 = I/c_1$ and $S_2 = I/c_2$ these ratios can be rewritten as follows:

$$\frac{S_1}{A_c} = \frac{I_c}{A_c c_1} = \frac{r^2}{c_1} \tag{a}$$

$$\frac{S_2}{A_c} = \frac{I_c}{A_c c_2} = \frac{r^2}{c_2} \tag{b}$$

Thus, for given values of c_1 and c_2, the most efficient cross section is the one with the largest value of radius of gyration, that is, the one in which the concrete area is concentrated as nearly as practical toward the extreme top and bottom surfaces.

The terms at the right of Eqs. (a) and (b) will be recognized as the lower kern and upper kern dimensions of the section, respectively, (see Art. 3.4D).

It is convenient to express the distances represented by Eqs. (a) and (b) in nondimensional form, in terms of the distances c_1 and c_2 to the top and bottom faces of the member. With $k_1 = r^2/c_2$ and $k_2 = r^2/c_1$ these ratios are

$$\frac{k_1}{c_1} = \frac{r^2}{c_1 c_2} \tag{c}$$

$$\frac{k_2}{c_2} = \frac{r^2}{c_1 c_2} \tag{d}$$

Consequently the single expression

$$Q = \frac{r^2}{c_1 c_2} \tag{4.17}$$

can be used as a convenient basis for comparing the flexural efficiency of competing cross sections of a given depth.

The efficiency factor Q can also be expressed in geometric terms. Noting that $h = c_1 + c_2$

$$Q = \frac{r^2}{c_1 c_2} \frac{c_1 + c_2}{h} \tag{e}$$

$$Q = \frac{k_1 + k_2}{h} \tag{4.18}$$

indicating that the Q factor is nothing more or less than the ratio of the total kern depth to the total section depth.

Clearly those I- and T-shaped cross sections with relatively thin webs and flanges will display higher Q factors than will cross sections with thicker parts. However, practical considerations place an upper limit on the degree of slenderness that can be achieved. The overall proportions of a beam must be chosen considering the possibility of lateral buckling of the loaded member, if it is not supported against lateral movement by connected construction. This is particularly a factor during the handling of precast members. Thin compression flanges always present the danger of local buckling when loaded. Thin overhanging flanges are vulnerable to breakage during the handling and erection of precast elements.

The minimum thickness of the web is often determined by minimum clearances needed for the prestressing tendons and the auxiliary reinforcement, and the requirements of concrete cover for the outermost steel. Although web thicknesses of 5 in. or less may be satisfactory to carry shear stresses with a reasonable amount of web reinforcement, such thin webs are often difficult to pour without risk of voids or air pockets. Normally a 6 in. web width should be considered the practical minimum. Web widths are usually less in European practice than in the United States.

In general, well-designed I beams have an efficiency factor close to 0.50. Q factors less than about 0.45 indicate too heavy a section, while values larger than about 0.55 indicate an excessively slender section of questionable practicality (Ref. 4.2).

4.8 STANDARD SECTIONS

Certain standard cross section shapes have evolved over the years for floor and roof panels, wall panels, beams, and columns, and for short- and medium-span highway bridge girders. Members having these standard shapes can be mass produced by precasting plants, often using long-line methods and permanent, reusable metal forms. Great cost savings are possible, compared with construction that requires special forming either in a precasting plant or at the construction site. Consequently, standard sections are often used, even though properties may not be optimum for a particular set of design constraints and even though the section efficiency could be improved by shape modification.

The most common standard sections used for building construction are described in Art. 12.2, and those shapes most often employed for bridges up to medium span are discussed in Art. 12.7.

In general, the properties of the standard section selected in a particular instance will exceed the minimum requirements and, as a result, the designer has some choice with respect to the prestress force and the eccentricity used. The discussion of the following article is particularly relevant in such instances.

4.9 SECTIONS HAVING EXCESS CAPACITY

In practical situations, very seldom will the concrete section chosen have exactly the required values of S_1 and S_2 as found by the methods of Art. 4.3, nor will the concrete centroid be exactly at the theoretically ideal level. Rounding upward of concrete dimensions, provision of broad flanges for functional reasons, or the use of standardized cross section shapes will normally result in a member whose section properties will exceed the minimum requirements. In such a case, the stresses in the concrete as the member passes from the unloaded stage to the full service load stage will stay within the allowable limits, but the limit stresses will not be obtained exactly. An infinite number of combinations of prestress force and eccentricity will satisfy requirements. Usually the design requiring the lowest value of prestress force, and the largest practical eccentricity, will be the most economical.

A typical situation is illustrated in Fig. 4.12. For practical reasons, a beam having a T-shaped cross section with a broad top flange has been selected. The section moduli S_1 and S_2 exceed the minimum requirements. At the bottom face, as the beam passes from the unloaded to the service load stage, the concrete stresses are within, and come close to, the allowable limits f_{ts} and f_{ci} as shown by Fig. 4.12c, for example. At the top face, because of the high location of the concrete centroid, the stress change is much smaller and the concrete stresses are easily contained within the range from f_{ti} to f_{cs}.

Three of the many possible solutions for such a case are illustrated by Figs. 4.12b, c, and d, corresponding to different combinations of prestress force and eccentricity. In Fig. 4.12b a relatively low value of P_i has been used (as confirmed by the low concrete centroidal stress compared with the other cases) combined with a high eccentricity (indicated by the slope of the stress distribution labeled $P_i + M_o$). In Fig. 4.12c a higher value of P_i has been selected. Since the stress distribution $P_i + M_o$ has about the same slope as before, the eccentricity must have been somewhat less than that for Fig. 4.12b. In the final case, shown in Fig. 4.12d, a substantially larger prestress force has been used, combined with a very small eccentricity.

All three cases illustrated by Fig. 4.12 meet the requirement that the stresses stay within the indicated limits in all stages between unloaded and full service load. However, the first choice would no doubt be the best, requiring the smallest value of prestress force. In addition, the large eccentricity would be advantageous in maximizing the ultimate flexural strength of the member, since it would offer the largest internal lever arm between tension and compression resultants should the beam be overloaded.

In cases such as that just illustrated, where the concrete section has excess capacity, Eqs. (4.4) and (4.6) for concrete centroidal stress and required eccentricity, respectively, do not apply, because the stress limits f_{ti} and f_{ci} are not realized exactly. However, those equations may easily be modified to suit the

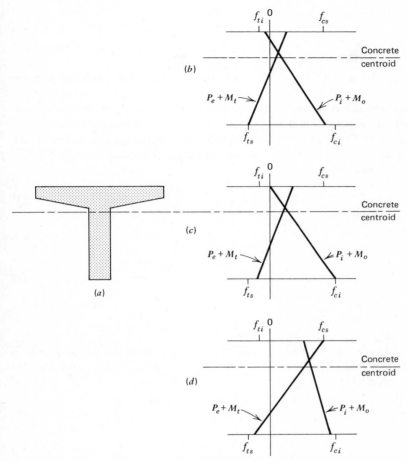

Figure 4.12   Alternate concrete stress distributions for section with excess capacity.

circumstances. If the desired values of concrete stress in the initial stage, at the top and bottom faces of the member, are respectively f_{1i} and f_{2i}, then the concrete centroidal stress in the initial condition is

$$f_{cci} = f_{1i} - \frac{c_1}{h}(f_{1i} - f_{2i})$$ (4.19)

The initial prestress force is given by Eq. (4.5) as before:

$$P_i = A_c f_{cci}$$ (4.5)

The required eccentricity is

$$e = (f_{1i} - f_{cci})\frac{S_1}{P_i} + \frac{M_o}{P_i} \tag{4.20}$$

Thus Eqs. (4.19) and (4.20) may be substituted for Eqs. (4.4) and (4.6) in such cases.

A graphical solution indicating all acceptable combinations of prestress force and eccentricity is helpful in making the best choice for a given concrete cross section (Ref. 4.9). There are four limit stresses to be satisfied, two at the initial unloaded stage and two at the full service load stage. The requirements may be restated as follows:

$$f_{ti} \geq -\frac{P_i}{A_c}\left(1 - \frac{ec_1}{r^2}\right) - \frac{M_o}{S_1} \tag{a}$$

$$f_{ci} \leq -\frac{P_i}{A_c}\left(1 + \frac{ec_2}{r^2}\right) + \frac{M_o}{S_2} \tag{b}$$

$$f_{ts} \geq -\frac{RP_i}{A_c}\left(1 + \frac{ec_2}{r^2}\right) + \frac{M_t}{S_2} \tag{c}$$

$$f_{cs} \leq -\frac{RP_i}{A_c}\left(1 - \frac{ec_1}{r^2}\right) - \frac{M_t}{S_1} \tag{d}$$

These equations may be rearranged to give the inverse of the initial prestress force as a linear function of eccentricity. For the initial stage, from Eqs. (a) and (b), respectively:

$$\frac{1}{P_i} \geq \frac{(-1 + ec_1/r^2)}{(f_{ti} + M_o/S_1)A_c} \tag{4.21}$$

$$\frac{1}{P_i} \geq \frac{(1 + ec_2/r^2)}{(-f_{ci} + M_o/S_2)A_c} \tag{4.22}$$

while for the service load stage, from Eqs. (c) and (d), respectively:

$$\frac{1}{P_i} \leq \frac{R(1 + ec_2/r^2)}{(-f_{ts} + M_t/S_2)A_c} \tag{4.23}$$

$$\frac{1}{P_i} \leq \frac{R(-1 + ec_1/r^2)}{(f_{cs} + M_t/S_1)A_c} \tag{4.24}$$

These functional relationships are plotted in Fig. 4.13 for a typical case. Equation (4.21) establishes a lower bound on $1/P_i$ (i.e., an upper bound on P_i) such that the tensile stress limit f_{ti} is not exceeded in the initial stage. Any value of $1/P_i$ above the line established by Eq. (4.21) is acceptable, as indicated by the shading. Similarly Eq. (4.22) establishes another lower bound on $1/P_i$ such that the compressive stress limit f_{ci} is not violated. Upper limits on $1/P_i$ are

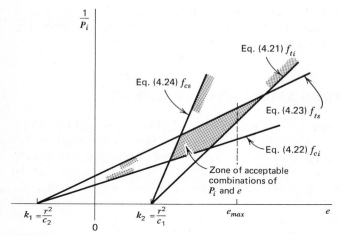

Figure 4.13   Variation   of   prestress   force   with eccentricity.

established by Eq. (4.23), based on the service load tensile stress limit f_{ts}, and by Eq. (4.24), based on the service load compressive stress limit f_{cs}. The zone indicating acceptable combinations of P_i and e that meet all four requirements is shown shaded on the graph.

It is interesting to note the results of setting $1/P_i$ equal to zero for each of Eqs. (4.21) through (4.24). Equations (4.21) and (4.24) indicate that $e = r^2/c_1$, that is, $e = k_2$, the lower kern dimension. In physical terms, an infinite value of P_i can be applied at the lower kern without violating stress limits at the top of the member, since that concrete stress would be zero for any value of P_i. Similarly, Eqs. (4.22) and (4.23), when set equal to zero, indicate that $e = -r^2/c_2$, that is, $e = k_1$, the upper kern dimension. An infinite value of P_i can be applied at the upper kern without violating stress limits at the bottom of the member. The eccentricities corresponding to k_1 and k_2 are shown in Fig. 4.13.

The maximum eccentricity that can be used without violating any of the four stress limits is found at the intersection of Eqs. (4.21) and (4.23) in Fig. 4.13. This also corresponds to the minimum acceptable value of P_i (i.e., maximum $1/P_i$), and would probably represent the most desirable solution. In many practical cases, a maximum value e_{max} would be established by physical limitations, based on the available distance c_2 reduced by the necessary concrete cover for the tendons, measured from the steel centroid. Given that condition, in the example of Fig. 4.13, the best value of $1/P_i$ is that at the intersection of e_{max} with Eq. (4.23).

Note that in Fig. 4.13 all lines have been shown with positive slope. This is not always true and for some cases the lines may have infinite slope or a negative slope. This is typically the case for T beams, in which the top flange is often sufficiently large that the loads can be carried without exceeding f_{cs}, even if no prestress force were used. In this case a negative slope is obtained for Eq. (4.24), and it can be disregarded altogether.

4.10 FLEXURAL DESIGN BASED ON LOAD BALANCING

It was pointed out in Art. 1.3 that the effect of a change in the alignment of a prestressing tendon in a beam is to produce a lateral force on the beam at that location. Prestressing a member with curved or harped tendons thus has the effect of introducing a set of transverse equivalent loads, and these may be treated just as any other external loads in finding moments or deflections. Each particular tendon profile produces its own unique set of equivalent transverse forces. Typical tendon profiles, with corresponding equivalent loads and moment diagrams, were illustrated in Fig. 1.8. Both Fig. 1.8 and Art. 1.3 should be reviewed carefully at this time.

The equivalent load concept offers an alternative approach to the determination of required prestress force and eccentricity. The prestress force and tendon profile can be established so that external loads that will act are exactly counteracted by the transverse forces resulting from prestressing. The net result, for that particular set of external loads, is that the beam is subjected only to axial compression, and no bending moment. Furthermore, if all external loads are of a sustained nature (as is the prestressing force) the member will have no vertical deflection. The selection of the load to be balanced is left to the judgment of the designer. Usually the balanced load chosen is the sum of the self-weight and superimposed dead load, but it may include a fraction of the anticipated live load.

The design approach described was introduced in the United States in 1963 as the *load-balancing method* (Ref. 4.8), although the concept was used in Europe some time earlier, where it was called moment balancing.

The fundamentals of the approach will be illustrated in the context of the simply supported uniformly loaded beam shown in Fig. 4.14a. The beam is to be designed for a balanced load consisting of its own weight w_o, the superimposed dead load w_d, and some fractional part of the live load denoted by $k_b w_l$. Since the external load is uniformly distributed, it is reasonable to adopt a tendon having a parabolic shape. It is easily shown that a parabolic tendon will produce a uniformly distributed upward load equal to

$$w_p = \frac{8Py}{l^2} \tag{4.25a}$$

where P is the magnitude of the prestress force, y is the maximum sag of the tendon measured with respect to the chord between its end points, and l is the span.

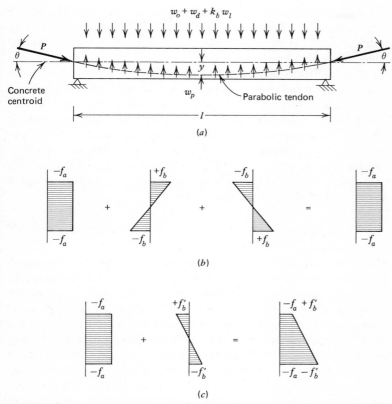

Figure 4.14 Load balancing for a uniformly loaded beam. (*a*) External and equivalent loads. (*b*) Concrete stresses due to axial and bending effects of prestress plus bending due to balanced external load. (*c*) Concrete stresses resulting when load $k_b w_l$ is removed.

If the downward load exactly equals the upward load from the tendon, these two loads cancel, and no bending stress is produced, as shown in Fig. 4.14*b*. The bending stresses due to prestress eccentricity are equal and opposite to the bending stresses resulting from the external load. The net resulting stress is uniform compression f_a equal to that produced by the axial force $P \cos \theta$. Excluding consideration of time-dependent effects, the beam would show no vertical deflection.

However, if the live load is removed or increased, then bending stresses and deflections will result because of the *unbalanced* portion of the load. Stresses due to this differential loading must be calculated and superimposed on the axial compression to obtain the net stresses for the unbalanced state. If we refer to Fig. 4.14c, the bending stresses f'_b resulting from removal of the partial live loading are superimposed on the uniform compressive stress f_a, resulting from the combination of eccentric prestress force and full balanced load to produce the final stress distribution shown.

Loads other than uniformly distributed would lead naturally to the selection of other tendon configurations. For example, if the external load consisted of a single concentration at midspan, a harped tendon such as that of Fig. 1.8a would be chosen, with maximum eccentricity at midspan, varying linearly to zero eccentricity at the supports. A third-point loading would lead the designer to select a tendon harped at the third points. A uniformly loaded cantilever beam would best be stressed using a tendon in which the eccentricity varied parabolically, from zero at the free end to y at the fixed support, in which case the upward reaction of the tendon would be

$$w_p = \frac{2Py}{l^2} \qquad (4.25b)$$

It should be clear that, for simple spans designed by the load balancing concept, it is necessary for the tendon to have zero eccentricity at the supports, because the moment due to superimposed loads is zero there. Any tendon eccentricity would produce an unbalanced moment (in itself an equivalent load) equal to the horizontal component of the prestress force times its eccentricity.

For spans continuous over supports this restriction does not apply. In Fig. 4.15a, if the prestress force is the same in the two spans adjacent to the interior support, and if the slope of the tendon is the same on either side, then the net bending moment applied to the beam at that location is zero. The only unbalanced load is the vertical force resulting from the change of tendon slope. This passes directly into the support. In such a case, the tendon may be raised to the maximum eccentricity permitted by requirements of concrete cover, maximizing the sag y in the adjacent spans and minimizing the prestress force required to carry the specified load. At the simply supported ends, the requirement of zero eccentricity must be retained.

At the free end of a cantilever beam, Fig. 4.15b, the steel eccentricity must be zero. The slope of the tendon there must match the slope of the concrete centroid, usually zero. In Fig. 4.15b, it is unlikely that the tendon slope θ_1 will equal the tendon slope θ_2; consequently, if the prestress force P_1 is the same as P_2, a net moment at the right support will result from prestressing. This could be avoided by using separate tendons for each span, each with its own value of prestress such that the horizontal components balance.

In practice, the load-balancing method of design is initiated by selection of a trial cross section, based on experience, or perhaps on an appropriate span–depth ratio. The tendon profile and prestress force are selected to balance the desired load. For that balanced load stage, the only net force on the concrete is axial compression, and the section need only be large enough to resist that force

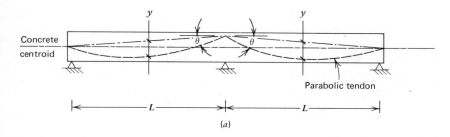

(a)

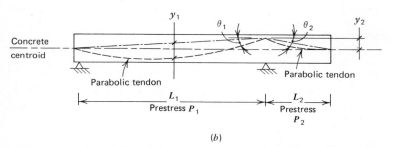

(b)

Figure 4.15 Load-balancing tendon profiles for uniformly loaded beams continuous over supports. (a) Two-span continuous beam. (b) Beam with cantilever.

and to provide room for the desired tendon profile. However, the trial section must be checked to insure that stresses are within the allowed limits should the live load be totally absent or fully in place, when bending stresses will be superimposed on the axial compressive stresses. There is no assurance that the section will be adequate for these load stages, nor that adequate strength will be provided should the member be overloaded. Revision may be necessary. Thus the load-balancing method is essentially a trial-and-error approach, and does not constitute a complete design method in itself.

It should further be observed that obtaining a uniform compressive concrete stress at the balanced load stage does not insure that the member will have zero deflection at that stage. The reason for this is that the uniform stress distribution is made up of two parts: that from the eccentric prestress force and that from the external loads. The first is sustained in nature and causes creep strain and creep deflection. The second is partially due to sustained dead load but may also include stresses due to transient live loads, which do not produce appreciable creep. A beam that is designed for a balanced load of which part is live load could be expected to show upward camber after a period of time.

In spite of these limitations, the load-balancing or equivalent-load approach provides the design engineer with a useful supplementary tool. For simple spans it leads the designer to choose a sensible tendon profile and focuses attention very early on the matter of deflection. But the most important advantages become evident in the design of indeterminate prestressed members, including both continuous beams and two-way slabs. For such cases, at least for one unique loading, the member carries only axial compression but no bending. This greatly simplifies the analysis.

EXAMPLE   Design of a Beam by Load Balancing

A post-tensioned beam is to be designed to carry a uniformly distributed load over a 30 ft span, as illustrated by Fig. 4.16a. In addition to its own weight, it must carry a dead load of 150 plf and a service live load of 600 plf. Concrete strength of 4000 psi will be attained at 28 days; at time of transfer of prestress force the strength will be 3000 psi. Prestress loss may be assumed at 20 percent of P_i. On the basis that about one quarter of the live load will be sustained over a substantial time period, k_b of 0.25 will be used in determining the balanced load. (Span = 9.1 m, $w_d = 2.2\,\text{kN/m}$, $w_l = 8.8$ kN/m, $f'_c = 28$ N/mm^2, and $f'_{ci} = 21$ N/mm^2.)

On the basis of an arbitrarily chosen span–depth ratio of 18, a trial section of 20 in. total depth is selected, having a 10 in. width. The calculated self-weight of the beam is

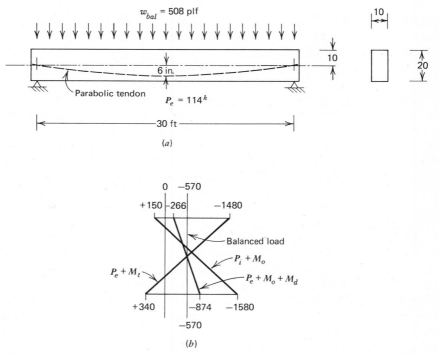

Figure 4.16 Example of design by load balancing. (*a*) Beam profile and cross section. (*b*) Flexural stresses at maximum moment section.

208 plf and the selected load to be balanced is

$$w_{bal} = w_o + w_d + k_b w_l = 208 + 150 + 150 = 508 \text{ plf}$$

Based on a minimum concrete cover from the steel centroid to the bottom face of the beam of 4 in., the maximum eccentricity that can be used for the 20 in. trial section is 6 in. A parabolic tendon will be used to produce a uniformly distributed upward tendon reaction. To equilibrate the sustained downward loading, the prestress force P_e after losses, from Eq (4.25), should be

$$P_e = \frac{w_{bal} l^2}{8y} = \frac{508 \times 900}{8 \times 0.5} = 114{,}000 \text{ lb (507 kN)}$$

and the corresponding initial prestress force is

$$P_i = \frac{P_e}{R} = \frac{114{,}000}{0.8} = 143{,}000 \text{ lb (636 kN)}$$

For the balanced load stage, the concrete will be subjected to a uniform compressive stress of

$$f_{bal} = \frac{114{,}000}{200} = -570 \text{ psi}$$

as shown in Fig. 4.16b. Should the partial live load of 150 plf be removed, the stresses to be superimposed on f_{bal} result from a net *upward* load of 150 plf. The section modulus for the trial beam is 667 in.[3] and

$$M_{unbal} = 150 \times \frac{900}{8} = 16{,}900 \text{ ft-lb}$$

Hence the unbalanced bending stresses at the top and bottom faces are

$$f_{unbal} = 16{,}900 \times \frac{12}{667} = 304 \text{ psi}$$

Thus the net stresses are

$$f_1 = -570 + 304 = -266 \text{ psi } (-1.8 \text{ N/mm}^2)$$
$$f_2 = -570 - 304 = -874 \text{ psi } (-6.0 \text{ N/mm}^2)$$

Similarly, if the *full* live load should act, the stresses to be superimposed are those due to a net *downward* load of 450 plf. The resulting stresses in the concrete at full service load are

$$f_1 = -570 - 910 = -1480 \text{ psi } (-10.2 \text{ N/mm}^2)$$
$$f_2 = -570 + 910 = +340 \text{ psi } (+2.3 \text{ N/mm}^2)$$

Stresses in the concrete with live load absent and live load fully in place are shown in Fig. 4.16b.

It is also necessary to investigate the stresses in the initial unloaded stage, when the member is subjected to P_i plus moment due to its own weight.

$$M_o = 208 \times \frac{900}{8} = 23{,}400 \text{ ft-lb}$$

Hence in the initial stage:

$$f_1 = -\frac{143,000}{200}\left(1 - \frac{6 \times 10}{33.35}\right) - \frac{23,400 \times 12}{667} = +150 \text{ psi } (+1.0 \text{ N/mm}^2)$$

$$f_2 = -\frac{143,000}{200}\left(1 + \frac{6 \times 10}{33.35}\right) + \frac{23,400 \times 12}{667} = -1580 \text{ psi } (-10.9 \text{ N/mm}^2)$$

The stresses in the unloaded and full service load stages must be checked against these permitted by Code. With $f'_c = 4000$ psi and $f'_{ci} = 3000$ psi the permitted stresses are:

$$f_{ti} = +165 \text{ psi } (+1.1 \text{ N/mm}^2) \qquad f_{ts} = +380 \text{ psi } (+2.6 \text{ N/mm}^2)$$

$$f_{ci} = -1800 \text{ psi } (-12.4 \text{ N/mm}^2) \qquad f_{cs} = -1800 \text{ psi } (-12.4 \text{ N/mm}^2)$$

The actual stresses, shown in Fig. 4.16b, are within these limits and acceptably close, and no revision will be made in the trial 10×20 in. (254×508 mm) cross section on the basis of stress limits.

The ultimate flexural strength of the members must now be checked, to insure that an adequate factor of safety against collapse has been provided. The required P_i of 143,000 lb will be provided using stranded Grade 250 cable, with $f_{pu} = 250,000$ psi and $f_{py} = 212,000$ psi. The maximum permitted initial stress is $0.70 \times 250,000 = 175,000$ psi. Accordingly the required area is

$$A_p = \frac{143,000}{175,000} = 0.82 \text{ in.}^2 \text{ (529 mm}^2)$$

This will be provided using eight $\frac{7}{16}$ in. strands, giving an actual area of 0.864 in.^{2} (Table 2.2). The resulting stresses at the initial and final stages are

$$f_{pi} = \frac{143,000}{0.864} = 166,000 \text{ psi}$$

$$f_{pe} = \frac{114,000}{0.864} = 132,000 \text{ psi}$$

Using the ACI approximate relation for steel stress at failure, according to Eq. (3.20), with steel ratio $\rho_p = 0.864/160 = 0.0054$, the stress

$$f_{ps} = f_{pu}\left(1 - 0.5\,\rho_p\,\frac{f_{pu}}{f'_c}\right)$$

$$= 250\left(1 - 0.5 \times 0.0054 \times \frac{250}{4}\right)$$

$$= 208 \text{ ksi}$$

However, according to Code, f_{ps} is not to be taken greater than f_{py} or $f_{pe} + 60,000$. The latter controls in this case, and f_{ps} is set equal to 192 ksi. Then

$$a = \frac{A_p f_{ps}}{0.85 f'_c b}$$

$$= \frac{0.864 \times 192}{0.85 \times 4 \times 10} = 4.88 \text{ in. (124 mm)}$$

The nominal flexural strength is

$$M_n = A_p f_{ps} \left(d - \frac{a}{2} \right) = 0.864 \times 192{,}000 \left(16 - \frac{4.88}{2} \right) \times \frac{1}{12}$$

$$= 187{,}000 \text{ ft-lb (254 kN-m)}$$

which must be reduced by the factor $\phi = 0.90$, as usual, to obtain design strength:

$$\phi M_n = 0.9 \times 187{,}000 = 168{,}000 \text{ ft-lb (228 kN-m)}$$

It will be recalled that the ACI load factors with respect to dead and live loads are, respectively, 1.4 and 1.7 (see Table 1.2). The safety factor obtained in the present case will be evaluated with respect to the service live load moment of 67,500 ft-lb, assuming that dead loads may be 1.4 times the calculated values, in keeping with the ACI requirements. Accordingly,

$$168 = 1.4(23.4 + 16.9) + F_l(67.5)$$
$$F_l = 1.65$$

This is slightly less than the requirement of 1.7. However, the deficiency could undoubtedly be made up by the addition of longitudinal reinforcing bars such as would be present to support the web reinforcement.

4.11 DESIGN BASED ON PARTIAL PRESTRESSING AND ULTIMATE STRENGTH

There is a distinct trend in current design practice toward the use of partially prestressed beams, in which flexural tensile stress or even cracking is permitted in the concrete in the service load stage or for occasional overloads. Cracks, if they occur, are usually small and well distributed, and normally close completely when the load that produced them is removed.

It is argued convincingly that cracking has long been an accepted feature of reinforced concrete members and that there is no reason to penalize prestressed concrete designs by requiring that cracks be eliminated completely, even though this is possible (Ref. 4.10). Furthermore, the condition of no tension or limited tension in a prestressed structure rarely exists. If combined effects including shear and torsion are taken into account, the calculated principal stresses usually exceed the tensile strength of the concrete. In regions of concentrated loads, load transfer, or anchorage of tendons, tensile stresses cannot be avoided. Also, in most cases, a structure is prestressed in only one direction, so that in the transverse direction it acts as ordinary reinforced concrete. In view of these facts, it is hard to justify a requirement for no flexural cracking.

The advantages of partial prestressing are important. A smaller prestress force will be required, permitting reduction in the number of tendons and anchorages. The necessary flexural strength may be provided in such cases either by a combination of prestressed tendons and non-prestressed reinforcing bars, or by an adequate number of high-tensile tendons prestressed to a level lower than the permitted limit. In some cases a combination of stressed and unstressed tendons is used. Since the prestressing force is less, the size of the bottom flange, which is required mainly to resist the compression when a beam is in the unloaded stage, can be reduced or eliminated altogether. This leads in turn to significant simplification and cost reduction in the construction of forms, as well as resulting in structures that are more pleasing esthetically. Furthermore, by relaxing the requirement for low service load tension in the concrete, a significant improvement can be made in the deflection characteristics of a beam. Troublesome upward camber of the member in the unloaded stage can be avoided, and the prestress force selected primarily to produce the desired deflection for a particular loading condition. The behavior of partially prestressed beams, should they be overloaded to failure, is apt to be superior to that of fully prestressed beams, because the improved ductility provides ample warning of distress. Such points have been discussed more fully in Art. 3.8.

The present ACI Code permits tensile stress in the concrete of $6\sqrt{f_c'}$ at full service load. This is slightly below the usual modulus of rupture, but it clearly amounts to partially prestressing because complete elimination of service load tension is not required. No cracking should occur if the tension is limited to this value, and the design methods presented earlier in this chapter are fully applicable.

The Code permits flexural tension as high as $12\sqrt{f_c'}$ in beams at full service load, provided that explicit calculations confirm that deflections are within specified limits. This tensile stress is substantially greater than the modulus of rupture of concrete, and tensile stresses calculated on the basis of an uncracked concrete section for such cases are *nominal stresses* only. Nevertheless they may serve as the basis for proportioning beam cross sections and the equations of Art. 4.3 used without modification.

However a more rational approach to the design of prestressed concrete beams is based on providing a member with *strength* sufficient to resist hypothetical overloads, which are calculated by applying *overload factors* greater than unity to the expected service loads. After the required concrete and steel areas are determined, an amount of prestress force may be specified such as to produce a member with the desired service load characteristics.

The design of structural members based on strength requirements is appealing, because in all but unusual cases the most important single characteristic of a structure is its strength, which establishes the degree of safety incorporated into its design. For *reinforced concrete* members, strength requirements usually provide the starting point in proportioning cross sections and determining steel areas. Only later is the design checked for satisfactory serviceability, with specific reference to cracking and deflection at the service load level. Checking of service load stresses is often dispensed with.

An analogous approach is proposed for prestressed concrete, although there are some complications. For reinforced concrete, consideration is usually limited to underreinforced beams, for which the steel is at the yield stress at failure. With the tensile force thus known, the compressive area of the cross section is easily calculated from the summation of horizontal forces. With the centroid of the compression area known, the internal resisting lever arm is known and an explicit equation can be written for the ultimate resisting moment. This equation can be rearranged to permit direct solution for the required concrete dimensions and tensile steel area (Ref. 4.11). For prestressed concrete, on the other hand, the stress in the steel at flexural failure is at some value f_{ps} usually less than the tensile strength f_{pu}. It may be more or less than the nominal yield stress f_{py}. The compression concrete area, which is a function of steel stress at failure, is not easily established at the outset of the design process, so the internal lever arm between compressive and tensile resultants is not known.

However, in practical cases, a trial concrete section may be found by assuming that the tendon stress at failure is 0.9 times the ultimate strength f_{pu}. Refinement will be found necessary only in cases when there is an unusually large percentage of steel (Ref. 4.12). For flanged sections, the internal lever arm at failure is very nearly equal to the distance from the tensile steel centroid to the middepth of the flange.

On this basis, a design procedure for partially prestressed beams may be developed as follows:

1. Find the required ultimate flexural strength M_u by applying overload factors to the calculated dead loads and specified service live loads. According to the usual specifications the nominal strength required of the member is $M_n = M_u/\phi$ where ϕ is a capacity reduction factor equal to 0.90 for bending.
2. A trial depth is assumed for the concrete section based on maximum span depth ratio or on experience. Top flange dimensions may be based on functional requirements or other criteria.
3. The internal lever arm z is assumed equal to the distance from the steel centroid to the middepth of the flange or, in the case of a rectangular section, equal to $0.80h$. If the steel stress at failure is taken to be $0.90f_{pu}$, then the required area of the tendon is

$$A_p = \frac{M_n}{0.9f_{pu}z} \qquad (4.26)$$

4. Assuming for design purposes that the actual concrete stress distribution can be replaced by an equivalent rectangular stress block at uniform stress intensity $0.85f'_c$ the required area of compression concrete is

$$A'_c = \frac{M_n}{0.85f'_c z} \qquad (4.27)$$

This gives the required area of the top flange, after making allowance for the contribution, if any, of the web area in compression. The trial section is modified if necessary.

5. The web width may now be chosen from requirements of shear strength or considering the practical needs for concrete cover for the tendons and other steel.

6. The amount of prestress force is chosen to produce the desired deflection characteristics for the member. In lieu of other requirements a criterion of zero deflection under the combined effect of prestress and total dead load may be selected, for example. The load balancing concept of Art. 4.10 is useful in determining the required prestress force.

7. Bonded prestressed reinforcement, together with nonprestressed bars used for stirrup support bars, are usually sufficient to insure that service-load cracks will be fine and well distributed. In some cases additional non-prestressed reinforcement may be added for purposes of crack control.

It will be noted that no mention has been made here of service load stresses, which may be considered almost irrelevant provided that all requirements of strength and serviceability are met. However, if service load stresses are to be checked, the method of Art. 3.9 is available.

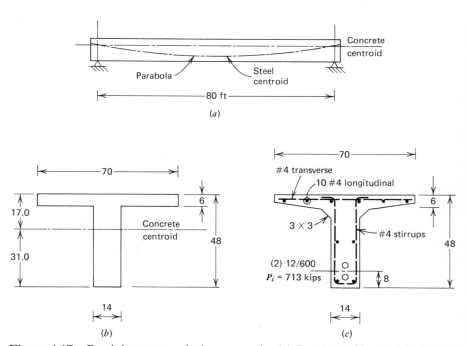

Figure 4.17 Partial prestress design example. (*a*) Beam profile. (*b*) Idealized section. (*c*) Final section.

EXAMPLE   Design Based on Strength Requirements and Partial Prestressing

A beam having T cross section is to be designed to carry a service live load of 1200 plf and superimposed dead load of 400 plf in addition to its own weight, on an 80 ft simple span, as shown in Fig. 4.17a. The member will be post-tensioned using tendons composed of Grade 250 stranded cable. Concrete strength at 28 days is specified to be 5000 psi. A design based on strength will be adopted, with the additional requirement that zero deflection is to be obtained under full service dead load. ($w_l = 17.5$ kN/m, $w_d = 5.8$ kN/m, span $= 24.4$ m, and $f'_c = 34$ N/mm^2.)

In lieu of other restrictions a trial member depth of 1/20 the span, or 4 ft (1219 mm), will be selected. Functional requirements dictate a flange width of 70 in. (1778 mm) having an average thickness of 6 in. (152 mm). Anticipated requirements for ducts and anchorages, as well as requirements for web reinforcement lead to a choice of 14 in. (356 mm) web width. The trial section, shown in Fig. 4.17b, has the following properties:

$$I_c = 229,000 \text{ in.}^4 \ (95.3 \times 10^9 \text{ mm}^4)$$
$$S_1 = 13,500 \text{ in.}^3 \ (221 \times 10^6 \text{ mm}^3)$$
$$S_2 = 7380 \text{ in.}^3 \ (121 \times 10^6 \text{ mm}^3)$$
$$c_1 = 17.0 \text{ in. } (432 \text{ mm})$$
$$c_2 = 31.0 \text{ in. } (787 \text{ mm})$$
$$A_c = 1010 \text{ in.}^2 \ (652 \times 10^3 \text{ mm}^2)$$
$$w_o = 1050 \text{ plf } (15.3 \text{ kN/m})$$

The dead and live load moments are:

$$M_o = \frac{1}{8} \times 1.050 \times 6400 = 840 \text{ ft-kips}$$

$$M_d = \frac{1}{8} \times 0.400 \times 6400 = 320 \text{ ft-kips}$$

$$M_l = \frac{1}{8} \times 1.200 \times 6400 = 960 \text{ ft-kips}$$

If we apply the usual ACI overload factors, the required flexural strength is

$$M_u = 1.4(840 + 320) + 1.7(960) = 3260 \text{ ft-kips}$$

and with $\phi = 0.90$ for bending, the member must have a nominal strength of

$$M_n = \frac{3260}{0.90} = 3620 \text{ ft-kips } (4909 \text{ kN-m})$$

The internal lever arm at ultimate load may be assumed equal to the distance between the steel centroid and the middepth of the compression flange. Anticipating the use of two tendons arranged vertically, with appropriate clearance and concrete cover, the steel centroid will be placed 8 in. from the bottom face of the beam at midspan. Thus the internal level arm is

$$z = 48 - 8 - 3 = 37 \text{ in.}$$

From Eq. (4.26) the tentative steel area required is

$$A_p = \frac{3620 \times 12}{0.9 \times 250 \times 37} = 5.22 \text{ in.}^2 \text{ (3368 mm}^2\text{)}$$

Two tendons will be used, each composed of 12 Grade 250 strands of 0.600 in. nominal diameter (see Appendix B), providing an area of 5.20 in.^{2} Check of the sheath diameter, which is 3 in., confirms that the proposed placement is satisfactory. The tendons will be draped to a parabolic profile with zero eccentricity at the supports and will be grouted after stressing.

From Eq. (4.27) the required compressive concrete area is

$$A_c' = \frac{3620 \times 12}{0.85 \times 5 \times 37} = 276 \text{ in.}^2$$

The full 70 in. flange width may be considered effective; hence the depth of the stress block at ultimate load is

$$a = \frac{276}{70} = 3.94 \text{ in.}$$

indicating that the revised internal lever arm is

$$z = 48 - 8 - \frac{3.94}{2} = 38 \text{ in.}$$

No practical difference in required steel area results.

The stress in the steel at ultimate load may now be estimated using the ACI approximate relation given by Eq. (3.20). With the actual steel ratio

$$\rho_p = \frac{5.20}{70 \times 40} = 0.00186$$

from Eq. (3.20) the steel stress at failure is

$$f_{ps} = f_{pu}\left(1 - 0.5\rho_p \frac{f_{pu}}{f_c'}\right)$$

$$= 250\left(1 - 0.5 \times 0.00186 \times \frac{250}{5}\right)$$

$$= 238 \text{ ksi (1640 N/mm}^2\text{)}$$

This is within 6 percent of the value of $0.90 \times 250 = 225$ ksi assumed in sizing the steel and no revision is called for.

The amount of pretensioning of the selected steel area will now be determined based on the specification that the full dead load of 1450 plf will be balanced by the uplift of the parabolic curved tendons. With sag $y = 48.0 - 8.0 - 17.0 = 23.0$ in. Equation (4.25) gives

$$P_e = \frac{(w_o + w_d)l^2}{8y} = \frac{1.450 \times 6400 \times 12}{8 \times 23.0} = 606 \text{ kips (2695 kN)}$$

If losses are assumed to be 15 percent then

$$P_i = \frac{606}{0.85} = 713 \text{ kips (3171 kN)}$$

and the initial stress in the tendons is

$$f_{pi} = \frac{713}{5.20} = 137 \text{ ksi}$$

According to the Code the permitted upper limit is $0.70 \times 250 = 175$ ksi; the actual initial prestress is 78 percent of this allowed value. Use of the lower value permits the desired zero deflection to be attained at full dead load.

In order to control cracking in the member prior to post-tensioning, non-prestressed longitudinal bars will be added in an amount equal to 0.0020 times the gross section of the concrete (see Art. 4.14). The total required area of

$$A_t = 0.0020(14 \times 48 + 6 \times 56) = 2.02 \text{ in.}^2 \text{ (1303 mm}^2\text{)}$$

is very nearly provided by 10 No. 4 bars. The arrangement of steel is given by Fig. 4.17c, which also shows the location of the two 12 strand tendons. The nonstressed bars will also aid the grouted tendons in controlling and distributing flexural cracking.

As a matter of interest, the nominal stresses will be calculated in the member for the unloaded and full service load stages. The stresses due to the component effects are as follows:

$$P_i: \quad f_1 = -\frac{713,000}{1010}\left(1 - \frac{23.0 \times 17.0}{227}\right) = +510 \text{ psi}$$

$$f_2 = -\frac{713,000}{1010}\left(1 + \frac{23.0 \times 31.0}{227}\right) = -2920 \text{ psi}$$

$$P_e: \quad f_1 = 510 \times 0.85 = +430 \text{ psi}$$

$$f_2 = -2920 \times 0.85 = -2480 \text{ psi}$$

$$M_o: \quad f_1 = \frac{840 \times 12,000 \times 17.0}{229,000} = -750 \text{ psi}$$

$$f_2 = \frac{840 \times 12,000 \times 31.0}{229,000} = +1360 \text{ psi}$$

$$M_d + M_l: \quad f_1 = \frac{1280 \times 12,000 \times 17.0}{229,000} = -1140 \text{ psi}$$

$$f_2 = \frac{1280 \times 12,000 \times 31.0}{229,000} = +2080 \text{ psi}$$

In the unloaded stage the top and bottom surface stresses are, respectively,

$$P_i + M_o: \quad f_1 = +510 - 750 = -240 \text{ psi}$$
$$f_2 = -2920 + 1360 = -1560 \text{ psi}$$

while in the full service load stage

$$P_e + M_t: \quad f_1 = +430 - 750 - 1140 = -1460 \text{ psi}$$
$$f_2 = -2480 + 1360 + 2080 = +960 \text{ psi}$$

Comparison of the bottom face tension with the ACI upper limit of $12\sqrt{5000} = 849$ psi indicates that the design does *not* satisfy the usual Code restriction on nominal flexural tension in prestressed members. However, an "escape clause" is included in the Code to the effect that the limiting tensile stress ". . . may be exceeded when it is shown experimentally or analytically that performance will not be impaired." In the present instance, the full required strength is provided, and service load performance is improved through the deflection control permitted by partial prestressing.

4.12 BOND STRESS, TRANSFER LENGTH, AND DEVELOPMENT LENGTH

In prestressed concrete beams there are certain forces acting which tend to cause the steel tendons to slip through the surrounding concrete. These produce bond stresses or shearing stresses acting on the interface between steel and concrete. The tendency to slip is resisted by a combination of adhesion, friction, and mechanical bond between the two materials. There are two types of bond stresses to consider: flexural bond stress and transfer bond stress.

Flexural bond stresses arise because of the change in tension along the tendon resulting from differences in bending moment at adjacent sections. They are proportional to the rate of change of bending moment, hence to the shear force, at a given location along the span. Provided that the concrete member is uncracked, the magnitude of flexural bond stress is very low. After cracking, flexural bond stresses are higher by an order of magnitude than before. They can be calculated using the same equations that have been developed for ordinary reinforced concrete members (Ref. 4.11). The resulting stress is only a nominal, average value, however, and immediately adjacent to the cracks the actual bond stresses bear little relation to the calculated values. On one side of a flexural crack, stresses are well below the nominal level and may even act in the opposite direction. On the other side of the same crack they are much higher and commonly cause local, nonprogressive destruction of bond.

Flexural bond stress need not be considered in designing prestressed concrete beams, either before or after cracking. Even though local bond failure may occur, general failure cannot take place as long as adequate end anchorage is provided for the tendon, either in the form of mechanical anchorages or strand embedment.

For pretensioned beams, when the external jacking force is released, the prestressing force is transferred from the steel to the concrete near the ends of the member by bond over a distance that is known as the *transfer length*. Within this length, the stress buildup is gradual from zero to the effective prestress level, as indicated by Fig. 4.18. Some slip often occurs between steel and concrete. A wire cut off flush with the end of a beam will normally sink into the concrete slightly, but this slip is confined to the extreme end of the tendon, and stability is restored under a combination of friction and mechanical bond.

The transfer length depends on a number of factors, including the steel tensile stress, the configuration of the steel cross section (e.g., wires vs. strands), the condition of the surface of the steel, and the suddenness with which the jacking force is released. Steel wires that are slightly rusted will require shorter transfer length than will clean bright wires. Tests indicate that if the release of jacking tension is sudden, as will be the case if the tendon is flame cut or parted with a grinding disc while under tension, the required transfer length will be substantially greater than if the force is gradually applied. Concrete strength appears to have little influence (Ref. 4.17).

It should be observed that, at the end of a pretensioned beam, the conditions resisting pullout are quite different from those existing for a steel bar in an ordinary reinforced concrete beam. When the bar is stressed in tension, there is a slight reduction in diameter because of the Poisson effect, with the result that there is a radial tension acting across the interface between steel and concrete. This tends to reduce the frictional resistance to slip. For a prestressed tendon, the diameter reduction has already taken place when the concrete is poured. When the jacking force is removed, the tension near the ends of the member is much less than before. This reduction in longitudinal stress is accompanied

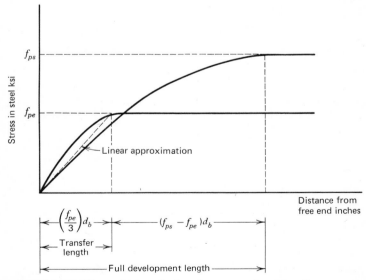

Figure 4.18 Transfer and development lengths for pretensioned strand.

by a slight increase in diameter of the steel, causing radial compression across the interface, which enhances the frictional resistance to pullout. This "swelling" has been shown to be important for wires, although in the more usual case of strands the mechanical resistance to slip provided by the irregular surface is at least equally important.

The effective prestress f_{pe} is essentially constant as the beam is loaded gradually up to the service load level. However, should it be overloaded there will be a large increase in steel stress until, at flexural failure a stress f_{ps} is attained that may be close to the tensile strength f_{pu} of the steel. Overstressing beyond service load produces somewhat reduced stresses within the original transfer length, as suggested by Fig. 4.18. A *development length* much greater than the original transfer length is required to reach the failure stress f_{ps} in the steel, as shown.

On the basis of tests of prestressing strand (Ref. 4.18), the effective prestress f_{pe} may be assumed to act at a transfer length from the end of the member equal to

$$l_t = \left(\frac{f_{pe}}{3}\right)d_b \tag{a}$$

where l_t is given in inches, the nominal strand diameter d_b is in inches, and the effective prestress f_{pe} is ksi. In investigating stresses near the ends of prestressed members such as short cantilevers, railroad ties, or truss members, it may be important to recognize that the full value of prestress force is not acting in the end region. Within the transfer length it is adequate and safe to assume a linear variation of prestress as shown in Fig. 4.18.

The same tests indicate that the additional distance past the original transfer length necessary to develop the failure strength of the steel is closely represented by the expression

$$l_t' = (f_{ps} - f_{pe})d_b \tag{b}$$

where the quantity in parentheses is the stress increment above the effective prestress level, in ksi units, to reach the calculated steel stress at flexural failure. Thus the total development length is

$$l_d = l_t + l_t'$$

$$= \left(\frac{f_{pe}}{3}\right)d_b + (f_{ps} - f_{pe})d_b \tag{c}$$

as shown in Fig. 4.18, or

$$l_d = (f_{ps} - \tfrac{2}{3}f_{pe})d_b \tag{4.28}$$

The ACI Code does not require that flexural bond stress be checked in either pretensioned or post-tensioned members, but for pretensioned strand it is required that the full *development length* given by Eq. (4.28) be provided beyond the critical bending section. Investigation may be limited to those cross sections nearest each end of the member that are required to develop their full flexural strength under the specified ultimate load.

In the event that sheathed tendons are employed near the ends of a span (see Art. 4.5) no prestress force will be transferred from the blanketed strands until the end of the sheathing is reached. From that point inward toward the center of the span, transfer bond is less than normally effective, because of the lack of vertical compression from the beam reaction and because flexural tensile stresses may exist in the concrete. Based on tests (Ref. 4.19) the Code requires that the development length given by Eq. (4.28) be doubled for sheathed tendons.

4.13 ANCHORAGE ZONE DESIGN

In prestressed concrete beams, the prestressing force is introduced as a load concentration, often acting over a relatively small fraction of the total member depth. For post-tensioned beams with mechanical anchorages, the load is applied at the end face, while for pretensioned beams it is introduced somewhat more gradually over the transfer length. In either case, the compressive stress distribution in the concrete becomes linear, conforming to that dictated by the overall eccentricity of the applied forces, only after a distance from the end roughly equal to the depth of the beam.

This transition of longitudinal compressive stress, from concentrated to linearly distributed, produces transverse (vertical) tensile stresses that may lead to longitudinal cracking of the member.

The pattern and magnitude of the concrete stresses depend on the location and distribution of the concentrated forces applied by the tendons. Numerous studies have been made using the methods of classical elasticity, photoelasticity, and finite element analysis. Typical results are given in Fig. 4.19 (Ref. 4.21). Here the beam is loaded uniformly over a height equal to $h/8$ at an eccentricity of $3h/8$. Contour lines are drawn through points of equal transverse tension, with coefficients expressing the ratio of transverse stress to average longitudinal compression. Typically there are high *bursting stresses* along the axis of the load a short distance inside the end zone, and high *spalling stresses* set up at the loaded face. These stresses will be less severe for pretensioned beams, where the load is introduced gradually by bond, than for post-tensioned beams where it is applied at the end face but, in either case, the neglect of transverse tension can result in distress or premature failure.

In many post-tensioned prestressed I beams, solid end blocks are provided as shown in Fig. 4.20. While these are often necessary to accommodate end anchorage hardware, they are of little use in reducing transverse tension or avoiding cracking. In fact, both analysis and tests have shown that beams with rectangular end blocks actually develop higher transverse tension for a given

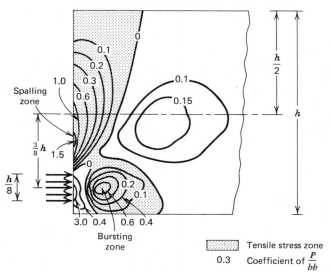

Figure 4.19   Contours of equal vertical stress (adapted from Ref. 4.21).

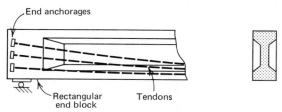

Figure 4.20   Post-tensioned I beam with rectangular end block.

prestress force than do otherwise identical beams without them (Ref. 4.21). If reinforcement is provided, stresses in the steel are higher than for beams without end blocks, and cracks are wider. Since the provision of end blocks adds appreciably to formwork cost, it is sound both from economic and structural considerations to omit them in pretensioned beams and also in post-tensioned beams (if anchorage clearances permit this), substituting in their place an adequate amount of steel reinforcement. Such reinforcement may be in the form of vertical bars of relatively small diameter and close spacing, and should be well anchored at the top and bottom of the member. Closed stirrups are used most often, looping around the main steel at the bottom and terminating in hooks or 90 degree bends at the top, as in Fig. 4.21.

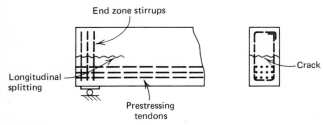

End zone stirrups

Longitudinal splitting

Prestressing tendons

Crack

Figure 4.21 End zone splitting in prestressed beam.

Methods of end zone analysis based on two-dimensional elastic theory, mentioned above, have been used as the basis for design of end zone reinforcement, and numerous charts are available giving patterns of stress for various distributions of end loading (Ref. 4.2). However, such analyses ignore some important aspects of the behavior of end zones. There is inelastic action at relatively low load because of the high concentration of stress in the concrete. The concrete must crack before end zone reinforcement becomes effective, yet the presence of cracks invalidates the analysis, as does the presence of the reinforcement.

Rational design of the reinforcement for end zones must recognize that horizontal cracking is likely. If adequate vertical reinforcement is provided so that the cracks are restricted to a few inches in length, and in width to one hundredth of an inch or less, then these cracks will not be detrimental to the performance of the beam either at service load level or at ultimate strength. They normally will not lengthen or widen as a result of the application of additional loads to the member, since in pretensioned and bonded post-tensioned beams the tension in the tendon in the end zones does not appreciably increase when loads are applied. Consequently the design of the end zone reinforcement can be based on conditions obtained upon initial prestressing, using a permissible stress for the stirrups that is low enough that crack widths are acceptably small.

For pretensioned members, on the basis of tests at the laboratories of the Portland Cement Association, Marshall and Mattock have proposed a very simple equation for the design of end zone reinforcement (Ref. 4.20). The total stirrup tension S is expressed in terms of the total longitudinal prestress force P by the relation

$$\frac{S}{P} = 0.0106 \frac{h}{l_t}$$

where h is the total beam depth and l_t is the transfer length. Tests indicate that the stirrup stress varies approximately linearly from maximum close to the end face to zero near the end of the crack. Thus, if f_s is a *permissible* stirrup stress when the initial prestress force P_i is applied, the average stress in the stirrups can be taken as $f_s/2$ and the total cross sectional area of stirrups necessary, A_t, is given by

$$\frac{A_t f_s}{2P_i} = 0.0106 \frac{h}{l_t}$$

or

$$A_t = 0.021 \frac{P_i h}{f_s l_t} \tag{4.29}$$

An allowable stress $f_s = 20,000$ psi has been found in tests to produce acceptably small crack widths. The transfer length l_t may either be calculated by Eq. (a) of Art. 4.13 or may be assumed to equal 50 times the nominal diameter of the strand. The required reinforcement having total area A_t should be distributed uniformly over a length equal to $h/5$ measured from the end face of the beam, and for most efficient crack control the first stirrup should be placed as close to the end face as possible.

It is recommended that vertical reinforcement according to Eq. (4.29) be provided for *all* pretensioned members unless tests or experience indicate that cracking does not occur at service or overload stages.

Equation (4.29), which is experimentally derived, does not apply to post-tensioned members, for which the prestressing force is applied at or near the end face rather than by bond stresses over a transfer length. For *post-tensioned* members, Gergely and Sozen have developed a method based on equilibrium conditions of the cracked anchorage zone, with the objective of limiting the length and width of the horizontal crack (Ref. 4.21).

Figure 4.22a shows the end region of a post-tensioned beam for which the prestressing force P_i is applied as a concentrated load at the end face, with eccentricity e from the concrete centroid. At some distance l from the end face, the compressive stress distribution is linear as shown. Figure 4.22b shows the forces and stresses acting on the freebody 0123 bounded by the edges of the member, by an assumed horizontal crack along the face 12, and by the inside end face 23 of the anchorage zone.

In general both a moment and shear force will be produced on the face 12 by the horizontal forces. The shear is resisted by aggregate interlock and the necessary resisting moment is provided by the tensile force T from the end zone reinforcement and the compressive resultant force C from the concrete. The height c of the free body, determined by the level of the crack, is established from the condition that the moment due to the horizontal forces will be a maximum at the level at which the crack forms. In practical cases, moments may be calculated at increments of height, starting at the bottom of the beam, and plotted as a function of distance from the bottom. Typical results are shown in Fig. 4.22c. At the level of the load, a net clockwise bending moment causing vertical tension deep within the end zone is indicated, gradually changing to net counterclockwise moment causing vertical tension near the end face in the upper part of the end region.

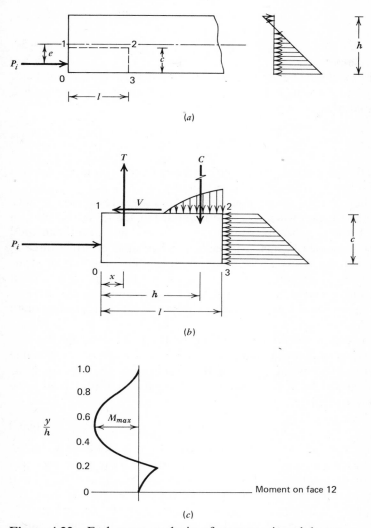

(a)

(b)

(c)

Figure 4.22   End zone analysis of post-tensioned beam.
(a) End of beam showing free body location. (b) Forces
on free body. (c) Variation of moment with depth.

Knowing the maximum bending moment to be resisted, the forces T and C
can be calculated if the distance between those forces can be estimated. For
post-tensioned beams, stirrups should be provided within a distance $h/2$ from
the end face to resist T, and the center of gravity of those stirrup forces is easily
found. The location of C must be estimated. It is usually assumed to be at a
distance h from the end face. Accordingly the tensile force to be resisted by the

end stirrups is

$$T = \frac{M_{max}}{h - x} \qquad (4.30)$$

where M_{max} is the maximum bending moment to be resisted and x is the distance from the end face to the centroid of the vertical steel within the distance $h/2$. The total required area of steel reinforcement is

$$A_t = \frac{T}{f_s} \qquad (4.31)$$

where f_s is an allowable stress chosen on the basis of crack control. A value of $f_s = 20,000$ psi has been found to be satisfactory.

The method described is simple conceptually and gives reasonable results. It is easily adapted to cases where the load is applied at several levels, and can also be used for I beams or beams of other shape. In common with the method presented for pretensioned beams, it is based on the initial prestress force P_i and permissible stirrup stress rather than strength. Since the stirrup stress recommended is less than half of the yield stress for the bar reinforcement currently used, and since the tendon force at the anchorage does not increase significantly as the beam is loaded to failure, an adequate margin of strength is assured.

In addition to vertical tensile stress causing splitting, end zone distress may be caused in post-tensioned beams by the high concentration of longitudinal compression under the bearing plates of the anchorages. The bearing stress on the concrete caused by post-tensioning anchorages when the initial force P_i acts should not exceed

$$f_{cp} = 0.6 f'_{ci} \sqrt[3]{A_2 / A_1} \qquad (4.32)$$

and should not exceed f'_{ci}, according to the ACI Code Commentary. In Eq. (4.32) A_1 is the bearing area of the anchor plate, and A_2 is the maximum area of the portion of the anchorage surface that is geometrically similar to, and concentric with, the area of the anchor plate of the post-tensioning steel. The definition of A_2 may be clarified by Fig. 4.23, which shows the loaded area A_1 under the anchor plate and the largest concentric area A_2 that can be superimposed.

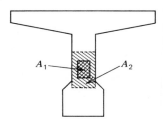

Figure 4.23 End bearing areas for posttensioned beam.

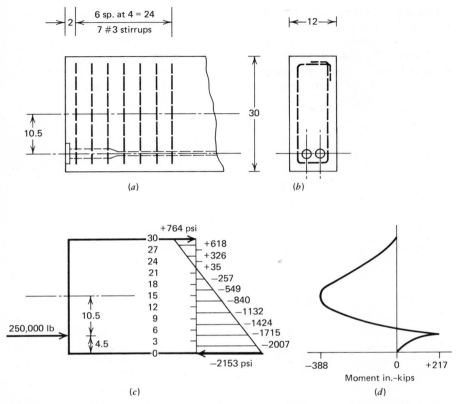

Figure 4.24 Design of anchorage zone reinforcement. (*a*) End zone.
(*b*) Cross section. (*c*) Forces and stresses. (*d*) Moments.

EXAMPLE   Design of End Zone Reinforcement
for Post-tensioned Beam

End zone reinforcement is to be designed for the rectangular post-tensioned beam shown
in Fig. 4.24*a*. An initial prestress force P_i of 250 kips is applied by two tendons having
eccentricity of 10.5 inches, producing longitudinal stresses in the concrete that vary linearly
from 2153 psi compression at the bottom to 764 psi tension at the top. Closed vertical
stirrups will be used as shown in Fig. 4.24*b*, at an allowable stress of 20,000 psi. ($b = 305$ mm,
$h = 762$ mm, $P_i = 1112$ kN, $e = 267$ mm, $f_2 = -14.8$ N/mm^2, $f_1 = +5.3$ N/mm^2, and
$f_s = 138$ N/mm^2.)

For computational purposes the beam will be divided into 3 in. increments of height,
and the concrete stress at the center of each increment will be assumed to act uniformly
through the depth of that increment. Values are given in Fig. 4.24*c*. The moments from
these stresses and from the concentrated tendon forces are computed at 3 in. intervals,
clockwise moments being taken positive. Results are given in Table 4.1 and are plotted in
Fig. 4.24*d*. It is seen that a maximum moment of 388 in.-kips is obtained, acting at a distance

Table 4.1 Moments at Horizontal Section of End Zone
Design Example

Distance from Bottom in.	Moment of Concrete Stresses in.-kips	Moment of Prestress Force in.-kips	Net Moment in.-kips
0	0	0	0
3	+108	0	+108
4.5	+217	0	+217
6	+418	−375	+43
9	+897	−1125	−228
12	+1514	−1875	−361
15	+2237	−2625	−388
18	+3035	−3375	−340
21	+3877	−4125	−248
24	+4731	−4875	−144
27	+5566	−5625	−59
30	+6349	−6375	−26

15 in. above the bottom of the beam such as to cause tension near the end face (spalling zone).

The centroid of the stirrup forces within a distance $h/2$ from the end face will be assumed to be at $x = 8$ in. Then from Eq. (4.30) the maximum tension to be resisted is

$$T = \frac{388,000}{30 - 8} = 17,600 \text{ lb (78 kN)}$$

The total amount of reinforcement in the spalling zone, based on the allowable stress of 20,000 psi, is found from Eq. (4.31):

$$A_t = \frac{17,600}{20,000} = 0.88 \text{ in.}^2 \text{ (568 mm}^2\text{)}$$

Four No. 3 closed loop stirrups provide an area of $4 \times 0.11 \times 2 = 0.88$ in.², exactly as required. The first stirrup will be placed 2 in. from the end face, followed by three stirrups at 4 in. spacing within the distance $h/2 = 15$ in. as shown in Fig. 4.24a. This places the steel centroid 8 in. from the end face as assumed.

A second moment maximum, of opposite sign and of value 217 in.-kips, is indicated by Fig. 4.24d, with associated tension at the level of the prestress force some distance inward from the end face (bursting zone). The tensile force of

$$T = \frac{217,000}{22} = 9860 \text{ lb (44 kN)}$$

can be accommodated by three additional stirrups, providing a total of seven no. 3 stirrups at 4 in. spacing. End zone reinforcement, shown in Fig. 4.24a, is thus included through a distance approximately equal to h from the end face.

4.14   CRACK CONTROL

A.   INTRODUCTION

Tensile stress due to flexure in concrete members at service load can be limited to any desired value, or eliminated completely, by prestressing. However, both technical and economic factors have resulted in a trend toward partial prestressing, such that tensile cracks may exist under normal conditions in service. For designs based on partial prestressing, it is advisable to give special attention to the matter of cracking, both from the viewpoint of appearance, and because of possible corrosion of the highly stressed steel tendons if exposed by excessively wide cracks.

Parameters of importance will respect to crack width have been established by tests and observation of structural performance. They include:

1. Surface characteristics of the tensile reinforcement, which may include both prestressed tendons and non-prestressed bar steel.
2. Distribution of steel over the concrete cross section.
3. Amount of concrete cover.
4. Ratio of total reinforcement area to concrete area.
5. Increase in steel stress as the member is loaded.
6. Concrete tensile strength.
7. Size and shape of the member.

Ideally, a method for controlling cracking should reflect the influence of each of these variables, although this does not appear practical at present.

Practical methods that have been proposed may be placed in one of two categories: (a) those based on limiting the nominal tensile stress in the concrete, and (b) those based on computation of probable maximum crack width, followed by comparison with limit values. The following paragraphs summarize two current proposals.

B.   CRACK CONTROL BASED ON NOMINAL CONCRETE TENSILE STRESS

The simplest method of crack control is based on calculation of a *nominal tensile stress* in the concrete at the load stage of interest, as proposed by Abeles (Refs. 4.22 and 4.23). By this method, the nominal concrete tensile stress is computed, based on properties of the concrete cross section assumed to be uncracked and homogeneous, even though that nominal stress exceeds the modulus of rupture. The maximum crack width is related to nominal tensile stress f_w by empirically derived equations, corresponding to crack widths w of 0.004 in., 0,008 in., and 0.012 in., as follows:

For strands:

$$f_{0.004} = 800 + 500(p - 0.3) \tag{4.33a}$$

$$f_{0.008} = 900 + 1200(p - 0.3) \tag{4.33b}$$

$$f_{0.012} = 1100 + 1300(p - 0.3) \tag{4.33c}$$

For round bars or smooth wires:

$$f_{0.004} = 700 + 450(p - 0.3) \tag{4.34a}$$

$$f_{0.008} = 850 + 600(p - 0.3) \tag{4.34b}$$

$$f_{0.012} = 1000 + 800(p - 0.3) \tag{4.34c}$$

where the nominal stresses f_w are expressed in psi, and p is the total *percentage* of steel, including both tendons and reinforcing bars, expressed in terms of the total beam depth times the width. Thus, if strands are used having a total area of 1.00 in.^{2} in a beam of width 12 in. and total depth 24 in., and if a maximum crack width of 0.008 in. is specified, then

$$p = \frac{100 \times 1.00}{12 \times 24} = 0.35 \text{ percent}$$

and, from Eq. (4.33b)

$$f_{0.008} = 900 + 1200(0.35 - 0.3) = 960 \text{ psi}$$

If the nominal tensile stress at service load exceeds the value of f_w computed in this way, then cracks having maximum width in excess of 0.008 in. could be expected, and the designer has the choice of either (a) increasing the amount of prestress force, so that the nominal tensile stress at service load is reduced to the value computed, or (b) increasing the steel ratio by adding reinforcing bars, so that the computed stress for the selected crack width limit is increased to the nominal value at service load.

It should be noted that Eqs. (4.33) and (4.34) are based on a limited number of tests, and must be regarded as tentative. In addition, the tests included only beams of rectangular cross section. The resulting equations may underestimate crack widths in T beams.

C. CALCULATION OF PROBABLE MAXIMUM CRACK WIDTH

Several methods have been proposed for direct calculation of crack widths.

The first approach uses the Gergely-Lutz equation, which provides the basis for ACI Code provisions relating to cracking in *reinforced concrete* beams (Refs. 4.22 and 4.24). While Code provisions are stated in slightly different form, the basic equation for predicting the maximum crack width at the tension face of a reinforced concrete beam is

$$w = 0.076Rf_s\sqrt[3]{d_cA} \tag{4.35}$$

in which w is the maximum width of crack in thousandth inches and f_s is the steel stress at the load for which crack width is to be determined, measured in ksi. The geometric parameters are shown in Fig. 4.25. Terms are defined

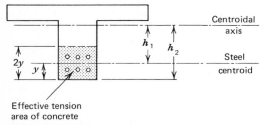

Figure 4.25   Geometric parameters used in Eq. (4.35).

as follows:

d_c = thickness of concrete cover measured from the tension face to the center of bar closest to that face, in.

R = ratio of distances from the tension face and from the steel centroid to the neutral axis, equal to h_2/h_1

A = concrete area surrounding one bar, equal to the total effective tension area of concrete surrounding reinforcement and having the same centroid, divided by the number of bars, in.^{2}

For *prestressed concrete* beams, it is proposed that the same equation be used, except that an incremental steel stress be used rather than f_s, the increment being equal to the increase in tension as the member is loaded from the decompression load to the load for which crack width is to be determined. The decompression load is defined here as the load that produces zero flexural stress at the bottom face of the beam. Computation of steel stress after cracking may be based on the method of Art. 3.9.

Equation (4.35) is based on experiments using normal deformed bar reinforcement. Available test evidence indicates that it can be used with reasonable accuracy for beams prestressed with strand, if supplementary deformed bar steel is present. If it is not, a modifying factor of 1.8 has been suggested, to account for the difference in bond properties of strand and deformed bars. If plain round rods or individual wires are used, rather than strand, a further than strand, a further modification of 1.5 to 2 is appropriate (Ref. 4.22).

Alternative equations for the prediction of crack width, also based on the incremental stress in the tendons, have been proposed by Nawy and Potyondy (Ref. 5.25), derived from tests of pretensioned beams having T- and I-shaped sections. Application requires determination of stresses using a cracked section analysis, as does the Gergely-Lutz method and consequently will prove laborious in practice. It appears at this writing that the Abeles method, based on nominal tensile stress, is both simple to use and acceptably accurate. It is probable that a variation of that method will eventually be included in the ACI Code.

D. PERMISSIBLE CRACK WIDTHS

From the viewpoint of appearance, crack widths up to about 0.015 in. will seldom be objectionable. With respect to protection of tendons and bar reinforcement against corrosion, the permissible crack width depends on conditions of exposure. For reinforced concrete members, present provisions of the ACI Code imply acceptable maximum crack widths of 0.016 in. for members with only interior exposure, and 0.013 in. for exterior exposure. ACI Committee 224 (Ref. 4.22) has recommended the values given in Table 4.2 for reinforced concrete members subject to various exposure conditions. These values are reasonably in agreement with those found in Ref. 4.23 for prestressed members, and may serve as a guide until recommendations are codified.

Table 4.2   Recommended Permissible Crack Widths

Exposure Condition	Maximum Allowable Crack Width	
	in.	mm
Dry air or protective membrane	0.016	0.41
Humidity, moist air, soil	0.012	0.30
De-icing chemicals	0.007	0.18
Seawater and seawater spray; wetting and drying	0.006	0.15
Water-retaining structures	0.004	0.10

E. CONCLUSION

It should be recognized that cracking in concrete beams is a random phenomenon, and that crack widths in a structure can exceed the computed maximum. Isolated cracks in excess of twice the computed maximum can sometimes occur, although generally the coefficient of variation of crack width is about 40 percent.

Limited test data indicate that the increase of maximum crack width due to sustained loading of about two years duration is about 100 percent. High cycle repeated loading increases crack widths by a factor that ranges from 1.5 to 4, depending on the load level.

No provisions are contained in the ACI Code pertaining specifically to crack widths in prestressed members. Special requirements are included, however, for the special case of beams with unbonded prestressing tendons, based on observations that such members develop larger cracks and fail at lower loads than do otherwise identical members with bonded tendons. For such cases, a minimum area of bonded reinforcement, A_s, is required as given by the equation:

$$A_s = 0.004A \tag{4.36}$$

where A is defined here as the area of that part of the gross concrete cross section between the flexural tension face and the center of gravity. This reinforcement is to be uniformly distributed over the precompressed tensile zone, as close as possible to the extreme tension face.

REFERENCES

4.1 Nilson, A. H., "Flexural Design Equations for Prestressed Concrete Members," *J. PCI*, Vol. 14, No. 1, February 1969, pp. 62–71.

4.2 Guyon, Y., *Prestressed Concrete*, Vol. I, Wiley, New York, 1960, 559 pp.

4.3 Guyon, Y., *Prestressed Concrete*, Vol. II, Wiley, New York, 1960, 741 pp.

4.4 Abeles, P. W., *Introduction to Prestressed Concrete*, Vol. I, Concrete Publications, Ltd., London, 1964, 384 pp.

4.5 Abeles, P. W., *Introduction to Prestressed Concrete*, Vol. II, Concrete Publications, Ltd., London, 1966, 355 pp.

4.6 Leonhardt, F., *Prestressed Concrete*, Wilhelm Ernest and Son, Berlin, 1964, 677 pp.

4.7 Libby, J. R., *Modern Prestressed Concrete*, Van Nostrand–Reinhold, New York, 1971.

4.8 Lin, T. Y., *Prestressed Concrete Structures*, Wiley, New York, 1963.

4.9 Magnel, G., *Prestressed Concrete*, McGraw-Hill, New York, 1954, 345 pp.

4.10 Thurlimann, B., *A Case for Partial Prestressing*, Bericht No. 41, Institut fur Baustatik, Swiss Federal Institute of Technology (ETH), Zurich, May 1971, pp. 252–301.

4.11 Winter, G. and Nilson, A. H., *Design of Concrete Structures*, 8th Ed., McGraw-Hill, New York, 1972, 615 pp.

4.12 Abeles, P. W., discussion of Ref. 4.1, *J. PCI*, Vol. 14, No. 6, December 1969, pp. 78–81.

4.13 Abeles, P. W., "Design of Partially Prestressed Concrete Beams," *J. ACI*, Vol. 64, No. 10, October 1967, pp. 669–677.

4.14 Nilson, A. H., discussion of Ref. 4.13, *J. ACI*, Vol. 65, No. 4, April 1968, pp. 345–347.

4.15 Lin, T. Y., "Load Balancing Method for Design and Analysis of Prestressed Concrete Structures," *J. ACI*, Vol. 60, No. 6, June 1963, pp. 719–742.

4.16 Janney, J. R., "Nature of Bond in Pre-Tensioned Prestressed Concrete," *J. ACI*, Vol. 25, No. 9, May 1954, pp. 717–736.

4.17 Hanson, N. W., "Influence of Surface Roughness of Prestressing Strand on Bond Performance," *J. PCI*, Vol. 14, No. 1, February 1969, pp. 32–45.

4.18 Hanson, N. W. and Kaar, P. H., "Flexural Bond Tests of Pretensioned Prestressed Beams," *J. ACI*, Vol. 30, No. 7, January 1959, pp. 783–802.

4.19 Kaar, P. H. and Magura, D. D., "Effect of Strand Blanketing on Performance of Pretensioned Girders," *J. PCI*, Vol. 10, No. 6, December 1965, pp. 20–34.

4.20 Marshall, W. T. and Mattock, A. H., "Control of Horizontal Cracking in the Ends of Pretensioned Prestressed Concrete Girders," *J. PCI*, Vol. 7, No. 5, October 1962, pp. 56–74.

4.21 Gergely, P. and Sozen, M. A., "Design of Anchorage Zone Reinforcement in Prestressed Concrete Beams," *J. PCI*, Vol. 12, No. 2, April 1967, pp. 63–75.

4.22 "Control of Cracking in Concrete Structures," Reported by ACI Committee 224, *J. ACI*, Vol. 69, No. 12, December 1972, pp. 717–752.

4.23 Abeles, P. W., "Design of Partially Prestressed Concrete Beams," *J. ACI*, Vol. 64, No. 10, October 1967, pp. 669–677.

4.24 Gergely, P. and Lutz, L. A., "Maximum Crack Width in Reinforced Concrete Flexural Members," *Causes, Mechanism, and Control of Cracking in Concrete, ACI Special Publication SP-20*, American Concrete Institute, Detroit, 1968, pp. 87–117.

4.25 Nawy, E. G. and Potyondy, J. C., "Flexural Cracking Behavior of Pretensioned Prestressed Concrete I and T Beams," *J. ACI*, Vol. 68, No. 5, May 1971, pp. 355–360.

PROBLEMS

4.1 A pretensioned prestressed beam has a rectangular cross section of 6 in. width and 20 in. total depth. It is built using normal-density concrete of design strength $f'_c = 4000$ psi, and strength at transfer of $f'_{ci} = 3000$ psi. Stress limits are as follows: $f_{ti} = 165$ psi, $f_{ci} = -1800$ psi, $f_{ts} = 380$ psi, and $f_{cs} = -1800$ psi. The effectiveness ratio R may be assumed equal to 0.80. For these conditions, find the initial prestress force P_i, and eccentricity e, such as to maximize the superimposed load moment $M_d + M_l$ that can be carried without exceeded stress limits. What uniformly distributed load can be carried on a 30 ft simple span? What tendon profile would you recommend?

4.2 A rectangular pretensioned concrete beam is to be designed to carry superimposed dead and live loads of 300 plf and 1000 plf, respectively, on a 40 ft simple span. Straight tendons will be used. Time-dependent losses will be approximately 16 percent of the initial stress in the steel. Determine the concrete dimensions (use $h = 2.5b$) and required prestress force and eccentricity, based on ACI limit stresses. Concrete strength $f'_c = 5000$ psi and $f'_{ci} = 4000$ psi.

4.3 A pretensioned beam is to carry a superimposed dead load of 600 plf and service live load of 1200 plf on a 55 ft simple span. A symmetrical I section with $b = 0.5h$ will be used. Flange thickness $h_f = 0.2h$ and web width $b_w = 0.4b$. The member will be prestressed using Grade 270 strands. Time-dependent losses are estimated at 20 percent of P_i. Normal density concrete will be used, with $f'_c = 5000$ psi and $f'_{ci} = 3000$ psi. (a) Using straight strands, find the required concrete dimensions, prestress force, and eccentricity. Select an appropriate number and size of tendons, and show by sketch their placement in the section. (b) Revise the design of part (a) using tendons harped at the third points of the span, with eccentricity reduced to zero at the supports. (c) Comment on your results. In both cases, ACI stress limits are to be applied. You may assume that deflections are not critical, and that a tensile stress of $12\sqrt{f'_c}$ is permissible at full service load.

4.4 The tee beam of Fig. P4.4 is to be used on an 80 ft roof span and must carry superimposed load (dead and live) of 70 psf of roof surface at full service condition. No topping slab is used. Using stress limitations in the unloaded and full service load stage as imposed by the ACI Code, and assuming 22 percent losses, determine the best combination of prestress force and eccentricity at midspan. Maintain at least 3 in. from the steel centroid to the bottom face of the concrete. Strands will be harped at midspan. Choose appropriate prestressing steel using Grade 270 stranded cable. For the section shown, $A_c = 782$ in.^{2}, $I_c = 169,000$ in.^{4}, $c_1 = 12.8$ in., $w_o = 815$ plf. Specify $f'_c = 5000$ psi and $f'_{ci} = 3500$ psi.

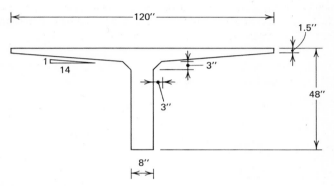

Figure P4.4

4.5 The double-tee roof beam of Fig. P4.5 is to be constructed using lightweight concrete having density 120 pcf with compressive strength $f'_c = 5000$ psi. At the time of release of pretensioning force, f'_{ci} will be 4000 psi. The member is intended for use on a 50 ft simple span, and must carry superimposed loads $w_d = 10$ psf and $w_l = 40$ psf uniformly distributed over the slab surface. Using ACI limit stresses, and assuming 15 percent losses, find the best combination of prestress force and eccentricity. Choose an appropriate size and number of Grade 250 strands. A minimum distance of 5 in.

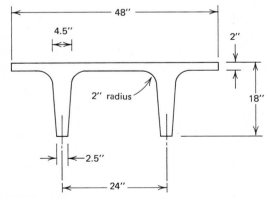

Figure P4.5

must be maintained from the steel centroid to the bottom face of the stems. What is the flexural efficiency of the beam section? Find the factor of safety against cracking and failure, both expressed in terms of live load increase. The section properties are $A_c = 208$ in.^{2}, $I_c = 5944$ in.^{4}, and $c_1 = 5.44$ in.

4.6 The I beam shown in Fig. P4.6 is post-tensioned by using two tendons that produce a total force $P_i = 390$ kips. A solid end block will be used having length equal to 3/4 the member height, to provide for anchorage hardware and bearing stresses. Design the end zone reinforcement for this member, using closed loop stirrups, at an allowable stress $f_s = 20{,}000$ psi. What is the minimum size bearing plate that should be used at the tendon anchorages, assuming that the central cone, which provides no bearing, has a diameter of 3 in. Concrete strengths $f'_c = 5000$ psi and $f'_{ci} = 3500$ psi.

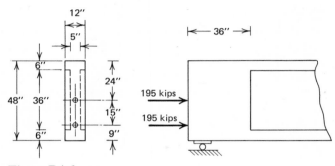

Figure P4.6

CHAPTER 5
SHEAR AND TORSION

5.1 INTRODUCTION

Chapters 3 and 4 have treated the flexural stresses and flexural strength of beams. Beams must also be safe against premature failures of other types, which may be more dangerous than flexural failure in the sense that, should catastrophic overloading and collapse occur, it might take place suddenly and without warning. Flexural shear failure, more properly called diagonal tension failure, is one example. Prestressed concrete beams normally contain special *shear reinforcement* to insure that flexural failure, which can be predicted accurately and which is usually preceded by obvious cracking and large deflections, will occur before shear failure, which is abrupt and more difficult to predict with accuracy.

Closely related to the shear stresses resulting from flexure in beams are those which are a consequence of torsion, or twisting of the beam about its long axis. Torsional shear stresses, too, produce diagonal tension in the concrete. *Torsional reinforcement*, similar to shear reinforcement and in many cases combined with it, is required in members that must resist significant twisting moments. The basic aspects of torsional design will be presented later in this chapter, following consideration of flexural shear stresses and shear reinforcement.

Neither flexural shear analysis nor torsional shear analysis is really concerned with shear stress as such. The shear stresses produced by actions of either type are usually much below the direct shear strength of the concrete. The real concern is with the *diagonal tension stress* in the concrete produced by shear stress, acting either alone or in combination with longitudinal normal stresses.

There are certain circumstances in which consideration of the direct shear strength of uncracked or cracked concrete is required. One example is the design of column brackets such as are used in precast construction to provide support for beams and girders. The *shear-friction theory*, a useful design tool for such cases, will be described in Ch. 12.

5.2 SHEAR AND DIAGONAL TENSION IN UNCRACKED BEAMS

When the loads acting on a prestressed concrete beam are relatively low, the beam will be free of cracks and the concrete response will be nearly elastic.

175

Under these circumstances shear stresses, flexural stresses, and the principal stresses resulting from their combined action may be found based on familiar equations of mechanics. The concrete shear stress at any location is given by

$$v = \frac{V_{net}Q}{I_c b} \tag{5.1}$$

where

V_{net} = net shear force at the cross section due to applied
loads and prestressing

Q = static moment about the neutral axis of that portion of
the cross section outside of the shear plane considered

I_c = moment of inertia of the cross section

b = width of the cross section at the shear plane considered

The bending stress in the concrete may be found by the equation

$$f = -\frac{P}{A_c} \pm \frac{Pey}{I_c} \mp \frac{My}{I_c} \tag{5.2}$$

where

P = prestress force

e = eccentricity of prestress force, measured positive downward

y = distance from the centroidal axis of the section to the point
considered

A_c = area of concrete cross section

M = moments due to applied loads

and the upper and lower signs of each pair apply to calculation of stresses above and below the centroidal axis, respectively.

The beneficial influence of prestressing in reducing diagonal tension in concrete beams becomes evident by considering two concrete beams, one with non-prestressed bar reinforcement as in Fig. 5.1a, and one prestressed, Fig. 5.1e.

A small element "a" located at the neutral axis of the reinforced concrete beam will be subjected to positive shear stresses v acting on its vertical faces, and negative shears of the same magnitude on the horizontal faces, as shown in Fig. 5.1b. Making use of Mohr's circle to find the principal stresses, (Fig. 5.1c) it is found that the principal tension f_1 is equal (in absolute value) to the shear stress intensity, and acts in a direction at 45 degrees to the axis of the beam, as shown in Fig. 5.1d. Equal principal compression acts in the perpendicular direction. Diagonal cracking, should it occur, will be at about 45 degrees to the horizontal axis of the member, as shown in idealized form in Fig. 5.1a.

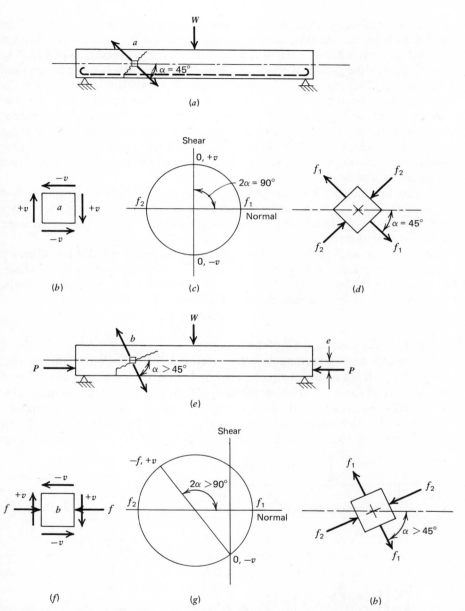

Figure 5.1 Effect of longitudinal prestress on diagonal tension and cracking.

The corresponding element "b" in the prestressed beam of Fig. 5.1e is subjected to identical shearing stresses v, Fig. 5.1f, and in addition is subjected to horizontal compressive stress f. The Mohr's circle construction of Fig. 5.1g indicates that the principal tension f_1 is reduced to a much lower value than that of Fig. 5.1c, and acts in a direction making a substantially larger angle with the horizontal beam axis, as seen in Fig. 5.1h. Consequently the diagonal tension crack of Fig. 5.1e is much flatter than before. If shear reinforcement is in the form of vertical stirrups, a larger number of those stirrups will cross the diagonal crack in the prestressed beam than would be true for the beam without prestressing, improving the effectiveness of the stirrups in transmitting shear across the crack.

It may also be seen from the principal stress constructions of Figs. 5.1c and 5.1g that diagonal tensile stress cannot be eliminated completely, no matter what the value of longitudinal compression, unless vertical precompression is introduced as well.

In addition to the effects just described, prestressing usually introduces a negative shear force, acting in an opposite sense to the load-induced shear, as a result of the inclination of the tendon, as shown in Fig. 5.2. Consequently, shear stresses in the uncracked beam are those corresponding to

$$V_{net} = V_{loads} - V_p \tag{5.3}$$

where V_p = the countershear of the tendons.

For beams having rectangular cross sections, the variation of shear stress through the depth of the member, given by Eq. (5.1), is parabolic, the value of v being zero at the top and bottom faces, and reaching a maximum at middepth. For beams of I cross section, such as Fig. 5.3a, commonly used for prestressed members, the shear stress increases abruptly at the transition from flange to web, because of the reduction of the section width b. The stress distribution

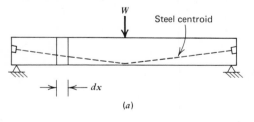

(a)

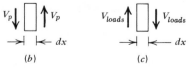

(b)   (c)

Figure 5.2 Effect of inclined tendons in reducing net shear force.

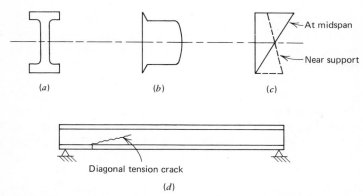

(a)   (b)   (c)

Diagonal tension crack

(d)

Figure 5.3 Diagonal tension cracking in prestressed concrete I beam. (*a*) Cross section. (*b*) Shear stress variation.
(*c*) Flexural stress variation. (*d*) Probable location of diagonal crack.

of Fig. 5.3*b* is typical of I beams, and is characterized by a nearly constant
value of v throughout the depth of the web.

The principal tensile stress in an I beam can be found from the shear stresses
of Fig. 5.3*b* and the longitudinal flexural stresses of Fig. 5.3*c*, which are usually
about as shown at the service load level.

Typically, for I beams, the maximum principal tension will not be found at
the neutral axis, where the shear stress is greatest, but rather will be near the
junction of the web and the lower flange, where the shear stress is also high,
but where the longitudinal compression is reduced by the effect of the applied
loads.

It should be noted further that the critical location for diagonal tension is
usually not adjacent to the supports, even though the net external shear is
highest there, because the longitudinal compression from prestressing is hardly
reduced from its full value by the small external moments acting. A flexural
stress distribution such as shown by the dotted line of Fig. 5.3*c* is typical, the
exact variation depending on prestress eccentricity. Substantial longitudinal
compression reduces the principal tensile stress near the supports. In addition,
vertical compressive stress from the beam reactions prevents diagonal cracking
close to the supports.

Consequently, diagonal tension cracking for uniformly loaded, simply supported prestressed I beams is likely to occur at about the quarter points of the
span, where the net shear forces are relatively large, and near the junction of
the web and lower flange, where longitudinal compressive stresses are low and
shear stresses are high. Should a diagonal crack form, it could be expected to
appear about as shown in idealized form in Fig. 5.3*d*. This is confirmed by
numerous tests.

The investigation of diagonal tension in uncracked beam webs is relevant mostly in predicting the load at which a diagonal crack will form, and in predicting the location and orientation of that crack. To base shear design upon an allowable tensile stress in the concrete at service load is unsafe, because relatively small increases in load above the service load level will produce disproportionate increases in diagonal tensile stress. This happens for two reasons.

First, consider the principal tensile stress at point a at the bottom of the web of the I beam shown in Fig. 5.4a. At service loads, the shear stress distribution and flexural stress distribution are shown by the solid lines of Figs. 5.4b and 5.4c, respectively, with values v and f at the point of interest. The principal tensile stress f_1 of Fig. 5.4d may be obtained graphically or analytically.

Suppose now that the loads are increased by 20 percent, producing the increased shear stresses and flexural stresses shown by the dotted lines of Figs. 5.4b and 5.4c, respectively. From the modified principal stress construction shown by the dotted lines of Fig. 5.4d, it is clear that reducing the flexural compression at point a to zero (which is achieved by a very modest increase in applied loads) together with a 20 percent increase in shear stress, is sufficient to produce a very large increase in principal tension. The increase shown is approximately 60 percent in the present case.

The second reason for disproportionate increase in tension is that the shear stress is calculated for the net shear, given by Eq. (5.3). As loads are increased,

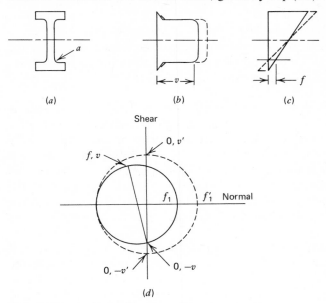

(a)   (b)   (c)

(d)

Figure 5.4 Principal stress increase upon overloading. (a) Cross section. (b) Shear stresses. (c) Flexural stresses. (d) Principal stress circle.

the external shear V_{loads} increases in direct proportion. However, V_p, the countershear from the inclined tendons, stays nearly constant. Thus a small percentage increase in loads may easily double the net shear for which the beam is to be designed.

In summary, principal stress calculations are useful in visualizing the flow of stresses in uncracked beams, and may provide useful information on the location and orientation of diagonal tension cracking. Such calculations also provide information on the load at which that crack may be expected. However, they must never be used to evaluate the degree of safety inherent in a design. A strength-based analysis is essential for that purpose.

5.3 DIAGONAL CRACKING SHEAR

Extensive testing has shown that two types of diagonal cracking can occur in prestressed beams: *flexure-shear cracking* and *web-shear cracking* (Refs. 5.1 and 5.2). These are illustrated by Figs. 5.5a and 5.5b, respectively.

Flexure-shear cracks occur after flexural cracking has taken place. The flexural crack extends more or less vertically into the beam from the tension face. When a critical combination of flexural and shear stresses develops at the head of the flexural crack, that crack propagates in an inclined direction, often quite flat, as indicated by Fig. 5.5a. If web reinforcement is not provided, such a crack may produce what is known as a *shear-compression failure*, in which the compression area of the concrete near the top of the beam, reduced by the diagonal crack, is inadequate to resist forces resulting from flexure.

While flexure-shear cracking is the more common type, web-shear cracking may occur as shown in Fig. 5.5b, especially near the supports of heavily prestressed beams with relatively thin webs. This type of cracking initiates in the

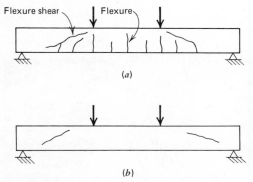

Figure 5.5 Types of inclined cracks. (*a*) Flexure-shear cracks. (*b*) Web-shear cracks.

web, without previous flexural cracking, when the principal tension in the concrete becomes equal to the tensile strength of the material. This type of web distress leads to the sudden formation of a large inclined crack and, if web reinforcement is not present, will lead to failure of the beam in one of the following modes:

a. Separation of the tension flange from the web, as inclined cracks extend horizontally toward the supports.
b. Crushing of the web due to high compression acting parallel to the diagonal cracks, as the beam is transformed into the equivalent of a tied arch.
c. Secondary inclined tension cracking near the supports, which separates the compression flange from the web.

Typically, web shear failures are more violent than flexure-shear failures.

Figure 5.6 shows both web-shear cracking and flexure-shear cracking in a pretensioned beam with stirrup-reinforced web, tested at the laboratories of

Figure 5.6 Web-shear cracking (left) and flexure-shear cracking (right) in continuous prestressed beam (courtesy Portland Cement Association).

the Portland Cement Association. The cracks have been marked in ink on the beam surface for emphasis.

For the case of flexure-shear cracking, tests have shown that the critical inclined crack has a horizontal projection at least equal to the effective beam depth d (Refs. 5.3, 5.4, and 5.5). Therefore, it is a flexural crack a distance d, in the direction of decreasing moment, from the section under consideration that is associated with the inclined crack causing failure. Tests further indicate that the formation of a *second* flexural crack, usually at about $d/2$ from the given section, is the event that triggers actual collapse.

Figure 5.7a shows an idealized representation of flexure-shear cracking in the combined stress region of a beam (Refs. 5.6 and 5.7). The flexural crack at section A initiates an inclined crack having a horizontal projection d, and

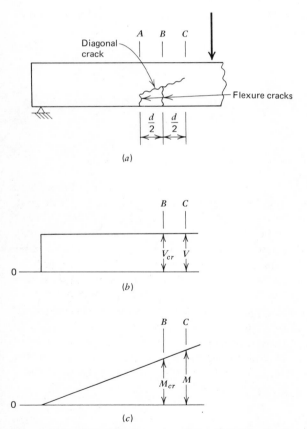

Figure 5.7 Flexure-shear cracking. (a) Idealized crack pattern. (b) Shear diagram. (c) Moment diagram.

terminating at the section C under consideration. A second flexural crack at section B is critical in precipitating failure. The shear and moment, at section C, are V and M, respectively, while the shear and moment at section B are V_{cr} and M_{cr}, as shown in Figs. 5.7b and 5.7c. The shears and moments shown are those produced by the *superimposed dead and live loads*, and act in addition to those produced by the member self-weight and produced by the prestressing tendon. The reason for distinguishing between moments and shears due to external loads and those due to self-weight will be clarified later.

The change in moment between sections B and C is equal to the area under the shear diagram between the two sections:

$$M - M_{cr} = \frac{1}{2}(V + V_{cr})\frac{d}{2}$$

or, since the difference between V and V_{cr} in the distance $d/2$ is small in most cases,

$$M - M_{cr} = \frac{Vd}{2}$$

Thus

$$\frac{M}{V} - \frac{M_{cr}}{V} = \frac{d}{2}$$

and

$$V = \frac{M_{cr}}{M/V - d/2} \tag{a}$$

This equation gives the shear V at section C, due to superimposed dead and live loads, when the moment at section B due to those loads is M_{cr}. Note that, while the shear V appears on the right side of Eq. (a) as well as the left, it is not necessary that the value of V be known to make use of the equation, but only the ratio M/V, which is a characteristic of any given load pattern and stays constant as the superimposed loads increase proportionately.

The total shear at section C when the flexural crack develops at section B is the sum of that given by Eq. (a) plus the shear V_o due to self-weight and the shear V_p carried by the vertical component of the force in the curved or draped tendon. Furthermore, tests indicate that an increment of shear equal to $0.6b_w d\sqrt{f'_c}$ is required, after the second flexural crack forms, for the inclined crack to develop, where b_w is the width of the section and d is the depth to the centroid of the prestressing steel (Refs. 5.3, 5.4, and 5.5). Thus the total shear force V_{ci} that would produce flexure-shear failure is given by

$$V_{ci} = 0.6b_w d\sqrt{f'_c} + \frac{M_{cr}}{M/V - d/2} + V_o + V_p \tag{b}$$

In most cases, in the part of a span in which flexure-shear cracking is likely, the tendon slope is very small. Consequently, V_p has a small value that may conservatively be neglected, resulting in

$$V_{ci} = 0.6 b_w d \sqrt{f'_c} + \frac{M_{cr}}{M/V - d/2} + V_o \qquad (5.4)$$

The cracking moment M_{cr} in Eq. (5.4) is, by definition, that moment from superimposed dead and live loads, and acts in addition to the moment due to self-weight. M_{cr} may be calculated based on the tensile concrete stress at the bottom face equal to the modulus of rupture of the concrete, taken equal to $6\sqrt{f'_c}$. Thus

$$f_o + \frac{M_{cr} c_2}{I_c} - f_{2p} = 6\sqrt{f'_c}$$

or

$$M_{cr} = \frac{I_c}{c_2} (6\sqrt{f'_c} + f_{2p} - f_o) \qquad (5.5)$$

where

f_o = flexural stress in the concrete at the bottom face of the beam, due to self-weight

c_2 = distance from concrete centroid to the bottom face

I_c = moment of inertia of the concrete cross section

f_{2p} = concrete compressive stress at the bottom face due to effective prestress force

The sign convention used here, consistent with that of the ACI Code, treats all stresses as absolute values, without positive or negative sense.

The reason for separate consideration of self-weight and external loads is that self-weight is usually uniformly distributed, while superimposed loads may have any distribution. By separating the loads in this way, the ratio of M/V in Eq. (5.4) remains constant as external loads increase, facilitating the calculations. It should also be noted that, while the analysis and design of web reinforcement to follow is based on ultimate strength at factored loads, the terms V_o and f_o used to predict diagonal cracking are to be based on the actual calculated self-weight without load factors.

Figure 5.8 shows the close agreement between Eq. (5.4) and available experimental data (Ref. 5.7).

The second type of cracking, web-shear cracking, occurs when the maximum principal tensile stress resulting from the combination of shear and flexural stress, equals the tensile strength of the concrete. The concrete behavior is reasonably elastic up to failure in tension, so calculations may be based upon the ordinary equations of elasticity.

Principal stress calculations and tests of typical beams indicate that a web-shear crack may be expected to occur at, or below, the centroid of the concrete

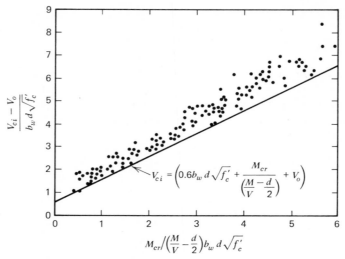

Figure 5.8 Comparison of Eq. (5.4) for V_{ci} with experimental data (Ref. 5.7).

section (see Art. 5.2 and Refs. 5.3, 5.4, 5.5). Beams for which the maximum principal tension is in the lower part of the cross section are likely to form flexural cracks, which lead to flexure-shear cracking rather than web-shear cracking. Consequently, the shear that will produce web-shear cracking may be estimated based on the principal tension at the concrete centroid.

The shear capacity of the member is reached if the principal tension becomes equal to the direct tensile strength of concrete, f_t'. Thus

$$\sqrt{v_{cw}^2 + \left(\frac{f_{cc}}{2}\right)^2} - \frac{f_{cc}}{2} = f_t'$$

where

v_{cw} = nominal shear stress in the concrete, $V_{cw}/b_w d$ due to *all* applied loads, dead and live

f_{cc} = compressive stress at the centroid of the concrete due to effective prestress force

Solving for the nominal shear stress corresponding to diagonal cracking, we obtain

$$v_{cw} = f_t' \sqrt{1 + \frac{f_{cc}}{f_t'}}$$

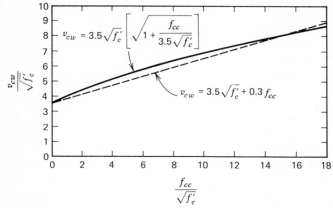

Figure 5.9 Nominal shear stress v_{cw} at web-shear cracking.

The direct tensile strength may conservatively be taken equal to $3.5\sqrt{f'_c}$, indicating that

$$v_{cw} = 3.5\sqrt{f'_c}\sqrt{1 + \frac{f_{cc}}{3.5\sqrt{f'_c}}} \tag{5.6}$$

Figure 5.9 shows the functional relationship of Eq. (5.6). It also indicates that the results of the principal stress calculation can be closely approximated by the much simpler expression

$$v_{cw} = 3.5\sqrt{f'_c} + 0.3f_{cc} \tag{5.7}$$

The use of Eq. (5.7) is therefore recommended as the basis for design.

The external shear V_{cw} at which web-shear cracking is likely, based on Eq. (5.7), is increased by the vertical component of the prestress force, V_p, which normally acts in the opposite sense to the load-induced shear. Thus

$$V_{cw} = b_w d(3.5\sqrt{f'_c} + 0.3f_{cc}) + V_p \tag{5.8}$$

In any given case, either flexure-shear or web-shear cracks may form. The shear force V_c at which diagonal cracking occurs should therefore be taken as the smaller of the two values V_{ci} and V_{cw}, given by Eqs. (5.4) and (5.8), respectively.

5.4   WEB REINFORCEMENT FOR SHEAR

It would be neither economical nor safe to design prestressed concrete beams of such proportions that all shear resistance is provided by the concrete alone.

Non-prestressed web reinforcement is employed, of the same general form as used for reinforced concrete beams. Such web steel not only increases the shear strength of beams, but also insures, should severe overloading produce a shear-related failure, that failure would be more ductile than otherwise. Yielding of the web reinforcement, accompanied by extensive concrete cracking, would give some warning of distress.

At least a minimum amount of web reinforcement is required in all prestressed beams. Exceptions may be made for members such as double-tee beams of short to medium span, which have proved to perform satisfactorily without such steel, or for slabs, where shear stress is characteristically low.

Infrequently, vertical or diagonal prestressing is used in the webs of beams. Although this offers the advantage that principal tensile stress and diagonal cracking in the concrete may be eliminated completely at service loads, such methods are not economical except in unusual cases. In addition, there is great practical difficulty controlling the amount of steel tension, because of large slip losses at the anchorages of the short tendons.

Typical forms of non-prestressed web reinforcement are shown in Fig. 5.10. For beams of ordinary dimensions, deformed reinforcing bars of sizes from No. 3 to No. 5 are common, and steel of Grades 40 or 60 is used. Steels of higher strength, used at corresponding higher stresses at service loads, are apt to permit excessively wide cracks. These not only would be visually objectionable, but would reduce the effectiveness of certain mechanisms of shear transfer, described later in this article. In addition, the relatively sharp bends required for stirrups might lead to damage if the higher strength, more brittle steels were used.

Because stirrup bars are necessarily rather short, in most cases it is not possible to develop the full yield strength of the bars by bond alone within the available length of embedment. For this reason, special anchorage is provided in the form of hooks or bends as shown in Fig. 5.10. At the bottom of a typical stirrup, the reinforcing bar is bent into the form of a U, offering positive resistance to pullout. At the top, inward or outward facing bends or hooks are used.

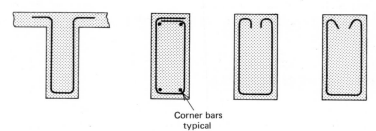

Corner bars
typical

Figure 5.10   Types of web reinforcement.

In most cases, small diameter longitudinal bars are added to prestressed beams, at the corners of the web reinforcement. These straight bars interlock with the stirrups to improve resistance to pullout, and serve the practical purpose of forming a rigid "cage" such that the web reinforcement can be fabricated outside of the beam forms, then dropped into position as a complete assembly.

The transfer of shear forces across the diagonally cracked section of a beam with web reinforcement may be understood with reference to Fig. 5.11. The figure shows the forces acting on a part of the beam between the diagonal cracked section and the adjacent support. Vertical U stirrups are shown at spacing s. For reasons already established, the analysis is based on conditions at the factored load stage, when the overloaded member is assumed to be at the point of incipient collapse.

Because of the presence of longitudinal compressive prestress in the concrete, the slope of the diagonal crack is generally considerably flatter than 45 degrees. It is assumed here, quite conservatively, that the horizontal projection of the crack has length d equal to the effective depth of the beam measured to the tendon centroid at the section of interest. Then, if the spacing of the web reinforcement in the direction of the member axis is s, the number of U stirrups crossing the diagonal crack is d/s. When the member is at incipient failure, the stirrups are stressed to their full yield strength f_y. It follows that the total contribution of the stirrups to transfer of shear across the cracked section is

$$V_s = \frac{A_v f_y d}{s} \tag{c}$$

where A_v is the total steel area of one stirrup, that is, two times the bar cross-sectional area for the typical case with U stirrups.

If the tendon centroid crosses the section of interest at slope θ, then the tendon transmits a shear force equal to the vertical component of the pre-

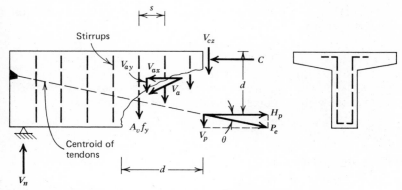

Figure 5.11 Shear transfer in partially cracked beam.

stressing force. Although the tendon force increases as the member is overloaded, it will be assumed conservatively that it has a value equal to the effective prestress P_e. Thus the vertical component is

$$V_p = P_e \sin \theta \tag{d}$$

A third contribution to shear transfer comes from frictional resistance along the naturally rough interface formed by the crack. Even though cracking will take place perpendicular to the direction of principal tension, such that no shear displacements might be expected, it has been confirmed by tests that a significant redistribution of internal forces takes place upon cracking, such that some tendency to slip exists along the interface. This is resisted by the roughness of the surface and the interlocking of the aggregate. The resisting force V_a associated with *aggregate interlock* acts on the free body in the direction represented in Fig. 5.11. Its vertical component is V_{ay}.

Finally, the concrete in the uncracked compression zone above the diagonal crack provides a resisting force V_{cz}.

Setting the summation of vertical forces equal to zero, Fig. 5.11, leads to the expression for nominal shear strength:

$$V_n = A_v f_y \frac{d}{s} + V_{cz} + V_p + V_{ay} \tag{5.9}$$

In spite of intensive research over a period of years, the magnitude of the individual contributions of V_{cz} and V_{ay} in Eq. (5.9) are not known. From tests, it appears that a conservative basis for design is to assume that their combined contribution is no less than V_c, the shear force that caused the diagonal crack to occur. The magnitude of V_c, in turn, may be determined either by web shear cracking or flexure shear cracking, and so is to be taken as the smaller of V_{ci} and V_{cw}, given by Eqs. (5.4) and (5.8), respectively.

If, in addition, the vertical component of the prestress force is neglected (this can be justified because of the small angle of tendon slope in the region of greatest interest), then Eq. (5.9) may be simplified to the following expression for ultimate shear strength:

$$V_n = A_v f_y \frac{d}{s} + V_c \tag{5.10}$$

If the "excess shear" above that which is resisted by the concrete is identified as $(V_n - V_c)$, and if the web reinforcement ratio is defined such that

$$\rho_v = \frac{A_v}{b_w s}$$

then Eq. (5.10) may be restated as

$$\frac{V_n - V_c}{b_w d} = \rho_v f_y \tag{5.11}$$

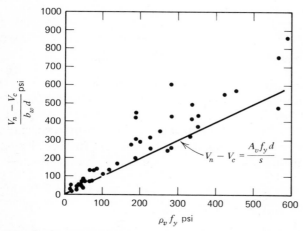

Figure 5.12   Increase in shear strength of a pre-stressed member due to web reinforcement (Ref. 5.5).

A comparison of the shear strength predicted by Eq. (5.11) with experimental data is given in Fig. 5.12. It is seen that the equation gives a conservative lower limit to the experimental data in all but a few cases; these too are close to the value given by Eq. (5.11).

5.5   SHEAR DESIGN CRITERIA OF THE ACI CODE

A.   DESIGN BASIS

The shear provisions of the ACI Code correlate directly with the development of the preceding articles. Design is to be based on conditions in the member at a hypothetical overload stage, with calculated dead loads and service live loads multiplied by the usual overload factors, except where otherwise noted.

   The design of cross sections subject to shear is to be based on the relation:

$$V_u \le \phi V_n \tag{5.12}$$

where

V_u = shear force applied at factored loads

V_n = nominal shear strength of the section

ϕ = strength reduction factor, taken equal to 0.85 for shear

The nominal shear strength, V_n, is calculated from the equation

$$V_n = V_c + V_s \tag{5.13}$$

where

V_c = nominal shear strength provided by the concrete

V_s = nominal shear strength provided by the shear reinforcement

The value of V_c is to be calculated according to Section B below.

The first critical section for shear is assumed to be at a distance $h/2$ from the face of a support, and sections located a distance less than $h/2$ are designed for the shear computed at $h/2$. This provision recognizes the beneficial effect of vertical compression in the concrete caused by the reaction. In special circumstances, those benefits do not obtain, and the shear at the support face may become critical.

B. NOMINAL SHEAR STRENGTH PROVIDED BY THE CONCRETE

The value of V_c in Eq. (5.13) is to be taken equal to the smaller of V_{ci} and V_{cw}, determined by flexure-shear cracking and web shear cracking, respectively. These values are based on Eqs. (5.4) and (5.8).

First, in Eq. (5.4) for flexure-shear cracking, the term $d/2$ may be deleted, for the sake of simplicity. This has the effect of relating flexure-shear cracking to the load that causes flexural cracking at the section considered, rather than at a distance $d/2$ from the section considered, and makes the equation somewhat more conservative. Then, with slight notational changes,

$$V_{ci} = 0.6\sqrt{f'_c}b_w d + V_o + \frac{V_i}{M_{max}}M_{cr} \qquad (5.14)$$

where b_w is the width of a rectangular section or the web width of a flanged section, and d is the depth from the compression face of the member to the centroid of the prestressing steel. On the basis of tests, the latter value need not be taken less than $0.80h$ for this and all other Code provisions relating to shear, except as specifically noted otherwise.

In Eq. (5.14) V_i and M_{max} are, respectively, the factored shear and bending moment at the section considered, resulting from the *superimposed* dead load and live load, and M_{cr} is the moment causing flexural cracking, computed by Eq. (5.5):

$$M_{cr} = \frac{I_c}{c_2}(6\sqrt{f'_c} + f_{2p} - f_o) \qquad (5.5)$$

V_o, in Eq. (5.14) is the shear due to the self-weight of the member, and is computed without load factor, and f_o in Eq. (5.5) is the flexural stress at the bottom face of the beam, due to member self-weight, also computed without load factor. The reason for separate consideration of self-weight has been explained earlier.

In applying Eq. (5.14), V_{ci} need not be taken less than $1.7\sqrt{f'_c}b_w d$, according to the Code.

The nominal shear strength corresponding to web-shear cracking is computed from Eq. (5.8) without modification:

$$V_{cw} = (3.5\sqrt{f'_c} + 0.3f_{cc})b_w d + V_p \tag{5.15}$$

where V_p is the vertical component of the effective prestress force at the section:

$$V_p = P_e \sin\theta \tag{5.16}$$

in which θ is the slope of the tendon centroid line at the section.

Alternatively to the use of Eq. (5.15), V_{cw} may be computed as the shear force corresponding to the dead load plus live load that results in a principal tensile stress of $4\sqrt{f'_c}$ at the centroid of the member, or at the intersection of the flange and web when the centroidal axis is in the flange.

For members with an effective prestress force not less than 40 percent of the tensile strength of the flexural reinforcement, an alternative to the use of Eqs. (5.14) and (5.15) is permitted. The shear force V_c may be taken equal to

$$V_c = \left(0.6\sqrt{f'_c} + 700\,\frac{V_u d}{M_u}\right)b_w d \tag{5.17}$$

In this equation, V_u and M_u are the factored shear and moment due to *all* loads, at the section considered, and the quantity $V_u d/M_u$ is not to be taken greater than 1.0. If Eq. (5.17) is used, V_c need not be taken less than $2\sqrt{f'_c}b_w d$ and must not be taken larger than $5\sqrt{f'_c}b_w d$. In this equation, d is the depth to the centroid of the prestressing tendons; the lower bound of $0.8h$ used elsewhere does not apply here.

Equation (5.17) is appealing in that it is simple to use compared with the more accurate Eqs. (5.14) and (5.15), but it may give very conservative and uneconomical results for certain classes of members.

C.   REQUIRED AREA OF WEB REINFORCEMENT

When shear reinforcement perpendicular to the axis of the member is used, its contribution to shear strength is

$$V_s = \frac{A_v f_y d}{s} \tag{5.18}$$

as derived in Art. 5.4, but the value of V_s is not to be taken larger than $8\sqrt{f'_c}b_w d$.

The total nominal shear strength V_n is found by summing the contributions of the steel and the concrete:

$$V_n = \frac{A_v f_y d}{s} + V_c \tag{5.19}$$

From Eq. (5.12), in the limiting case, and Eq. (5.13):

$$V_u = \phi V_n$$
$$= \phi(V_s + V_c)$$

from which

$$V_u = \phi \left(\frac{A_v f_y d}{s} + V_c \right)$$ (5.20)

The required cross sectional area of one stirrup, A_v, may be calculated by suitable transposition of Eq. (5.20):

$$A_v = \frac{(V_u - \phi V_c)s}{\phi f_y d}$$ (5.21)

Normally, in practical design, the engineer will select a trial stirrup size, for which the required spacing is found. Thus, a more convenient form of Eq. (5.21) is:

$$s = \frac{\phi A_v f_y d}{V_u - \phi V_c}$$ (5.22)

If the spacing determined for the trial stirrup size is too close for placement economy or practicality, or if it is so large that maximum spacing requirements control over too great a part of the beam span, then a revised bar size is selected and the calculation repeated.

D. MINIMUM WEB REINFORCEMENT

At least a certain minimum area of shear reinforcement is to be provided in all prestressed contrete members, where the total factored shear force V_u is greater than one-half the shear strength ϕV_c provided by the concrete. However, based on successful performance, the following types of members are excepted from this requirement:

1. Slabs and footings.
2. Concrete joist construction (including ribbed members such as double-tee beams).
3. Beams with a total depth not greater than the largest of 10 in., $2\frac{1}{2}$ times the thickness of the flange, and $\frac{1}{2}$ the web width.

The minimum area of shear reinforcement to be provided in all other cases is to be taken equal to the smaller of the following values:

$$A_v = 50 \frac{b_w s}{f_y}$$ (5.23)

and

$$A_v = \frac{A_p}{80} \frac{f_{pu}}{f_y} \frac{s}{d} \sqrt{\frac{d}{b_w}}$$ (5.24)

in which A_p is the cross sectional area of the prestressing steel, f_y is the yield stress of the stirrup steel, and f_{pu} is the ultimate tensile strength of the pre-stressing steel. All other terms are as previously defined.

Equation (5.23) will generally require greater minimum web steel than Eq. (5.24); thus the latter equation generally controls. However, it may be applied only if the effective prestress force is not less than 40 percent of the tensile strength of the tensioned reinforcement.

The ACI Code contains, in addition, certain restrictions on the maximum spacing of web reinforcement to insure that any potential diagonal crack will be crossed by at least a minimum amount of web steel. For prestressed members, this maximum spacing is not to exceed the smaller of $0.75h$ or 24 in. If the value of V_s exceeds $4\sqrt{f'_c}b_w d$, these limits are reduced by one-half.

E. LIGHTWEIGHT CONCRETE

Lightweight aggregate concretes are used with increasing frequency for pre-stressed members. Although the provisions of the ACI Code for shear design that have just been summarized pertain to members using normal weight con-crete, they may be applied to those built of lightweight concrete with the fol-lowing modification:

    a. When the split-cylinder strength f_{ct} is specified for the lightweight con-crete, the provisions for V_c shall be modified by substituting $f_{ct}/6.7$ for $\sqrt{f'_c}$, but the value of $f_{ct}/6.7$ shall not exceed $\sqrt{f'_c}$.

    b. When f_{ct} is not specified, all values of $\sqrt{f'_c}$ affecting V_c and M_{cr} shall be multiplied by 0.75 for "all-lightweight" concrete and 0.85 for "sand-lightweight" concrete.

F. ANCHORAGE OF WEB STEEL

Web reinforcement should be carried as close to the compression and tension surfaces of the member as cover requirements and the proximity of other reinforcement will permit. According to the Code, stirrups must extend a dis-tance d from the extreme compression face and must be anchored at both ends by one of the following means:

    a. A standard hook plus an effective embedment of $0.5l_d$. The $0.5l_d$ of em-bedment of a stirrup leg shall be taken as the distance between the mid-depth of the member, $d/2$, and the start of the hook (point of tangency).

    b. Embedment above or below the middepth, $d/2$, of the beam on the com-pression side for a full development length l_d but not less than 24 bar diameters, or for deformed bars or deformed wire 12 in.

    c. For No. 5 bars and D31 wire and smaller, bending around the longi-tudinal reinforcement through at least 135 degrees, plus, for stirrups with design stress exceeding 40,000 psi, an effective embedment of $0.33l_d$. The $0.33l_d$ embedment of a stirrup leg shall be taken as the distance between the middepth of the member $d/2$ and start of the hook (point of tangency).

The basic development length l_d is to be taken as

$$l_d = \frac{0.04 A_b f_y}{\sqrt{f'_c}}$$

(5.25a)

but not less than

$$l_d = 0.0004d_b f_y \qquad (5.25b)$$

where

$$A_b = \text{bar cross-sectional area, in.}^2$$
$$d_b = \text{bar diameter, in.}$$

For "all-lightweight" concrete this length is increased by 33 percent, while for "sand-lightweight" it is increased by 18 percent.

The dimensions of hooks have been standardized, and for stirrups are shown in Fig. 5.13. For such reinforcement, the minimum inside diameter of bends should not be less than 4 bar diameter for No. 5 bars and smaller, and not less than 6 bar diameters up to No. 8 bars.

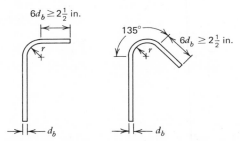

Figure 5.13 Standard hooks for stirrups and ties.

G. DESIGN PRACTICE

It is clear that the design of web reinforcement becomes quite complex even for ordinary cases. This is particularly true if V_c is based on the more refined approach using Eqs. (5.14) and (5.15) for V_{ci} and V_{cw}, respectively, because many of the parameters in those equations vary depending upon the location along the span. Use of a computer program will greatly facilitate the calculation of required stirrup spacings.

Alternatively, it may be advantageous to determine web steel requirements by plotting the variation of applied and resisting shears along the span, as shown in Fig. 5.14 for a uniformly loaded member. The excess shear may be quickly established at any location from such a diagram, and a practical arrangement of stirrups selected. In placing stirrups, usually three or four constant spacings are selected, to approximate the continuously varying requirement such as indicated by Fig. 5.14.

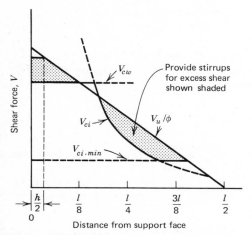

Figure 5.14   Basis for design of stirrups for uniformly loaded beam.

5.6   EXAMPLE: DESIGN OF WEB REINFORCEMENT FOR SHEAR

The unsymmetrical I beam of Fig. 5.15 is to carry a superimposed dead load of 345 plf and service live load of 1220 plf in addition to its own weight of 255 plf. It is to be built of concrete having $f'_c = 5000$ psi and is prestressed using multiple wire tendons with $f_{pu} = 275,000$ psi to an effective force $P_e = 288$ kips. Find the required spacing of vertical U stirrups at a point 10 ft from the left support, if f_y for the stirrup steel is 40,000 psi. ($w_o = 3.72$ kN/m, $w_d = 5.03$ kN/m, $w_l = 17.80$ kN/m, $f'_c = 35$ N/mm², $f_{pu} = 1896$ N/mm², $f_y = 276$ N/mm², $P_e = 1281$ kN, and the section at $x = 3.05$ m.)

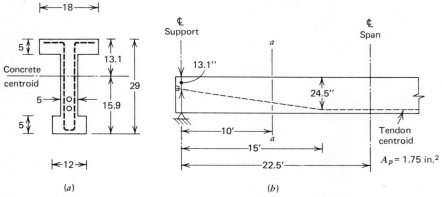

Figure 5.15   Shear design example. (a) Cross section. (b) Profile.

It is easily established that the properties of the uncracked concrete cross section are: $I_c = 24{,}200$ in.^{4}, $A_c = 245$ in.^{2}, and $r^2 = 99$ in.^{2}. $(10.1 \times 10^9$ mm^4, 158×10^3 mm^2, and 64×10^3 mm^2.)

The tendon depth d through the central part of the span is 24.5 in. and the eccentricity $e = 11.4$ in. From a 15 ft distance, the eccentricity is reduced linearly to zero at the support. Thus, at the section of interest, the eccentricity is

$$e = 11.4 \times \frac{10}{15} = 7.6 \text{ in. (193 mm)}$$

The corresponding depth d is $13.1 + 7.6 = 20.7$ in. In accordance with the Code, the effective depth in shear calculations will be assumed at $0.80 \times 29 = 23.2$ in. (589 mm).

The nominal shear strength for flexural-shear cracking is found with the aid of Eqs. (5.14) and (5.5). At the given section, the stress in the concrete at the bottom face due to prestress alone is

$$f_{2p} = -\frac{P_e}{A_c}\left(1 + \frac{ec_2}{r^2}\right)$$

$$= -\frac{288{,}000}{245}\left(1 + \frac{7.6 \times 15.9}{99}\right)$$

$$= -2600 \text{ psi}$$

The self-weight moment and shear at $x = 10$ ft are, respectively,

$$M_o = \frac{w_o x}{2}(l - x)$$

$$= \frac{0.255 \times 10}{2}(45 - 10)$$

$$= 45 \text{ ft-kips (61 kN-m)}$$

$$V_o = w_o \left(\frac{l}{2} - x\right)$$

$$= 0.255 \left(\frac{45}{2} - 10\right)$$

$$= 3.19 \text{ kips (14.19 kN)}$$

The moment M_o produces a tensile stress at the bottom of the beam equal to

$$f_o = \frac{M_o c_2}{I_c}$$

$$= \frac{45{,}000 \times 12 \times 15.9}{24{,}200}$$

$$= 355 \text{ psi}$$

Then, from Eq. (5.5)

$$M_{cr} = \frac{I_c}{c_2}(6\sqrt{f_c'} + f_{2p} - f_o)$$

$$= \frac{24,200}{15.9}(6\sqrt{5000} + 2600 - 355)\frac{1}{12,000}$$

$$= 339 \text{ ft-kips } (460 \text{ kN-m})$$

The shear and moment at the section 10 ft from the support, resulting from the superimposed dead load of 345 plf and live load of 1220 plf, are respectively

$$V_i = 1.565\left(\frac{45}{2} - 10\right)$$

$$= 19.56 \text{ kips}$$

$$M_{max} = \frac{1.565 \times 10}{2}(45 - 10)$$

$$= 274 \text{ ft-kips}$$

Thus, from Eq. (5.14) the value of V_{ci} is

$$V_{ci} = 0.6\sqrt{f_c'}b_w d + V_o + \frac{V_i}{M_{max}}M_{cr}$$

$$= 0.6\sqrt{5000} \times 5 \times 23.2 + 3190 + \frac{19,560}{274,000} \times 339,000$$

$$= 32,310 \text{ lb } (144 \text{ kN})$$

Note that the lower limit of $1.7\sqrt{5000} \times 5 \times 23.2 = 13,940$ lb does not control here.

The nominal shear strength for web shear cracking is found from Eq. (5.15). With $P_e = 288$ kips, the centroidal stress in the concrete is

$$f_{cc} = \frac{288,000}{245} = 1170 \text{ psi}$$

The vertical component of the effective prestress force is

$$V_p = 288 \times \frac{11.4}{15 \times 12}$$

$$= 18.24 \text{ kips}$$

Then, from Eq. (5.15),

$$V_{cw} = (3.5\sqrt{f_c'} + 0.3f_{cc})b_w d + V_p$$
$$= (3.5\sqrt{5000} + 0.3 \times 1170) \times 5 \times 23.2 + 18,240$$
$$= 87,660 \text{ lb } (390 \text{ kN})$$

In the present case, flexure-shear cracking controls, and $V_c = V_{ci} = 32,310$ lb $= 32.31$ kips (144 kN)

The total shear force at $x = 10$ ft at factored loads is

$$V_u = [1.4(0.255 + 0.345) + 1.7 \times 1.220]12.5$$
$$= 36.43 \text{ kips (162 kN)}$$

Thus the excess shear stress, $(V_u - \phi V_c) = \phi V_s = 36.43 - 0.85 \times 32.31 = 8.97$ kips, is well below the upper limit of $8 \times 0.85\sqrt{5000} \times 5 \times 23.2 = 55.8$ kips and is also below $4 \times 0.85\sqrt{5000} \times 5 \times 23.2 = 27.9$ kips so that normal spacing limitations apply.

For trial purposes, No. 3 U stirrups will be selected, providing an area per stirrup of $A_v = 2 \times 0.11 = 0.22$ in.^{2} From Eq. (5.22),

$$s = \frac{\phi A_v f_y d}{V_u - \phi V_c}$$

$$= \frac{0.85 \times 0.22 \times 40{,}000 \times 23.2}{8970}$$

$$= 19.3 \text{ in. (490 mm)}$$

Checking minimum web steel area by Eqs. (5.23) and (5.24):

$$A_v = 50 \frac{b_w s}{f_y}$$

$$= \left(\frac{50 \times 5}{40{,}000}\right) s$$

$$= 0.00625s$$

and

$$A_v = \frac{A_p f_{pu}}{80 f_y} \frac{s}{d} \sqrt{\frac{d}{b_w}}$$

$$= \frac{1.75}{80} \times \frac{275}{40} \frac{s}{23.2} \sqrt{\frac{23.2}{5}}$$

$$= 0.01396s$$

The smaller of the two requirements controls, and for No. 3 stirrups with $A_v = 0.22$ in.^{2} the maximum spacing $s = 35$ in. In addition, the maximum spacing is not to exceed the smaller of 24 in. or $0.75 \times 29 = 22$ in. The calculated requirement of $s = 19.3$ in. controls in any case. This will be rounded off to $s = 18$ in. for practical reasons.

5.7 TORSION IN CONCRETE STRUCTURES

Reinforced or prestressed concrete members may be subjected to torsional moments, causing a member to twist about its long axis. While such torsional moments may act alone, more often they act in conjunction with bending moments and shear forces.

For many years, designers of concrete structures have tended to regard torsion as a secondary effect, relying upon the capacity of a typical indeterminate struc-

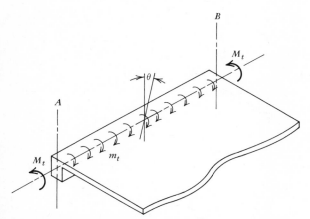

Figure 5.16   Spandrel beam subject to torsion.

ture to redistribute internal forces until an alternative equilibrium state is found. A common example occurs in the design of spandrel beams supporting the edge of a monolithic floor, as shown in Fig. 5.16. A distributed load applied to the floor causes twisting moments m_t to be applied, more or less uniformly along the length of the edge beam. These are equilibrated by resisting torques M_t provided by the building columns at A and B. Spandrel beam cross sections near midspan tend to rotate with respect to the corresponding sections near the columns, as shown.

If no special attention is given to torsion in designing the spandrel and its reinforcement, some torsional cracking is likely to occur, reducing its stiffness and its capacity to provide edge restraint for the slab. If the slab is reinforced accordingly, in most cases no difficulty will be experienced.

While indeterminate structures seek to accommodate to the assumptions of the designer in this way, it is dangerous to attempt to exploit this to too great an extent. Redistribution in some cases may be accompanied by excessive cracking and large deflections. In other cases, the required ductility may not be available.

Furthermore, in many types of structures, torsion is a primary design condition. The beam of Fig. 5.17a, for example, carries a cantilevered slab, and must possess adequate torsional resistance to carry the load. The box girder bridge of Fig. 5.17b, when loaded in one traffic lane as indicated by the shaded area, develops torsional stresses that are a dominant part of the design. Other examples are easily found, such as helical stairways and curved beams. Engineers may expect to encounter many such design problems in which torsion is the primary loading.

The behavior of concrete structures carrying torsion or combined loading is not yet fully understood. Research in recent years has shed much light on

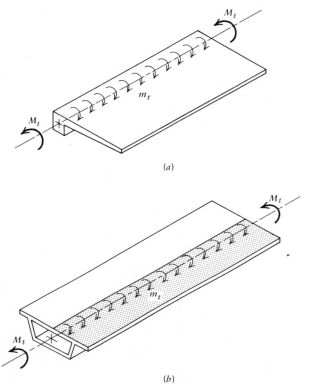

Figure 5.17 Torsion members. (*a*) Cantilevered slab. (*b*) Box girder bridge.

this behavior, yet present recommendations are based largely on test observation, not theory. Specific requirements governing the design of *reinforced* concrete members for torsion and combined loading were included for the first time in the 1971 ACI Code. These have been included with no essential change in the current 1977 Code.

Code provisions do not include coverage of prestressed concrete members subject to torsion. It appears, however, that an approach similar to that use for reinforced concrete is applicable, and tentative recommendations have been proposed (Ref. 5.10). The approach, which will be summarized in the following articles, combines theory with experimental observation, in arriving at a practical design method. The material presented must be regarded as tentative however, subject to revision as new information is developed.

5.8   **TORSION DESIGN OF PRESTRESSED CONCRETE**

In studying the behavior of prestressed concrete members subject to loading that combines torsion, bending, and flexural shear, it is first necessary to discuss the effects of torsion acting alone. For simplicity, the subject will be introduced with reference to rectangular members, but the conclusions apply to more complicated shapes with slight modifications, as will be discussed further.

A.   TORSION IN BEAMS WITHOUT WEB REINFORCEMENT

Figure 5.18a shows a portion of a prismatic member *without prestress force*, with equal and opposite torques T acting at each end. If the material is elastic, St. Venant's torsion theory indicates that torsional shear stresses are distributed over the cross section as shown by the solid lines in Fig. 5.18b. The largest shear stress occurs at the middle of the wide faces and is equal to

$$t_{max} = \frac{T}{\eta x^2 y} \tag{5.26}$$

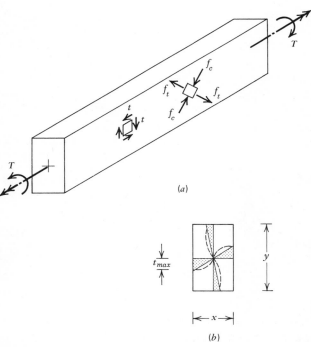

(a)

(b)

Figure 5.18   Stresses caused by torsion.

where η is a coefficient that depends upon the shape of the cross section, and x and y are, respectively, the shorter and longer sides. If the material is inelastic, the stress distribution is similar, as shown by the dashed lines, and the maximum shear stress is still given by Eq. (5.26) except that η assumes a different value.

Shear stresses act in pairs on an element at or near the wide surface, as shown in Fig. 5.18a. It is easily shown that this state of stress corresponds exactly to a state described by equal tension and compression stresses on the faces of an element at 45 degrees to the direction of shear.

When the diagonal tension stresses exceed the tensile strength of the concrete, a crack forms at some accidentally weaker location, and spreads immediately across the beam as shown in Fig. 5.19a. Tests confirm that the crack

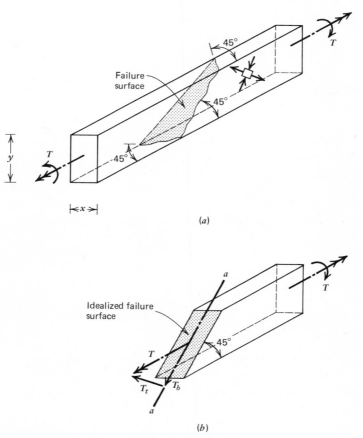

(a)

(b)

Figure 5.19 Torsional cracking of beam without web reinforcement. (a) Skew bending failure. (b) Idealized failure model.

forms at 45 degrees on the near face, and that the extensions of the crack on the two narrower faces are also at about 45 degrees with the member axis. The fracture line on the far face connects the cracks at the short faces, establishing a warped failure surface.

For purposes of analysis, this surface can be replaced by a plane section inclined at 45 degrees to the axis as in Fig. 5.19b. The applied torque T can be resolved into a component T_b causing bending about the axis a-a of the failure plane, and a component T_t that causes twisting. Tests indicate that failure is associated with the bending component, not the twisting.

The section modulus of the failure plane about a-a is

$$Z = \frac{1}{6} \frac{x^2 y}{\sin 45°}$$

and the maximum tensile stress resulting from the moment component T_b is

$$f_t = \frac{T_b}{Z} = \frac{6T \sin 45° \cos 45°}{x^2 y}$$

Simplified, this becomes

$$f_t = \frac{T}{\frac{1}{3} x^2 y} \tag{5.27}$$

It is seen that the tension stress calculated by this *skew bending theory* is identical with the St. Venant's shear stress of Eq. (5.26) with $\eta = \frac{1}{3}$.

If f_t were the only stress acting, cracking should occur when f_t becomes equal to f_r', the modulus of rupture of concrete, usually taken as $7.5\sqrt{f_c'}$. However, at right angles to the tension, there is equal compression. This results in a reduction in the tensile strength of about 15 percent (see Art. 2.10). Consequently, a crack forms and the unreinforced member fails when $f_t = 6\sqrt{f_c'}$. Thus the failure torque T_{cr} of a non-prestressed beam without web steel (or the cracking torque of one with web steel) can be predicted from the equation

$$T_{cr} = 6\sqrt{f_c'}(\tfrac{1}{3} x^2 y) \tag{5.28}$$

For *prestressed* concrete members without web steel, an analogous development is valid. Failure is attained when the maximum principal tensile stress, due to the combined action of torsion and compression, reaches the direct tensile strength of the concrete, which for present purposes is taken equal to $0.10 f_c'$. On this basis it is shown in Ref. 5.9 that the cracking torque of a prestressed beam is given by the equation

$$T_{cr}' = 6\sqrt{f_c'}\sqrt{1 + 10 f_{cc}/f_c'}(\eta x^2 y) \tag{5.29}$$

or $T_{cr}' = T_{cr}\sqrt{1 + 10 f_{cc}/f_c'}$, where f_{cc} is the average longitudinal prestress P_e/A_c.

Equation (5.29) permits experimental evaluation of the shape factor η based on measured cracking torque. From tests of 218 prestressed rectangular beams, with varying eccentricity of prestress (Ref. 5.10) it appears that a reasonably conservative lower bound for the shape factor η is given by

$$\eta = \frac{0.35}{0.75 + (x/y)} \tag{5.30}$$

For *flanged sections*, the torsional strength may be taken conservatively as the sum of the torsional strengths of the web and projecting flanges. Accordingly, the term $\eta x^2 y$ in Eq. (5.29) is replaced by $\sum \eta x^2 y$, where x and y are, respectively, the smaller and larger side dimensions of each of the component rectangles. T and L sections may be subdivided so as to maximize $\sum \eta x^2 y$. The effective width of the projecting flanges should not be taken greater than 3 times the flange thickness.

Based on limited testing, it appears that the ACI Code approach for non-prestressed *box sections* applies to prestressed box sections also (Ref. 5.8). For such members with a wall thickness h not less than $x/4$, where x is the overall width of the box section, the torsional strength may be taken as that if a comparable solid rectangular section with the same overall dimensions. If the wall thickness h is less than $x/4$ but greater than $x/10$, the torsional strength of the box section is reduced by the factor $4h/x$ on the right-hand side of Eq. (5.29).

B.   TORSION IN BEAMS WITH WEB REINFORCEMENT

To obtain increased resistance to torsion, in both non-prestressed and prestressed beams, reinforcement is provided consisting of closely spaced closed stirrups and longitudinal bars. Even though a member may be adequately reinforced in this way, as in Fig. 5.20, the concrete cracks at a torque equal to, or only somewhat larger than, that in an unreinforced member. Only after cracking does the reinforcement become effective. The cracks form a spiral pattern as shown for one single crack in Fig. 5.19a. Actually, a great number of such cracks develop at close spacing.

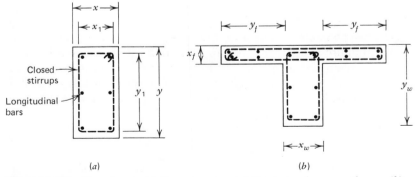

Figure 5.20 Torsion   reinforcement.   (a) Rectangular   section.   (b) Flanged section.

Upon cracking, the torsional resistance of the concrete in a *non-prestressed member* drops to about half of that of the uncracked member, the remainder being resisted by the reinforcement. Failure occurs by skew bending. The stirrup steel may or may not be stressed to its yield strength, depending upon the location of the crack and orientation of the stirrup leg.

The torsional strength of a *non-prestressed member* can be analyzed considering the equilibrium of the internal forces that are transmitted across the potential failure surface shown in Fig. 5.21. The figure shows the partially cracked failure surface, including the compression zone of concrete (shaded) and the horizontal and vertical stirrup forces S_h and S_v of all the stirrups intersecting the failure surface, except for those located in the compression zone.

It is shown in Ref. 5.11 that the total resisting torque contributed by the steel reinforcement is given by the expression

$$T_s = \alpha_t \frac{x_1 y_1}{s} A_t f_y$$

where

s = spacing of stirrups along the axis of the member, in.

A_t = cross-sectional area of one stirrup leg, in.^{2}

f_y = yield strength of stirrup steel, psi

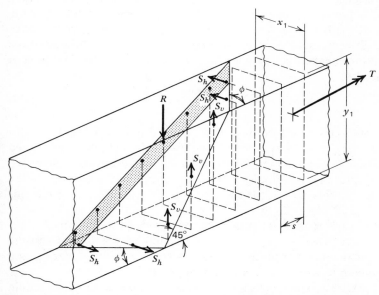

Figure 5.21   Torsion resistance of cracked beam with web steel.

and the coefficient α_t accounts for crack geometry, stirrup stress at failure, and other parameters. This coefficient has been established empirically as

$$\alpha_t = 0.66 + 0.33 \frac{y_1}{x_1} \qquad (5.31)$$

not to exceed 1.5.

For non-prestressed members, after cracking, the torque T_c resisted by the concrete is diminished to about half the cracking torque. Taking the ratio of the two conservatively to be 40 percent, then from Eq. (5.28)

$$T_c = 0.4(\tfrac{1}{3}x^2 y)6\sqrt{f_c'} \qquad (5.32)$$

The total nominal torsion strength for a non-prestressed member is then

$$T_n = T_c + T_s$$

or

$$T_n = 2.4\sqrt{f_c'}\,\frac{x^2 y}{3} + \alpha_t \frac{x_1 y_1}{s} A_t f_y \qquad (5.33)$$

This torque will be developed only if the stirrups are sufficiently closely spaced so that any failure surface will intersect an adequate number of stirrups.

The role of the longitudinal bar reinforcement is not fully understood but it has been shown by tests that T_n can be developed only if such reinforcement is provided. Its chief functions are probably (1) to anchor the stirrups, particularly at the corners, which enables them to develop their full yield strength, and (2) to provide at least some resisting torque themselves by dowel action, where they cross the failure surface. It is customary to design torsional members such that the volume of longitudinal steel is equal to the volume of the transverse reinforcement. It is easily verified that this is so if the total area of longitudinal steel is

$$A_l = 2A_t \frac{x_1 + y_1}{s} \qquad (5.34)$$

For *prestressed members* subject to torsion, limited tests show that the ultimate torsional strength can be expressed as the sum of the strengths contributed by the concrete and the web reinforcement, just as for non-prestressed members. The effect of the prestress is to increase the contribution of the concrete to the ultimate torsional strength, while the contribution of the reinforcement remains unchanged.

Figure 5.22 illustrates that, for non-prestressed members, the concrete resisting torque after cracking, T_c, is only a fraction of the torque causing cracking, T_{cr}. The reduced resistance is taken equal to 40 percent of the cracking torque, as pointed out earlier, in present design practice.

Likewise for prestressed members, the resistance of the concrete after cracking is only a fraction, but a greater fraction, of the torque causing cracking. Accord-

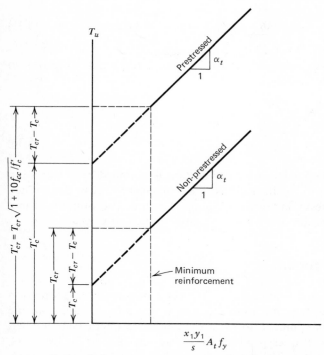

Figure 5.22   Ultimate torque for reinforced and prestressed concrete members (Ref. 5.10).

ingly the ultimate torque for a prestressed member can be expressed as

$$T_n = T'_c + T_s$$

or

$$T_n = T'_c + \alpha_t \frac{x_1 y_1}{s} A_t f_y$$

where the terms of T_s are exactly as defined earlier for non-prestressed members, and T'_c is the torsional resistance of the concrete after cracking.

It is proposed in Ref. 5.8 that the reduction in concrete torque, upon cracking, for a prestressed concrete beam be taken equal to that reduction upon cracking for the equivalent non-prestressed member. This is illustrated by Fig. 5.22. From Eq. (5.32) the torsional resistance, after cracking, of a non-prestressed beam is

$$T_c = 0.133(x^2 y)6\sqrt{f'_c}$$

Thus, with reference to Fig. 5.22

$$T'_c = T_{cr}\sqrt{1 + 10 f_{cc}/f'_c} - (T_{cr} - T_c)$$

or

$$T'_c = (\eta x^2 y) 6 \sqrt{f'_c} (\sqrt{1 + 10 f_{cc}/f'_c} - k) \tag{5.35}$$

where $k = (1 - T_o/T_{cr}) = (1 - 0.133/\eta)$.

Then the total nominal resisting torque T_n for a rectangular prestressed member with web reinforcement is

$$T_n = T'_c + T_s$$

or

$$T_n = (\eta x^2 y) 6 \sqrt{f'_c} (\sqrt{1 + 10 f_{cc}/f'_c} - k) + \alpha_t \frac{x_1 y_1}{s} A_t f_y \tag{5.36}$$

The equivalent expression for a flanged section is obtained by substitution of $\sum \eta x^2 y$ for $\eta x^2 y$ in Eq. (5.36). In such case the coefficient k may be determined on thg basis of the largest component rectangle. For a box section, the reduction factor $4h/x$ may be applied within the limits indicated earlier.

5.9 TORSION PLUS SHEAR

It was pointed out in Art. 5.7 that concrete members designed to carry torsion alone are quite unusual. It is much more common that a beam subject to the usual moments and shears must also resist torsion. In an uncracked member, shear forces as well as torques produce shear stresses. It must be expected, therefore, that simultaneous application of shear forces and torques will produce an interaction that will reduce the strength of a member compared with what it would be if shear or torsion were acting alone.

A. COMBINED LOADING IN BEAMS WITHOUT WEB REINFORCEMENT

No satisfactory theories of this complex interaction have yet been developed so that reliance must be placed on the available experimental evidence (Refs. 5.10, 5.12, and 5.13). Recommendations must be regarded as tentative.

Tests have shown that the interaction between torsion and shear for prestressed beams without web reinforcement can be adequately represented by a circular curve. Let V_{cr} and T_{cr} be the cracking shear and cracking torque of the prestressed member when subjected, respectively, to flexural shear or to torsion alone, computed according to the methods of Arts. 5.3 and 5.8.* It will be recalled that, for all practical purposes, failure occurs at these same values almost immediately following cracking, so that, for members without web reinforcement, V_{cr} and T_{cr} adequately represent their ultimate strengths in the two modes. Furthermore, let V_n and T_n, respectively, represent the shear capacity and the torsion capacity under combined loading, that is, when the

---

* Note that T_{cr} was defined for the prestressed beam as T'_{cr} by Eq. (5.29). The prime will be deleted from this point on for the sake of simplification.

member is subject to simultaneous flexural shear and torsion. Available test results are reasonably well represented by the circular interaction equation

$$\left(\frac{V_n}{V_{cr}}\right)^2 + \left(\frac{T_n}{T_{cr}}\right)^2 = 1 \tag{5.37}$$

where

V_n = shear force at failure under combined loading

T_n = torsional moment at failure under combined loading

V_{cr} = the lesser of V_{ci} and V_{cw} computed according to Art. 5.3

$T_{cr} = 6\sqrt{f'_c}\sqrt{1 + 10f_{cc}/f'_c}\sum\eta x^2 y$

A graphical representation of this equation is shown in Fig. 5.23. It is seen that this interaction curve is quite favorable, that is, the two modes do not very strongly interfere with each other. For instance, if a member carries a torque $T_{cr}/2$, that is, one half of its pure torsion capacity, the curve shows that it can carry simultaneously about $0.85V_{cr}$, that is, only about 15 percent less than it could carry if no torsion were present at all.

After suitable algebraic transformation, Eq. 5.37 results in the following:

$$V_n = \frac{V_{cr}}{\sqrt{1 + \left(\frac{V_{cr}}{T_{cr}}\right)^2 \left(\frac{T_n}{V_n}\right)^2}} \tag{5.38}$$

$$T_n = \frac{T_{cr}}{\sqrt{1 + \left(\frac{T_{cr}}{V_{cr}}\right)^2 \left(\frac{V_n}{T_n}\right)^2}} \tag{5.39}$$

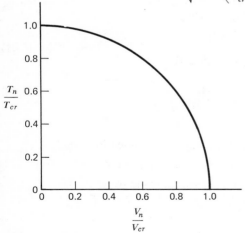

Figure 5.23 Interaction curve for combined torsion plus flexural shear.

The terms in the numerators of Eqs. (5.38) and (5.39) are the cracking stresses for shear and torsion, respectively, if shear or torsion is acting alone. The factors in the denominators of these equations account for the interaction between torsion and shear.

Note further that, while the unknowns V_n and T_n appear on the right sides of these two equations, it is not necessary to know their values at the outset of the calculations, but only to know the ratio of torsion to flexural shear at the section of interest, T_n/V_n, or in the design case, T_u/V_u, which is constant and known for given loads.

B. COMBINED LOADING IN BEAMS WITH WEB REINFORCEMENT

While experimental verification is sparse, it appears reasonable to proceed, in designing members with web reinforcement subject to combined loading, following the same general approach established for members without web reinforcement. Pending more extensive research, both experimental and analytical, the following assumptions are made:

1. In members with stirrups, the portion of the total torsion carried by the concrete is determined by the same type of interaction equation as in members without stirrups; that is, a circular interaction law holds.
2. To carry the excess torque, above that resisted by the concrete, the same amount of reinforcement must be provided in members subject to combined loading as would be required for members carrying torsion alone. This torsional reinforcement is to be added to that required in the same member for carrying bending moments and flexural shears.

On the basis of the first assumption and with reference to Eqs. (5.38) and (5.39), the interaction equations for the nominal shear and torsion carried by the concrete, in beams with web reinforcement, are

$$V_c^* = \frac{V_c}{\sqrt{1 + (\beta T_n/V_n)^2}} \tag{5.41}$$

$$T_c^* = \frac{T_c'}{\sqrt{1 + (V_n/\beta T_n)^2}} \tag{5.42}$$

where

V_c^* = shear force carried by concrete under combined loading

T_c^* = torsion force carried by the concrete under combined loading

V_c = the lesser of V_{ci} and V_{cw} computed according to Art. 5.3

$T_c' = 6\sqrt{f_c'}(\sqrt{1 + 10f_{cc}/f_c'} - k)\sum \eta x^2 y$

$\beta = \dfrac{1}{2}\left(\dfrac{V_c}{T_c'}\right)$

$$k = 1 - 0.133/\eta$$

$$\eta = \frac{0.35}{0.75 + x/y}$$

The basis of Eqs. (5.41) and (5.42) is found in Ref. 5.10.

From the second assumption above, if the torque T_u actually applied to the member is larger than that carried by the concrete, then reinforcement must be provided to carry the excess. Recasting Eq. (5.36) to apply to the combined stress case, we obtain

$$T_n = T_c^* + \alpha_t \frac{x_1 y_1}{s} A_t f_y \qquad (5.43)$$

where T_c^* is given by Eq. (5.42).

For the design case, setting $T_n = T_u$ at factored loads, and transposing terms, one obtains

$$(T_u - T_c^*) = \alpha_t \frac{x_1 y_1}{s} A_t f_y$$

from which

$$A_t = \frac{(T_u - T_c^*)s}{\alpha_t f_y x_1 y_1} \qquad (5.44)$$

Note that the web reinforcement for torsion, determined by Eq. (5.44), must be in the form of closed stirrups, and is in addition to that required for flexural shear. The latter is to be found by Eq. (5.18), with the substitution of V_c^* from Eq. (5.41) for V_c in that equation.

For design purposes, it is consistent with earlier procedures to introduce the capacity reduction factor $\phi = 0.85$ for torsion in computing the nominal strengths. Thus, for design,

$$A_t = \frac{(T_u - \phi T_c^*)s}{\alpha_t \phi f_y x_1 y_1} \qquad (5.45)$$

where T_u is the design torque at factored loads.

C. MAXIMUM AND MINIMUM WEB REINFORCEMENT

To avoid brittle failure upon cracking, a minimum amount of web reinforcement be provided in members subject to combined stress. Tests reported in Ref. 5.10 indicate that the minimum web reinforcement required by ACI Code for flexural shear is insufficient to insure ductility in beams with high ratio of torsion to shear. Accordingly, it is recommended that a beam should be reinforced for no less than the cracking torque.

Consideration must also be given to the possibility of over-reinforcing the member such that a sudden compressive failure of the concrete might occur before the stirrup steel yields. To avoid this type of failure, an upper limit must be placed on web reinforcement by specifying a maximum nominal torque $T_{u,max}$. Based on available tests, it is recommended in Ref. 5.8 as follows:

1. For members subject to torsion alone:

$$T_{n,max} = C\sqrt{f'_c}\sqrt{1 + 10f_{cc}/f'_c}(\sum \eta x^2 y) \qquad (5.46)$$

where

$$C = 14 - 13.33\left(\frac{f_{cc}}{f'_c}\right)$$

2. For members subject to combined loading:

$$T^*_{n,max} = \frac{C'\sqrt{f'_c}}{\sqrt{1 + \left(\frac{C'}{10}\right)^2 \left(\frac{V_n}{T_n}\right)^2 \left(\frac{\sum \eta x^2 y}{b_w d}\right)^2}}(\sum \eta x^2 y) \qquad (5.47)$$

$$V^*_{u,max} = \frac{10\sqrt{f'_c}}{\sqrt{1 + \left(\frac{10}{C'}\right)^2 \left(\frac{T_n}{V_n}\right)^2 \left(\frac{b_w d}{\sum \eta x^2 y}\right)^2}}(b_w d) \qquad (5.48)$$

where $C' = C\sqrt{1 + 10f_{cc}/f'_c}$

D. LIMITATIONS

To insure the development of ultimate torsional strength and to control cracking and stiffness at service load, the maximum yield strength of the stirrup reinforcement should be limited to 60 ksi. In order to properly control spiral cracking, the maximum spacing of torsional stirrups should not exceed $(x_1 + y_1)/4$ or 12 in. whichever is smaller. Longitudinal bars must be provided, well distributed around the perimeter of the closed stirrups, at a spacing that should not exceed 12 in.

For reinforced concrete members, the ACI Code permits the torsional effect to be neglected if the torsional shear stress is less than 25 percent of the cracking stress. This same requirement would seem justified for prestressed beams. Specifically, the influence of torsion may be neglected if T_u is less than

$$T_{u,min} = 1.5\sqrt{f'_c}\sqrt{1 + 10f_{cc}/f'_c}(\sum \eta x^2 y) \qquad (5.49)$$

5.10 EXAMPLE: DESIGN OF PRESTRESSED BEAM FOR COMBINED LOADING

The rectangular beam of 30 ft clear span shown in Fig. 5.24 is to carry a superimposed dead load of 1.85 kips/ft and service live load of 1.20 kips/ft, both at eccentricity of 9 in., in addition to its own weight of 0.38 kips/ft. The beam is prestressed with a force after losses of $P_e = 300$ kips, with steel centroid at effective depth 24 in. The specified 28 day

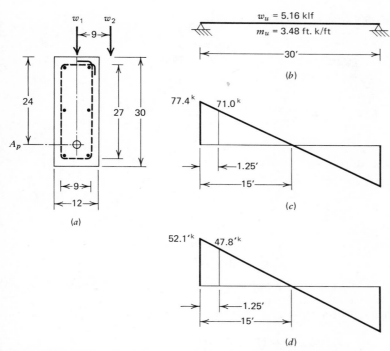

Figure 5.24 Torsion design example. (a) Cross section. (b) Loads. (c) Shear. (d) Torque.

concrete strength $f'_c = 5000$ psi. Design the reinforcement required for shear and torsion, at a section $h/2$ from the support face, using steel of $f_y = 40,000$ psi. (Span $= 9.14$ m, $w_o = 5.5$ kN/m, $w_d = 27.0$ kN/m, $w_l = 17.5$ kN/m, $e = 229$ mm, $P_e = 1334$ kN, $d = 618$ mm, $f'_c = 34$ N/mm², and $f_y = 276$ N/mm².)

The usual ACI load factors are applied to obtain the factored loads:

$$w_1 = 1.4 \times 0.38 = 0.53 \text{ kips/ft}$$
$$w_2 = 1.4 \times 1.85 + 1.7 \times 1.20 = 4.63 \text{ kips/ft}$$

The total shear force and torque at the face of supports are, respectively,

$$V_u = 5.16(30/2) = 77.4 \text{ kips}$$
$$T_u = 4.63(9/12)(30/2) = 52.1 \text{ ft-kips}$$

In accordance with the ACI Code provisions for shear, the first critical section will be assumed at a distance $h/2 = 1.25$ ft from the support face. The values of shear and torque at that section are, respectively, 71.0 kips and 47.8 ft-kips as shown in Fig. 5.24.

First, for reference, from Eq. (5.30) with $x/y = 12/30 = 0.40$,

$$\eta = \frac{0.35}{0.75 + 0.40} = 0.304$$

and

$$\eta x^2 y = 0.304 \times 144 \times 30$$
$$= 1310 \text{ in.}^3$$

while

$$b_w d = 12 \times 24$$
$$= 288 \text{ in.}^2$$

With the concrete stress at the section centroid

$$f_{cc} = \frac{P_e}{A_c} = \frac{300,000}{12 \times 30} = 833 \text{ psi}$$

from Eq. (5.49)

$$T_{u,min} = 1.5\sqrt{f_c'}\sqrt{1 + 10f_{cc}/f_c'}(\eta x^2 y)$$
$$= 1.5\sqrt{5000}\sqrt{1 + 8330/5000}(1310)$$
$$= 227,000 \text{ in.-lb} = 18.9 \text{ ft-kips}$$

The actual nominal torsion of 47.8 ft-kips is well above this value, confirming that torsion must be considered in designing the member.

The upper limits of torsion and shear are determined from Eqs. (5.47) and (5.48), respectively, with

$$C = 14 - 13.33(833/5000) = 11.78$$
$$C' = 11.78\sqrt{1 + 8330/5000} = 19.23$$

$$T_{u,max}^* = \frac{C'\sqrt{f_c'}}{\sqrt{1 + \left(\frac{C'}{10}\right)^2 \left(\frac{V_u}{T_u}\right)^2 \left(\frac{\eta x^2 y}{b_w d}\right)^2}}(\eta x^2 y)$$

$$= \frac{19.23\sqrt{5000}}{\sqrt{1 + \left(\frac{19.23}{10}\right)^2 \left(\frac{71.0}{47.8 \times 12}\right)^2 \left(\frac{1310}{288}\right)^2}}\left(\frac{1310}{12000}\right)$$

$$= 101 \text{ ft-kips} > 47.8 \text{ ft-kips}$$

$$V_{u,max}^* = \frac{10\sqrt{f_c'}}{\sqrt{1 + \left(\frac{10}{C'}\right)^2 \left(\frac{T_u}{V_u}\right)^2 \left(\frac{b_w d}{\eta x^2 y}\right)^2}}(b_w d)$$

$$= \frac{10\sqrt{5000}}{\sqrt{1 + \left(\frac{10}{19.23}\right)^2 \left(\frac{47.8 \times 12}{71.0}\right)^2 \left(\frac{288}{1310}\right)^2}}\left(\frac{288}{1000}\right)$$

$$= 150 \text{ kips} > 71 \text{ kips}$$

It is confirmed that the maximum values of forces acting are below the allowed upper limits in each case.

The interaction equations will next be employed to determine the contribution of the concrete section to resisting torsion and shear forces. With

$$k = 1 - \frac{0.133}{\eta}$$

$$= 1 - \frac{0.133}{0.304}$$

$$= 0.563$$

then from Eq. (5.35):

$$T'_c = 6\sqrt{f'_c}(\sqrt{1 + 10 f_{cc}/f'_c} - k)(\eta x^2 y)$$

$$= 6\sqrt{5000}(\sqrt{1 + 8330/5000} - 0.563)\left(\frac{1310}{1000}\right)$$

$$= 595 \text{ in.-kips}$$

For V_c, the approximate Eq. (5.17) will be used:

$$V_c = \left(0.6\sqrt{f'_c} + 700 \frac{V_u d}{M_u}\right) b_w d$$

but not less than $2\sqrt{f'_c}b_w d$ and not to exceed $5\sqrt{f'_c}b_w d$. The upper limitation controls in this case and

$$V_c = 5\sqrt{5000} \times 288/1000 = 102 \text{ kips}$$

Then with $\beta = \frac{1}{2}(102/595) = 0.086$, application of Eq. (5.42) results in

$$T^*_c = \frac{T'_c}{\sqrt{1 + \left(\frac{V_u}{\beta T_u}\right)^2}}$$

$$= \frac{595}{\sqrt{1 + \left(\frac{71.0}{0.086 \times 47.8 \times 12}\right)^2}}$$

$$= 339 \text{ in.-kips}$$

While Eq. (5.41) indicates

$$V^*_c = \frac{V_c}{\sqrt{1 + \left(\frac{\beta T_u}{V_u}\right)^2}}$$

$$= \frac{102}{\sqrt{1 + \left(\frac{0.086 \times 47.8 \times 12}{71.0}\right)^2}}$$

$$= 83.8 \text{ kips}$$

The web steel required for torsion will be in the form of closed stirrups placed with $1\frac{1}{2}$ in. cover measured to the center of the steel, as shown in Fig. 5.24, giving $x_1 = 9$ in. and $y_1 = 27$ in. From Eq. (5.31):

$$\alpha_t = 0.66 + 0.33 \left(\frac{27}{9}\right)$$

$$= 1.65$$

but not to exceed 1.50, which controls in this case. The required cross sectional area of *one leg* of a torsion stirrup is found from Eq. (5.45):

$$A_t = \frac{(T_u - \phi T_c^*)s}{\alpha_t \phi f_y x_1 y_1}$$

$$= \frac{(47.8 \times 12 - 0.85 \times 339)s}{1.50 \times 0.80 \times 40 \times 9 \times 27}$$

$$= 0.0245s \text{ in.}^2$$

The maximum spacing of such stirrups is not to exceed the smaller of 12 in. or:

$$s_{max} = \frac{x_1 + y_1}{4}$$

$$= \frac{9 + 27}{4}$$

$$= 9 \text{ in.}$$

which controls here.

Next the required reinforcement for flexural shear will be found. Since $V_u = 71.0$ kips is less than $V_c^* = 83.8$ kips, only the minimum steel is needed for flexural shear. From Eq. (5.23)

$$A_v = \frac{50b_w s}{f_y}$$

$$= \frac{50 \times 12}{40,000}s$$

$$= 0.015s$$

The minimum required cross sectional area per vertical leg is therefore $A_v/2 = 0.0075s$. This minimum requirement is easily met by the stirrups provided for torsion.

No. 4 bars will be selected for the closed hoop stirrup reinforcement, the area of one vertical leg being 0.20 in.^{2} Setting this provided area equal to the requirement of $0.0245s$ indicates the required spacing is

$$\frac{0.20}{0.0245} = 8.16 \text{ in.}$$

A practical spacing of 8 in. will be selected.

The required longitudinal non-prestressed reinforcement is found from Eq. (5.34):

$$A_l = 2A_t \frac{x_1 + y_1}{s}$$

$$= 2 \times 0.0245(9 + 27)$$

$$= 1.62 \text{ in.}^2$$

This will be met by six No. 5 bars, arranged as shown in Fig. 5.24, which provide a total area of 1.84 in.^{2} The maximum spacing of 12 in. is very nearly met by the arrangement of 6 bars, allowing for placement clearances.

REFERENCES

5.1   ASCE–ACI Joint Committee 426, "The Shear Strength of Reinforced Concrete Members," Chs. 1–4, *J. Struct. Div., ASCE,* Vol. 99, No. ST6, June 1973, pp. 1091–1187.

5.2   MacGregor, J. G. and Hanson, J. M., "Proposed Changes in Shear Provisions for Reinforced and Prestressed Concrete Beams," *J. ACI,* Vol. 66, No. 4, April 1969, pp. 276–288.

5.3   MacGregor, J. G., Sozen, M. A., and Siess, C. P., "Strength and Behavior of Prestressed Concrete Beams with Web Reinforcement," Structural Research Series No. 201, University of Illinois, August 1960.

5.4   Sozen, M. A., Zwoyer, E. M., and Siess, C. P., *Strength in Shear of Beams without Web Reinforcement,* Bulletin No. 452, University of Illinois, Engineering Experimental Station, Urbana, 1959.

5.5   MacGregor, J. G., Sozen, M. A., and Siess, C. P., "Strength of Concrete Beams with Web Reinforcement," *J. ACI,* Vol. 62, No. 12, December 1965, pp. 1503–1519.

5.6   ACI Standard *Building Code Requirements for Reinforcement Concrete,* ACI 318–63, American Concrete Institute, Detroit, 1963, 143 pp.

5.7   ACI Committee Report *Commentary on Building Code Requirements for Reinforced Concrete,* ACI 318–63, American Concrete Institute Special Publication SP–10, 1965, 91 pp.

5.8   Zia, P. and McGee, W. D., "Torsion Design of Prestressed Concrete," *J. PCI,* Vol. 19, No. 2, March–April 1974, pp. 46–65.

5.9   Hsu, T. T. C., "Torsion of Structural Concrete—Uniformly Prestressed Members Without Web Reinforcement," *J. PCI,* Vol. 13, No. 2, April 1968, pp. 34–44.

5.10   McGee, W. D. and Zia, P., *Prestressed Concrete Members Under Torsion, Shear, and Bending,* Research Report, Department of Civil Engineering, North Carolina State University, Raleigh, N. C., July 1973, 212 pp.

5.11   Winter, G. and Nilson, A. H., *Design of Concrete Structures,* 8th Ed., McGraw-Hill., New York, 1972, 615 pp.

5.12   GangaRao, H. V. S. and Zia, P., Rectangular Prestressed Beams in Torsion and Bending, *J. Struct. Div., ASCE,* Vol. 99, No. STI, January 1973, pp. 183–198.

5.13   Henry, R. L. and Zia, P., "Prestressed Beams in Torsion, Bending, and Shear," *J. Struct. Div., ASCE,* Vol. 100, No. ST5, May 1974, pp. 933–952.

5.14   Mitchell, D. and Collins, M. P., "Detailing for Torsion," *J. ACI,* Vol. 73, No. 9, September 1976, pp. 506–511.

PROBLEMS

5.1 Establish the required spacing of No. 3 U stirrups at a beam cross section subject
to factored-load shear v_u of 35.55 kips and moment M_u of 474 ft-kips. Web width
$b_w = 5$ in., effective depth $d = 24$ in., and total depth $h = 30$ in. The concrete shear
contribution may be based on the approximate relationship of Eq. (5.17). Use $f_y =$
40,000 psi for stirrup steel, and take $f'_c = 5000$ psi.

5.2 The pretensioned beam shown in Fig. P5.2 is designed to carry a superimposed dead
load of 500 plf and live load of 900 plf in addition to its own weight of 300 plf on a
50 ft simple span. Ten 1/2 in. diameter strands having $f_{pu} = 270,000$ psi are used to
provide an effective prestress force P_e of 218 kips. The strands are positioned with
eccentricity 12.5 in. at midspan and deflected at the third points to zero eccentricity
at the supports. Normal density concrete is used, with $f'_c = 5000$ psi. (a) Prepare a
diagram showing the values of V_u, V_{ci}, and V_{cw} as a function of distance along the
span. (b) Superimpose on the same diagram the values obtained by the simplified
equation (5.17). (c) Based on the excess shears obtained in part (a) find the required
spacing of No. 3 vertical U stirrups along the span. Stirrups will have yield stress
$f_y = 40,000$ psi. For the section shown, $A_c = 288$ in.^{2}, $I_c = 28,700$ in.^{4}, $c_1 = 13.5$ in.,
$A_p = 1.45$ in.^{2}

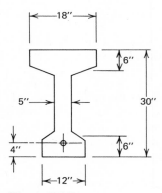

Figure P5.2

CHAPTER 6
PARTIAL LOSS OF PRESTRESS FORCE

6.1 INTRODUCTION

The lack of success experienced in early attempts to prestress concrete was due, in most cases, to failure to appreciate the significance of the inevitable partial loss of prestress force. Doubts relative to the permanence of prestressing persisted into the 1940s. It was only with the success of the dramatic bridges of Freyssinet, such as that shown in Fig. 1.1, that the engineering profession began to accept that prestress losses could be calculated and allowed for in the design, and that their effect could be minimized through careful selection of the proper materials.

As discussed in Art. 1.7, losses of prestressing force can be grouped into two categories: those that occur immediately during construction of the member, and those that occur over an extended period of time. The *prestress jacking force* P_j may be immediately reduced by losses due to friction, anchorage slip, and elastic shortening of the compressed concrete. In this book, the prestress force, after those losses, has been called the *initial prestress force* P_i. As time passes, the force gradually reduces further, rapidly at first but then more slowly, because of length changes resulting from shrinkage and creep of the concrete, and because of relaxation of the highly stressed steel. After a period of many months, or even years, further stress changes become insignificant, and a nearly constant prestress force is attained. This is defined as the *effective prestress force* P_e.

The jacking pressure, P_j, is the largest force that will act on the steel tendon during the normal life of a member, and the jacking operation may be thought of as a performance test of the tendon.

For pretensioned members, P_j never acts on the concrete, but only on the permanent anchorages of the casting bed. The tension is reduced along the length of the strand by friction at cable deflection points and beam end forms. In addition, the steel force is reduced, immediately upon transfer, by elastic shortening of the concrete.

For post-tensioned members, the jacking force is, in fact, actually applied to the concrete during stressing, but it exists at its full value only at the jacking

221

end of the member. Elsewhere it is diminished by frictional losses. Immediately upon transfer, the post-tensioning force is reduced by anchorage slip. Elastic shortening accounts for further losses.

It may be concluded that the jacking force P_j is of somewhat secondary interest to the designer, although the instantaneous losses must be estimated, in order to know what force to specify at the jacks.

Of primary interest are the initial prestress P_i immediately after transfer, and the final or effective prestress P_e after all losses have occurred. These were related in Art. 3.3 in terms of the effectiveness ratio, R, by the equation

$$P_e = RP_i \tag{3.1}$$

All time-dependent losses, specifically those due to creep, shrinkage, and relaxation, all of which affect both pretensioned and post-tensioned members, are included in the coefficient R.

The estimation of losses may be done on several different levels. In most cases, in practical design, detailed calculation of losses is not necessary. It is possible to adopt reasonably accurate lump sum approximations of prestress loss. Such expressions are included in the ACI Code Commentary, the AASHTO Interim Specification for Bridges (Ref. 6.1) and other documents, and are summarized in Art. 6.2.

For cases in which greater accuracy is required, it is necessary to estimate the separate losses, taking account of the special conditions of member geometry, material properties, and construction methods that apply. Methods for making more detailed estimates of this type are outlined in Arts. 6.3 through 6.10 of this chapter. The information on material properties found in Chapter 2 will be helpful.

Accuracy of loss estimation may be still further improved by accounting for the interdependence of time-dependent losses, using discrete time intervals for the calculations. A practical method for doing so is described in Art. 6.11.

For prestressed structures of major importance, or for which unusual methods or materials are to be used, it may be advisable to base loss calculations on specific information obtained for the materials to be used, methods of curing, ambient exposure conditions, and other such construction information. For structures such as precast or cast-in-place segmental cantilever bridges, for example, it may be appropriate and necessary to obtain this information, in order to maintain control of the geometry of the bridge during construction.

Actual losses, which may be greater or smaller than the estimated losses, have no effect on the ultimate flexural strength of a prestressed beam. However, losses do affect service load behavior such as deflection or camber, cracking load, and crack widths, as well as deformations during construction. The overestimation of prestress losses, which may seem to be on the conservative side, can actually be as detrimental as underestimation. Overestimation may lead the designer to specify too much prestress, resulting in excessive camber and troublesome horizontal movements in structures. It is necessary that the best possible appraisal of losses be made in each case, commensurate with the importance of the work at hand.

6.2   LUMP SUM ESTIMATES OF LOSSES

As early as 1958, ACI-ASCE Joint Committee 423 recognized the need for approximate expressions to be used to estimate prestress losses in cases of routine design. The following values were recommended in Ref. 6.2 for lump sum losses, including those due to elastic shortening, shrinkage, creep, and relaxation, but excluding losses due to friction and anchorage slip:

> For pretensioning: 35,000 psi (241 N/mm^2)
>
> For post-tensioning: 25,000 psi (172 N/mm^2)

Losses due to friction, assumed to apply only to post-tensioned members, were to be calculated separately, by the equations of Art. 6.6 of this chapter.

This basis for the calculation of losses was incorporated in the 1963 ACI Code and is also contained in the current ACI Code Commentary. Many thousands of prestressed concrete structures have been built from designs based on these losses, and where member sizes, materials, construction procedures, amount of prestress, and environmental conditions are not out of the ordinary, this approach has proved quite satisfactory.

The same lump sum values were included in the AASHO (AASHTO) Specifications then in effect for highway bridges. Nearly all prestressed concrete bridges now in service were designed using these values and, in general, the performance and serviceability of these bridges have been excellent.

These loss values are based on use of normal weight concrete, normal prestress levels, and average conditions of exposure.

Modifications are included in the 1975 AASHTO Interim Specification (Ref. 6.1), however, which provides that the lump sum losses of Table 6.1 be used for prestressed members or structures of usual design. The modifications reflect research that has shown that certain of the assumptions made in the original development of lump sum loss values could be improved. This is particularly true with respect to steel relaxation loss, but applies to some extent to shrinkage and concrete creep losses as well.

Table 6.1 includes concrete strengths of 4000 and 5000 psi. However, the lump sum loss values may be used for bridges with concrete strengths 500 psi above or below the values of 4000 and 5000 psi listed in the table headings. Thus the range of concrete strength covered may be considered to extend from 3500 to 5500 psi. The values were developed on the assumption that the full allowable compressive stress of concrete is required by stress conditions during the life of the member. For structures or elements where the concrete strength is determined on the basis of the nominal minimums in the specifications, and where

Table 6.1   AASHTO Lump Sum Losses (Ref. 6.6)

Type of Prestressing Steel	Total Loss	
	$f'_c = 4{,}000$ psi (27.58 N/mm^2)	$f'_c = 5{,}000$ psi (34.47 N/mm^2)
Pretensioning: Strand		45,000 psi (310.26 N/mm^2)
Post-tensioning:[a] Wire or strand	32,000 psi (220.63 N/mm^2)	33,000 psi (227.53 N/mm^2)
Bars	22,000 psi (151.68 N/mm^2)	23,000 psi (158.58 N/mm^2)

[a] Losses due to friction are excluded. Friction losses should be computed according to Art. 6.5.

full utilization of the allowable compressive stresses does not occur during the life of the structure, the lump sum loss values given will be somewhat conservative (Ref. 6.1).

The lump sum loss values presented in the ACI Code and the AASHTO Specifications include elastic shortening losses, as well as the time-dependent losses due to shrinkage, creep, and relaxation. Elastic shortening losses, easily calculated by the method given in Art. 6.5, must be deducted from the lump sum losses if the recommended values are used as the basis for determining the effectiveness ratio R of Eq. (3.1).

It is to be emphasized that the treatment of losses as lump sum quantities is recommended only for "standard" conditions. For members of unusual proportions, exceptionally long span, or of lightweight concrete, for example, a separate estimate of the individual losses should be made using the methods described in the following articles.

6.3   DETAILED ESTIMATION OF LOSSES

For cases where lump sum estimates of loss are inadequate, it is necessary to estimate each of the losses separately, using either assumed data or, for major works, using data developed for the particular job at hand. The separate contributions are then summed to obtain the total loss.

The detailed calculation of prestress losses due to the various contributing factors is complicated because the rate of loss due to one effect is continually

being altered by changes in stress due to other causes. For example, the relaxation of stress in the tendons is affected by length changes due to creep of
concrete. Rate of creep, in turn, is altered by change in tendon stress. It is
extremely difficult to separate the net amount of loss due to each factor under
different conditions of stress, environment, loading, and other uncertain factors.

The following six articles provide the theoretical background necessary to
determine the separate loss effects. The instantaneous losses due to anchorage
slip, elastic shortening of the concrete, and friction are discussed in Arts. 6.4,
6.5, and 6.6, respectively, while the time-dependent losses associated with concrete creep, concrete shrinkage, and steel relaxation are treated in Arts. 6.7,
6.8, and 6.9.

Time-dependent losses are treated here as if they occurred independently,
although certain arbitrary adjustments, based on more precise calculations,
are recommended to account for their interdependence. If greater refinement
is necessary, a step-by-step approach, such as that described in Art. 6.11, may
be used.

6.4 ANCHORAGE SLIP

In post-tensioned members, when the jacking force is released, the steel tension
is transferred to the concrete by special anchorages of one type or another (see
Appendix B). Inevitably there is a small amount of slip at the anchorages upon
transfer, as the wedges seat themselves into the tendons, or as the anchorage
hardware deforms. A similar situation is obtained in pretensioning, when the
prestressing force is transferred from the jacks to the permanent anchorages
of the casting bed through strandholding chucks. In either case, anchorage
slip loss may be compensated by overstressing, provided its magnitude is known.

Its magnitude will depend on the particular prestressing system or hardware
used. The wide variety of anchorages precludes any generalization. The most
reliable source of information may be the manufacturer of the hardware selected
or, better still, laboratory tests of the specific equipment.

Given the amount of slip characteristic of the specified hardware, the anchorage slip loss can easily be calculated from the expression

$$\Delta f_{anc} = \frac{\Delta l}{l} E_p \qquad (6.1)$$

where

Δl = amount of slip

l = tendon length

E_p = elastic modulus of the prestressing steel

Equation (6.1) is based on the assumption that the slip is uniformly distributed
over the length of the tendon. This will generally be so for pretensioning, and

will usually also apply for post-tensioning, particularly if the tendon is well lubricated and the duct is free of excessive wobble. However, if frictional losses are high, the anchorage slip loss may be concentrated mostly near the end of the tendon, requiring special consideration (Ref. 6.3).

The importance of anchorage slip depends on the length of the member or casting bed. For very short tendons, anchorage set will produce high slip losses. For long post-tensioned members, or for pretensioning using long casting beds, slip losses become insignificant.

6.5   ELASTIC SHORTENING OF THE CONCRETE

When prestress force is transferred to a member, there will be elastic shortening of the concrete as it is compressed. For pretensioned members, in which the tendon is bonded to the concrete at the time of transfer, the change in steel strain is the same as the concrete compressive strain at the level of the steel centroid, and losses may be calculated accordingly. For post-tensioned members in which all tendons are stressed at once, the elastic deformation of the concrete takes place when the jacking force is applied, and there is automatic compensation for elastic shortening loss, which therefore need not be calculated. This will not be the case, however, if several tendons are tensioned sequentially.

First considering pretensioned beams, the concrete compressive stress at the level of the steel centroid, when eccentric prestress plus self-weight are acting, immediately after transfer, is

$$f_{cs} = -\frac{P_i}{A_c}\left(1 + \frac{e^2}{r^2}\right) + \frac{M_o e}{I_c} \tag{6.2}$$

where

P_i = initial prestress force (see below)

A_c = area of concrete section

e = eccentricity of steel centroid with respect to concrete centroid

r = radius of gyration of concrete section

M_o = moment due to self-weight of the member

I_c = moment of inertia of concrete section

Introducing the modular ratio $n_p = E_p/E_c$, the loss of stress in the tendon due to elastic shortening of the concrete is

$$\Delta f_{el} = n f_{cs} \tag{6.3}$$

The value of E_c to be used in computing n_p must be that of the concrete at the time of tensioning.

Some comment is necessary regarding the value of prestress force P_i to be used in Eq. (6.2). P_i is the prestress force after the losses being calculated have occurred. It is usually adequate to estimate P_i as about 10 percent less than P_j. It may be corrected later, but such refinement is rarely justified.

The loss of prestress due to elastic shortening of pretensioned beams will vary along the length of the member, but is is generally sufficient to calculate losses at the section or sections of maximum moment.

For post-tensioned beams, if all the steel is tensioned at once there will be no loss due to elastic shortening. However, for the common case where multiple tendons are used, with the tendons tensioned in sequence, there will be losses. The first tendon anchored will lose stress when the second is tensioned, the first and second will lose stress when the third is tensioned, etc. The elastic shortening loss can be calculated for each tendon in turn, starting with the last tendon, for which there will be no loss. The procedure is time-consuming if there are more than a few tendons, however, and is further complicated by the uncertainty as to when the self-weight is to be introduced. In practical cases, it is adequate to calculate the loss of stress as equal to 1/2 the value obtained using Eqs. (6.2) and (6.3).

Note that for pretensioned beams the stress loss in the tendons can be different at different sections along the beam, depending on the concrete stress change at the sections under consideration. In contrast, for post-tensioned beams, the steel is not bonded at this stage and the elastic shortening loss will be the same everywhere along the tendon, neglecting friction effects. In applying Eq. (6.2) to post-tensioned beams, the average concrete stress f_{cs} between anchorages may be used.

For the increasingly common types of design in which pretensioning and post-tensioning are combined, the loss of stress in the pretensioned strands as post-tensioning is introduced must not be neglected.

6.6 LOSSES DUE TO FRICTION

For post-tensioned members, usually the tendons are anchored at one end and stretched with the jacks at the other end. As the steel slides through the duct, frictional resistance is developed, with the result that the tension at the anchored end is less than the tension at the jack. The total friction loss is the sum of the *wobble friction* due to unintentional misalignment, and the *curvature friction* due to the intentional curvature of the tendon. These effects will be considered separately first, then combined.

Wobble friction loss would be present even if a straight tendon were specified because, in actual cases, the duct cannot be perfectly straight. The amount of loss depends on the type of tendon and duct used, as well as on the care taken during construction. The incremental stress loss dP due to wobble friction, in a short length dx of tendon, can be expressed as

$$dP = KP \, dx \qquad\qquad \text{(a)}$$

where the prestress force P is a function of distance x along the span, and where K is a wobble friction coefficient, expressed in units of pounds loss per pound of prestress force per foot of duct. Typical ranges of values have been established by tests. The values given in Table 6.2 are those found in the ACI Code Commentary and in the PCI Recommendations (Ref. 6.5).

Table 6.2   Friction Coefficients for Post-Tensioning Tendons[a]

Type of Tendon	Wobble Coefficient K per Foot	Curvature Coefficient μ
Tendons in flexible metal sheathing		
Wire tendons	0.0010–0.0015	0.15–0.25
7-wire strand	0.0005–0.0020	0.15–0.25
High strength bars	0.0001–0.0006	0.08–0.30
Tendons in rigid metal duct		
7-wire strand	0.0002	0.15–0.25
Pregreased tendons		
Wire tendons and		
7-wire strand	0.0003–0.0020	0.05–0.15
Mastic-coated tendons		
Wire tendons and		
7-wire strand	0.0010–0.0020	0.05–0.15

[a] Adapted with permission of the American Concrete Institute from ACI Building Code 318–77.

The equation for those losses associated with the *intended* curvature of the tendon will be developed with reference to Fig. 6.1. Figure 6.1a shows a curved tendon subjected to a force P_s at the jacking end. The reduced force at a distance l is P_x. In most practical cases, the actual tendon curve can be replaced by a circular arc for calculating friction loss, as suggested in the sketch.

The loss of force in the short length defined by the angle change $d\alpha$ is dP, as shown in Fig. 6.1b. Here P is the value of the prestress force at the location considered. The equilibrium polygon of forces acting on the short segment, shown in Fig. 6.1c, indicates that the component of force normal to the tendon

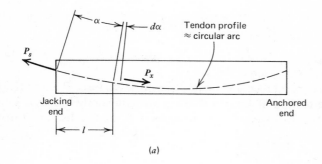

(a)

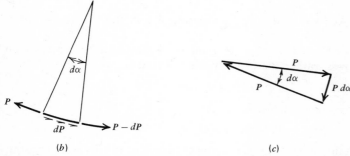

(b)   (c)

Figure 6.1 Loss of prestress due to curvature friction. (a) Tendon geometry. (b) Frictional effect in incremental length. (c) Force polygon.

is equal to $P \, d\alpha$. If the coefficient of friction between tendon and duct is μ, the incremental stress loss dP due to curvature friction is

$$dP = \mu P \, d\alpha \qquad \text{(b)}$$

Values of μ have been established by experiment also, and are given in Table 6.2.

Combining Eqs. (a) and (b), the sum of wobble and curvature losses in the incremental length is

$$dP = KP \, dx + \mu P \, d\alpha$$

The friction loss is conveniently expressed as the ratio dP/P at the location considered. If we do this, then integrate between appropriate limits,

$$\int_{P_x}^{P_s} \frac{dP}{P} = \int_0^l K \, dx + \int_0^\alpha \mu \, d\alpha$$

$$\ln \frac{P_s}{P_x} = Kl + \mu\alpha$$

This leads to the desired relation between the prestress force P_s at the jack and the reduced value P_x at a distance l from the jack:

$$P_s = P_x e^{Kl + \mu\alpha} \qquad (6.4)$$

where e is the base of natural logarithms.

Equation (6.4) was derived recognizing that the prestress force P is a function of distance along the tendon. If frictional losses are sufficiently low, it is satisfactory to calculate the losses based on the tension P_x at the distance l from the jack:

$$P_s - P_x = KP_x l + \mu P_x \alpha$$

from which

$$P_s = P_x(1 + Kl + \mu\alpha) \qquad (6.5)$$

According to the ACI Code, this approximation is acceptable if $(Kl + \mu\alpha) \leq 0.30$.

The relations established by Eqs. (6.4) and (6.5) may also be expressed in terms of *loss in stress*, rather than loss in force. From Eq. (6.4):

$$P_x = P_s e^{-(Kl + \mu\alpha)}$$

and the loss of force due to curvature friction is

$$\Delta P_{fr} = P_s - P_x = P_s(1 - e^{-(Kl + \mu\alpha)})$$

Dividing by the tendon area A_p gives the loss in stress due to curvature friction:

$$\Delta f_{fr} = f_s(1 - e^{-(Kl + \mu\alpha)}) \qquad (6.6)$$

where f_s is the tendon stress at the jack. Alternately, from the approximate relation given by Eq. (6.5)

$$\Delta P_{fr} = P_s - P_x = P_x(Kl + \mu\alpha)$$
$$\approx P_s(Kl + \mu\alpha)$$

or, in terms of stresses:

$$\Delta f_{fr} = f_s(Kl + \mu\alpha) \qquad (6.7)$$

For tendon profiles composed of a combination of straight and curved segments, the losses may be calculated progressively, starting at the jacking end. For each segment, the force at the end nearest the jack is equivalent to P_s, and is equal to the reduced force P_x calculated at the end of the preceding segment.

A geometric problem often encountered, in determining prestress losses due to friction, is to fit a circular arc through three known points, for example the tendon coordinates at the two ends and midpoint of a span, and to find the central angle α. If the curve is relatively flat, as is usually true, an approximate calculation will suffice. In Fig. 6.2, if the central angle is α, the slope at either end is $\alpha/2$. Then

$$\tan\frac{\alpha}{2} = \frac{m}{x/2} = \frac{2m}{x}$$

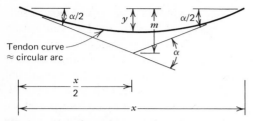

Figure 6.2 Approximate determination of central angle for a tendon.

The distance m is approximately equal to twice the sag y. Also, for small angles, the tangent of an angle is about equal to the angle itself, measured in radians. Consequently,

$$\frac{\alpha}{2} = \frac{4y}{x}.$$

and

$$\alpha = \frac{8y}{x} \text{ radians} \tag{6.8}$$

If the angle change is too large for these approximations to be acceptable, a graphical determination of α may prove convenient.

6.7 CREEP OF CONCRETE

Creep of concrete was discussed in Art. 2.11, in which it was pointed out that concrete subjected to a sustained compressive force will first deform elastically, then will continue to deform over an extended period of time. The *ultimate creep coefficient* was defined by Eq. (2.7):

$$C_u = \frac{\varepsilon_{cu}}{\varepsilon_{ci}} \tag{2.7}$$

where ε_{ci} is the initial elastic strain and ε_{cu} is the *additional* strain in the concrete, after a long period of time, due to creep. Typical values of C_u range from 2 to 4. An average value of 2.35 has been recommended where specific data are not available.

In prestressed concrete members, the compressive stress at the level of the steel is sustained in nature, and the resulting concrete creep is an important source of loss of prestress force.

The interdependence of time-dependent losses was mentioned in Art. 6.3. In prestressed members, the compressive force causing concrete creep is not constant, but diminishes with the passage of time, because of relaxation of the steel and shrinkage of the concrete, as well as because of length changes associated with creep itself. This interdependence may be accounted for by adopting a step-by-step approach in calculating time-dependent losses, in which the stresses acting at the beginning of a specific time interval, causing the next increment of deformation, or relaxation, reflect all losses that have occurred up to that time. The PCI Method of calculating losses, described in Art. 6.11, uses such an approach incorporating four time intervals. For present purposes, losses are treated individually, for better appreciation of the role played by each. Practical calculations are often carried out on this basis as well, with arbitrary adjustments to account for interdependence.

The concrete stress, which provides the basis for creep loss calculations, is that at the level of the steel centroid, when the eccentric prestress force plus all sustained loads are acting. Equation (6.2) may be used, except that the moment M_o should be replaced by the moment due to *all* dead loads, plus that due to any portion of the live load that may be considered sustained. To account, in an approximate way, for the gradual reduction of prestress force as creep, shrinkage, and relaxation occur, it is recommended that a value of $0.9P_i$ be substituted for P_i for creep calculations. For precast members that later receive a cast-in-place slab or topping, the moment of inertia of the composite section should be used in calculating the stresses caused by loads applied after the cast-in-place concrete has hardened.

After f_{cs} is found, the loss of steel stress associated with concrete creep can be determined from the expression

$$\Delta f_{cr} = C_u n f_{cs} \tag{6.9}$$

where $n = E_p/E_c$ as usual.

For pretensioned and grouted post-tensioned members, the loss of prestress due to creep will depend on the concrete stress at the particular section of interest. The loss due to creep will usually be calculated at the section or sections of maximum moment. For unbonded post-tensioned beams, however, the reduction in steel stress will be more or less uniform along the entire length of the tendon. In creep loss calculations for this case, an average value of f_{cs} between the anchorages may be used.

If, for improved accuracy of loss estimation, a step-by-step analysis of time-dependent losses is to be made, the creep-time relation given by Eq. (2.10) may be employed. For other than "standard" conditions of loading and humidity, Eqs. (2.11) and (2.12) may be introduced.

6.8 CONCRETE SHRINKAGE

Drying shrinkage of concrete permits a reduction of strain in the prestressing steel equal to the shrinkage strain of the concrete. The resulting steel stress reduction is an important component of the total prestress loss for all types of prestressed concrete beams.

Ultimate concrete strains resulting from drying shrinkage may fall in the range from about 500×10^{-6} to 1000×10^{-6}. It was recommended in Art. 2.11(b) that the ultimate shrinkage strain for moist-cured concrete be taken equal to 800×10^{-6} in the absence of specific data, and that for steam-cured concrete a value of 730×10^{-6} be adopted. The time rates of shrinkage for these two cases were given by Eqs. (2.13a) and (2.13b), and the correction factors for other than "standard" conditions of humidity were given by Eqs. (2.14a) and (2.14b).

Only the part of the shrinkage that occurs after transfer of prestressing force to the member need be considered. For pretensioned construction, transfer commonly takes place only 24 hours after pouring, and nearly all of the shrinkage takes place subsequent to that time. However, post-tensioned members are seldom stressed at an earlier age than seven days, and often much later than that. The curves of Fig. 2.15 indicate that about 10 to 15 percent of the ultimate shrinkage may already have occurred at seven days. If stressing is delayed until age 28 days, about 35 to 45 percent of the shrinkage would have occurred.

For total shrinkage loss calculation, or for calculations based on the step-by-step approach, the amount of shrinkage occurring in the specific time interval is the difference between the shrinkage at the beginning of the interval and that at the end. For such determinations, Fig. 2.15 and the equations of Art. 2.11 may be used.

Once the amount of concrete shrinkage strain has been determined, the loss of tensile stress in the steel resulting from that shrinkage can easily be found, by multiplying the strain by the modulus of elasticity of the prestressing steel:

$$\Delta f_{sh} = E_p \varepsilon_{sh} \qquad (6.10)$$

where ε_{sh} is the amount of shrinkage strain occurring during the period under consideration.

6.9 RELAXATION OF STEEL

Prestressing tendons are held stressed at essentially constant length during the lifetime of a member, although there is some reduction in length due to concrete creep and shrinkage. As was discussed in Art. 2.6, there will be a gradual reduction of stress in the steel under these conditions due to *relaxation*, even though the length is held nearly constant. The amount of relaxation depends on the intensity of steel stress as well as time and, for the usual stress-relieved steel, the ratio of reduced stress f_p to initial stress f_{pi} can be estimated using Eq. (2.1):

$$\frac{f_p}{f_{pi}} = 1 - \frac{\log t}{10} \left(\frac{f_{pi}}{f_{py}} - 0.55 \right) \qquad (2.1)$$

where f_{py} is the effective yield stress, t is the time in hours after stressing, $\log t$ is to the base 10, and f_{pi}/f_{py} is not less than 0.55. For present purposes, this relation may be restated in terms of the loss of steel stress resulting from relaxation:

$$\Delta f_{rel} = f_{pi} \frac{\log t}{10} \left(\frac{f_{pi}}{f_{py}} - 0.55 \right) \qquad (6.11)$$

For step-by-step loss analysis, the loss increment in any time interval resulting from steel relaxation may be based on Eq. (2.2), which may be restated as

$$\Delta f_{rel} = f_{pi} \left(\frac{\log t_n - \log t_r}{10} \right) \left(\frac{f_{pi}}{f_{py}} - 0.55 \right) \qquad (6.12)$$

in which t_n is the time at the end of the interval and t_r is the time at the beginning of the interval. The same equation is useful in estimating relaxation loss for pretensioned members, for which the relaxation loss that takes place before the concrete is cast should be subtracted from the total relaxation loss to obtain the change in steel stress as the beam ages from the initial to the final condition.

Relaxation loss will be diminished because of the effects of concrete shrinkage and creep, which reduce the stress intensity in the steel. This interaction may be accounted for in an approximate way be substituting $0.90f_{pi}$ for f_{pi} in the above equations.

Special low-relaxation steels are used with increasing frequency in current practice. For such steels, the loss of prestress due to relaxation may be estimated at about 25 percent of that predicted by Eq. (6.11) or Eq. (6.12).

6.10   EXAMPLE: CALCULATION OF SEPARATE LOSSES

The beam shown in Fig. 6.3 is to be post-tensioned using twelve 1/2 in. (12.7 mm) diameter Grade 270 strands in a single flexible duct. The total jacking tension of 300 kips (1334 kN) will be applied to all cables at once, when the concrete is at age 28 days. Jacking will be at one end only, and it has been determined by test that slip of 0.10 in. (2.54 mm) can be expected at the anchorage. Other design data are as follows:

$$A_p = 12 \times 0.153 = 1.836 \text{ in.}^2 \ (1185 \text{ mm}^2)$$
$$A_c = 524 \text{ in.}^2 \ (338 \times 10^3 \text{ mm}^2)$$
$$I_c = 22{,}040 \text{ in.}^4 \ (9.17 \times 10^9 \text{ mm}^4)$$
$$r^2 = 42.06 \text{ in.}^2 \ (27.1 \times 10^3 \text{ mm})$$
$$w_o = 546 \text{ plf} \ (7.97 \text{ kN/m})$$
$$E_c = 4{,}000{,}000 \text{ psi} \ (27.6 \times 10^3 \text{ kN/mm}^2)$$
$$E_p = 27{,}000{,}000 \text{ psi} \ (186 \times 10^3 \text{ kN/mm}^2)$$
$$f'_c = 5000 \text{ psi} \ (34 \text{ kN/mm}^2)$$
$$C_u = 2.35$$

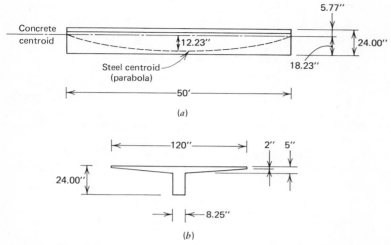

Figure 6.3 Beam for loss calculation example of Art. 6.10. (*a*) Profile. (*b*) Cross section.

Find the separate contributions to loss of prestress force at the end of a five year period, during which the sustained load may be taken equal to the self-weight of the beam.

The estimate of loss of prestress will be based on consideration of each of the separate contributions to total loss, as outlined in Arts 6.4 through 6.9. The interdependence of creep, shrinkage, and relaxation losses will be accounted for in an approximate way by a downward adjustment of the force for which these losses are calculated.

(A) ANCHORAGE SLIP LOSS

From Eq. (6.1), with estimated slip of 0.10 in.:

$$\Delta f_{anc} = \frac{0.10}{50 \times 12} \times 27 \times 10^6$$

$$= 4500 \text{ psi (31 N/mm)}$$

(B) ELASTIC SHORTENING LOSS

With all 12 strands tensioned at once with a single jack, the elastic shortening of the concrete will take place during the jacking operation, and will be fully compensated by additional extension of the jack. As a result, elastic shortening loss is

$$\Delta f_{el} = 0$$

(C) FRICTION LOSS

The actual parabolic tendon profile will be approximated as a circular arc for calculating friction losses. From Eq. (6.8) the central angle for the circular arc is about equal to

$$\alpha = \frac{8 \times 12.23}{50 \times 12} = 0.163 \text{ radian}$$

Consulting Table 6.2 for values of the wobble coefficient and the curvature friction coefficient for 7-wire strands in a flexible duct, representative values $K = 0.0010$ and $\mu = 0.20$ are selected. The parameter

$$(Kl + \mu\alpha) = (0.0010 \times 50 + 0.20 \times 0.163)$$
$$= 0.0826$$

is substantially less than 0.30, indicating that the approximate friction loss Eq. (6.7) may be used. The steel stress at the jack end of the tendon at this stage is equal to the jacking tension less the anchorage slip loss. With $f_{pj} = 300,000/1.836 = 163,000$ psi, the stress at the jack is

$$f_s = 163,000 - 4500 = 158,500 \text{ psi}$$

and, from Eq. (6.7),

$$\Delta f_{fr} = 158,500 \times 0.0826$$
$$= 13,100 \text{ psi } (90 \text{ N/mm}^2)$$

This results in an initial stress in the steel, after all instantaneous losses, but before the time-dependent losses, of

$$f_{pi} = f_{pj} - \Delta f_{anc} - \Delta f_{el} - \Delta f_{fr}$$
$$= 163,000 - 4500 - 0 - 13,100$$
$$= 145,400 \text{ psi } (1003 \text{ N/mm}^2)$$

corresponding to an initial prestress force of

$$P_i = 145,400 \times 1.836 \times \frac{1}{1000}$$

$$= 267 \text{ kips } (1188 \text{ kN})$$

(D) CREEP LOSS

The loss in tension due to concrete creep will be calculated at the maximum moment section at midspan, for the condition of prestress plus self-weight. In order to account, in an approximate way, for the gradual reduction of prestress force due to creep, shrinkage, and relaxation as creep goes on, the prestress force used in computation will be reduced to 0.9 P_i or 240 kips. The maximum moment produced by the beam weight is

$$M_o = \tfrac{1}{8} \times 546 \times 50^2 = 171,000 \text{ ft-lb}$$

and, from Eq. (6.2), the concrete stress at the level of the steel centroid is

$$f_{cs} = -\frac{240,000}{524}\left(1 + \frac{12.23^2}{42.06}\right) + \frac{171,000 \times 12 \times 12.23}{22,040}$$

$$= -948 \text{ psi}$$

Then from Eq. (6.9), with $n_p = E_p/E_c = 6.75$, the loss of stress in the steel resulting from concrete creep is

$$\Delta f_{cr} = 2.35 \times 6.75 \times 948$$
$$= 15,000 \text{ psi } (103 \text{ N/mm}^2)$$

(E) SHRINKAGE LOSS

Shrinkage loss calculation will be based on an assumed ultimate shrinkage strain for the concrete of 800×10^{-6}. The amount of shrinkage affecting the stress in the tendon is that which occurs after stressing and anchoring the steel at concrete age 28 days. From Fig. 2.15, it is seen that, for moist-cured concrete, 44 percent of the ultimate shrinkage could be expected to occur before that time. Consequently the remaining shrinkage is $800 \times 10^{-6} \times 0.56 = 448 \times 10^{-6}$, and from Eq. (6.10) the loss in steel stress associated with that strain reduction is

$$\Delta f_{sh} = 27 \times 10^{6} \times 448 \times 10^{-6}$$
$$= 12{,}100 \text{ psi (83 N/mm}^{2})$$

(F) RELAXATION LOSS

The gradual reduction of steel stress resulting from the combined effects of creep, shrinkage, and relaxation will be accounted for in determining relaxation loss by using a reduced value of prestress force of $0.9P_i$ in the calculation. The corresponding steel stress is $0.9 \times 145{,}000 = 131{,}000$ psi. Referring to Fig. 2.4, we see that the effective yield stress for Grade 270 strand is $f_{py} = 230{,}000$ psi. Then from Eq. (6.11), at time 5 years or 44,000 hours, the loss of stress in the steel due to relaxation is estimated to be

$$\Delta f_{rel} = 131{,}000 \times \frac{4.64}{10} \left(\frac{131}{230} - 0.55 \right)$$

$$= 1200 \text{ psi* (8 N/mm}^{2})$$

(G) SUMMARY AND COMPARISON WITH LUMP SUM ESTIMATES

The losses of prestress due to all causes are summarized in Table 6.3. The initial jacking stress f_{pj} of 163,000 psi is reduced by instantaneous losses due to slip, shortening, and friction, to an initial prestress f_{pi} of 145,400 psi. After a five-year period from the time of transfer, that initial tension is further reduced by creep, shrinkage, and relaxation effects to an effective prestress f_{pe} of 117,100 psi.

The losses are also expressed as a percentage of the initial stress f_{pi} in Table 6.3. It is seen that instantaneous losses total 12 percent, while time-dependent losses are 19 percent of f_{pi}. The effectiveness ratio R for the beam is $117{,}100/145{,}400 = 0.81$.

It is of interest to compare the results of the calculations with the lump sum estimates based on recommendations of ACI and AASHTO. For lump sum losses, including those due to elastic shortening, creep, shrinkage, and relaxation, for post-tensioned beams, the ACI Code Commentary gives a value of 25,000 psi, while the AASHTO lump sum losses from Table 6.1 are 33,000 psi. By the calculations just completed, the comparable figure is 28,300 psi. It may be concluded that, for the present case at least, use of either of the lump sum estimates would be satisfactory.

---

* It should be noted that the relaxation loss of this example is unusually low. This is a result of the low steel stress f_{pi}. The steel area for this beam was selected on the basis of strength requirements. The initial prestress of 300 kips was determined by deflection requirements and was less than the maximum allowable based on stress limits.

Table 6.3 Summary of Losses for Example of Art. 6.10

Source	Loss psi	Loss N/mm^2	Loss Percent of f_{pi}
Anchorage slip	4,500	31	3
Elastic shortening	0	0	0
Friction	13,100	90	9
Creep	15,000	103	10
Shrinkage	12,100	83	8
Relaxation	1,200	8	1

6.11 ESTIMATION OF LOSSES BY THE TIME STEP METHOD

The loss calculations of the preceding articles, and the example just presented, recognized the interdependence of creep, shrinkage, and relaxation losses in an approximate way, by an arbitrary reduction of 10 percent of the initial prestress force P_i to obtain the force for which creep and relaxation losses were calculated. For cases requiring greater accuracy, losses may be calculated for discrete time steps over the period of interest. The prestress force causing losses during any time step is taken equal to the value at the end of the preceding time step, accounting for losses due to all causes up to that time. Accuracy may be improved to any desired degree by reducing the length and increasing the number of time steps. Computer programs are available for such analysis (Ref. 6.4).

A step-by-step method has been developed by the PCI Committee on Prestress Losses that uses only a small number of time steps and, consequently, is well suited for use in calculations by slide rule or electronic calculator, as well as by computer (Ref. 6.5). The time interval for each step is increased with the age of the concrete. Four time steps are used as follows:

1. For pretensioned members: from the time of anchorage of the prestressing steel until the age of prestressing the concrete.
   For post-tensioned members: from the time when curing ends until the age of prestressing the concrete.
2. From the end of step (1) until age 30 days, or the time when a member is subjected to load in addition to its own weight.
3. From the end of step (2) until age 1 year.
4. From the end of step (3) until the end of service life.

The PCI method for determining losses due to the interrelated time-dependent effects will produce a more accurate estimate than the method suggested in Arts. 6.7, 6.8, and 6.9, and the accuracy may be still further improved, within the general format of the PCI method, by increasing the number of time steps. When significant changes in loading are expected, time intervals other than those recommended may be used. The cost of such refinement, of course, is additional computational effort. This may or may not be justified in a given case.

REFERENCES

6.1 *Interim Specifications—Bridges*—1975, AASHTO Subcommittee on Bridges and Structures, American Association State Highway and Transportation Officials, Washington, 1975, pp. 41–79.

6.2 "Tentative Recommendations for Prestressed Concrete," reported by ACI–ASCE Joint Committee, 423, *J. ACI*, Vol. 54, No. 7, January 1958, pp. 548–578.

6.3 Huang, T., "Anchorage Take-up Loss in Posttensioned Members," *J. PCI*, Vol. 14, No. 4, August 1969, pp. 30–35.

6.4 Sinno, R. and Furr, H. L., "Computer Program for Predicting Prestress Loss and Camber," *J. PCI*, Vol. 17, No. 5, September–October 1972, pp. 27–38.

6.5 "Recommendations for Estimating Prestress Losses," reported by PCI Committee on Prestress Losses, *J. PCI*, Vol. 20, No. 4, July–August 1975, pp. 43–75.

6.6 Discussion of Ref. 6.5, *J. PCI*, Vol. 21, No. 2, March–April 1976, pp. 108–126.

6.7 *PCI Design Handbook*, Prestressed Concrete Institute, Chicago, 1971, pp. 4.38–4.40, 5.57–6.61.

6.8 Tadros, M. K., Ghali, A., and Dilger, W. H., "Time-Dependent Prestress Loss and Deflection in Prestressed Concrete Members," *J. PCI*, Vol. 20, No. 3, May–June 1975, pp. 86–98.

PROBLEMS

6.1 List the sources of loss of prestress force that must be accounted for in the design of (a) pretensioned members and (b) post-tensioned members. Present your answer in tabular form, elaborating on a simple yes or no response where appropriate.

6.2 An alternate design has been prepared using the same member cross-section and prestressing strand described in the example of Art. 6.10. However, the alternate design will be pretensioned using straight cables at constant eccentricity $e = 8$ in. The jacking force is 300,000 lb as before. Compute all losses for the pretensioned beam and express as percentages of initial prestress P_i. High early strength concrete is used, with steam curing, and the prestress force will be transferred at 3 days for the pretensioned beam. Concrete design strength $f'_c = 5000$ psi as before. Compare the results of your calculations and those of the example beam with the values suggested for post-tensioned and pretensioned beams in the ACI Code Commentary. Discuss.

6.3 The beam shown in Fig. P6.3, of 70 ft span, is post-tensioned using eighteen $\frac{1}{2}$ in. diameter Grade 270 strands in a single tendon having a parabolic profile, with $e = 18$ in. at midspan and zero at the supports. (The curve may be approximated by

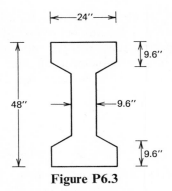

Figure P6.3

a circular arc for loss calculations.) The jacking force $P_j = 618$ kips. Calculate losses due to slip, elastic shortening, friction, creep, shrinkage, and relaxation. Use the methods of Arts. 6.3 to 6.10; the time-step approach of Art. 6.11 need not be employed here. Express your results in tabular form, as percentages of initial prestress P_i. Creep effects may be assumed to occur under the combination of prestress force plus self-weight. The beam is moist-cured and is prestressed when the concrete is at age 7 days. Anchorage slip $= 0.25$ in., coefficient of strand friction $= 0.20$, coefficient of wobble friction $= 0.0010$, creep coefficient $= 2.35$. Member properties are as follows: $A_c = 737$ in.^{2}, $I_c = 192,000$ in.^{4}, $c_1 = c_2 = 24$ in., $f'_c = 5000$ psi, $E_c = 4,000,000$ psi, $E_p = 27,000,000$ psi, and $w_c = 150$ pcf.

CHAPTER 7

COMPOSITE BEAMS

7.1 TYPES OF COMPOSITE CONSTRUCTION

The term composite construction, applied to prestressed concrete, usually refers to construction in which a precast concrete member acts in combination with cast-in-place concrete, poured at a later time and bonded to it. Often the precast element is a pretensioned slab or single- or double-tee beam. In such cases, a relatively thin topping slab is used, often unreinforced but sometimes containing wire mesh. Another frequently employed form of composite construction combines a pretensioned precast I beam with a cast-in-place reinforced concrete slab, to form a composite member having a bulb tee section. In either case, the cast-in-place slab meets functional requirements by providing a smooth, useful surface and, in addition, substantially stiffens and strengthens the precast unit. A pretensioned composite member may be further prestressed by post-tensioning after the slab has hardened.

Composite construction offers the advantages of precasting, including factory prefabrication of standardized sections, reuse of forms, long-line tensioning of strands, and excellent quality control. On the construction site, formwork and scaffolding are largely eliminated, permitting rapid field erection of the structure, with little interference to work or traffic below.

Composite construction may take many forms. The types of members most common to United States practice are shown in Fig. 7.1. In each case, the precast (*PC*) part of the section is shown shaded, while the cast-in-place (*CIP*) portion is left unshaded to differentiate the two.

The bridge girder section shown in Fig. 7.1a has been used extensively for short-to-medium-span highway bridges. The dimensions of the precast I sections have been standardized by AASHTO in six sizes, ranging in depth from 28 to 72 in. (Ref. 7.1 and Appendix A). The unsymmetrical I section is used in conjunction with a cast-in-place roadway slab, creating a bulb tee beam with a composite concrete centroid close to the underside of the slab.

The single-tee section beam shown in Fig. 7.1b is often used for medium- to long-span roof deck and floor systems, as in parking garages, for example. With the increasing use of partial prestressing, which avoids the need for large bottom flanges to resist heavy initial prestressing forces, such cross sections are found suitable for members of all types including bridges as well as buildings. They are normally placed side by side, with flange tips in contact. The

241

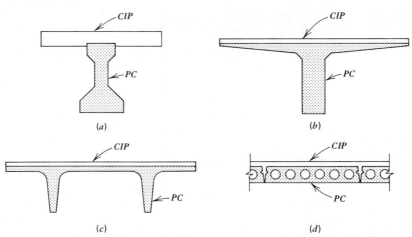

Figure 7.1 Typical composite sections. (*a*) AASHTO bridge girder. (*b*) Single-tee girder. (*c*) Double-tee beam. (*d*) Hollow-core slab.

thickness of the topping slab is typically 2 to 3 in. for buildings, but may be substantially deeper for bridges. The construction may include intermediate diaphragms, often prestressed laterally to insure that the entire assembly acts as a unit.

The double tee beam of Fig. 7.1*c* is typical of the production of numerous precasting plants. Such beams are widely used for short and medium spans, mostly for floors and roofs in buildings, and are often designed for composite action with a 2 in. topping slab. The same comments apply to the hollow-core precast deck planks shown in cross section in Fig. 7.1*d*.

The essential prerequisite for composite action is good bond between the precast concrete and the cast-in-place concrete. Flexural shear causes a tendency for horizontal slip along the plane between the two components. Considerable resistance to slip is provided by the natural adhesion and friction between the poured-in-place and the precast concrete. In many cases the top surface of the precast element is left rough, screeded but not troweled, to improve the transfer of shear by friction and mechanical interlock. For members with a broad surface of contact, such as in Figs. 7.1*b*, *c*, and *d*, no other provision is made for shear transfer, as a rule. For the more heavily loaded bridge girders of Fig. 7.1*a*, with a smaller contact interface, the web reinforcement of the precast beam is projected upward into the cast-in-place slab. This provides dowel action in resisting slip, and locks the two components together to insure the development of maximum frictional resistance.

In almost all cases, the quality of concrete specified and attained in the precast member is superior to that in the cast-in-place part of a composite section. Concrete cast under plant conditions, where quality control is easily maintained, is generally of strength from 4000 to 6000 psi. Concrete cast on the construction site is of more variable quality and lower strength, usually in the range from 3000 to 4000 psi. Such differences must be accounted for in design.

7.2 LOAD STAGES

A composite member must perform in a satisfactory way under any load or combination of loads that may act upon it during its useful life. The analysis and design of composite sections may require consideration of several, or all, of the following load stages:

1. Initial prestress P_i immediately after transfer.
2. Initial prestress P_i plus self-weight of the precast member.
3. Effective prestress P_e plus member self-weight.
4. Effective prestress P_e plus all noncomposite dead loads including the weight of the wet concrete slab.
5. Effective prestress P_e plus both noncomposite and composite dead loads plus service live loads.
6. Maximum overload.

Loads introduced before the cast-in-place concrete hardens cause stresses associated with bending of the precast section, about its own centroidal axis. Loads applied after the cast-in-place concrete hardens cause bending about the centroid of the composite member. Stresses already present in the precast part of the member are modified and, in addition, stresses are introduced in the newly placed concrete.

In some cases, it is economical to carry all superimposed loads by composite action. This can be done through the use of temporary shoring of the precast unit during the period when the slab is poured and is curing. When shores are removed, the weight of the slab, as well as all subsequently applied loads, cause bending about the composite centroid.

As a general rule, stresses resulting from load stages 1 through 5 may be found based on the assumption of elastic behavior, with section properties calculated for the noncomposite or composite beam, whichever is appropriate.

Tests have proved that when composite members are subject to overloads, the full strength of the combined section is developed, provided that effective shear transfer is maintained across the interface between components (Refs. 7.2 and 7.3). Both steel and concrete are normally stressed well into their inelastic ranges, and the consequences of strain discontinuities are minimal. The strength of composite members may be calculated as if the construction were homogeneous.

Normally the load stages that control the design of composite prestressed beams are stage 2, when limitations on tensile and compressive stresses at the top and bottom, respectively, of the precast unit must be satisfied, stage 5, when service load stress limits on compression at the top and tension at the bottom of the composite section must not be exceeded, and stage 6, when the member must develop adequate strength to resist overloads, developing a suitable margin of safety.

7.3 SECTION PROPERTIES AND ELASTIC FLEXURAL STRESSES

In calculating stresses in composite beams, it is necessary to differentiate between loads acting on the precast beam and those introduced after the cast-in-place part of the section is added, when full composite action can be developed. Stresses produced by bending of the composite member may be superimposed directly upon those already present in the precast portion. Clearly, bending is about a different centroid in each case, and two different sets of section properties must be used.

Notation is established by reference to Fig. 7.2, which shows a precast I section to which is added a cast-in-place slab. In referring to section properties, the subscripts p and c relate, respectively, to properties of the precast and composite sections. Similarly, dead loads affecting only the precast portion will be subscripted p, while those causing stresses associated with composite action will be subscripted c.

Elastic stresses acting on the member at any stage may be found by the methods of Ch. 3, using the appropriate section properties. It will be assumed that the member is uncracked at all stages of present interest.

The stresses at various load stages, for a typical composite beam, are shown in Fig. 7.3. Immediately after transfer, the initial prestress force P_i acts on the

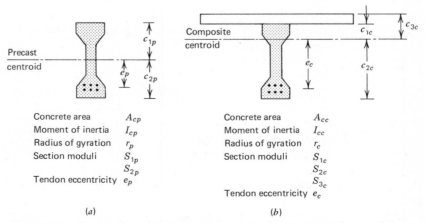

Figure 7.2 Properties of precast and composite cross sections. (*a*) Precast section. (*b*) Composite section.

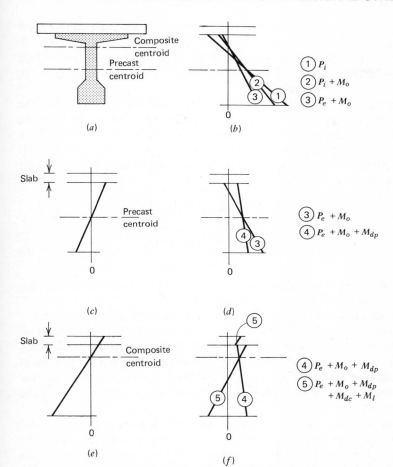

Figure 7.3   Elastic stresses in an uncracked composite beam.
(a) Cross section. (b) Prestress plus self-weight. (c) Increment
due to noncomposite loads. (d) Prestress plus noncomposite
loads. (e) Increment due to composite loads. (f) Prestress plus
noncomposite and composite loads.

member. Normally, the self-weight of the precast portion is immediately superimposed. The stresses at the top and bottom of the precast beam are given by
distribution (2) of Fig. 7.3b and are, respectively:

$$f_1 = -\frac{P_i}{A_{cp}}\left(1 - \frac{e_p c_{1p}}{r_p^2}\right) - \frac{M_o}{S_{1p}} \tag{7.1a}$$

$$f_2 = -\frac{P_i}{A_{cp}}\left(1 + \frac{e_p c_{2p}}{r_p^2}\right) + \frac{M_o}{S_{2p}} \tag{7.1b}$$

where M_o is the moment due to the self-weight of the precast member, and other terms are as previously defined.

It will be assumed that all time-dependent losses occur at this point, so that concrete stresses are gradually modified to those shown as distribution (3), when P_e acts, together with self-weight.

Usually the only important noncomposite dead load other than that of the precast beam itself is the weight of the wet concrete slab. This causes bending about the centroid of the precast unit, with stresses as shown in Fig. 7.3c. These stresses, when superimposed on those already present, produce distribution (4) of Fig. 7.3d. At this stage, the stresses at the top and bottom of the precast concrete beam are, respectively:

$$f_1 = -\frac{P_e}{A_{cp}}\left(1 - \frac{e_p c_{1p}}{r_p^2}\right) - \frac{M_o + M_{dp}}{S_{1p}} \tag{7.2a}$$

$$f_2 = -\frac{P_e}{A_{cp}}\left(1 + \frac{e_p c_{2p}}{r_p^2}\right) + \frac{M_o + M_{dp}}{S_{2p}} \tag{7.2b}$$

where M_{dp} is moment due to dead loads, exclusive of the member self-weight, that cause bending of the noncomposite section.

After the freshly poured concrete slab has hardened and acquired its strength, the effective centroid shifts upward to that of the composite section, and all loads applied subsequently cause bending about the composite centroid. These include dead loads applied after the slab has hardened, such as pavement surface, piping, and sidewalks for bridges, or finish floors, ceilings, and suspended utilities in the case of buildings. Live load almost always acts on the composite section only.

The incremental stresses due to composite loads, shown in Fig. 7.3e, are superimposed on prior stresses in the precast section to produce the stress distribution (5) shown in Fig. 7.3f. Note that, since there are no prior stresses in the slab (disregarding shrinkage effects), distribution (5) shows a stress discontinuity at the level of the interface between precast and cast-in-place components. The stresses in the precast concrete at stage (5) are given by the equations:

$$f_1 = -\frac{P_e}{A_{cp}}\left(1 - \frac{e_p c_{1p}}{r_p^2}\right) - \frac{M_o + M_{dp}}{S_{1p}} - \frac{M_{dc} + M_l}{S_{1c}} \tag{7.3a}$$

$$f_2 = -\frac{P_e}{A_{cp}}\left(1 + \frac{e_p c_{2p}}{r_p^2}\right) + \frac{M_o + M_{dp}}{S_{2p}} + \frac{M_{dc} + M_l}{S_{2c}} \tag{7.3b}$$

while those at the top and bottom of the slab are, respectively,

$$f_3 = -\frac{M_{dc} + M_l}{S_{3c}} \tag{7.3c}$$

$$f_4 = -\frac{M_{dc} + M_l}{S_{4c}} \tag{7.3d}$$

In these equations, M_{dc} is the moment caused by dead loads introduced after composite action is obtained, and M_l is the moment due to the superimposed live loads.

It has already been noted that the precast concrete is ordinarily of higher quality than the cast-in-place concrete, which must be placed and cured under field conditions. The elastic stresses in the composite beam will be affected by the difference in stiffness of the concretes. This difference may be accounted for in the calculations by making use of the transformed section concept, by means of which the cast-in-place concrete of lower grade may be transformed into a smaller equivalent amount of precast concrete of higher quality.

Figure 7.4a shows the actual composite cross section composed of two grades of concrete, while Fig. 7.4b shows the equivalent transformed homogeneous section. At any level of the cross section, a distance y above the centroidal axis, the strains must be the same in each. If f_c and f_{cp} are, respectively, the concrete stresses at the level y in the actual and equivalent sections, and if E_c and E_{cp} are, respectively, the elastic moduli of the two concretes then, since the strains are equal:

$$\frac{f_c}{E_c} = \frac{f_{cp}}{E_{cp}}$$

or

$$f_c = \frac{E_c}{E_{cp}} f_{cp} = n f_{cp}$$

where $n =$ the modular ratio of the two concretes, a number normally less than unity.

The equivalent section will provide the proper resistance if the differential compressive force is the same in either case, that is:

$$dC = f_c b \, dy = f_{cp} b_{tr} \, dy$$

substituting $n f_{cp}$ for f_c and cancelling like terms:

$$b_{tr} = nb \qquad (7.4)$$

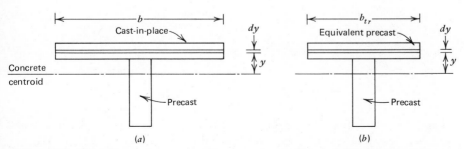

Figure 7.4   Transformed composite cross section. (a) Actual section. (b) Transformed section.

That is, a *reduced width* b_{tr}, based on the modular ratio n, is to be substituted for the actual width b in the calculation of section properties. After this substitution, the section properties may be found as if the beam were composed uniformly of the higher quality concrete.

EXAMPLE   Calculation of Elastic Flexural Stresses in Bridge Girder

A 3 ft depth AASHTO Type II girder, precast and pretensioned, will be used with a 5.75 in. × 96 in. cast-in-place slab to form a composite beam that will span 55 ft between simple supports. The cross section geometry is shown in Fig. 7.5a. The precast beam will

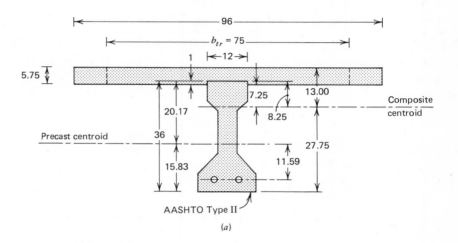

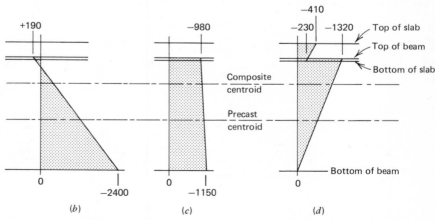

Figure 7.5 AASHTO bridge girder cross section and stress distributions. (a) Cross section. (b) $P_i + M_o$. (c) $P_e + M_o + M_{dp}$. (d) $P_e + M_o + M_{dp} + M_{dc} + M_l$.

be made using concrete with $f'_c = 5000$ psi and $E_c = 4.07 \times 10^6$ psi, while the slab concrete has $f'_c = 3000$ psi and $E_c = 3.15 \times 10^6$ psi. An initial prestress force of 468 kips, applied 11.59 in. below the centroid of the precast beam, is reduced by time-dependent losses to 398 kips. ($h = 914$ mm, slab $= 146 \times 2438$ mm, span 16.76 m, beam $f'_c = 34$ N/mm^2, slab $f'_c = 21$ N/mm^2, beam $E_c = 28.1 \times 10^3$ kN/mm^2, slab $E_c = 21.7$ kN/mm^2, $P_i = 2081$ kN, $P_e = 1770$ kN, and $e = 294$ mm.) The loads and corresponding moments to be carried are as follows:

Precast girder:	$w_o = 385$ plf	$M_o = 146$ ft-kips
	(5.6 kN/m)	(198 kN-m)
Concrete slab:	$w_{dp} = 575$ plf	$M_{dp} = 218$ ft-kips
	(8.4 kN/m)	(296 kN-m)
Superimposed dead load:	$w_{dc} = 185$ plf	$M_{dc} = 70$ ft-kips
	(2.7 kN/m)	(95 kN-m)
Live load:	$w_l = 1158$ plf	$M_l = 438$ ft-kips
	(16.9 kN/m)	(594 kN-m)

Find the flexural stresses in the beam corresponding to the following load combinations: (a) initial prestress plus self-weight of the precast beam, (b) effective prestress plus all noncomposite dead loads, and (c) effective prestress plus full service loads.

The properties of the AASHTO Type II precast beam are available from Appendix A and are summarized in Table 7.1. The girder self-weight is immediately superimposed when the initial prestress force is applied to the precast girder, and stresses in the concrete

Table 7.1 Summary of Section Properties for AASHTO Bridge Girder Example

Precast Beam	Composite Beam
$A_{cp} = 369$ in.^{2} (238×10^3 mm^2)	$A_{cc} = 799$ in.^{2} (515×10^3 mm^2)
$c_{1p} = 20.17$ in. (512 mm)	$c_{1c} = 8.25$ in. (210 mm)
$c_{2p} = 15.83$ in. (402 mm)	$c_{2c} = 27.75$ in. (705 mm)
$I_{cp} = 50{,}980$ in.^{4} (21.2×10^9 mm^4)	$c_{3c} = 13.00$ in. (330 mm)
$r_p^2 = 138$ in.^{2} (89.0×10^3 mm^2)	$c_{4c} = 7.25$ in. (184 mm)
$s_{1p} = 2528$ in.^{3} (41.4×10^6 mm^3)	$I_{cc} = 149{,}000$ in.^{4} (62.0×10^9 mm^4)
$s_{2p} = 3220$ in.^{3} (52.8×10^6 mm^3)	$r_c^2 = 162$ in.^{2} (105×10^3 mm^2)
	$S_{1c} = 18{,}000$ in.^{3} (295×10^6 mm^3)
	$S_{2c} = 5300$ in.^{3} (87×10^6 mm^3)
	$S_{3c} = 11{,}400$ in.^{3} (187×10^6 mm^3)
	$S_{4c} = 20{,}550$ in.^{3} (337×10^6 mm^3)

at the top and bottom of the section may be found using Eqs. (7.1a) and (7.1b):

$$f_1 = -\frac{P_i}{A_{cp}}\left(1 - \frac{e_p c_{1p}}{r_p^2}\right) - \frac{M_o}{S_{1p}}$$

$$= -\frac{468,000}{369}\left(1 - \frac{11.59 \times 20.17}{138}\right) - \frac{146,000 \times 12}{2528}$$

$$= +190 \text{ psi } (+1.3 \text{ N/mm}^2)$$

$$f_2 = -\frac{P_i}{A_{cp}}\left(1 + \frac{e_p c_{2p}}{r_p^2}\right) + \frac{M_o}{S_{2p}}$$

$$= -\frac{468,000}{369}\left(1 + \frac{11.59 \times 15.83}{138}\right) + \frac{146,000 \times 12}{3220}$$

$$= -2400 \text{ psi } (-16.5 \text{ N/mm}^2)$$

as shown in Fig. 7.5b.

The freshly poured concrete slab causes stresses in the precast section due to the additional noncomposite moment of 218 ft-kips. From Eqs. (7.2a) and (7.2b):

$$f_1 = -\frac{P_e}{A_{cp}}\left(1 - \frac{e_p c_{1p}}{r_p^2}\right) - \frac{M_o + M_{do}}{S_{1p}}$$

$$= -\frac{398,000}{369}\left(1 - \frac{11.59 \times 20.17}{138}\right) - \frac{(146 + 218) \times 12,000}{2528}$$

$$= -980 \text{ psi } (-6.8 \text{ N/mm}^2)$$

$$f_2 = -\frac{P_e}{A_{cp}}\left(1 + \frac{e_p c_{2p}}{r_p^2}\right) + \frac{M_o + M_{do}}{S_{2p}}$$

$$= -\frac{398,000}{369}\left(1 + \frac{11.59 \times 15.83}{138}\right) + \frac{(146 + 218) \times 12,000}{3220}$$

$$= -1150 \text{ psi } (-7.9 \text{ N/mm}^2)$$

The properties of the composite cross section must now be found. With modular ratio $n = 3.15/4.07 = 0.775$, the transformed width of the compression flange is $b_{tr} = 0.775 \times 96 = 75$ in. as shown in Fig. 7.5a, providing a compression flange area of 430 in.^{2} If one takes moments of areas about the top face of the slab to locate the composite centroid:

$$c_{3c} = \frac{369 \times 24.92 + 430 \times 2.87}{369 + 430} = 13.00 \text{ in.}$$

Accordingly, the distances c_{1c} and c_{2c} from the composite centroid to the top and bottom faces of the precast section are, respectively, 8.25 and 27.75 in., and the distance c_{4c} to the bottom of the slab is 7.25 in., as shown in Fig. 7.5a.

The moment of inertia of the transformed slab concrete about its own centroidal axis is

$$I_{slab} = \frac{1}{12} \times 75 \times 5.75^3 = 1190 \text{ in.}^4$$

and, making use of the transfer axis theorem, the moment of inertia of the composite section about its own axis is

$$I_{cc} = 50980 + 369(27.75 - 15.83)^2 + 1190 + 430(13.00 - 2.87)^2$$
$$= 149,000 \text{ in.}^4$$

The section moduli to the top and bottom of the precast section and to the top and bottom of the slab are, respectively:

$$S_{1c} = \frac{149,000}{8.25} = 18,000 \text{ in.}^3$$

$$S_{2c} = \frac{149,000}{27.75} = 5300 \text{ in.}^3$$

$$S_{3c} = \frac{149,000}{13.00} = 11,400 \text{ in.}^3$$

$$S_{4c} = \frac{149,000}{7.25} = 20,550 \text{ in.}^3$$

All section properties for the composite section are summarized in Table 7.1.

The incremental stresses applied at the top and bottom of the precast member as composite dead and live loads are introduced are

$$f_1 = -\frac{(70 + 438)12,000}{18,000} = -340 \text{ psi} (-2.3 \text{ N/mm}^2)$$

$$f_2 = +\frac{(70 + 438)12,000}{5300} = +1150 \text{ psi} (+7.9 \text{ N/mm}^2)$$

These stresses associated with composite action are superimposed on the stresses already present because of the bending of the noncomposite section, Fig. 7.5c, to obtain the total service load stresses

$$f_1 = -980 - 340 = -1320 \text{ psi} (-9.1 \text{ N/mm}^2)$$
$$f_2 = -1150 + 1150 = 0$$

at the top and bottom faces, respectively, as shown in Fig. 7.5d. The stresses at the top and bottom faces of the concrete slab may found similarly, except that the stresses found for the transformed slab area must be transformed back, in turn, to stresses acting on the actual concrete, multiplying by the modular ratio n. Based on Eqs. (7.3c) and (7.3d) these stresses are:

$$f_3 = -\frac{(70 + 438)12,000}{11,400} \times 0.775 = -410 \text{ psi} (-2.8 \text{ N/mm}^2)$$

$$f_4 = -\frac{(70 + 438)12,000}{20,550} \times 0.775 = -230 \text{ psi} (-1.6 \text{ N/mm}^2)$$

The final stress distribution for the composite section at full service load is as shown by Fig. 7.5d.

7.4 FLEXURAL STRENGTH

If proper provision is made for the transfer of horizontal shear forces across the interface between the components of a composite member, then the entire cross section can be considered effective in the calculation of ultimate flexural strength.

At large compressive strains, the difference in elastic moduli of the cast-in-place and precast concrete, which led to use of a transformed compressive flange width in elastic calculations, has no meaning and, consequently, the calculations should be based on the full effective flange width. Furthermore, the relatively small strain discontinuity at the interface between precast and cast-in-place concrete, resulting from prior bending of the noncomposite precast section, may be ignored without serious consequences at this stage. However, the differences in concrete compressive stress at a given strain in the two materials will produce a discontinuity in concrete stress at the interface, as illustrated by Fig. 7.6.

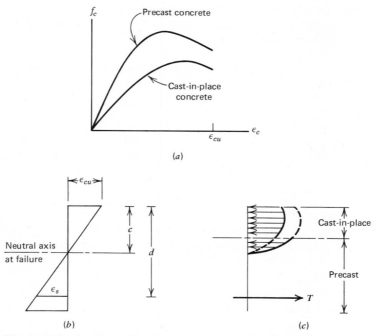

Figure 7.6 Strain and stress distributions for a composite section at failure load. (*a*) Comparative stress-strain curves. (*b*) Strains at failure. (*c*) Stresses at failure.

Figure 7.6a shows compressive stress–strain curves typical of the precast and cast-in-place concrete. The distribution of strain in the concrete at incipient failure is represented in Fig. 7.6b. The stress distributions shown in Fig. 7.6c are obtained from the respective stress–strain curves, the curve of higher stress applying below the interface, and the curve of lower stress applying above the interface.

To account for such a stress distribution in design would result in complicated expressions for failure moment. It is unnecessary to do so in most cases, because for the tee section the ultimate neutral axis is usually quite high in the section and often, in fact, is above the interface level. In addition, the resisting moment is governed by the steel and not the concrete strength. Thus, in most practical cases, the strength calculations may be based on a homogeneous section composed of the weaker, cast-in-place, concrete.

Calculations should be based on an effective flange width, as usual for tee sections. The ACI recommendations given in Art. 3.7 for monolithic beams may be used for composite members as well. In applying the criteria to sections such as shown in Figs. 7.1b or 7.1c, the average thickness of the combined cast-in-place and precast flanges should be used.

EXAMPLE   Ultimate Flexural Strength of Composite Bridge Girder

Find the ultimate flexural strength of the 36 in. AASHTO Type II bridge girder, with cast-in-place composite slab, studied in the preceding example and shown in cross section in Fig. 7.5a. The prestressing steel consists of two 28 wire tendons having a total cross section of 2.75 in.^{2} The ultimate strength of the steel is $f_{pu} = 250,000$ psi. ($A_p = 1774$ mm^2, $f_{pu} = 1723$ N/mm^2, and $h = 914$ mm.)

The ultimate flexural strength will be determined based on the ACI approximate expression for stress in the steel at failure.

First the effective compressive flange width will be determined, using the ACI criteria described in Art. 3.7:

$$b \leq \tfrac{1}{4} \times 55 \times 12 = 165 \text{ in.}$$

$$b \leq (16 \times 5.75 + 12) = 104 \text{ in.}$$

$$b \leq 96 \text{ in. (controls)}$$

The steel ratio is

$$\rho_p = \frac{A_p}{bd} = \frac{2.75}{96 \times 36.51} = 0.00078$$

The steel stress at failure will be found based on the approximate relations contained in the ACI Code. From Eq. (3.20) the failure stress is calculated to be

$$f_{ps} = f_{pu} \left(1 - 0.5\rho_p \frac{f_{pu}}{f'_c} \right)$$

$$= 250(1 - 0.5 \times 0.00078 \times 250/3)$$

$$= 240 \text{ ksi } (1655 \text{ N/mm}^2)$$

However, according to the Code, the failure stress is not to exceed the yield stress f_{py}, which is 212 ksi for Grade 250 strand, nor is it to exceed the stress $f_{pe} + 60$ ksi, which in the present case is $398/2.75 + 60 = 205$ ksi. The last limit is seen to control here, and the stress at failure will be assumed to be 205 ksi (1414 N/mm²).

The flange thickness of 5.75 in. is greater than the Code criterion

$$1.4 d\rho_p \frac{f_{ps}}{f'_c} = 1.4 \times 36.51 \times 0.00078 \times \frac{205}{3}$$

$$= 2.72 \text{ in.}$$

indicating that the neutral axis will be in the cast-in-place flange. Consequently the beam may be treated as a rectangular beam of width 96 in. in calculating flexural strength. By Eq. (3.18),

$$a = \frac{A_p f_{ps}}{0.85 f'_c b}$$

$$= \frac{2.75 \times 205}{0.85 \times 3 \times 96} = 2.30 \text{ in.}$$

and from Eq. (3.19), the nominal strength is

$$M_n = A_p f_{ps} \left(d - \frac{a}{2} \right)$$

$$= 2.75 \times 205(36.51 - 1.15)/12$$

$$= 1661 \text{ ft-kips (2252 kN-m)}$$

corresponding to a design strength $\phi M_n = 0.90 \times 1661 = 1495$ ft-kips (2027 kN-m). This value will be compared with the required strength found by applying the usual ACI over-load factors to dead and live loads:

$$M_u = 1.4(146 + 218 + 70) + 1.7(438)$$

$$= 1353 \text{ ft-kips (1835 kN-m)}$$

confirming that adequate strength is available should the member be overloaded.

7.5 HORIZONTAL SHEAR TRANSFER

As flexural loading is applied to a composite prestressed beam such as that shown in Fig. 7.7a, there is a tendency for the cast-in-place slab to slip horizontally, the bottom face of the slab tending to move outward with respect to the top face of the precast web, which tends to displace inward. If this slip is not prevented, the flange and the web will act as two separate beams, each resisting its portion of the load independently by bending about its own centroidal axis, as in Fig. 7.7b. The development of full composite action depends on the prevention of slip.

To prevent slip, there must be a means for transferring shear forces across the interface between the two components of the composite member. The

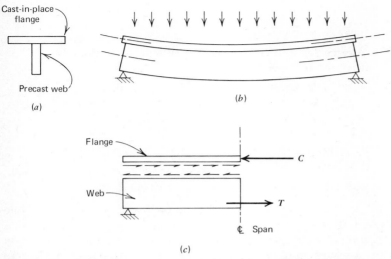

Figure 7.7 Composite action in tee-beam. (a) Section. (b) Non-composite behavior. (c) Shear stresses on interface.

shear forces produced by normal bending loads act inward on the slab, toward the section of maximum moment, and outward on the web, as shown in Fig. 7.7c.

Shear resistance along the interface may be provided by the natural adhesion and friction between the cast-in-place and the precast concrete. It will be enhanced if the top of the precast unit is deliberately roughened, rather than troweled smooth. This is usually done, and for composite beams having a broad contact surface, such as those of Figs. 7.1b, c, and d, no other provision need be made for transfer of shear force. Tests have confirmed that full composite behavior is assured up to the flexural failure load in members of this type.

For more heavily loaded beams having a smaller contact interface, such as that of Fig. 7.1a, vertical stirrups placed in the beam web to resist diagonal tensile stresses are usually extended upward, and anchored in the cast-in-place slab. This not only provides slip resistance through dowel action, but also improves frictional resistance by holding the two components in intimate contact. In addition, a roughened surface is usually specified. In special cases, shear keys may be formed in the top of the web, projecting upward into the flange, although these are actually ineffective until some slip occurs.

For an elastic uncracked beam, the intensity of the horizontal shearing stress due to bending can be calculated from the familiar expression

$$v_h = \frac{VQ}{Ib_v} \qquad (7.5a)$$

where

v_h = shear stress intensity, psi

V = external shear force at the section due to the composite dead and live loads, lb

Q = static moment about the centroidal axis of the entire section of the compression area of the cross section, from the horizontal plane considered to the extreme compression face, in.^{3}

I = moment of inertia of the entire section about its own centroidal axis, in.^{4}

b_v = width of the shear plane under investigation, in.

While Eq. (7.5a) was used to calculate the interface shearing stress at failure in early research, (Refs. 7.3 and 7.4), it was recognized that it does not give a true representation of stresses because the influence of cracking is ignored and because of the assumption of elastic concrete response. An equally valid, and simpler, basis for comparison is provided by calculating the nominal shear stress intensity at failure, defined by the equation

$$v_h = \frac{V}{b_v d} \tag{7.5b}$$

where d is the distance from the extreme compression face of the member to the centroid of the prestressing steel, for the entire composite section. Present design procedures are based on nominal shear stress limits, calculated by Eq. (7.5b), determined by test.

According to ACI Code, full transfer of horizontal shear forces may be assumed when all of the following are satisfied:

1. Contact surfaces are clean, free of laitance, and intentionally roughened to a full amplitude of approximately 1/4 in.
2. At least minimum ties are provided.
3. Web members are designed to resist the total vertical shear.
4. All shear reinforcement is fully anchored into all interconnecting elements.

In these provisions, minimum tie requirements are those established for diagonal tension by Eqs. (5.23) and (5.24). The spacing of ties must not exceed four times the least dimension of the supported element (i.e., the slab thickness) nor 24 in. Ties for horizontal shear may consist of single bars or wire, multiple leg stirrups, or the vertical legs of welded wire fabric. In all cases suitable anchorage is to be provided.

If all of the requirements above are not met, then the adequacy of the member to transfer horizontal forces must be checked based on the relation

$$V_u \leq \phi V_{nh} = \phi(v_{nh} b_v d) \tag{7.6}$$

where V_u is the shear force at factored loads, V_{nh} is the nominal shear strength, and the strength reduction factor $\phi = 0.85$. According to ACI Code, the following maximum values of v_{nh} are to be applied:

1. When ties are not provided, but the contact surfaces are clean, free of laitance, and intentionally roughened, $v_{nh} = 80$ psi.
2. When minimum tie requirements are met, and the contact surfaces are clean and free of laitance, but not intentionally roughened, $v_{nh} = 80$ psi.
3. When minimum tie requirements are met and the contact surfaces are clean, free of laitance, and intentionally roughened, $v_{nh} = 350$ psi.

Minimum tie requirements and intentional roughness are as previously stated.

An alternative approach to designing for horizontal shear, also permitted by Code, is to provide for transfer of the maximum compression or tension force that must act on either component of the composite section at flexural failure. With reference to Fig. 7.7c, the total flexural compression C or tension T may be easily determined. The maximum shear force that can be transferred between the sections of maximum and zero moment can be calculated on the basis of the shear-friction theory of Art. 12.4 (Ref. 7.5), and is dependent on the number and yield strength of the stirrups crossing the interface as well as upon the surface roughness. This approach is based on the acceptance of slight movement along the interface at severe overloads, such that the elastic distribution of horizontal shear stress becomes irrelevant. This alternative analysis is specifically required when the calculated value of V_u exceeds $\phi(350b_v d)$.

EXAMPLE   Investigation of Horizontal Shear Transfer

The AASHTO Type II girder with cast-in-place slab studied in the preceding examples contains web reinforcement consisting of No. 4 U stirrups that are extended upward into the slab and anchored by a standard 90 degree bend. The proposed spacing of Grade 60 stirrups varies from 5 in. (127 mm) on centers at the supports to a maximum of 21 in. (533 mm) on centers through the central part of the span. A total of 29 stirrups is provided in each half of the span. The top surface of the precast beam is screeded such that it meets Code requirements for "intentional roughening," with approximately 0.25 in. (6.35 mm) full amplitude. Determine if the shear transfer mechanism provided is adequate.

The factored load is computed from actual dead load and service live loads by the usual ACI procedures:

$$w_u = (385 + 575 + 185)1.4 + 1185 \times 1.7$$
$$= 3618 \text{ plf (53 kN/m)}$$

corresponding to a shear of

$$V_u = 3618 \times 55/2 = 99,500 \text{ lb (443 kN)}$$

For the composite beam, the effective depth to the steel centroid is 36.51 in. and the width of the shear interface at the top of the precast member is 12 in.

According to the Code, for roughened surface and ties, the design shear strength may be taken equal to $\phi V_{nh} = 0.85 \times 350 \times 12 \times 36.51 = 130$ kips, well above the value of $V_u = 99.5$ kips. The maximum spacing of the ties must not exceed four times the slab thickness, nor 24 in., according to the Code. The proposed maximum spacing of 21 in. will satisfy both criteria.

For comparison, the design will be checked using the shear-friction theory. The total force to be transferred, in order to develop the flexural capacity of the member, is easily found, based on the steel stress at ultimate load of 205 ksi (see the Example in Art. 7.4). For the prestressing steel of area 2.75 in.^{2} this corresponds to a tensile (or compressive) thrust of

$$T = C = 2.75 \times 205,000 = 564,000 \text{ lb (2509 kN)}$$

With a friction factor between cast-in-place and precast concrete of 1.0, according to the Code, the required steel area crossing the interface is found from Eq. (12.4) to be

$$A_{vf} = \frac{V_u}{\phi f_y \mu}$$

$$= \frac{564,000}{0.85 \times 60,000 \times 1.0} = 11.06 \text{ in.}^2 \text{ (7136 mm}^2\text{)}$$

The proposed total of 29 stirrups, each of area 0.40 in.^{2}, provides

$$A_v = 29 \times 0.40 = 11.60 \text{ (7484 mm}^2\text{)}$$

thus meeting requirements according to the shear-friction theory.

7.6 SHEAR AND DIAGONAL TENSION

There are no special problems associated with the design of composite pre-stressed beams to resist shear and diagonal tension. In general, the concepts and design specifications of Ch. 5 apply to composite members without change. Because shear design is based on conditions in the member at factored loads, that is, at incipient failure, it is not relevant whether the loads are applied to the precast section alone or to the composite member.

The entire composite member way be assumed to resist vertical shear, as-suming it to behave as a monolithically-cast member of the same cross-sectional shape. The calculation of V_c may usually be based upon the strength of the concrete in the precast part of composite members (normally of the higher quality) because most of the shear resistance is provided by the precast web rather than by the cast-in-place flange.

As usual, the nominal shear stress is computed on the basis of the web width. For I sections such as that of Fig. 7.1a, it is appropriate and conservative to use the narrowest width of the web, disregarding the top flange of the precast section. For sections having a tapered web, such as Fig. 7.1c, it is acceptable to base the calculations on the average width of the stems.

Web reinforcement is normally not necessary or provided for slab units such as Fig. 7.1d, or for double tees (actually ribbed slab units) such as Fig. 7.1c. For other cases, such as single tees, Fig. 7.1b, and I-sections (Fig. 7.1a) stirrups are provided. The stirrups are carried up into the slab and suitably anchored

with a 90 degree bend or the equivalent. Such web steel serves several purposes. It reinforces against failure due to diagonal tensile stress, it provides
against failure by slip between the components along the interface and, in
addition, it prevents upward buckling of the flange of the girder because of
longitudinal compression caused by bending.

REFERENCES

7.1 AASHTO, *Specifications for Highway Bridges*, 11th Ed., American Association of
State Highway and Transportation Officials, Washington, D.C., 1973, 469 pp.

7.2 Hanson, N. W., "Precast-Prestressed Concrete Bridges: (2) Horizontal Shear Connections," *J. Res. and Dev. Lab.*, Portland Cement Association, Vol. 2, No. 2, May
1960, pp. 38–58.

7.3 Saemann, J. C. and Washa, G. W., "Horizontal Shear Connections Between Precast
Beams and Cast-in-Place Slabs," *J. ACI*, Vol. 61, No. 11, November 1964, pp. 1383–
1409.

7.4 ACI–ASCE Committee 333, "Tentative Recommendations for the Design of Composite Beams and Girders for Buildings," *J. ACI*, Vol. 57, No. 6, December 1960,
pp. 609–628.

7.5 Mast, R. F., "Auxiliary Reinforcement in Concrete Connections," *J. Struct. Div.*
ASCE, Vol. 94, No. ST6, June 1968, pp. 1485–1504.

7.6 Mattock, A. H. and Kaar, P. H., "Precast Prestressed Concrete Bridges: (4) Shear
Tests of Continuous Girders," *J., Res. and Dev. Lab.*, Portland Cement Association,
Vol. 3, No. 1, January 1961, pp. 19–46.

PROBLEMS

7.1 The uniformly loaded 50 ft span composite T beam of Fig. P7.1 incorporates a cast-
in-place slab with $f'_c = 3000$ psi. The total steel area $A_p = 1.73$ in.^{2}, and separate
calculations indicate that the steel stress at failure is $f_{ps} = 230,000$ psi. Determine
the number and spacing of No. 4 U stirrups of strength $f_y = 50,000$ psi, to insure
composite action through shear transfer across the interface between components.
The top face of the precast T section is left intentionally rough.

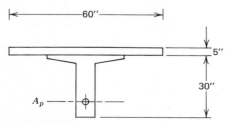

Figure P7.1

7.2 A parking deck structure is planned, composed of parallel 42 × 96 in. precast single-tee beams, placed side-by-side, as shown in Fig. P7.2. After erection of the tees, a 5 in. cast-in-place slab will be poured that will act in a composite sense with the precast members. The precast concrete has strengths $f'_c = 5000$ psi and $f'_{ci} = 3500$ psi, while the cast-in-place concrete is of strength $f'_c = 3000$ psi. It is proposed that the beams be pretensioned, using 1/2 in. diameter Grade 250 straight strands, such that they will carry their own weight plus that of the wet concrete slab without exceeding ACI stress limits, and that, after the slab has hardened, they are further prestressed by post-tensioning, using additional 1/2 in. diameter strands, so as to carry the full service load, including 150 psf live load, meeting ACI stress limitations. Losses may be assumed at 15 percent for pretensioning and 12 percent for post-tensioning. (a) Determine the required pretensioning force and number of 1/2 in. diameter strands. (b) Find the required additional force to be applied by post-tensioning, and the number of post-tensioned strands. (c) Calculate the flexural stresses in the concrete at all critical load stages. (d) What suggestions do you have for the improvement of the design? Properties of the single-tee section are: $A_c = 834$ in.^{2}, $I_c = 127,000$ in.^{4}, $c_1 = 15.3$ in.

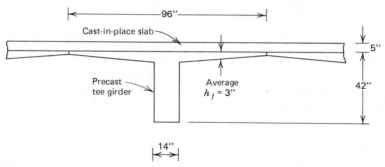

Figure P7.2

CHAPTER 8

CONTINUOUS BEAMS AND FRAMES

8.1 SIMPLE SPANS VERSUS CONTINUITY

Most prestressed concrete construction in the United States at the present time consists of statically determinate beams and girders, floor and roof deck panels, and wall units. There are several reasons for this. In contrast to reinforced concrete construction, which is mostly cast-in-place and for which continuity is the natural condition, a large proportion of prestressed concrete is also precast. This offers great advantages by avoiding forming, shoring, and tensioning in the field, and permits high quality construction at low cost. But the structure arrives on the site in pieces, much as does a steel structure, and extra expense and effort is needed to obtain continuity.

In addition, for continuous spans, the diagram of maximum design moments has local peaks, usually at the supports. For concrete structures using ordinary non-prestressed bar steel, the resisting moment is easily varied to match the controlling moments at various sections, by cutting off or bending bars where they are not needed. For prestressed members, the main reinforcement is often a continuous tendon of constant cross section, the area of which is determined by requirements at the section of greatest moment. For continuous spans in which moment requirements vary greatly along the total length, this may result in an uneconomical design.

Frictional losses may also become large for continuous prestressed spans, for which the tendon profile is likely to have several changes of curvature.

Finally, as will be discussed in more detail later, statically indeterminate prestressed beams characteristically develop *secondary moments* as a result of prestressing, introducing a complication to the design process.

However, there are important advantages associated with indeterminate structures of prestressed concrete, as for structures of other types. Design moments are smaller, for given spans and loads, than for determinate structures. Stiffness is increased and deflection is reduced. By continuing post-tensioning tendons over several spans, fewer anchorages are required, and the labor cost of stressing is greatly reduced. Joint rigidity in continuous frames provides an important mechanism to resist horizontal loads such as are induced by wind, blast, or seismic forces.

261

As a result of the advantages, continuous prestressed concrete construction is increasingly common in the United States, and this trend may be expected to continue. Two-way, continuous, flat plate slabs are used extensively, and have proven both functional and highly economical. For medium and long span bridges, the economic and esthetic advantages of continuity are dominant considerations. Many ingenious arrangements have been developed to avoid the problems listed earlier, such as high frictional losses of prestress, and the need to accommodate to moment variation along the spans.

In many instances, precast pretensioned components are post-tensioned together in the field to obtain the advantages of continuity, as well as the economy associated with plant production. This system has been widely exploited for medium span bridges, for which entire spans are often precast and pretensioned to carry their own weight and construction loads, then post-tensioned at the construction site to provide continuity for superimposed dead and live loads. Segmentally precast bridges of long span are normally designed for full continuity.

Continuous prestressed construction is well established in Europe, and may be expected to become common in the United States as a result of further technical development and changing economic conditions (Refs. 8.1, 8.2, and 8.3).

8.2   TENDON PROFILES AND STRESSING ARRANGEMENTS

The tendon profiles used for continuous spans are closely related to the variation of bending moment due to the dead and live loads, just as was true for statically determinate, simple span beams. In general, moments resulting from prestressing should vary in the same way as those moments due to the applied loads, and act in the opposite sense. It follows that a reasonable tendon profile may be established by dividing all ordinates of the applied load moment diagram by a constant to obtain tendon eccentricities along the span.

For example, for the two-span continuous beam of Fig. 8.1a, a uniformly distributed load will produce the moment diagram of Fig. 8.1b. Moments vary parabolically, reaching a maximum value of $wl^2/8$ at the central support. The moment at the center of each span is $wl^2/16$. Accordingly, a tendon might be selected for which the eccentricity varied parabolically, with maximum eccentricity over the central support, and eccentricity just half that amount at midspan, as shown in Fig. 8.1c.

While this will result in a *concordant tendon*, described later, in Art. 8.7, it would probably not be the best arrangement. Improved economy would be obtained using a tendon with the maximum possible eccentricity, at both midspan and center support, as in Fig. 8.1d. A smaller prestress force would be required, using such a profile, than would be necessary for the case shown in Fig. 8.1c. This may be confirmed by recalling the principle of load balancing,

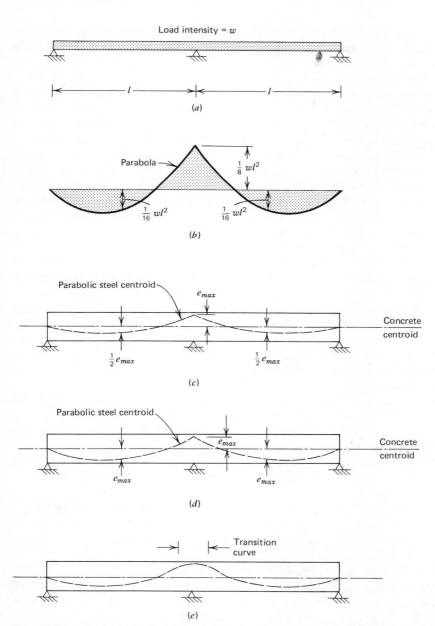

Figure 8.1 Basis for selecting tendon profile. (*a*) Loads. (*b*) Moment due to loads. (*c*) Tendon profile based on moment diagram. (*d*) Tendon profile based on maximum sag. (*e*) Practical tendon arrangement.

or equivalent loads, described in Art. 4.10, which confirms that the prestress force required to balance a given loading is minimized by maximizing the sag (Refs. 8.4 and 8.5).

The load-balancing approach generally provides the best insight in determining the tendon profile for continuous beams, often revealing possibilities not clearly shown by other methods. Designing for load balancing, the engineer is led to select a profile that will produce equivalent loads on the beam that are equal and opposite to those resulting from the applied loads. A distributed load would be carried by a parabolic tendon, a set of concentrated loads by a segmentally linear tendon, etc., as was true for the simple spans discussed in Art. 4.10. At the simply supported ends of exterior spans of continuous beams, the eccentricity should be zero, because of the load-induced moments are zero there. At interior supports, the eccentricity may be the maximum value permitted by requirements of concrete protection for the steel.

Practical considerations preclude the sharp change in tendon slope shown at the center support of the beam of Fig. 8.1d. In real cases, a transition curve would be used, as shown in Fig. 8.1e. The length of the transition curve varies, depending on the dimensions of the beam and the flexibility of the tendon and duct. In general, it may be of the order of 20 percent of the span length. The difference in equivalent load produced by the idealized tendon of Fig. 8.1d and the more practical arrangement of Fig. 8.1e, with a transition curve, may be accounted for in the analysis, but is usually neglected. While service load behavior will be slightly different than assumed, the ultimate flexural capacity is not affected.

The several reversals of curvature typical of post-tensioning tendons for continuous beams may result in very high frictional losses. For slabs (Fig. 8.2a) the concrete depth is small relative to span lengths and therefore, the required tendon curvatures are small. In such cases, continuous tendons may be used over three, four, or sometimes five spans without excessive frictional losses. For other cases, special arrangements may be used to avoid difficulty.

For example, a two-span beam such as that of Fig. 8.1e, might be tensioned from both ends simultaneously by using two jacks. Alternately, the beam might be jacked from only one end, but overtensioned temporarily to bring the tension in the farther span up to the desired value. After this, the jacking force is reduced to the specified initial level.

Other tendon arrangements for post-tensioned cast-in-place construction are shown in Fig. 8.2. The needed eccentricity of tendon may be achieved without excessive cable curvatures by curving the bottom flange of the girder, as in Fig. 8.2b. The effective eccentricity is the distance from the steel centroid to the concrete centroid, the depth of which varies as shown.

The overlapping intermediate anchorages of Fig. 8.2c reduce the length of the prestressing units and thus reduce frictional losses. The tendons are brought

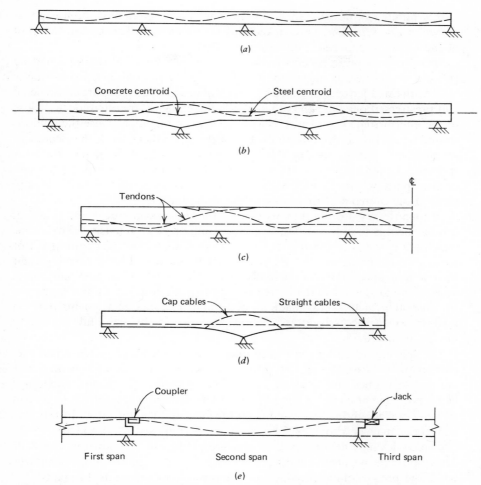

Figure 8.2 Tendon arrangements for cast-in-place continuous beams. (*a*) Continuous tendons in slab. (*b*) Beam with varying depth. (*c*) Use of intermediate anchorages. (*d*) Cap cables. (*e*) Span-by-span construction.

out of the upper surface of the beam. Long stressing cavities must be provided to accommodate the jacks and anchorages. These cavities are later filled with unstressed concrete. It is usually necessary, when such a scheme is used, to place several straight tendons over the entire length of the beam initially, to prevent cracking at the intermediate supports that results from the large effective eccentricity (Ref. 8.1).

In a number of designs, short discontinuous cap cables have been used, as shown in Fig. 8.2d. These are jacked and anchored in pockets cast in the soffit of the beam on either side of the intermediate supports.

Span-by-span prestressing of continuous beams may be accomplished by splicing of tendons, as suggested by Fig. 8.2e. High strength bars are normally used, with threaded ends engaged by coupling sleeves. The spans are constructed and prestressed one after the other. While the couplers are often located close to the intermediate supports, this leads to some difficulty because the tendons should be as close as possible to the top of the beam there, while the clearances required for splicing prevent this optimum arrangement. A better scheme is to locate the tendon splices at construction joints at the 1/5 points of the successive spans, where the individual tendons may be distributed vertically, still keeping the centroid of the group at the desired level.

In many cases, for continuous beams, the most economical and practical arrangement is to assemble the structure using precast pretensioned elements, which are post-tensioned after assembly to provide for partial continuity. For short to medium spans, the elements span between supports, carrying their own weight and construction loads as simple spans. After post-tensioning, added dead load and live loads are carried by continuous action. For long span bridges, often each span is made up of a number of precast segments that are post-tensioned successively as erection proceeds. In this case, full continuity may be obtained.

The splicing of tendons in continuous beams made up of pretensioned precast spans is illustrated by Fig. 8.3a. After placing the precast elements, they are post-tensioned one span at a time in sequence, a temporary anchorage being provided at each support. The post-tensioning tendon for the next span is then coupled, and it is stressed from the far end, then anchored. In this way continuity may be provided for resisting superimposed dead and live loads.

Cap cables may also be used to join precast beams, as shown in Fig. 8.3b. These provide negative bending resistance over the intermediate supports, while the pretensioning provides for the positive moments in the spans.

The construction of a long span bridge by the cantilever method is illustrated by Fig. 8.3c. In this case short segments of the central span are precast or cast-in-place sequentially. The tendons that are necessary over the supports are successively curved downward into the webs of the girder and are anchored to the segments as they are progressively set in place, cantilevering outward toward midspan. Continuity cables start at the top of the girder, about at the points of contraflexure. These tendons curve downward so as to be at the bottom of the girder at midspan. They are tensioned and anchored in recesses formed into the top of the girder.

The variations are many, for both cast-in-place and precast construction, and considerable engineering ingenuity has been demonstrated in the development of special techniques. For continuous members of all types, it is absolutely

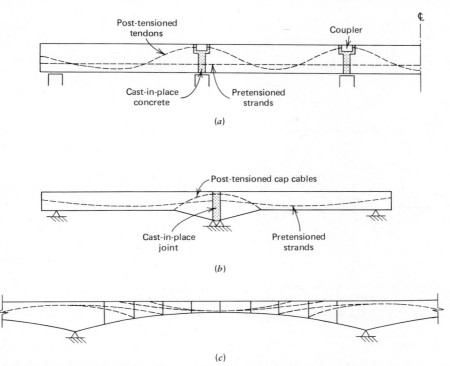

Figure 8.3   Tendon arrangements for continuous beams using precast elements. (*a*) Coupled continuous tendons. (*b*) Cap cables at intermediate support. (*c*) Precast segments post-tensioned in sequence.

essential that provision be made for the axial shortening associated with post-tensioning.

8.3   ELASTIC ANALYSIS FOR THE EFFECTS OF PRESTRESSING

When an eccentric prestressing force is applied to a statically *determinate* beam, shown in Fig. 8.4, bending moments are induced, equal to the product of the force times the distance between the steel centroid and the concrete centroid. The beam will deflect when prestressed, usually cambering upward, but no external reactions are produced. If the effect of member self-weight is excluded from consideration, the compressive stress resultant *C* coincides with the centroid of the prestressing steel, as shown.

For a statically *indeterminate* beam, the action is more complex. The moment just described, which will now be referred to as the *primary moment*, causes a

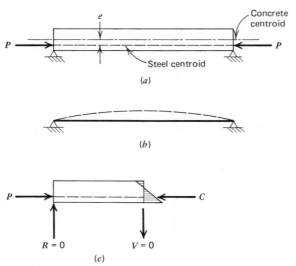

Figure 8.4 Statically determinate beam. (*a*) Beam profile. (*b*) Deflection due to prestressing. (*c*) Free body diagram of portion of beam.

tendency for the beam to deflect as before, but it is restrained by the redundant system of supports. Reactions are produced at those supports, giving rise to *secondary moments* in the beam. In this case, the total moment produced at any section by prestressing is the sum of the primary and secondary moments.

The effect of prestressing a statically indeterminate beam may be understood with reference to Figs. 8.5 and 8.6. The beam of Fig. 8.5*a* is subjected to a prestressing force *P* with a constant eccentricity *e*. The primary bending moment *Pe* would cause the central part of the continuous beam to rise off its support, as in Fig. 8.5*b*, if it were free to do so. It is restrained against this displacement by the redundant support system, however. To provide this restraint, a downward force *R* is developed at the center support, as shown in Fig. 8.5*c*. This force is equilibrated by the reactions *R*/2 at each end of the continuous span. The actual deflected shape of the continuous beam, subjected to the prestressing force *P*, and constrained to zero deflection at all supports, is represented in Fig. 8.5*d*.

The support forces due to prestressing can be found using the classical method of superposition (Ref. 8.6). Appropriate redundant reactions are selected such that their removal will result in a statically stable and determinate primary structure. The redundants are replaced by unknown forces, and the values of these forces adjusted so that zero deflection is obtained at the corresponding support locations.

For the present example, it would be convenient to treat the center support force as the redundant. With that redundant restraint removed, the deflection

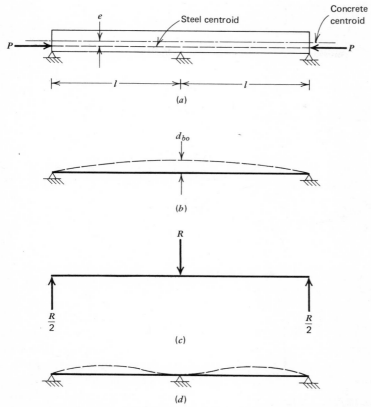

Figure 8.5   Forces and deflections for statically indeterminate beam. (*a*) Beam profile. (*b*) Deflection if center support were removed. (*c*) Reactions at supports due to prestressing. (*d*) Actual deflection due to prestressing.

d_{bo} of Fig. 8.5*b*, due to the applied prestress force, can be found by any convenient method, such as moment-area, conjugate beam, virtual work, etc. The force R of Fig. 8.5*c* is then found from the condition that it must produce an equal and opposite deflection, so that the sum of the two deflection components at that location is zero.

The bending moments for the beam of Fig. 8.5 are shown in Fig. 8.6. Since the eccentricity is constant, for this example, the primary moment $M_1 = Pe$ is constant (Fig. 8.6*a*). The reactions resulting from prestressing produce the secondary moments $M_2 = Rl/2$ at the center support. Since the secondary moments of any continuous prestressed beam are caused by forces acting at the supports only, these secondary moments must always vary linearly between the supports, as shown here.

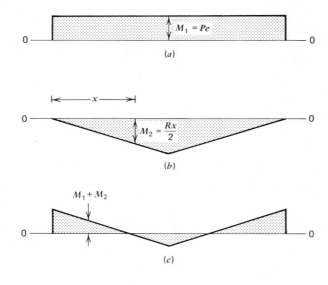

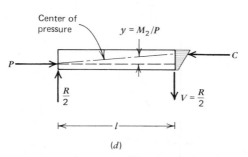

Figure 8.6 Moments and thrust line for statically indeterminate beam. (*a*) Primary moments due to prestressing. (*b*) Secondary moments due to support reactions. (*c*) Total moments due to prestressing. (*d*) Free body diagram of one-half beam.

The total moment due to prestressing the indeterminate beam is equal to the sum of the primary and secondary moments, and is shown in Fig. 8.6*c*. The points of zero bending moment may be identified with the points of inflection for the deflection curve of Fig. 8.5*d*.

The magnitude of the secondary moments in any given case depends on the particular tendon profile selected. For special cases, the secondary moments may be zero (see Art. 8.7), but this is not usually so. They are often comparable to the primary moments, and in many cases may be larger, even though they are called secondary.

The centroid of the concrete stress distribution for a continuous beam will not, in general, be at the same level as the steel centroid, as was true for simple span beams, because of the existence of secondary moments. This is shown for the present example by the free body diagram of Fig. 8.6d. The clockwise secondary moment, equal to the reaction $R/2$ times the distance l to the center support, is equilibrated by the internal counterclockwise couple, consisting of the compressive resultant C times the lever arm to the steel centroid. Elsewhere along the span, the displacement to the *center of pressure*, or *thrust line*, from the steel centroid varies linearly with distance from the support, in the same way as does the secondary moment M_2. Specifically, referring to Fig. 8.6d,

$$y = \frac{M_2}{P} \tag{8.1}$$

where

y = distance from steel centroid to thrust line

M_2 = secondary moment due to prestressing

P = prestress force

Note that the primary moments are directly proportional to the prestress force. Consequently the reactions due to prestressing, and the secondary moments are also proportional to the prestress force, as are the total moments generated by prestressing. It follows that the displacement y of the thrust line from the steel centroid does not change as losses gradually reduce the prestress force from P_i to P_e. The location of the thrust line for a given steel profile is fixed.

The concrete stresses resulting from prestressing a continuous beam may be found from the equations of Art. 3.4, except that e^*, the eccentricity of the thrust line with respect to the concrete centroid, must be substituted for e, the eccentricity of the steel centroid, because the center of compression no longer coincides with the center of tension. Thus, for a continuous beam, the longitudinal stresses in the concrete at the top and bottom face, resulting from initial prestress are

$$f_1 = -\frac{P_i}{A_c}\left(1 - \frac{e^* c_1}{r^2}\right) \tag{8.2a}$$

$$f_2 = -\frac{P_i}{A_c}\left(1 + \frac{e^* c_2}{r^2}\right) \tag{8.2b}$$

while, after all losses have occured, the effective prestress force produces the concrete stresses

$$f_1 = -\frac{P_e}{A_c}\left(1 - \frac{e^* c_1}{r^2}\right) \tag{8.3a}$$

$$f_2 = -\frac{P_e}{A_c}\left(1 + \frac{e^* c_2}{r^2}\right) \tag{8.3b}$$

where e^* is the distance from the thrust line to the concrete centroid, and all other terms are previously defined. Note that e^* is negative when the thrust line is above the neutral axis.

The support reactions that result from prestressing a statically indeterminate beam produce shear forces, as well as bending moments, and these should be considered in the analysis. It will be found, however, that the shear forces are generally much less significant than the secondary moments.

An example of the calculation of secondary moments, thrust line, and stresses resulting from prestressing a continuous beam will be found in Art. 8.5, following the development of an alternative approach to the analysis of such members.

8.4 EQUIVALENT LOAD ANALYSIS

The total moments resulting from prestressing a continuous member may be found directly, without considering the separate contributions of primary and secondary moments, by the method of equivalent loads. The equivalent loads produced by various prestressing tendon profiles were described in Art. 1.3 (see also Fig. 1.8), and the use of the equivalent load approach in the design of statically determinate simple span beams was presented in Art. 4.10.

The equivalent load approach is based on consideration of the transverse forces that are applied to a member wherever there is a change in the alignment of the prestressing tendons. These forces produce moments, just as any other system of external loads. The stresses resulting from these moments must be combined with the uniform axial compression, P/A_c, due to prestressing to obtain the total stresses at any section.

The concept of equivalent loads is particularly advantageous for continuous beams. The transverse forces that correspond to the particular tendon profile are found, making use of the relations developed in Arts. 1.3 and 4.10. The structure can then be analyzed for the effects of these equivalent loads by using any of the available methods for indeterminate analysis, such as moment distribution or matrix analysis.

For an indeterminate structure, the moments found from such an analysis are the *total moments* due to prestressing, and include the secondary moments due to support reactions as well as the primary moments due to tendon eccentricity. Secondary moments may be found, if needed, by subtracting the primary moments, easily determined, from the total moments obtained from the equivalent load analysis.

If the equivalent loads due to prestressing should be exactly equal and opposite to the applied loads, then all transverse forces cancel. For this unique balanced load condition, there are no bending moments applied to the beam. No flexural stresses exist, but only the axial stresses produced by the longitudinal component of the prestressing force. For such a condition, there are no displacements of the beam other than axial shortening, and the question of determinacy or indeterminancy becomes irrelevant (Refs. 8.4 and 8.5). However, should the balancing load be removed or should an increment of load be added, moments must be found for the unbalanced portion of the load. To obtain the net concrete stresses, the stresses due to these moments may be added to the uniform compressive stress resulting from prestressing.

The equivalent load method simplifies the analysis and design of indeterminate beams by eliminating, in service load analysis, the need to calculate the reactions and secondary moments due to prestressing. When such secondary moments must be found, in connection with ultimate load analysis, the equivalent load method provides the most convenient way to obtain those secondary moments, by subtracting the primary from the total moments. Furthermore, it is an aid to the designer in selecting the most advantageous tendon profile and in understanding the effects of linear transformation and concordancy of tendons, discussed in Arts. 8.6 and 8.7.

While the method of superposition of deflections is quite convenient where there are only one or two redundant reactions, for more highly indeterminate members the method of equivalent loads permits a more systematic solution, and is better suited for use with existing computer programs.

8.5   EXAMPLE: INDETERMINATE PRESTRESSED BEAM

The two-span rectangular beam of Fig. 8.7a has width $b = 12$ in. and total depth $h = 22$ in. It is prestressed using a continuous tendon having a parabolic profile in each span, with eccentricities as indicated. The beam will carry an effective prestress force P_e, after all losses, of 200 kips. Differences in tension along the span due to friction may be neglected. Find the primary, secondary, and total moments resulting from prestressing, as well as the support reactions and location of the thrust lines: (1) using the method of superposition of deflections, and (2) using the method of equivalent loads. Find the concrete stresses at support B due to prestressing. ($b = 305$ mm, $h = 559$ mm, $e = +152$, -152, $+152$ mm, span $= 2 \times 9.14$ m, and $P_e = 890$ kN.)

(1)   METHOD OF SUPERPOSITION

The primary moments due to the prestress force are easily found by multiplying the eccentricities of Fig. 8.7a by the prestress force of 200 kips, assumed constant over the full 60 ft length. The resulting primary moments are given by Fig. 8.7b.

The given structure is indeterminate to the first degree. Following the usual procedure for the method of superposition, a redundant is selected such that its removal will leave a stable and determinate primary structure. In this case, the reaction at B will be treated as redundant; the primary structure becomes a single span beam, simply supported at A and C.

This primary structure will first be subjected to the moments M_1 due to prestressing, and the deflection found at point B. This deflection is numerically equal to the distance

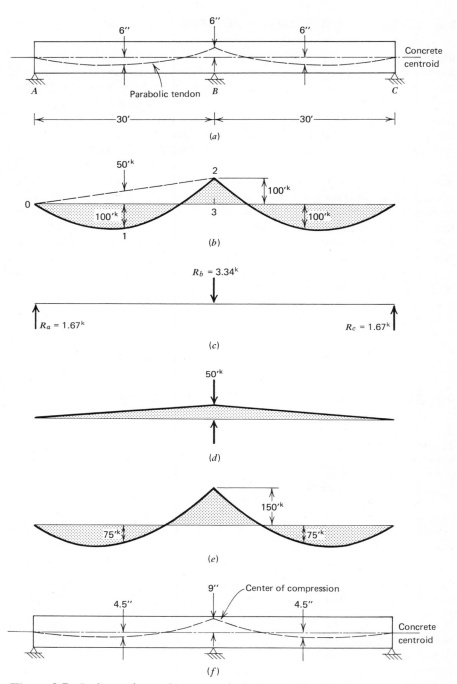

Figure 8.7 Indeterminate beam analysis by method of superposition. (a) Beam profile. (b) Primary moments M_1. (c) Reactions due to prestress. (d) Secondary moments M_2. (e) Total moments $M_1 + M_2$. (f) Thrust line due to prestress.

of point A, on the elastic curve, from the horizontal tangent to the elastic curve through point B. This can easily be found using the second moment area principle (Ref. 8.6). First, it is convenient, in taking moments of the M/EI area, to divide the diagram for span AB into the positive area included within the parabola 012 and the negative triangular area 023 (Fig. 8.7b). Then, when we take moments about A, the deflection sought is equal to

$$d_{bo} = \frac{1}{EI} [(150 \times 30 \times \tfrac{2}{3} \times 15) - (100 \times 30 \times \tfrac{1}{2} \times 20)]$$

$$= \frac{15,000}{EI} \text{ ft}$$

upward; that is, the beam would rise off the support B if not restrained by a still-unknown downward force R_b at that point.

Next the primary structure, of span AC, will be subjected to the unknown reaction R_b with corresponding reactions at A and C of $R_b/2$, as shown by Fig. 8.7c. The resulting moment diagram is linear, of the shape shown by Fig. 8.7d, with a maximum value $15R_b$. The downward deflection of point B due to the force R_b is

$$d_{bb} = \frac{1}{EI} (15R_b \times 30 \times \tfrac{1}{2} \times 20) = \frac{4500}{EI} R_b$$

For satisfaction of the condition of compatibility, the upward deflection due to the primary prestressing moments, d_{bo}, must equal d_{bb}, the downward deflection due to R_b, that is, the net deflection must be zero at the support. Thus

$$4500R_b = 15,000$$
$$R_b = 3.34 \text{ kips}$$
$$R_a = R_c = 1.67 \text{ kips (7.43 kN)}$$

The secondary moment M_2 varies linearly from 0 at the exterior supports to the value of $1.67 \times 30 = 50$ ft-kips at support B, as indicated by Fig. 8.7d. These secondary moments are superimposed on the primary moments M_1, to obtain the total moments due to prestressing shown in Fig. 8.7e.

The thrust line resulting from the application of prestress is presented in Fig. 8.7f. Its location is found by computing distances from the steel centroid line using Eq. (8.1). Thus, at B, the center of compression is

$$y_b = \frac{50 \times 12}{200} = 3 \text{ in. (76 mm)}$$

above the steel centroid, or 9 in. above the concrete centroid. Similar calculations indicate that at midspan the thrust line is 1.5 in. above the steel centroid or 4.5 in. below the concrete centroid. The deviation of the thrust line from the steel centroid varies linearly from 0 at the exterior supports to 3 in. at the center support.

The location of the thrust line may also be found directly, from the total moments of Fig. 8.7e, by using the condition that these moments are produced by the compressive resultant, acting at its own eccentricity, e^* from the concrete centroid. Thus, at B,

$$e^* = \frac{150 \times 12}{200} = 9 \text{ in. (229 mm)}$$

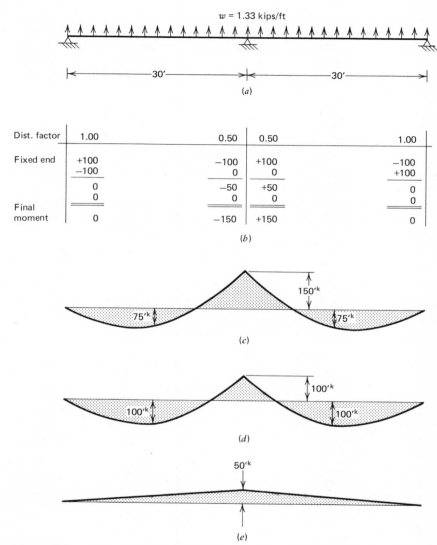

$w = 1.33$ kips/ft

30'

30'

(a)

Dist. factor	1.00		0.50	0.50		1.00
Fixed end	+100		−100	+100		−100
	−100		0	0		+100
	0		−50	+50		0
	0		0	0		0
Final moment	0		−150	+150		0

(b)

150'k

75'k

75'k

(c)

100'k

100'k

100'k

(d)

50'k

(e)

Figure 8.8 Indeterminate beam analysis by method of equivalent loads. (a) Equivalent load from prestressing. (b) Analysis by moment distribution. (c) Total moments M. (d) Primary moments M_1. (e) Secondary moments $M_2 = M - M_1$.

276

while at midspan,

$$e^* = \frac{75 \times 12}{200} = 4.5 \text{ in. (114 mm)}$$

The concrete stresses at the top and bottom face at B are found using Eqs. (8.3a) and (8.3b). With $A_c = 264 \text{ in.}^2$, $I_c = 10{,}600 \text{ in.}^4$, and $r^2 = 40.2 \text{ in.}^2$ these stresses are, respectively,

$$f_1 = -\frac{200{,}000}{264}\left(1 + \frac{9 \times 11}{40.2}\right) = -2620 \text{ psi } (-18.1 \text{ N/mm}^2)$$

$$f_2 = -\frac{200{,}000}{264}\left(1 - \frac{9 \times 11}{40.2}\right) = +1110 \text{ psi } (+7.7 \text{ N/mm}^2)$$

(2)   METHOD OF EQUIVALENT LOADS

The same results may be found by using the method of equivalent loads. From Eq. (4.25a) of Art. 4.10 it is known that a parabolic tendon having total sag y will produce a uniformly distributed upward load on a member equal to

$$w_p = \frac{8Py}{l^2} \tag{4.25}$$

For the present case, the sag, measured with respect to a line between tendon locations at the supports of either span, is 9 in. Thus

$$w_p = \frac{8 \times 200 \times 9}{30^2 \times 12} = 1.33 \text{ kips/ft (19.4 kN/m)}$$

acting upward, as in Fig. 8.8a. The two-span indeterminate beam will be analyzed for this load, using the method of moment distribution (Ref. 8.6). Fixed end moments at the left and right ends of each span are $1.33 \times 30^2/12 = 100$ ft-kips. These are recorded, with appropriate signs, in Fig. 8.8b. Two cycles of moment distribution are executed to obtain the final moments of 0 at the exterior supports and 150 ft-kips at the center support. The final moment diagram is given in Fig. 8.8c. These are the *total* moments due to prestressing, and include the contributions of both primary and secondary moments. Primary moments are easily found, multiplying the tendon eccentricity by the value of P_e, and are shown in Fig. 8.8d. Secondary moments are determined by subtracting primary from total moments, and are given by the diagram of Fig. 8.8e. All results are identical to those obtained by the method of superposition. The thrust line and concrete stresses are found just as before.

With the total effect of prestressing established, there is little difficulty in superimposing the effects of other loads to establish net moments and stresses at any location.

8.6   LINEAR TRANSFORMATION

It will be noted, from the review of Arts. 8.3 and 8.4, that the thrust line, locating the center of pressure in any span of an indeterminate beam, has the same basic shape as the steel centroid line in that span. Its profile may be obtained by rotating the profile of the steel centroid line an appropriate amount about its end. This is so because the deviation of the thrust line from the steel centroid is directly proportional to the secondary moment, which in turn varies linearly with distance from the support.

This procedure, by which a line of given characteristic shape is rotated about one end or the other, without changing that shape within the span, is known as *linear transformation*. The thrust line is said to be a linearly transformed version of the steel centroid line.

It is an interesting fact, of considerable practical importance, that *any steel profile may be linearly transformed to a new position in a span, yet produce exactly the same thrust line as before*. The reactions induced by prestressing will differ for different steel profiles, and the secondary and primary moments will be different, but the total moment, that is, the sum of the primary and secondary moments, will be unchanged. Consequently, the thrust line must be in the same position.

This will be illustrated by the beams of Figs. 8.9 and 8.10. In each case, all conditions are the same as for the beam shown in Fig. 8.7, except that linearly transformed versions of the original steel profile are used.

The beam of Fig. 8.9a uses a parabolic tendon in each span, with the same 9 in. sag as before. However, the steel centroid passes through the concrete centroid at the center support B as well as at the exterior supports A and C. The analysis was performed using the method of superposition. The primary moments M_1 of Fig. 8.9b, when applied to the beam, require the reactions shown in Fig. 8.9c to maintain zero support deflections. The secondary moments of Fig. 8.9d, when superimposed upon the primary moments, produce the total moments due to prestressing, shown in Fig. 8.9f. These are seen to be identically the same as the final moments obtained for the same beam, with the tendon profile shown in Fig. 8.7a. The thrust line, shown in Fig. 8.9f, is also identically the same as before.

Another alternative design is shown in Fig. 8.10a. Again a parabolic tendon with the same 9 in. sag is used, but in this case with 9 in. eccentricity at the center support. Primary moments are obtained and shown in Fig. 8.10b. For this particular moment diagram analysis by the method by superposition indicates that there is no tendency for the beam to move up or down from its support at B, that is, the deflection at B of the primary structure AC, when loaded with moments M_1, is zero. As a result, there are no induced reactions and no secondary moments. The total moments of Fig. 8.10e are identical to the primary moments of Fig. 8.10b. Once again, the same thrust line is obtained, because the final moments due to prestress are the same as in the previous two cases.

Figures 8.7, 8.9, and 8.10 should be studied carefully and compared. Primary moments, prestress reactions, and secondary moments are completely different in each case, yet the same thrust line is obtained and, consequently, the same concrete stresses will be produced by prestressing.

The examples confirm that a tendon profile may be linearly transformed without modifying the thrust line produced. This is always so. Although the

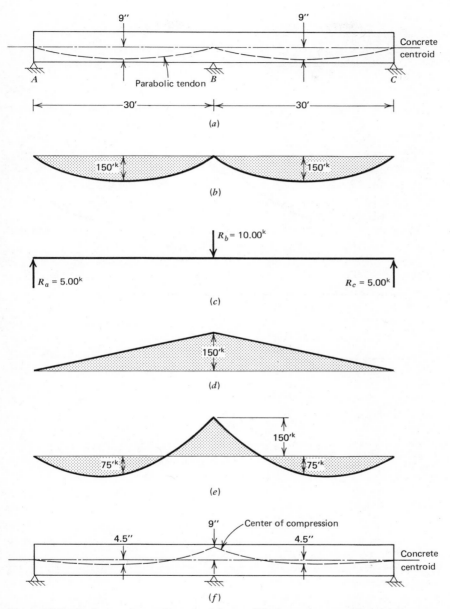

Figure 8.9 Indeterminate beam with modified tendon profile. (*a*) Beam profile. (*b*) Primary moments M_1. (*c*) Reactions due to prestress. (*d*) Secondary moments M_2. (*e*) Total moments $M_1 + M_2$. (*f*) Thrust line due to prestress.

279

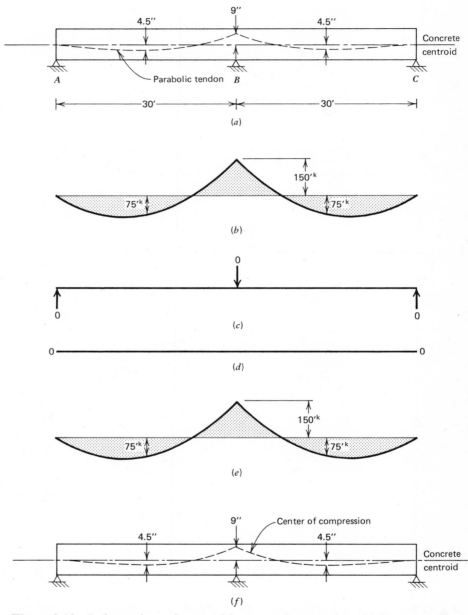

Figure 8.10 Indeterminate beam with concordant tendon. (*a*) Beam profile. (*b*) Primary moments M_1. (*c*) Reactions due to prestress. (*d*) Secondary moments M_2. (*e*) Total moments $M_1 + M_2$. (*f*) Thrust line due to prestress.

280

reason may not be immediately evident, it will become so upon consideration from the point of view of equivalent loads. The same tendon shape was used for all three cases. The equivalent upward load, 1.33 kips per foot, was unchanged by the small rotations of the steel centroid line. Consequently the total moments, obtained from that equivalent load, must be the same in all three cases, even though the primary and secondary moments must differ.

It is a necessary restriction that the transformed steel centroid line must still intersect the concrete centroid at the freely supported ends of continuous spans. Changes in the eccentricity at the free end would produce changes in the moment applied at the beam end. This represents a modification of the equivalent load, which would produce a different diagram of total moment and different thrust line.

The concept of linear transformation is of great use to the designer of prestressed concrete structures, because it permits the relocation of the steel centroid, as may be desirable to maintain adequate concrete cover for the tendon, for example, without changing the thrust line or the concrete stresses in the structure.

8.7   CONCORDANT TENDONS

The tendon profile selected for use in the beam of Fig. 8.10 was unique because for that particular tendon no reactions were generated by prestressing and, consequently, no secondary moments were developed. The thrust line produced by prestressing coincided with the steel centroid line, as would be the case for a simple span, statically determinate beam. Such a tendon is called a concordant tendon.

There are any number of concordant tendons possible for a given continuous prestressed concrete beam. The most obvious one is a steel profile, which coincides everywhere with the concrete centroid. For this case, no primary bending moments are generated by prestressing, and so no support reactions are possible, and no secondary moments. This observation is of limited practical use, however, because centroidally prestressed beams are highly uneconomical, in general.

The beam examples of Figs. 8.7, 8.9, and 8.10 suggest another basis for concordancy: a tendon that coincides with the thrust line obtained using a nonconcordant tendon is itself a concordant tendon. The steel profile used for the example of Fig. 8.10 was selected in this way, and for that profile no prestress reactions and no secondary moments were found. The proof of concordancy for such a tendon is simple. It has been shown that the thrust line in any given case is a linearly transformed steel centroid line. Any other linearly transformed version of the steel centroid line would produce identically the same thrust line, *including the one that matches the thrust line itself.* Consequently a tendon which follows that thrust line is concordant.

Actually, *any valid moment diagram for a continuous member provides the basis for a concordant tendon profile*, with the steel eccentricity taken equal to a constant times the moment ordinate at any point. This too may be simply proved. For any arbitrary system of loads, the moment diagram for the span in question is obtained on the basis that there is no deflection at the supports. If the beam deflections were to be calculated at the supports, using moment area theorems or other means, those deflections would be zero. A steel centroid line that has eccentricities directly proportional to the ordinates of any such moment diagram would produce primary moments varying in the same way. Support deflections of the primary structure, acted upon by those moments, would also be zero. No reactions or secondary moments would be produced by prestressing, and the requirements for concordancy would be satisfied.

While use of a concordant tendon in a given instance offers the possibility of simplified analysis, there is little practical advantage in terms of structural behavior. The most economical design in a given case is usually obtained with the steel centroid as high as possible over the supports, and as low as possible near midspan, an arrangement that will not generally result in a concordant tendon.

8.8 CONCRETE STRESSES IN THE ELASTIC RANGE

There is no special difficulty associated with the calculation of concrete stresses for the initial and service load stages for indeterminate prestressed beams. The moments M_o, M_d, and M_l due respectively to member self-weight, superimposed dead load, and service live load, must be found for each of the sections of interest by an analysis that accounts for the effects of continuity. As for any indeterminate structure, a continuous prestressed concrete beam or frame must be analyzed for alternate live loadings to determine the maximum moments at all critical sections. The investigation of minimum moments in the spans should not be neglected, as they may be of sign opposite to the maximum moments.

For initial conditions, immediately after transfer, the effect of prestressing is found using Eqs. (8.2a) and (8.2b). At midspan, where gravity moments are generally positive, the stresses in the concrete at the top and bottom faces of the beam are, respectively,

$$f_1 = -\frac{P_i}{A_c}\left(1 - \frac{e^* c_1}{r^2}\right) - \frac{M_o}{S_1} \tag{8.4a}$$

$$f_2 = -\frac{P_i}{A_c}\left(1 + \frac{e^* c_2}{r^2}\right) + \frac{M_o}{S_2} \tag{8.4b}$$

The same equations apply for the negative bending regions near the supports, except that the sign of the stress associated with M_o is reversed in each case. The eccentricity of the thrust line, e^*, is negative if measured upward from the concrete centroid; otherwise it is positive.

At the full service load stage, when all prestress losses are assumed to have already occurred, concrete stresses due to prestressing are found based on Eqs. (8.3a) and (8.3b), and stresses due to the total service load are superimposed. With $M_t = M_o + M_d + M_l$, the resulting stresses in the positive bending region at the top and bottom faces of the concrete are, respectively,

$$f_1 = -\frac{P_e}{A_c}\left(1 - \frac{e^*c_1}{r^2}\right) - \frac{M_t}{S_1} \qquad (8.5a)$$

$$f_2 = -\frac{P_e}{A_c}\left(1 + \frac{e^*c_2}{r^2}\right) + \frac{M_t}{S_2} \qquad (8.5b)$$

As before, the sign of the stress associated with the gravity moments must be reversed in determining net stress in the negative bending regions.

According to ACI Code, service load stresses may be based on the properties of the uncracked concrete section, even though the nominal concrete tensile stress may be as high as $12\sqrt{f_c'}$, well above the modulus of rupture.

The method of load balancing offers considerable simplification in determining the concrete stresses within the elastic range. The equivalent load that results from prestressing may be easily found, referring to Arts. 1.3 and 4.10. If the external loads acting are just equal and opposite to the equivalent loads, then there is no bending, no flexural stress, and no deflection (except axial) of the continuous member. Consequently an indeterminate analysis becomes unnecessary. The net stress in the concrete is simply uniform compression, P_e/A_c, for the balanced load stage. Usually this load state is that produced by effective prestress plus total dead load plus any sustained live load.

When the remainder of the service live load is applied, bending of the continuous member results, and the concrete stresses due to that increment of load must be found by an analysis that accounts for continuity. These flexural stresses must be superimposed at any section on the axial compression produced by the balanced loading. Since the flexural analysis need include only the unbalanced fraction of the live load, the use of an approximate method of analysis for moments is fully justified.

While the method of load balancing avoids the immediate need to calculate reactions and secondary moments due to prestressing, they must eventually be found in order to evaluate the factor of safety against collapse. Secondary moments and shears from prestressing may add to, or subtract from, the moments and shears due to gravity loads.

8.9 FLEXURAL STRENGTH

The ultimate flexural strength should always be checked, for continuous prestressed concrete beams, just as for simple spans, because the desired degree of safety against collapse is not automatically insured by satisfaction of stress limits at service load. Load factors, such as those of the ACI Code, are applied to the calculated dead loads and service live loads to obtain the minimum hypothetical overload that the member should be capable of resisting. Moments corresponding to these overloads are determined at all critical sections, and compared with the flexural strength of the beam at those sections. The moment analysis may be performed by using any of the standard methods for continuous beams and frames. The strength of sections in flexure, in turn, can be found by the methods of Art. 3.7, incorporating the usual strength reduction factors.

For several reasons the load-balancing approach to the analysis of continuous members is not useful at overload stages or at incipient failure. When overloaded, the member is well beyond the range of elastic response, and the superposition of stresses, which is implicit in load balancing, is not valid. Also, the equivalent loads computed for load-balancing analysis are usually determined for the effective prestress force P_e, which is assumed to have constant value along the span and to remain unchanged as loads are applied. These conditions are at least approximately met up to service load, but not much beyond that stage. When the beam is severely overloaded, the stress in the tendon increases, the amount of the increase depending on the location along the span, whether or not the tendons are grouted or otherwise bonded to the concrete, and the extent of concrete cracking. Any calculation of equivalent load would have to recognize this change in tendon stress, a procedure that would involve great practical difficulty.

For any indeterminate structure, moments may be found based on an elastic analysis, or based on the assumption of some degree of plastic behavior. Plastic analysis assumes the formation of one or more *plastic hinges* at critical moment sections, followed by some amount of *redistribution of the elastic moments*, until finally a collapse mechanism is formed. This type of analysis, for prestressed concrete structures, will be discussed in Art. 8.10.

It is conservative to perform the strength analysis based on elastic moments. The moments at all sections are considered to increase linearly with load until, at some location, the capacity of the beam or frame is reached, establishing the failure load. This procedure is conservative, in that it neglects the capacity of almost all beams and frames to redistribute moments, to some extent, before actual collapse. For concrete structures it is also inconsistent, because the flexural strength of individual sections is computed on the basis of nonlinear, inelastic material behavior, even though the beam or frame is assumed to respond elastically. However, because of the difficulty in predicting rotation capacities, present United States practice for both reinforced and prestressed concrete members follows essentially this procedure. It is always on the safe side to neglect moment redistribution. The actual failure load would not be less, and may be substantially more, than that computed.

Thus, the ultimate moments that must be resisted may be found, for the factored loads, by using any of the well-known methods for analysis of elastic beams and frames. Ordinarily, for manual solutions performed using a slide rule or an electronic calculator, the method of moment distribution is used, while for computer solutions the matrix methods, incorporated in packaged programs, are almost universally adopted (Ref. 8.6).

In either case, members are represented by their centerlines. Moments of inertia, upon which member stiffnesses are based, may be computed for the uncracked concrete sections, neglecting the influence of the steel and that of cracking. Provided that a consistent set of assumptions is adopted for all members of the indeterminate structure, no significant error will result from this, because it is the relative stiffnesses of the members that are of consequence, not the absolute stiffnesses, in determining moments.

Loads to be included in the elastic flexural analysis are the member self-weight, the superimposed dead loads, and the live loads, each with the appropriate load factor specified by the Code. It has been pointed out already that load balancing is not appropriate at the ultimate load stage and, therefore, equivalent loads due to prestressing are not to be included. The secondary moments resulting from prestressing *must* be included, however, using a load factor of 1.0.

The proper treatment of secondary moments in the ultimate load analysis of indeterminate prestressed structures have been the subject of much debate (Refs. 8.7 to 8.11). In the 1971 ACI Code, it was stated that the effect of moments due to prestressing, including secondary moments, shall be neglected when calculating the overload moments. It was also stated that behavior shall be determined by elastic analysis, with only a modest amount of redistribution of moments due to plastic hinging permitted. The accompanying ACI Code Commentary stated that the secondary moments produced by the prestress force in a nonconcordant tendon disappear at the capacity at which, because of plastic hinge formation, the structure becomes statically determinate. Therefore, according to that edition of the Commentary, the overload moments at the critical sections of a continuous prestressed beam are only those due to dead and live loads.

That such a procedure is inconsistent and, in some cases unsafe, was pointed out in Refs. 8.7 to 8.10 and elsewhere. The secondary moments do exist and influence the elastic moments at all sections of the structure through the full range of loads up to failure.

The only circumstances under which secondary moments may be legitimately ignored are when a concordant tendon is specified (in which case there are no secondary moments, by definition), or when full moment redistribution is possible, through formation of plastic hinges that have adequate rotation capacity. The procedure established by the 1971 ACI Code, by which only limited rotation was permitted at critical sections, on the one hand, but secondary moments were ignored, on the other, was clearly in error. The 1977 Code correctly requires consideration of secondary moments, using a load factor of 1.0, up to and including the ultimate load.

Secondary moments are to be found on the basis of the effective prestress force, P_e. While the force in the tendon does increase significantly as loads on the structure are increased, because of bending of the members (Fig. 3.5), this does not represent a change in the *prestressing force* that produced the secondary moments, any more than the similar increase in steel stress in a reinforced concrete beam changes that beam to a prestressed beam. The force resulting from prestressing is unchanged, and the secondary moments are unchanged, as the load increases, up to the ultimate load or the load that produces the first plastic hinge.

8.10 MOMENT REDISTRIBUTION AND LIMIT ANALYSIS

If the loads acting on an indeterminate structure should gradually be increased, the limiting flexural capacity will eventually be reached at one (or possibly more than one) section of the structure. If the member at that location possesses the capacity to rotate plastically, at a resisting moment that is essentially constant, then *redistribution of moments* is possible. If the loads are such as to produce a sufficient number of plastic hinges in a given case, then a collapse mechanism will form, and the collapse load can be calculated on the basis that each hinging section provides a resistance equal to its flexural strength. After the formation of one or more plastic hinges, the ratios between moments at the critical sections will no longer be the same as the elastic moment ratios.

The principles of limit analysis, based on plastic behavior, are well known and will not be developed in detail here (see Ref. 8.12). The essential aspects can be demonstrated by means of the simple example shown in Fig. 8.11. Figure 8.11a shows a single span beam with fixed support at the left end and roller support at the right, the structure thus being indeterminate to the first degree. It carries a single concentrated load at midspan. That load is increased gradually until the elastic bending moment at the fixed support, $\frac{3}{16}Pl$, is just equal to the plastic moment capacity of the beam section M_n. This load is

$$P = \frac{16M_n}{3l} = 5.33\,\frac{M_n}{l} \tag{a}$$

At this stage the positive moment under the load is $\frac{5}{32}Pl$, as shown in Fig. 8.11b. The beam still responds elastically everywhere but at the left support, where plastic rotation occurs. At that point, the actual fixed support can be replaced for purposes of analysis with a plastic hinge offering a known resisting moment M_n. Because a redundant reaction has been replaced by a known moment, the beam is now statically determinate.

The load can be increased further until the moment under the load also becomes equal to M_n (assuming here that the beam has equal capacity in positive and negative bending), when the second hinge forms. The structure

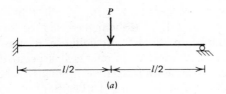

(a)

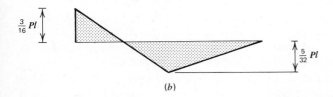

(b)

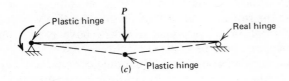

(c)

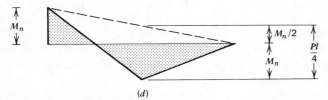

(d)

Figure 8.11 Moment redistribution in statically indeterminate beam. (*a*) Indeterminate beam. (*b*) Elastic
moment diagram. (*c*) Collapse mechanism. (*d*) Plastic
moment diagram.

then forms a mechanism, as shown in Fig. 8.11*c*, and collapse occurs. The
moment diagram at the collapse load is shown in Fig. 8.11*d*.

The magnitude of the load causing collapse is easily calculated from the
geometry of Fig. 8.11*d*:

$$M_n + \frac{M_n}{2} = \frac{Pl}{4}$$

from which

$$P = \frac{6M_n}{l} \qquad\qquad\qquad\text{(b)}$$

By comparison of Eqs. (a) and (b) it is evident that an increase in P of 12.5 percent is possible for this example, beyond that load which caused the formation
of the first plastic hinge, before the beam will actually collapse. Because of the
formation of plastic hinges, a redistribution of moments has occurred such
that, at failure, the ratio between positive and negative moments is equal to
the ratio of resisting moments *provided* in designing the beam, rather than the
ratio of elastic moments.

There is a direct relation between the amount of redistribution to be achieved
and the amount of plastic rotation required at the critical sections of a beam
to produce the desired redistribution. In general, the greater the modification
of the elastic moment ratio the greater the rotation capacity required to accomplish this change. If the beam of Fig. 8.11 has been designed with resisting
moments consistent with the elastic moment diagram of Fig. 8.11b, no rotation
would have been required at the two critical sections, and the beam would
(theoretically) have yielded at the same instant at the left support and at midspan. On the other hand, if the resisting moment at the left support had been
deliberately reduced (and the resistance at midspan correspondingly increased)
then substantial plastic rotation at the support would have been required
before the strength at midspan could be realized.

The simple example chosen illustrates clearly the difference between elastic
moment analysis and plastic moment analysis, and the necessity for plastic
rotation capacity at the location of hinges if the failure load predicted by
plastic analysis is to be achieved. Plastic analysis is widely used for steel structures, where rotation capacity is usually adequate because of the great ductility
of the steel. It has not been generally accepted for reinforced or prestressed
concrete structures, because of the more limited amount of rotation that can
be achieved at the hinging sections, and the practical difficulty of predicting
the rotation capacity that is available in given cases.

It has been shown experimentally and analytically that prestressed concrete
sections with relatively small amounts of steel are capable of substantial plastic
rotation, while those with relatively large amounts of steel behave in a more
brittle fashion. Accordingly and in lieu of more exact calculations of rotation
requirements and capacities, the ACI Code permits a limited amount of redistribution of elastic moments depending upon the reinforcement index. Defining

$$\omega = \frac{\rho f_y}{f'_c}$$

$$\omega' = \frac{\rho' f_y}{f'_c}$$

$$\omega_p = \frac{\rho_p f_{ps}}{f'_c}$$

where

$$\rho = \frac{A_s}{bd}$$

$$\rho' = \frac{A'_s}{bd}$$

$$\rho_p = \frac{A_p}{bd}$$

it is stated in the Code that the negative moments due to factored dead and live loads calculated by elastic theory for any assumed loading arrangement, at the supports of continuous prestressed beams with sufficient bonded steel to insure control of cracking, may be increased or decreased by not more than

$$p = 20\left(1 - \frac{\omega + \omega_p - \omega'}{0.30}\right) \tag{8.6}$$

percent, provided that these modified negative moments are also used for final calculations of the moments at other sections in the span corresponding to the same loading condition. Such an adjustment may only be made when the section at which the moment is reduced is so designed that $(\omega + \omega_p - \omega')$ is equal to or less than 0.20.

In this way, many of the economic and practical benefits of plastic analysis may be realized without the complexity of a true plastic analysis of the indeterminate prestressed concrete structure.

It is worth repeating that, for prestressed structures in which full redistribution of moments cannot be assured, it is necessary to *include* the secondary moments due to prestressing when calculating the moments at critical sections. These secondary moments disappear only at the stage of loading at which the structure is converted to a statically determinate condition through the formation of plastic hinges moving through the necessary rotation angles.

8.11   INDETERMINATE FRAMES

All of the fundamentals of the behavior of indeterminate structures that have been presented in studying beams apply with equal validity to frames. For frames too, prestressing generally develops secondary as well as primary moments. As for beams, the equivalent load approach is useful in establishing optimum tendon profiles, and may avoid the necessity for considering secondary moments, at least up to the service load stage. In frames, special attention must be paid to the axial shortening of members which accompanies prestressing, because, if the structure is restrained against this tendency to shorten, the intended prestress may not be achieved, and large secondary moments may be caused.

The rigid jointed portal frame of Fig. 8.12, indeterminate to the first degree, will serve to illustrate certain fundamental principles. The uniformly distributed dead and live loads acting on the girder lead to selection of a parabolic tendon profile, with the steel centroid close to the top surface of the girder at the columns and near the bottom face at midspan, maximizing the sag. The moments produced at the girder-to-column joints by the eccentric girder tendon will be balanced by countermoments produced by the column tendon eccentricity there. At the column bases, where hinged supports are provided, the tendon eccentricity is zero.

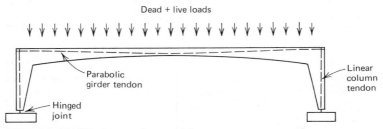

Figure 8.12 Prestressed portal frame.

Figure 8.13*a* shows the equivalent transverse load acting on the girder as a result of the curvature of the tendon. This load produces an upward deflection, accompanied by rotation of the knee joints, which causes inward displacement at the bottom of the columns. The supports prevent this displacement, and reaction forces act outward on the columns.

The axial component of prestress force causes a tendency for the girder to shorten, as in Fig. 8.13*b*. This too causes outward reactions on the frame at the bottom of the columns, producing flexural deformations of both columns and girder. The outward forces due to support restraint tend to produce tensile stress in the girder. This causes a reduction in the effective prestress, which must be accounted for in the design.

The deformations and reactive forces caused by dead and live loads are similar in nature. Figure 8.13*c* shows the vertical reactions and inward-directed thrust at the bases of the columns, typical of any portal frame.

When prestressing force and dead load effects are superimposed as in Fig. 8.13*d*, in most designs the net transverse load on the girder will be upward, and the girder will deflect upward accordingly. Support reactions are obtained by superposition of those of the type shown in Figs. 8.13*a*, *b*, and *c*. For this load stage, it is likely that the net horizontal reaction at the columns will be

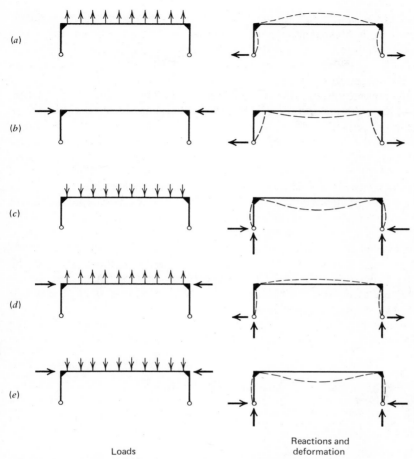

Loads

Reactions and
deformation

Figure 8.13 Effects of prestressing and loading of portal frame.
(*a*) Equivalent load of prestress. (*b*) Axial component of prestress.
(*c*) Superimposed dead and live loads. (*d*) Prestress and dead load.
(*e*) Prestress and dead and live loads.

outward, rather than inward as would usually be the case for non-prestressed portal frames.

Finally, when the full service load acts, together with prestress and superimposed dead and live loads, the girder deflects downward, as in Fig. 8.13*e*. The thrust at the base of the columns is now inward, but it will be much less than otherwise would be obtained, because of the combined effects of girder shortening and flexure resulting from prestress. This reduction of foundation force permits lighter foundations to be used. In addition, column moments, being directly proportional to the horizontal thrust, will be much reduced. This may permit prestressing in the columns to be eliminated, with tensile stresses in the columns to be resisted by ordinary bar reinforcement.

The relative magnitudes of the various effects just discussed and, consequently, the direction of the reactive forces and displacements, depends not only on the magnitudes of prestress force and applied loads, but on the relative stiffness of the columns and the girder. Stiff columns produce a high degree of restraint, large reduction of prestress in the girder (see Fig. 8.13b), and large moments at the knee joints such as to produce downward deflection of the girder at midspan. Slender columns will deform more readily, permitting axial shortening of the girder with little restraint or loss of prestress. The horizontal thrust at the supports will be less, as well as the column moments.

Time-dependent deformation of the concrete due to shrinkage and creep assumes great importance when constructing prestressed frames, particularly of long span. The columns must be designed to permit the inevitable axial shortening of the girder without suffering damage themselves. Several ingenious schemes have been devised to accomplish this. The slender bridges over the Marne by Freyssinet (see Fig. 1.1) were very shallow portal frames, which used a triangulated support at each end, providing the equivalent of very stiff columns. The sloping compression members of the end support frames could be adjusted by hydraulic jacks and wedges (Fig. 8.14) when shortening of the beam was sufficient to cause noticeable girder deflection at midspan.

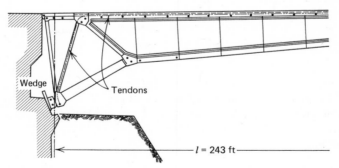

Figure 8.14 Freyssinet's portal frame with adjustable inclined struts at the supports (after Ref. 8.2).

In other designs, the shortening has been accommodated by use of a sliding joint detail. Figure 8.15 shows a portal frame support of this type, used for the Rosenstein Bridge in Stuttgart. Jacks provided the needed inward movement, as shrinkage and creep deformations occurred, maintaining the desired reactions and controlling bending moments applied at the ends of the span.

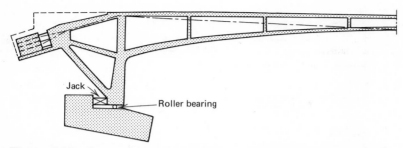

Figure 8.15 Support detail of the Rosentein Bridge at Stuttgart (after Ref. 8.2).

REFERENCES

8.1   Leonhardt, F., "Continuous Prestressed Concrete Beams," *J. ACI*, Vol. 24, No. 7, March 1953, pp. 617–634.

8.2   Leonhardt, F., *Prestressed Concrete Design and Construction*, Wilhelm Ernst and Sons, Berlin, 1964, 676 pp.

8.3   Abeles, P. W., *Introduction to Prestressed Concrete*, Vol. 2, Concrete Publications, Ltd., London, 1966.

8.4   Lin, T. Y., "Load Balancing Method for Design and Analysis of Prestressed Concrete Structures," *J. ACI*, Vol. 60, No. 6, June 1963, pp. 719–742.

8.5   Discussion of Ref. 8.4, *J. ACI*, Vol. 60, No. 12, December 1963, pp. 1843–1881.

8.6   Norris, C. H., Wilbur, J. B., and Utku, S., *Elementary Structural Analysis*, 3rd Ed., McGraw-Hill, New York, 1976, 673 pp.

8.7   Lin, T. Y. and Thornton, K., "Secondary Moment and Moment Redistribution in Continuous Prestressed Concrete Beams," *J. PCI*, Vol. 17, No. 1, January–February 1972, pp. 1–20.

8.8   AASHTO, *Interim Specifications for Bridges*—1975, American Association of State Highway and Transportation Officials, Washington, D.C., 1975.

8.9   Mattock, A. H., "Discussion of Proposed Revision of ACI 318–63: Building Code Requirements for Reinforced Concrete," *J. ACI*, Vol. 67, No. 9, September 1970, p. 710.

8.10 Mattock, A. H., discussion of Ref. 8.7, *J. PCI*, Vol. 17, No. 4, July–August 1972, pp. 86–88.

8.11 Mattock, A. H., Yamazaki, J., and Kattula, B. T., "Comparative Study of Prestressed Concrete Beams, With and Without Bond," *J. ACI*, Vol. 68, No. 2, February 1971, pp. 116–125.

8.12 Winter, G. and Nilson, A. H., *Design of Concrete Structures*, McGraw-Hill, New York, 1972, 615 pp.

PROBLEMS

8.1   The prestressed concrete beam shown in Fig. P8.1 is fixed at the left end and roller-supported at the right. It is post-tensioned with a single tendon having a parabolic

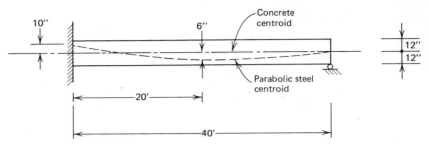

Figure P8.1

profile, with indicated eccentricities. (a) Locate the pressure line due to application of a prestress force of 240 kips. (b) Find the primary, secondary, and total moments due to prestressing at the face of the fixed support. (c) What is the magnitude and direction of the reaction produced at the roller by prestressing? (d) What minor adjustment could be made in the tendon profile to produce a concordant tendon?

8.2 A concrete beam having width 12 in. and total depth 24 in. is continuous over two 48 ft spans with hinge or roller supports at three points. It is post-tensioned with tendons providing effective prestress P_e after losses of 230,000 lb. The tendon profile in each span is parabolic, with 0 eccentricity at the exterior supports, -8 in. eccentricity at the interior support, and $+8$ in. eccentricity at the center of each span. Using the method of equivalent loads: (a) Find the primary moments resulting from prestressing. (b) Find the support reactions and secondary moments resulting from prestressing. (c) Draw the combined moment diagram resulting from prestressing and locate the pressure line along the span. (d) Find the distributions of concrete flexural stress at midspan and at the interior support resulting from: (1) effective prestress plus total dead load of 500 plf, and (2) effective prestress plus total dead load plus a superimposed live load of 300 plf.

8.3 Solve Problem 8.2 using the method of superposition (consistent deformation). Comment on the relative merits of the alternative methods of analysis.

CHAPTER 9
DEFLECTIONS

9.1 INTRODUCTION

Prestressed members are typically more slender than reinforced concrete members, because of the use of higher strength materials, and because of more refined techniques of design and construction. With a lower ratio of dead to live load, they may be used on much longer spans. Under such circumstances, the matter of deflections demands special attention.

In some circumstances, the main concern is the total deflection due to the combined effects of prestress and full service loading. In other cases, the important deflection may be that due to live load alone. Often, it is mainly the long-term deflection due to the combination of prestress and sustained loads that is of concern.

Failure to give adequate attention to deformations may cause trouble in various forms. For many members, particularly those designed for full prestressing rather than partial prestressing, the problem is excessive upward deflection, or camber, which as a result of concrete creep increases with time. Camber of bridge girders, for example, may result in an uneven road profile, producing uncomfortable or even dangerous ride characteristics. Excessive camber of roof decks may interfere with proper drainage.

For floors, excessive upward or downward displacements may cause cracking of partitions or other nonstructural elements, ill-fitting windows or doors, or possible misalignment of sensitive machinery. In some cases, differential vertical displacement, such as between adjacent precast floor units, caused by unintentional variation of material properties, prestress force, or eccentricity, may cause difficulty.

By prestressing, it is possible to control deflections to a remarkable degree. A beam of given cross section is apt to be considerably more stiff, if prestressed, than if merely reinforced. Reduction of cracking means that all, or nearly all, of the cross section is effective in contributing to the moment of inertia. In addition, net deflection in service may be minimized or even eliminated altogether by balancing the load-induced moments with prestress moments acting in the opposite sense. However, prediction of deflection of prestressed members is complicated by the gradual reduction of prestress force due to the various losses, and by changes in curvature due to concrete creep.

295

For a typical member, application of prestress force will produce upward camber. The effect of concrete shrinkage, creep, and relaxation is gradually to reduce the camber produced by the initial force, as that force is diminished. However, the creep effect is twofold. While it produces loss of prestress force, tending to reduce the camber, creep strains in the concrete usually increase negative curvatures and, hence, increase the camber. Generally the second effect predominates, and camber increases with time, in spite of the reduction of prestress force.

Dead and live loads are usually such as to produce downward deflections. In the case of sustained loads, these too are time dependent, because of concrete creep.

In considering the effect of creep on deflections, it may be noted that, if a balanced load stage is obtained under the combined action of prestress and long-term transverse loads, so that a uniform compression prevails in the concrete at all sections, then the effects of creep on deflections are nullified, and near-zero deflection may be maintained. This balanced load stage may prove a useful reference datum in design.

The control of flexibility in design, or the prediction of deflection, can be approached at any of several levels of accuracy, depending upon the nature and importance of the work. In many cases, it is sufficient to place limitations on the span-depth ratio, based on past experience or Code limitations (see Art. 4.7 for beams and Arts. 10.6 and 10.16 for slabs). If deflections are to be calculated, the approximate method described in Art. 9.3 will be found sufficiently accurate for most design purposes.

In special circumstances where it is important to obtain the best possible information on deflections at all important load stages, such as for long span bridges, the most satisfactory approach is to use a summation procedure based on incremental deflections at discrete time steps, as described in Art. 9.5. In this way, the time-dependent changes of prestress force, material properties, and loading can be accounted for accurately.

9.2   BASIS FOR THE CALCULATIONS

If the prestress force is accurately known, if the materials are stressed only within their elastic ranges, and if the concrete remains uncracked, then the calculation of deflection of a prestressed flexural member presents no special difficulty. Camber resulting from prestressing can be calculated either on the basis of curvatures, or directly from the prestress moment diagram, using familiar tools such as the moment-area method. Alternately, the effect of prestressing may be considered in terms of equivalent loads. Deflections due to dead and live loads are then calculated as for any other flexural member, and are superimposed on prestress deflections to obtain net values at the load stages of interest.

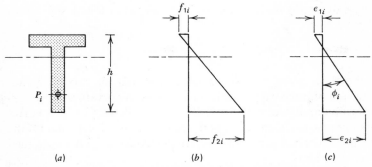

(a)   (b)   (c)

Figure 9.1 Stresses and strains due to initial prestress force P_i. (a) Cross section. (b) Stresses. (c) Strains.

The concrete strains and stresses in a typical beam, due to the application of initial prestress force P_i, may appear as shown in Fig. 9.1a. Concrete stresses are found from the equations of Ch. 3, after which the strains are easily obtained by the relation $\varepsilon_c = f_c/E_c$. If the total depth of the section is h, then the curvature at a particular section due to P_i is

$$\phi_{pi} = \frac{\varepsilon_{2i} - \varepsilon_{1i}}{h} \tag{9.1}$$

with due regard for sign. If tensile strain is taken positive, as usual, then a negative sign will indicate concave downward curvature, and upward camber, for a simple span.

Concrete stresses and strains in the member after losses are shown in Fig. 9.2. Stresses decrease, compared with those of Fig. 9.1, because of the loss of prestress force. However, because of the combined effects of shrinkage and creep,

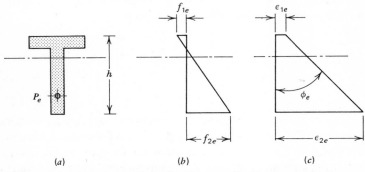

(a)   (b)   (c)

Figure 9.2 Stresses and strains due to effective prestress force P_e after losses. (a) Cross section. (b) Stresses. (c) Strains.

there is an increase of strains in the compressive sense. After losses, the curvature is

$$\phi_{pe} = \frac{\varepsilon_{2e} - \varepsilon_{1e}}{h} \tag{9.2}$$

For computational purposes, it is convenient to consider the curvature after losses, ϕ_{pe}, as the sum of three parts: (1) the instantaneous curvature ϕ_{pi} occurring immediately upon application of P_i, (2) the change in curvature $d\phi_1$ corresponding to loss of prestress from relaxation, shrinkage, and creep, and (3) the change in curvature $d\phi_2$ resulting from creep of the concrete under sustained compression (Ref. 9.1). Thus

$$\phi_{pe} = \phi_{pi} + d\phi_1 + d\phi_2 \tag{9.3}$$

The curvatures ϕ_{pi} and ϕ_{pe} vary along a span. Values at intervals may be calculated so as to establish the shape of the curvature diagram, which may then be treated as an elastic load in deflection calculations.

In many cases, in computing deflections due to prestress force, it is simpler to work with moments rather than curvatures. For statically determinate beams, the prestress moment diagram is directly proportional to the eccentricity diagram, since $M = Pe$. Moment ordinates are converted to M/EI ordinates, and the M/EI diagram considered to be an elastic load in finding deflections by the moment-area or conjugate beam method. The equivalence of the two methods is obvious, since from elementary mechanics

$$\phi = \frac{M}{E_c I_c} = \frac{Pe}{E_c I_c} \tag{9.4}$$

Thus, for the beam of Fig. 9.3a, having a parabolic tendon of eccentricity e at midspan, diminishing to zero at the supports, a parabolic moment diagram with maximum ordinate Pe is obtained. This is readily converted to the M/EI diagram of Fig. 9.3b. If we apply the moment area method, the flexural displacement Δ due to prestress P is found by taking moments of the M/EI area, between midspan and support, about the support point:

$$\Delta = \frac{Pe}{EI} \times \frac{l}{2} \times \frac{2}{3} \times \frac{5}{8} \times \frac{l}{2}$$

$$= \frac{5}{48} \frac{Pel^2}{EI}$$

This, and other cases that occur frequently, are summarized in Fig. 9.4 for reference. Figures 9.4b, c, and d give the midspan deflections for tendons harped at midspan, at the third points, and at the quarter points of the span, respectively, and passing through the concrete centroid at the supports in all cases. Figure 9.4e gives the midspan deflection produced by a straight tendon having constant eccentricity e.

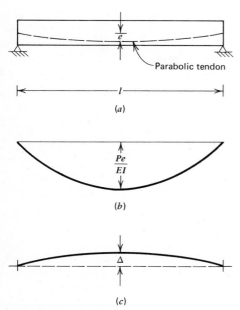

Figure 9.3 Deflection due to prestressing. (*a*) Profile. (*b*) Elastic loads.
(*c*) Deflection curve.

Other cases may be obtained by superposition. For example, if the parabolic
tendon of Fig. 9.4*f* has eccentricity e_1 at the supports, plus an incremental
eccentricity e_2 at midspan, the total deflection at midspan due to prestressing
is found by superimposing cases (a) and (e) as shown in Fig. 9.4*f*.

A third alternative in finding the deflection due to prestressing is to translate
the prestress effect into equivalent loads, permitting use of handbook equations
for deflections such as are available for the usual loadings.

To illustrate that identical results may be obtained by the method of equivalent loads, it will be recalled that the equivalent upward load produced on
a concrete member by a parabolic tendon is

$$w = \frac{8Pe}{l^2} \tag{4.25}$$

It may be confirmed in any standard reference that the deflection due to a
uniform load on a simple span is

$$\Delta = \frac{5}{384} \frac{wl^4}{EI}$$

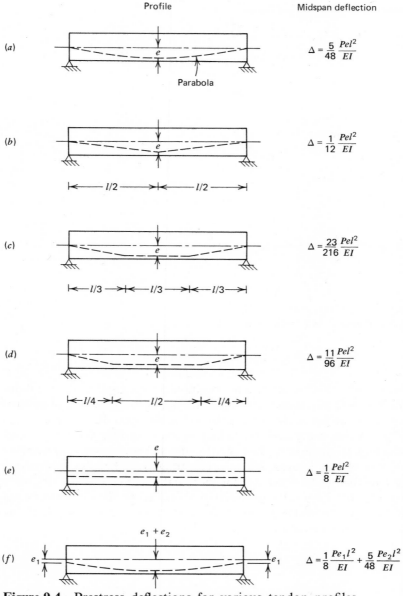

Figure 9.4 Prestress deflections for various tendon profiles.

Substituting the equivalent prestress load:

$$\Delta = \frac{5 \times 8}{384} \frac{Pel^4}{l^2 EI}$$

$$= \frac{5}{48} \frac{Pel^2}{EI}$$

as already found by the method of moment areas. Similar confirmation may be obtained for the other load cases shown.

If the beam or slab is uncracked, the moment of inertia used in the calculations may be taken as that of the gross concrete cross section without serious error. If there is an unusually large amount of reinforcing steel present, accuracy will be improved by the use of the properties of the transformed section.

If cracking is present, the stiffness of a member may be substantially reduced. However, even partially prestressed concrete members crack only at discrete locations. Between cracks, the flexural stiffness is approximately that of the uncracked concrete section. In such cases, use of an *effective moment of inertia* is recommended, as described in Art. 9.4.

9.3   APPROXIMATE METHOD FOR DEFLECTION CALCULATION

While deflection at intermediate states may be important in certain cases, normally to be considered are the initial stage, when a beam is acted upon by the initial prestress force P_i and its own weight, and one or more combinations of load in service, when the prestress force is reduced by losses to P_e and when deflections are modified by concrete creep under sustained loads.

The *short term deflection* Δ_{pi} due to the initial prestress force P_i may be found based on the variation of curvature along the span, making use of moment area principles. The initial curvatures ϕ_{pi} may be calculated from strains (Eq. 9.1), but it is usually more direct to work from the prestress moment diagram, and the corresponding variation of $P_i e/E_c I_c$ along the span. For common cases, the midspan deflection Δ_{pi} may be calculated directly by the equations in Fig. 9.4.

Usually Δ_{pi} is upward, and for normal conditions the member self-weight is superimposed immediately upon prestressing. The immediate downward deflection Δ_o due to self-weight, which is usually uniformly distributed, is easily found by conventional methods. The net deflection upon prestressing is

$$\Delta = -\Delta_{pi} + \Delta_o \tag{9.5}$$

where negative values indicate upward displacement.

In consideration of *long term effects*, reference is made to Eq. (9.3), which indicates that the curvatures (or deflections) due to prestressing force P_e after losses may be computed as the sum of the initial curvatures (or deflections) plus changes due to reduction of prestress and due to concrete creep. Equation (9.3) may be restated as follows:

$$\phi_{pe} = -\frac{P_i e_x}{E_c I_c} + (P_i - P_e)\frac{e_x}{E_c I_c} - \left(\frac{P_i + P_e}{2}\right)\frac{e_x}{E_c I_c}C_u \tag{9.6}$$

where C_u is the creep coefficient (see Ch. 2). The subscript x used with e indicates that the eccentricity varies along the span. The first term in Eq. (9.6) is the initial negative curvature, the second term is the reduction in that initial curvature because of the loss of prestress, and the third term is the increase in negative curvature because of concrete creep. Here the important approximation is made that creep occurs under a constant prestress force, equal to the average of the initial and final values.

Corresponding to that approximation, the final deflection of the member under the action of P_e is

$$\Delta = -\Delta_{pi} + (\Delta_{pi} - \Delta_{pe}) - \frac{\Delta_{pi} + \Delta_{pe}}{2}C_u$$

or simply

$$\Delta = -\Delta_{pe} - \frac{\Delta_{pi} + \Delta_{pe}}{2}C_u \tag{9.7}$$

where the first term is easily obtained by direct proportion:

$$\Delta_{pe} = \Delta_{pi}\frac{P_e}{P_i} \tag{9.8}$$

The long term deflection due to self-weight is also modified by creep, and may be obtained applying the creep coefficient to the instantaneous value. Thus the total member deflection, after losses and creep deflections when effective prestress and self-weight act, is given by

$$\Delta = -\Delta_{pe} - \frac{\Delta_{pi} + \Delta_{pe}}{2}C_u + \Delta_o(1 + C_u) \tag{9.9}$$

The deflection due to superimposed loads may now be added, with creep coefficient introduced to account for the long term effect of the sustained dead loads, to obtain the net deflection at full service loading:

$$\Delta = -\Delta_{pe} - \frac{\Delta_{pi} + \Delta_{pe}}{2}C_u + (\Delta_o + \Delta_d)(1 + C_u) + \Delta_l \tag{9.10}$$

where Δ_d and Δ_l are the immediate deflections due to superimposed dead and live loads, respectively.

9.4   EFFECTIVE MOMENT OF INERTIA

It has been suggested earlier that, if a member is uncracked at the load stages for which deflection is to be calculated, then the calculations may be based on the moment of inertia of the gross concrete cross section. If cracking does exist, then the effective flexural stiffness may be substantially reduced. For partially prestressed members, for example, where cracking can be expected at service load, use of the gross cross section could introduce serious error.

For reinforced concrete beams, Branson has shown that a reduced, or *effective moment of inertia* (Ref. 9.2), may be used as follows:

$$I_e = \left(\frac{M_{cr}}{M_{max}}\right)^3 I_g + \left[1 - \left(\frac{M_{cr}}{M_{max}}\right)^3\right] I_{cr} \qquad (9.11)$$

not to exceed I_g, where

I_g = moment of inertia of the gross concrete section

I_{cr} = moment of inertia of the fully cracked transformed concrete section

M_{cr} = cracking moment for the beam

M_{max} = maximum moment acting on the simple span

It is seen that $I_{cr} < I_e \leq I_g$ and that I_e approaches I_{cr} the more M_{max} exceeds M_{cr}.

Equation (9.11) has been widely used and is included in the ACI Code recommendations for reinforced concrete beams.

The Code is not clear regarding the use of Eq. (9.11) for the deflection of *prestressed members* in the cracked range, but does require that deflection computations be based on the transformed cracked section and on bilinear moment-deflection relationships.

Based on test results (Ref. 9.3), Branson has recommended that Eq. (9.11) be used for bonded prestressed concrete members, either with or without non-prestressed tension steel, loaded into the cracking range (see also Refs. 9.4, 9.5, and 9.6). Use of $E_c I_e$ represents adoption of a secant modulus of rigidity, and appears to satisfy the intent of Code provisions. In computing I_{cr} for use in Eq. (9.11), it is normally acceptable to use the neutral axis of the "fully cracked" transformed cross section, accounting for the steel area in the usual way, but disregarding the effect of prestress force in modifying the neutral axis location (Ref. 9.7).

Often in practice the engineer is concerned not so much with total deflection as with the incremental deflection, for example as the live load is applied. In such cases, because of the nonlinear relation between load and deflection resulting from the increase of cracking (see Fig. 4.1), it is necessary first to calculate the deflection before the load increment is applied, using the appropriate

I_e from Eq. (9.11), then to calculate the deflection after the load is added, using a new value of I_e as appropriate, and finally to substract the first from the second value to obtain the desired increment of deflection.

9.5 REFINED CALCULATIONS USING INCREMENTAL TIME STEPS

In calculating the deflection resulting from prestress force, the method presented in Art. 9.3 treated time-dependent changes in a very approximate way. Two load stages were considered: the initial stage, when prestress P_i acted, and the final stage, after all time-dependent losses, when the prestress force P_e. With reference to Eq. (9.6), the initial curvature $P_i e_x/E_c I_c$ was reduced to account for the prestress loss $(P_i - P_e)$, then increased to account for the effect of creep strain in increasing the curvatures along the span. In computing the last component, we made the approximation that concrete creep occurred under a constant prestress force, equal to the average value $(P_i + P_e)/2$. Such an approach should prove sufficiently accurate for all but unusual cases.

For greater refinement, it is necessary to account for time-dependent changes in prestress force in a way that recognizes the interaction of the effects of creep, shrinkage, and relaxation. Creep does not proceed under a constant force, but rather under a force that is continuously reducing because of the combined effects of shrinkage, relaxation, and creep itself. This may be accounted for using a summation procedure, based on the incremental changes occuring in a series of discrete time steps (Ref. 9.1). Such a step-by-step method, while still approximate, permits improvement in accuracy to any desired degree by reducing the length, and increasing the number, of the time steps considered.

The determination of curvatures and deflections by such means requires information not only on the ultimate creep, shrinkage, and relaxation coefficients, but also on the variation of those quantities with time. The information contained in Ch. 2 will prove useful in this respect (see also Refs. 9.4 and 9.5).

For the step-by-step method, Eq. (9.6) is replaced, in effect, by the following summation, to obtain the curvature ϕ_{pt} at any section at time t:

$$\phi_{pt} = -\frac{P_i e_x}{E_c I_c} + \sum_0^t (P_{n-1} - P_n)\frac{e_x}{E_c I_c} - \sum_0^t (C_n - C_{n-1})P_{n-1}\frac{e_x}{E_c I_c} \quad (9.12)$$

where the subscripts $(n-1)$ and (n) define the beginning and end of a particular time step. It will be recalled that the first term is the instantaneous curvature occuring upon application of the prestress force P_i, the second term is the decrease in curvature corresponding to the loss of prestress from creep, shrinkage, and relaxation, and the third term is the increase in curvature resulting from creep.

The prestress force at the end of any time step is equal to the initial prestress P_i less the losses caused by shrinkage, creep, and relaxation. Losses caused by shrinkage, and relaxation could easily be obtained by application of the shrinkage and relaxation coefficients and time functions of Ch. 2. However, the effect of creep must be accounted for by summing the curvature changes in all time steps up to the time (t), because the force causing creep is continuously reducing.

In practice, it is convenient to treat all losses in the same summation. Curvature changes represented by the second and third terms of Eq. (9.12) are obtained concurrently at each step, by a sequence of calculations that accounts both for prestress loss from all causes and creep curvature, and provides for the summation indicated symbolically by Eq. (9.12).

First, the initial curvature, term 1 of Eq. (9.12), is determined, either from Eq. (9.1) or Eq. (9.4). Then, for the next and each subsequent time step, the following sequence of calculations is performed (refer to Fig. 9.5):

1. Obtain the gross increase in creep strain at each extreme fiber, $\Delta\varepsilon_{1gross}$ and $\Delta\varepsilon_{2gross}$ by multiplying the stress at the beginning of the time step by the *increment* of unit creep strain for that interval.
2. Determine the corresponding creep strain at the level of the steel centroid.
3. Sum the creep strain determined in Step 2 and the shrinkage strain *increment* for the time interval, to obtain the total change in strain at the level of the steel centroid.
4. Multiply the total strain found in Step 3 by E_p, and add the increment of relaxation loss to obtain the total steel stress loss for the interval.

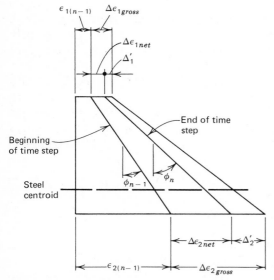

Figure 9.5   Strain changes and rotations at time step n.

5. Find the change in concrete stress at the extreme fibers corresponding to the loss in steel stress, and divide by E_c to obtain the corresponding strain changes Δ'_1 and Δ'_2.

6. Determine the net changes in creep strain at the extreme fibers, $\Delta\varepsilon_{1net}$ and $\Delta\varepsilon_{2net}$, by substracting the strain changes of Step 5 from the gross changes of Step 1.

7. Obtain the increase in curvature

$$(\phi_n - \phi_{n-1}) = \frac{\Delta\varepsilon_{2net} - \Delta\varepsilon_{1net}}{h}$$

from the net strains determined in Step 6, and sum with the curvatures present at the beginning of the time step to obtain total curvatures.

8. Find the stresses in the extreme fibers at the end of the time interval by finding the algebraic sum of the initial stress and the change in stress determined in Step 5. These are the stresses with which the computational sequence begins at the next time step.

The effect of the computational sequence just described is to calculate creep curvature, term 3 of Eq. (9.12), based on the prestress force at the beginning of the time step, then to calculate the curvature change due to losses, term 2 of Eq. (9.12), based on the shrinkage and relaxation occurring during the time step, and the creep corresponding to the prestress force acting at the beginning of the time step.

The calculations described must be performed at a sufficient number of locations along the span to establish the shape of the curvature diagram with reasonable accuracy, at least at midspan, the quarter points, and the supports. The calculation of beam deflections from the curvature diagram is a routine matter, and may proceed using the moment area method or other means.

The instantaneous and long term deflections due to transverse loads may now be superimposed, to obtain net deflections at the load stages of interest. In this case, creep does not require the summation approach, because the sustained load causing creep is constant. Instantaneous deflections due to the sustained load may be multiplied directly by the creep coefficient to obtain long term deflections.

9.6 EXAMPLE OF DEFLECTION CALCULATIONS

Calculate the midspan deflection of the 40 ft span I beam of Fig. 9.6 at age 0, 30, 180, and 360 days, using the step-by-step method of Art. 9.5. Compare the resulting deflection at 360 days with that obtained using the approximate method of Art. 9.3. The member, originally studied in connection with elastic stress analysis in Art. 3.4, is to carry its own weight of 183 plf and will be subjected to a service live load of 550 plf. (Span = 12.19 m,

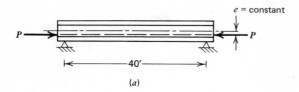

e = constant

P → ← P

|← 40' →|

(a)

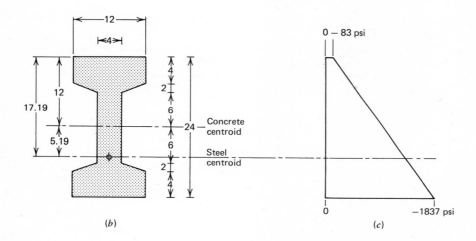

(b)

0 − 83 psi

0   −1837 psi

(c)

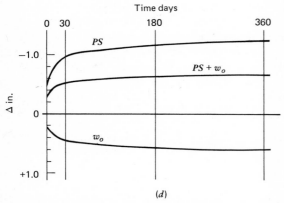

Time days

0   30   180   360

PS

PS + w_o

w_o

Δ in.

−1.0

0

+1.0

(d)

Figure 9.6 Deflection example. (a) Elevation. (b) Cross section. (c) Concrete stresses due to $P_i = 169$ kips. (d) Midspan deflection.

$w_o = 2.7$ kN/m, and $w_l = 8.0$ kN/m.) The following data are given:

$$P_i = 169,000 \text{ lb (752 kN)} \qquad\qquad I_c = 12,000 \text{ in.}^4 \ (4.99 \times 10^9 \text{ mm}^4)$$
$$A_p = 0.966 \text{ in.}^2 \ (623 \text{ mm}^2) \qquad\quad r^2 = 68.2 \text{ in.}^2 \ (44.0 \times 10^3 \text{ mm}^2)$$
$$f_y = 210,000 \text{ psi (1448 N/mm}^2) \qquad E_c = 4,030,000 \text{ psi (27.8 kN/mm}^2)$$
$$f_{pi} = 175,000 \text{ psi (1207 N/mm}^2) \qquad C_u = 2.35$$
$$A_c = 176 \text{ in.}^2 \ (114 \times 10^3 \text{ mm}^2) \qquad \varepsilon_{sh,u} = 800 \times 10^{-6}$$

The member will be constructed of normal density concrete, moist cured, and will be prestressed at age 7 days.

It is convenient to determine deflections due to prestress, self-weight, and superimposed loads separately, then to superimpose the results.

In the calculations of Art. 3.4 it is shown that the concrete stresses due to P_i, at the top and bottom of the section, are respectively -83 and -1837 psi. The corresponding concrete strains are

$$\varepsilon_1 = \frac{f_1}{E_c} = \frac{83}{4,030,000} = 21 \times 10^{-6}$$

$$\varepsilon_2 = \frac{f_2}{E_c} = \frac{1837}{4,030,000} = 456 \times 10^{-6}$$

Then, from Eq. (9.1), the initial curvature is

$$\phi_{pi} = \frac{\varepsilon_{2i} - \varepsilon_{1i}}{h}$$

$$= \frac{-456 + 21}{24} \times 10^{-6} = -18.14 \times 10^{-6} \text{ rad/in.}$$

The identical result may be obtained from Eq. (9.4):

$$\phi_{pi} = -\frac{P_i e_x}{E_c I_c}$$

$$= \frac{169,000 \times 5.19}{4,030,000 \times 12,000} = -18.14 \times 10^{-6} \text{ rad/in.}$$

The corresponding upward camber may be found by the moment area method, or by reference to Fig. 9.4b:

$$\Delta_{pi} = \phi_{pi} \frac{l^2}{8}$$

$$= -18.14 \times 10^{-6}(40 \times 12)^2/8$$

$$= -0.52 \text{ in. (13 mm)}$$

The time-dependent changes in deflection due to relaxation, shrinkage, and concrete creep will be determined based on the material information given in Ch. 2.

The ultimate creep coefficient C_u of 2.35 corresponds to a unit creep strain of

$$\delta_u = \frac{C_u}{E_c} = \frac{2.35}{4,030,000} = 0.583 \times 10^{-6}$$

The time variation of δ may be obtained from Eq. (2.10b). For example, at 30 days:

$$\delta_t = \frac{30^{0.60}}{10 + 30^{0.60}} \times 0.583 \times 10^{-6}$$

$$= 0.254 \times 10^{-6}$$

Similar calculations result in the data summarized in the second column of Table 9.1. The increment of creep strain for each time step is given in column 3.

Shrinkage calculations must account for the fact that the beam is poured and commences volumetric change 7 days before stressing, hence, at time -7 days. With $\varepsilon_{sh,u} = 800 \times 10^{-6}$ and time function as given by Eq. (2.13a), a typical calculation is as follows:

$$\varepsilon_{sh,30} = \frac{37}{35 + 37}(800 \times 10^{-6})$$

$$= 411 \times 10^{-6}$$

Calculations at other time steps yield the data of column 4 of Table 9.1, with the increments in each step in column 5.

Loss of stress in the steel due to relaxation is given by Eq. (2.1). With yield stress of 210 ksi and initial stress of 175 ksi, the stress ratio at 30 days, or 720 hours, is

$$\frac{f_p}{f_{pi}} = 1 - \frac{\log 720}{10}\left(\frac{175}{210} - 0.55\right)$$

$$= 0.919$$

corresponding to a loss ratio of $1.000 - 0.919 = 0.081$. Similar calculations at all time steps provide the information of column 6, Table 9.1, with the incremental changes given in column 7.

The calculation of time-dependent changes in curvature and deflection can now proceed, following steps 1 through 8 of Art. 9.5. For purposes of demonstrating the method, only three time steps will be used.

Table 9.1   Time-Dependent Parameters for Loss Calculations
(Example 9.6)

(1) Time	(2) Creep	(3)	(4) Shrinkage	(5)	(6) Relaxation	(7)	(8) Increment
Days	δ_t $\times 10^{-6}$	$\Delta\delta_t$ $\times 10^{-6}$	$\varepsilon_{sh,t}$ $\times 10^{-6}$	$\Delta\varepsilon_{sh,t}$ $\times 10^{-6}$	f_p/f_{pi}	$1 - f_p/f_{pi}$	$\Delta(1 - f_p/f_{pi})$
-7			0				
0	0		133	133	1.000		
30	0.254	0.254	411	278	0.919	0.081	0.081
180	0.404	0.150	674	263	0.897	0.103	0.022
360	0.451	0.047	730	56	0.888	0.112	0.009

The first time step will be taken from the time of prestressing, time 0, to time 30 days. At the beginning of that time step concrete fiber stresses are

$$f_1 = -83 \text{ psi}$$
$$f_2 = -1837 \text{ psi}$$

Applying the unit creep increment of 0.254×10^{-6} for the first step results in gross creep strains of

$$\Delta\varepsilon_{1gross} = 83 \times 0.254 \times 10^{-6} = 21 \times 10^{-6}$$
$$\Delta\varepsilon_{2gross} = 1837 \times 0.254 \times 10^{-6} = 467 \times 10^{-6}$$

The gross creep at the level of the prestressing steel is

$$\Delta\varepsilon_{pgross} = \left[21 + \frac{17.19}{24}(467 - 21)\right] \times 10^{-6}$$

$$= 340 \times 10^{-6}$$

The shrinkage strain increment for the first time step, from Table 10.1, is 278×10^{-6}. The relaxation of steel stress, based on the incremental loss ratio is

$$\Delta f_{p,rel} = 0.081 \times 175{,}000$$
$$= 14{,}200 \text{ psi}$$

Consequently the total loss of steel stress during time step 1 is

$$\Delta f_p = (\varepsilon_{cr} + \varepsilon_{sh})E_p + \Delta f_{p,rel}$$
$$= (340 + 278) \times 10^{-6} \times 27 \times 10^6 + 14{,}200$$
$$= 30{,}900 \text{ psi}$$

The corresponding changes in concrete stress at the top and bottom face are:

$$\Delta f_1 = +\frac{\Delta P}{A_c}\left(1 - \frac{ec_1}{r^2}\right)$$

$$= \frac{0.966 \times 30{,}900}{176}\left(1 - \frac{5.19 \times 12}{68.2}\right)$$

$$= +14 \text{ psi}$$

$$\Delta f_2 = +\frac{\Delta P}{A_c}\left(1 + \frac{ec_2}{r^2}\right)$$

$$= \frac{0.966 \times 30{,}900}{176}\left(1 + \frac{5.19 \times 12}{68.2}\right)$$

$$= +324 \text{ psi}$$

These stresses are divided by the elastic modulus of the concrete to obtain the corresponding changes in concrete strain:

$$\Delta_1' = 14/4{,}030{,}000 = 3 \times 10^{-6}$$
$$\Delta_2' = 324/4{,}030{,}000 = 80 \times 10^{-6}$$

The gross strains, first obtained, are now adjusted by these values to obtain the net strains at the top and bottom faces of the concrete section:

$$\Delta\varepsilon_{1net} = (21 - 3) \times 10^{-6} = 18 \times 10^{-6}$$
$$\Delta\varepsilon_{2net} = (467 - 80) \times 10^{-6} = 387 \times 10^{-6}$$

The curvature increment during the first time step is easily found based on these strains:

$$\phi_{30} - \phi_0 = \frac{(-387 + 18)10^{-6}}{24} = -15.38 \times 10^{-6}$$

Thus the total curvature, as of the end of time step 1, is

$$\phi_{pi} + \Delta\phi = (-18.14 - 15.38)10^{-6}$$
$$= -33.52 \times 10^{-6}$$

This curvature, which is constant along the span as a result of the constant eccentricity, is easily translated into upward deflection at midspan:

$$\Delta_{30} = \phi_{30}\frac{l^2}{8}$$

$$= -33.52 \times 10^{-6}\frac{(40 \times 12)^2}{8}$$

$$= -0.97 \text{ in. } (-25 \text{ mm})$$

Concrete stresses at the top and bottom faces at the beginning of the next time step are obtained by taking the algebraic sum of the stresses at the start of the first time step and the change in stress that resulted from losses:

$$f_1 = -83 + 14 = -69 \text{ psi}$$
$$f_2 = -1837 + 324 = -1513 \text{ psi}$$

The results of all calculations described to this point are summarized in Table 9.2 at time 30 days. Corresponding calculations at the second and third time steps are summarized as well.

Based on total curvature at the end of each time step, found by the summation process just described, the upward cambers due to prestress force at times 0, 30, 180, and 360 days are respectively 0.52, 0.97, 1.18, and 1.24 in., as given in the final column of Table 9.2. These cambers are plotted as a function of time in days in Fig. 9.6d.

Next the deflections due to the self-weight of 183 plf are found. The instantaneous deflection, downward, is

$$\Delta_o = \frac{5wl^4}{384E_cI_c}$$

$$= \frac{5 \times 183(40 \times 12)^4}{384 \times 4,030,000 \times 12,000 \times 12}$$

$$= 0.218 \text{ in. (6 mm)}$$

Table 9.2 Summary of Calculations for Deflection due to Prestress (Example 9.6)

Time	Concrete Stress at Start of Time Step		Gross Creep Strain Increment		Gross Steel Strain Increment	Shrinkage Strain Increment	Steel Relaxation Increment	Total Stress Loss Increment	Concrete Stress Change Due to Losses	
Days	f_1 psi	f_2 psi	$\Delta\varepsilon_{1g}$ $\times 10^{-6}$	$\Delta\varepsilon_{2g}$ $\times 10^{-6}$	$\Delta\varepsilon_p$ $\times 10^{-6}$	$\Delta\varepsilon_{sh}$ $\times 10^{-6}$	$\Delta f_{p,rel}$ psi	Δf_p psi	Δf_1 psi	Δf_2 psi
0										
30	−83	−1837	21	467	340	278	14,200	30,900	+14	+324
180	−69	−1513	10	227	165	263	3,850	15,400	+7	+162
360	−62	−1351	3	64	47	56	1,575	4,400	+2	+46

Time	Concrete Strain Change Due to Losses		Net Creep Strain Increment		Curvature Increment	Total Curvature	Midspan Deflection
Days	Δ'_1 $\times 10^{-6}$	Δ'_2 $\times 10^{-6}$	$\Delta\varepsilon_{1net}$ $\times 10^{-6}$	$\Delta\varepsilon_{2net}$ $\times 10^{-6}$	$\Delta\phi$ $\times 10^{-6}$ rad	$\sum\phi$ $\times 10^{-6}$ rad	Δ_p in.
0							
30	+3	+80	18	387	15.38	18.14	0.52
180	+2	+40	8	187	7.46	33.52	0.97
360	+1	+11	2	53	2.13	40.98	1.18
						43.11	1.24

The time-dependent increase in this value is most conveniently found by introducing the creep coefficient $C_u = 2.35$, with time multipliers obtained by Eq. (2.10a):

$$\Delta_t = \Delta_o(1 + C_t)$$
$$\Delta_{30} = 0.218(1 + 0.435 \times 2.35) = 0.44 \text{ in. (11 mm)}$$
$$\Delta_{180} = 0.218(1 + 0.693 \times 2.35) = 0.57 \text{ in. (14 mm)}$$
$$\Delta_{360} = 0.218(1 + 0.774 \times 2.35) = 0.61 \text{ in. (15 mm)}$$

These values, too, are plotted as a function of time in Fig. 9.6d, and the net deflection due to the combined effect of prestress and dead load is shown.

The instantaneous deflection due to application of the live load of 550 plf is

$$\Delta_l = 0.218 \times \frac{550}{183} = 0.66 \text{ (17 mm)}$$

Thus the net deflection at time 360 days, due to prestress, and dead and live loads will be

$$\Delta_{net} = -1.24 + 0.61 + 0.66$$
$$= +0.03 \text{ in. (1 mm)}$$

The beam would be almost level at this load stage, but with the short term live load removed, a net upward camber of 0.63 in. could be expected.

Component deflections and net deflections at the end of each time step are summarized in Table 9.3. Column 5 represents the beam camber for the unloaded member, while column 6 is the deflection with the full live load acting.

Table 9.3   Summary of Deflections (Example 9.6)

(1) Time	(2) Δ_p		(3) Δ_o		(4) Δ_l		(5) $\Delta_p + \Delta_o$		(6) $\Delta_p + \Delta_o + \Delta_l$	
Days	in.	mm	in.	mm	in.	mm	in.	mm	in.	mm
0	−0.52	−13	+0.22	+6	+0.66	+17	−0.30	−8	+0.36	+9
30	−0.97	−25	+0.44	+11	+0.66	+17	−0.53	−13	+0.13	+3
180	−1.18	−30	+0.57	+14	+0.66	+17	−0.61	−15	+0.05	+1
360	−1.24	−31	+0.61	+15	+0.66	+17	−0.63	−16	+0.03	+1

For comparison, prestress camber at 360 days will be found using the approximate method of Art. 9.3. The loss of prestress will be taken the same as for the previous calculations, and at the end of 360 days will total

$$\Delta f_p = 30{,}900 + 15{,}400 + 4400$$
$$= 50{,}700 \text{ psi (350 N/mm}^2)$$

as shown in Table 9.2. This corresponds to loss in force of $0.966 \times 50,700 = 49,000$ lb. Thus

$$P_e = P_i - \Delta P$$
$$= 169 - 49$$
$$= 120 \text{ kips (534 kN)}$$

The immediate deflection upward due to prestress is

$$\Delta_{pi} = -0.52 \text{ in. (13 mm)}$$

as before, while

$$\Delta_{pe} = -0.52 \times \frac{120}{169}$$

$$= -0.37 \text{ in. (9 mm)}$$

The creep coefficient at time 360 days is $C_t = 0.774 \times 2.35 = 1.82$. Thus, from Eq. (9.7) the total deflection due to prestress force at 360 days is estimated at

$$\Delta_{360} = -\Delta_{pe} - \frac{\Delta_{pi} + \Delta_{pe}}{2} C_t$$

$$= -0.37 - \frac{0.52 + 0.37}{2} \times 1.82$$

$$= -1.18 \text{ in. (30 mm)}$$

This compares very favorably with the value of 1.24 in. obtained by the step-by-step approach. Agreement would not normally be so good.

In the present case, the step-by-step method was demonstrated using only three time steps, with increments of loss and deflection calculated at ages 30, 180, and 360 days. If deflections are sufficiently critical that use of the step-by-step method is indicated, at least 9 or 10 steps should be used. A suggested sequence might use calculations at ages from 1 day to 3 years, for example, with short steps at the beginning of the sequence and longer steps at the end. While the work would become tedious if performed manually, the deflection analysis is easily programmed for solution by digital computer.

9.7 COMPOSITE MEMBERS

Determination of the deflection of composite prestressed concrete beams introduces few new concepts, although there are practical complications because of the need to relate the time-dependent material parameters to the time-sequence of construction operations, such as casting the slab, achievement of full composite action, and possible step-by-step tensioning of the steel. Appropriate section properties must be used at the various stages in the computations.

Even if the approximate approach of Art. 9.3 is followed, it is normally necessary to use two time-steps, the first from time of transfer of prestress until the time of casting the slab, and the second from the time the slab is cast until the service load stage, when all losses may be assumed to have occurred.

Initial camber due to prestress, and deflection due to self-weight of the precast unit and weight of the freshly poured slab may be found by procedures already described, with no change, using properties of the precast section. The effect of creep due to prestress and other sustained loads, together with the effect of losses of prestress force, must be determined in two stages: prior to and after casting of the slab. Appropriate values of shrinkage, creep, and relaxation coefficients may be established by applying the time functions of Ch. 2 to the ultimate values of the parameters. Live load deflection may be calculated in the usual way, using properties of the composite beam.

A new consideration in the case of composite beams is the effect of differential shrinkage between the precast and cast-in-place parts of the section. Shrinkage of the slab after casting will always be greater than the continued shrinkage of the precast section. The resulting increment of downward deflection of the composite member may be significant, although shrinkage stresses and strains tend to be reduced by concrete creep.

Calculation of deflection of composite members is discussed in Refs. 9.4, 9.5, and 9.8. The reader is referred to those sources for details relating to specific cases.

9.8 ALLOWABLE DEFLECTIONS

The deflections that are considered acceptable vary widely depending on the particular type of construction and circumstances. Functional requirements of the member or structure may impose limits. Nonstructural elements carried by the prestressed construction may be damaged if deflections due to short or long term loads are too great. Drainage of long roof spans may be affected. Riding properties of bridges may be unsatisfactory if the supporting structure is too flexible.

Certain limits are included in the ACI Code, applicable to building construction. These are given in Table 9.4. The deflection limitation in each case, expressed as a fractional part of the span, depends on the type of member and supported construction. In some cases the limit applies to live load deflection only, while in other cases it applies to incremental deflections expected after attachment of nonstructural elements.

For bridges, the AASHTO Specification requires that, for simple or continuous spans, the deflection due to live load plus impact should not exceed 1/800 of the span, except on bridges in urban areas used in part by pedestrians, on which the ratio preferably shall be 1 1000. The deflection of cantilever arms due to live load plus impact is limited to 1/300 of the cantilever arm except for the case including pedestrian use, where the ratio preferably shall be 1/375 according to the Specification.

Table 9.4 Maximum Allowable Computed Deflections of the ACI Code[a]

Type of Member	Deflection to be Considered	Deflection Limitation
Flat roofs not supporting or attached to nonstructural elements likely to be damaged by large deflections	Immediate deflection due to the live load, L	$\dfrac{l}{180}$[*]
Floors not supporting or attached to nonstructural elements likely to be damaged by large deflections	Immediate deflection due to the live load, L	$\dfrac{l}{360}$
Roof or floor construction supporting or attached to nonstructural elements likely to be damaged by large deflections	That part of the total deflection which occurs after attachment of the non-structural elements, the sum of the long-time deflection due to all sustained loads and the immediate deflection due to any additional live load.[†]	$\dfrac{l}{480}$[‡]
Roof or floor construction supporting or attached to nonstructural elements not likely to be damaged by large deflections		$\dfrac{l}{240}$[§]

[a] Adapted with permission of the American Concrete Institute from ACI Building Code 318–77.

[*] This limit is not intended to safeguard against ponding. Ponding should be checked by suitable calculations of deflection, including the added deflections due to ponded water, and considering long-time effects of all sustained loads, camber, construction tolerances, and the reliability of provisions for drainage.

[†] The long-time deflection may be reduced by the amount of deflection which occurs before attachment of the nonstructural elements. This amount shall be determined on the basis of accepted engineering data relating to the time-deflection characteristics of members similar to those being considered.

[‡] This limit may be exceeded if adequate measures are taken to prevent damage to supported or attached elements.

[§] But not greater than the tolerance provided for the nonstructural elements. This limit may be exceeded if camber is provided so that the total deflection minus the camber does not exceed the limitation.

316

REFERENCES

9.1 "Deflections of Prestressed Concrete Members," ACI Committee 435, *J. ACI*, Vol. 60, No. 12, December 1963, pp. 1697–1727.

9.2 Branson, D. E., "Instantaneous and Time Dependent Deflections of Simple and Continuous Reinforced Concrete Beams," *HPR Report No. 7*, Part 1, Alabama Highway Department, Bureau of Public Roads, August 1963, pp. 1–78.

9.3 Shaikh, A. F. and Branson, D. E., "Non-Tensioned Steel in Prestressed Concrete Beams, "*J. PCI*, Vol. 15, No. 1, February 1970, pp. 14–36.

9.4 Branson, D. E., "The Deformation of Non-Composite and Composite Prestressed Concrete Members," ACI Special Publication SP–43, *Deflections of Concrete Structures*, American Concrete Institute, Detroit, 1974, pp. 83–127.

9.5 Branson, D. E. and Kripanarayanan, K. M. "Loss of Prestress, Camber, and Deflection of Non-Composite and Composite Prestressed Concrete Structures," *J. PCI*, Vol. 16, No. 5, September–October 1971, pp. 22–52.

9.6 *PCI Design Handbook*, Prestressed Concrete Institute, Chicago, 1971.

9.7 "Deflections of Continuous Concrete Beams," ACI Committee 435, *J. ACI*, Vol. 70, No. 12, December 1973, pp. 781–787.

9.8 Branson, D. E., *Deformation of Concrete Structures*, McGraw-Hill, New York, 1977, 546 pp.

PROBLEMS

9.1 The concrete T beam shown in Fig. P9.1 is post-tensioned at an initial force $P_i = 229$ kips, which reduces after 1 year to an effective value $P_e = 183$ kips. In addition to its own weight, the beam will carry a superimposed short term live load of 21.5 kips at midspan. Using the approximate method of Art. 9.3 find (a) the initial deflection of the unloaded girder, and (b) the deflection at age 1 year of the loaded girder. The following data are given: $A_c = 450$ in.^{2}, $c_1 = 8$ in., $I_c = 24{,}600$ in.^{4}, $E_c = 3{,}500{,}000$ psi, $C_u = 2.5$.

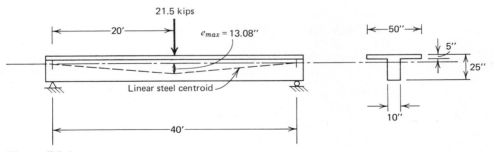

Figure P9.1

9.2 Find the deflections of the beam of Problem 9.1 by using the method of incremental time steps described in Art. 9.5. Consider the beam at time zero, 1 month, 3 months, 6 months, and 1 year. The following additional data are given: $A_p = 1.31$ in.^{2}, $f_y =$

210,000 psi, $f_{pi} = 175,000$ psi, $\varepsilon_{sh,u} = 650 \times 10^{-6}$. Use material properties as given in Ch. 2. The beam is poured 3 days before transfer, and is steam cured. Compare with the results of Problem 9.1 and comment.

9.3 The standard double-tee section beam of Fig. P9.3 is to be used on a simple span of 54 ft. Tendons are harped at the third points, with eccentricities varying as shown in the sketch. The initial prestress in the steel is 140,000 psi; after time-dependent losses this reduces to 77,000 psi. Using the approximate method of Art. 9.3, compute the deflections of the member at the following load stages: (a) immediately after transfer, when initial prestress and self-weight act. (b) after all time-dependent losses, when effective prestress and self-weight act. (c) Same as (b) but with short term live load of 275 plf acting. The following data are given: $A_c = 267$ in.^{2}, $I_c = 7550$ in.^{4}, $c_1 = 5.5$ in., $A_p = 1.52$ in.^{2}, $w_o = 275$ plf, $f'_c = 5000$ psi, $C_u = 2.0$, $E_c = 4,030,000$ psi, and $E_p = 27,000,000$ psi. Note that the application of full live load will produce flexural cracking.

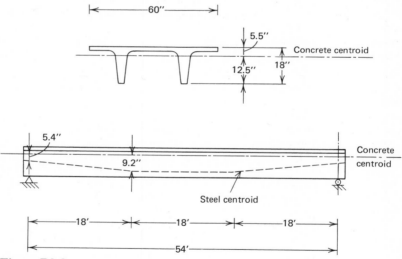

Figure P9.3

CHAPTER 10

SLABS

10.1 INTRODUCTION

Prestressed concrete slabs are used in civil engineering structures of many types, to provide flat, useful surfaces such as for floors, roofs, decks, or walls. In its most basic form, a slab is a plate, the thickness of which is small relative to its length and width. Usually the thickness is constant. The slab may be supported by walls, but more often it is carried by concrete beams that are generally poured monolithically with the slab, by structural steel beams, or directly by columns with no beams or girders.

Beam-supported slabs may be supported along two opposite edges only, as in Fig. 10.1*a*, in which case the structural action is essentially *one-way*. Loads applied to the surface are carried by the slab spanning in the direction perpendicular to the supported edges. On the other hand, there may be supports on all four sides of a slab panel, as in Fig. 10.1*b*, so that *two-way* action is obtained. Intermediate beams may be introduced to subdivide the slab, as shown in Fig. 10.1*c*. If the ratio of the short to the long side of a rectangular slab panel is less than about 0.5, most of the load is carried in the short direction, because of the greater stiffness associated with the shorter span length. Thus one-way action may be obtained, in effect, even though supports exist on four edges.

Prestressed concrete slabs are often carried directly by columns, as in Fig. 10.1*d*, without the use of beams or girders. Such slabs are described as *flat plates*. While flat plates are generally cast in place, just as for the other types of slabs described, they may also be cast at ground level and lifted into their final position in the structure by jacks at the columns. They are termed *lift slabs* in this case. Generally steel columns are used.

Closely related to the flat plate is the grid slab shown in Fig. 10.1*e*. To reduce dead load, voids are formed in the lower surface of the slab in a rectilinear pattern by means of reusable metal, fiberboard, or plastic form inserts. A two-way ribbed construction results. Generally inserts are omitted near the columns, resulting in a solid slab better able to resist the local concentration of moments and shears.

The term *flat slab* is reserved for the type of beamless construction shown in Fig. 10.1*f* (although in a literal sense all the slab forms described are flat slabs). Flat slab construction is characterized by a locally thickened portion

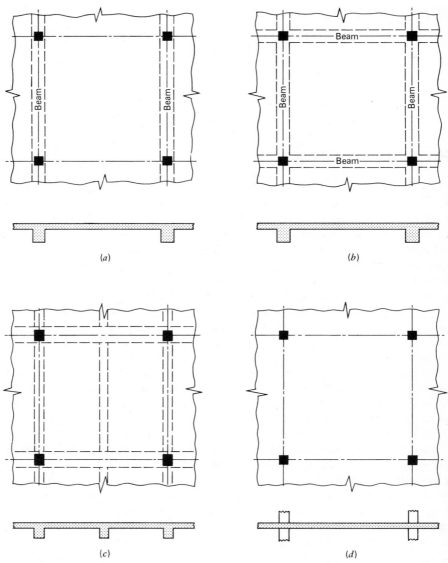

Figure 10.1 Types of slabs. (*a*) One-way slab. (*b*) Two-way slab. (*c*) One-way slab. (*d*) Flat plate slab. (*e*) Grid slab. (*f*) Flat slab.

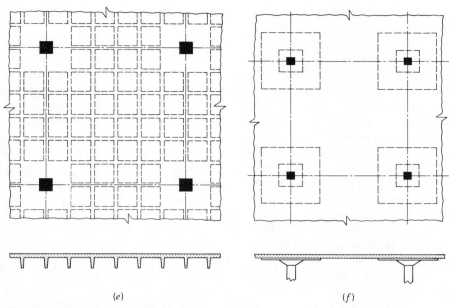

(e)   (f)

Figure 10.1 (cont.)

of the slab, termed a dropped panel, centered on the column, or by flared column tops, or both. The purpose of these devices is to increase shear strength and negative bending resistance at the columns. The design trend is away from the use of either dropped panels or flared columns, in favor of flat plates incorporating special reinforcement to serve the same purpose.

Prestressed concrete slabs are usually designed for dead and live loads assumed to be uniformly distributed over the entire surface of an area bounded by column centerlines or beam centerlines. Pattern live loadings, for which certain panels are unloaded, may be considered to obtain maximum and minimum moments. Concentrated loads require special study. They are always supported by a width of slab greater than the contact width, because of two-way action, or in the case of one-way slabs, by means of lateral distribution steel that is always present. Very heavy fixed concentrated loads may require supporting beams.

The principal reinforcement in prestressed slabs generally consists of stranded cable or multiwire tendons, typically spaced between about 2 and 5 ft center-to-center, depending on the loads, spans, and slab thickness. Variable eccentricity is almost always specified, with a basic parabolic profile derived from the uniform loads to be carried, but incorporating local concave downward transition curves over the column centerlines or supporting beams. The concrete protection for the tendons should not be less than 1 in. if the surface is exposed to earth or weather, and not less than 3/4 in. if it is not exposed to weather or in contact with the ground, according to ACI Code.

Economic and construction considerations have generally resulted in the selection of greased and wrapped unbonded tendons for slabs. These considerations include higher friction during stressing of tendons of the type intended for later grouting, the necessity to protect unwrapped tendons against corrosion during construction, and the problems associated with grouting a large number of tendons in small diameter ducts. Non-prestressed bar reinforcement is commonly added in one-way slabs for lateral distribution steel. When unbonded tendons are used in one- or two-way slabs, bar steel is often added to control cracking and enhance flexural strength. It also increases shear strength at the columns of flat plate construction.

Prestressed concrete slabs must exhibit satisfactory behavior at all stages of loading. Allowable stresses must not be exceeded at the unloaded or full service load stages. Camber, deflection, and vibration frequency and amplitude in service must be within acceptable limits. Adequate strength must be provided to resist the specified degree of overloading.

Any of these requirements may serve as the starting point in proportioning the slab. Recognizing that deflections may govern for relatively thin members such as slabs, many designers start with an assumed slab depth, based on maximum span/depth ratios or personal experience, to insure adequate stiffness. For some types of slabs, notably flat plates, shear is critical, and the initial estimate of slab thickness may be such as to satisfy shear strength requirements at the columns.

The concept of load balancing is specially useful for slabs, and usually provides the basis for establishing the best tendon profile, as well as the prestress force required to produce zero deflection for the selected load. The load to be balanced is usually the full dead load, or in some cases, dead load plus some small fraction of the service live load.

10.2 ONE-WAY SLABS

It has been noted that for one-way slabs the main structural action is in the direction perpendicular to the two supported edges. It follows that the principal prestressing tendons are placed perpendicular to the supports, as shown for a single-span slab in Fig. 10.2a. Normally unbonded strands or unbonded multiple wire tendons are employed. Consistent with the principle of load balancing, a parabolic tendon profile would be selected for the usual case of uniformly distributed load, with eccentricity varying from maximum at midspan to zero at the supported edges.

It is convenient for design purposes to isolate a typical slab strip of unit width, as shown in Fig. 10.2a. The load applied per unit area of slab surface is then equivalent to a distributed load, per unit length, along the strip of span

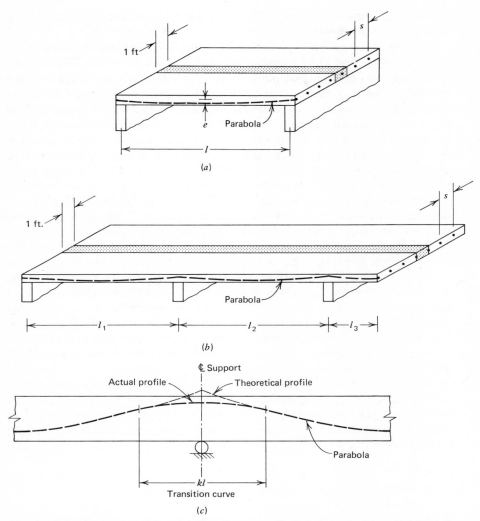

Figure 10.2 One-way slabs. (*a*) Simple span. (*b*) Continuous spans. (*c*) Detail at interior support.

l. All the equations developed in earlier chapters for beams can be applied, with no change, to the slab strip under consideration.* The required prestressing force determined will be that per unit width of slab. This can easily be translated into a required spacing *s* for tendons of known capacity. As a general guide,

---

* This simplified analysis, which neglects lateral pressures between adjacent slab strips due to the Poisson effect, is slightly conservative. The slab will actually be slightly stiffer and stronger than assumed, but the difference is small and is almost always disregarded.

the recommended maximum spacing of tendons is about six times the slab thickness (Ref. 10.1).

One-way slabs are often continuous over several supports or cantilevered, as suggested by Fig. 10.2b. A design approach similar to that for simple spans is followed but, in this case, the continuous tendon may be raised over the interior supports to the maximum negative eccentricity permitted by requirements of concrete cover. Parabolic profiles are used in each span, with relatively short, concave-downward transition curves over the interior supports. These transitions have the effect of delivering the downward reaction from each tendon over a finite length kl, as in Fig. 10.2c, rather than at a point, as would be true for the theoretically correct but impractical profile shown. In ordinary cases, the value of k may be about 0.20. The difference between concentrated and distributed reactions may be accounted for in the design, but is usually disregarded, since the reversed curvature has only a minor influence on the elastic moments, and it does not affect the ultimate moment capacity.

The tendons may be continuous over two, three, or more spans. Because of the shallow depth of slabs, as compared with beams, the prestress loss due to friction is not so severe, and it does not preclude several reversals of curvature. The effect of frictional losses in slabs may be further minimized by jacking alternate tendons from opposite ends, or for very long tendons, by jacking each tendon from both ends.

In addition to the main prestressed steel perpendicular to the supports, one-way slabs should be provided with reinforcement in the direction parallel to the supports. This serves the purpose of controlling cracks due to shrinkage of the concrete or due to a decrease in temperature. It also serves to distribute any concentrated loads. Reinforcement for shrinkage and temperature effects and load distribution may be non-prestressed bar steel, as for ordinary reinforced concrete construction. The ACI Code specifies the following minimum ratios of reinforcement area to gross concrete area:

Slabs where Grade 40 or 50 deformed bars are used	0.0020
Slabs where Grade 60 deformed bars or welded wire fabric (smooth or deformed) are used	0.0018
Slabs where reinforcement with yield strength exceeding 60,000 psi measured at a yield strain of 0.35 percent is used	$\dfrac{0.0018 \times 60{,}000}{f_y}$

In no case are such reinforcing bars to be placed farther apart than five times the slab thickness or more than 18 in., and in no case is the steel ratio to be less than 0.0014. Use of non-prestressed bar steel does not eliminate shrinkage or temperature cracks, but does insure that these will be very narrow "hairline" cracks, well distributed throughout the slab and not detrimental in any way.

An alternative, which may completely avoid cracking, is to use centroidal post-tensioned tendons, parallel to the supported edges, to provide a uniform compressive stress in that direction. This scheme is not practical for narrow one-way slabs, because short prestressing is neither economical nor accurate, but it has been successful for wide slabs. If such an arrangement is used, a minimum concrete compression of about 125 psi should be maintained. Prestressing a slab in the transverse direction has the effect of reducing losses associated with elastic shortening and creep in the longitudinal direction, but it can be shown that the reduction is not significant.

The design of one-way slabs will seldom be controlled by shear, although shear strength should be checked by the usual equations for beams. The critical section is to be taken a distance $h/2$ from the support face. One-way slabs, essentially wide shallow beams, are more apt to be critical in flexure or governed by deflection. For slabs designed by the load-balancing method, it is the deflection due to the *unbalanced* load (usually the live load) that is important. In calculations, the moment of inertia of the gross concrete cross section may ordinarily be used.

The ACI Code requires that deflections be calculated for slabs, as well as for all other prestressed members, and that the computed deflections should not exceed the limits given in Table 9.4.

Span/depth ratios provide a convenient starting point in proportioning one-way slabs. For single-span solid slabs, values between 22 and 28 are common. For fully continuous spans, ratios between 30 and 35 are often seen, while for cantilevers, an upper limit of about 16 appears reasonable. The total required thickness is usually rounded to the next higher 1/4 in. for slabs up to 6 in. in thickness, and to the next higher 1/2 in. for thicker slabs.

A practical consideration that must not be overlooked in the design of slabs prestressed longitudinally, or both longitudinally and transversely, is that axial shortening of the slab must not be prevented by conditions at the supports. This shortening may be particularly significant for multiple span members of substantial total length, or for very wide slabs. The maximum length of a slab between construction joints should be limited to about 150 ft to minimize the effect of slab shortening, as well as to avoid excessive loss of prestress due to friction.

10.3   TWO-WAY SLABS WITH ALL EDGES SUPPORTED: BEHAVIOR

Two-way slab systems may be supported by walls or relatively stiff beams on all four sides of each panel. Whereas the one-way slabs discussed in the preceding article deform under load into a cylindrical surface (Fig. 10.3a), a two-way edge-supported slab will bend into a dished shape (Fig. 10.3b). At any location, the slab is curved in both principal directions and, consequently, moments

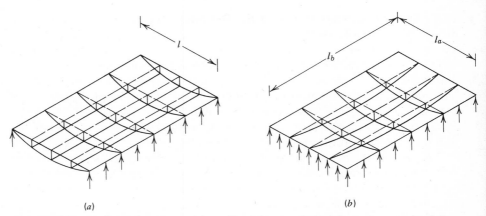

(a)   (b)

Figure 10.3 Deflected shape of uniformly loaded edge-supported slabs. (a) One-way slab with two edges supported. (b) Two-way slab with four edges supported.

exist in both directions. Prestressing tendons are placed in two directions, parallel to the edges of the slab, each set providing for its share of the applied load.

Inspection of Fig. 10.3b will show that the curvature of the central part of the slab in the short direction is greater than that in the long direction. Since the bending moment is directly proportional to curvature, it may be concluded that the bending moment in the short direction is larger than that in the long direction. Furthermore, the short-span curvature is less near the short edges of the panel than at the center of the slab. Consequently, a variation of short-span moments exists across the width of the slab, moments reducing markedly as the supported edges are approached. Similar behavior is apparent in the long direction.

Loads applied to two-way slabs cause twisting moments, as well as bending moments. Careful study of Fig. 10.3b indicates that slab strips in either direction, at any location except the slab centerlines, must twist in order to conform to the flexural rotations in the perpendicular direction. The internal twisting moments developed by two-way slabs tend to reduce the bending moments that must be resisted.

It may be clear from this short discussion that the determination slab design moments, in even the relatively simple two-way slab shown, is a fairly difficult problem. While solutions are available, based on application of the theory of elasticity, practical cases are complicated by the continuity of the slab over one or more of the edges, torsional and vertical deflection of the edge beams, varying panel proportions, etc. The more important variables are incorporated in an approximate way in practical methods of analysis.

10.4 TWO-DIRECTIONAL LOAD BALANCING FOR EDGE-SUPPORTED SLABS

The concept of load balancing, introduced in Chapter 1 and developed further in Chapter 4, is a useful tool for the analysis and design of two-way wall- or beam-supported slabs. The objective of load balancing for slabs, as for beams, is to provide an equivalent upward load from the curved tendons, such as to exactly balance a specified downward load. For that unique loading, the slab is subjected only to a uniform compressive stress in its own plane, resulting from the prestress force. Neither bending moments nor twisting moments will exist and, consequently, the analysis is very much simplified. If the external load is sustained in nature, as is the prestress force, the slab will exhibit neither camber nor deflection.

Two-directional load balancing for slabs differs from linear load balancing for beams, in that the equivalent load on the slab produced by the tendons in one direction either adds to, or subtracts from, the equivalent load from the tendons in the perpendicular direction. The fractional part of the load to be carried by the tendons in either direction is more or less arbitrary, the only strict requirement being satisfaction of statics. Consideration of indeterminancy is avoided for the unique balanced load that produces no deflection.

The fundamentals of two-directional load balancing will be demonstrated in the context of the rectangular, wall-supported slab of Fig. 10.4. The load to be balanced is generally the dead load, and is uniformly distributed. This leads naturally to the choice of parabolic tendon profiles in each direction as shown. Simply supported edges, in turn, govern the choice of zero eccentricity over the walls.

From Eq. (4.25a) of Ch. 4, the upward equivalent load, uniformly distributed, applied to the slab by parabolic tendons in the short span direction is

$$w_{pa} = \frac{8P_a y_a}{l_a^2} \qquad (10.1a)$$

where w_{pa} is the upward load in terms of force per unit area of slab surface, P_a is the effective prestress force after losses in the l_a direction per unit of length along side l_b, and y_a is the maximum eccentricity of those tendons with respect to the middepth of the slab. Similarly the tendons in the direction l_b produce an upward equivalent load of

$$w_{pb} = \frac{8P_b y_b}{l_b^2} \qquad (10.1b)$$

For design, the sum of the two upward components is set equal to the load to be balanced:

$$w_b = \frac{8P_a y_a}{l_a^2} + \frac{8P_b y_b}{l_b^2} \qquad (10.2)$$

and the required prestressing forces P_a and P_b determined accordingly.

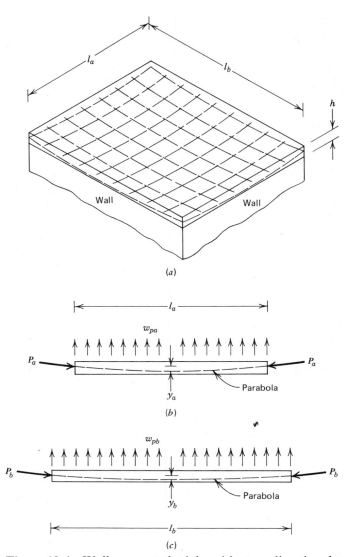

Figure 10.4 Wall-supported slab with two-directional tendon layout.

Note that many combinations of P_a and P_b will satisfy the requirement of statics given by Eq. (10.2).

For rectangular panels, in general, the economical choice is to carry most of the load in the short direction. However, it is usually desirable to maintain a certain minimum degree of precompression in the long direction, to control cracking, and to provide for improved distribution of any locally applied load.

This can be used to reduce the prestress required in the short direction by the amount w_{pb} from Eq. (10.1b).

Under the action of prestressing forces P_a and P_b plus the applied load w_b, the slab will be in a state of uniform compression P_a/bh in the direction of l_a and P_b/bh in the direction of l_b, where h is the slab thickness and b is the width of the unit strip, in appropriate units. Theoretically, the slab should be a completely level surface for this special loading, although this state will be only approximated in practice. This is because of uncertainties connected with losses and because of time-dependent effects on deflections.

If the slab is subjected to an incremental load above the balanced load, moments due to the unbalanced portion of the load may be determined using the methods of classical elasticity, or the approximate methods described in Art. 10.5. The resulting stresses in the slab (within the elastic range) are found by superimposing the uniform compression from the balanced loading and the flexural stresses associated with the moments due to the unbalanced loading. In the direction of l_a:

$$f_1 = -\frac{P_a}{bh} - \frac{M_a h}{2I_c}$$

$$f_2 = -\frac{P_a}{bh} + \frac{M_a h}{2I_c}$$

(10.3a)

at the top and bottom face of the slab, respectively, while in the direction of l_b:

$$f_1 = -\frac{P_b}{bh} - \frac{M_b h}{2I_c}$$

$$f_2 = -\frac{P_b}{bh} + \frac{M_b h}{2I_c}$$

(10.3b)

where M_a and M_b are the moments associated with the unbalanced portion of the load in the l_a and l_b directions, respectively, per unit strip of slab, and I_c is the moment of inertia of a unit strip of the slab section, which is assumed uncracked. Stresses in the unloaded stage, and stresses at full service loading, may be found in this way and compared against specified limits.

The arrangement of tendons suggested by Fig. 10.4 is not the only possibility, or even the best, from points of view other than load balancing. If an additional load is applied, the full service live load for example, the slab will deflection downward, and the behavior described in Art. 10.3 will obtain. A greater concentration of tendons in a central band in either direction would be more rational and more economical for that loading, although a slab designed with banded tendons would not be a level surface if the live load were removed. A banded arrangement of tendons would produce a slab with a greater strength reserve, should it be overloaded, than would one with the same number of tendons at uniform spacing.

In two-way slabs, a practical problem may arise due to interference of the tendons passing in perpendicular directions in certain regions. In the simply supported panel shown in Fig. 10.4, for example, such tendon interference will occur in the central region and at the corners. For thicker slabs, it is sufficiently accurate to use the average eccentricity for calculations in each direction; the loads will redistribute accordingly, should severe overloading occur. For thinner slabs, for which the tendon diameter represents a more substantial fraction of the slab depth, it is advisable to use actual eccentricities, recognizing that stacking is unavoidable.

10.5 PRACTICAL ANALYSIS FOR UNBALANCED LOADING

If the loading applied to an edge-supported slab deviates from the balanced loading, the slab will deflect either upward or downward, and moments must be found recognizing the indeterminate nature of even a simply supported rectangular panel. The most usual situation is the application of live loads, causing downward deflection, or the consideration of overloads. While the classical methods of elastic analysis provide solutions for very idealized situations, practical complications intrude and, as a result, approximate methods are favored that do account for these complicating factors, if only in a simplified way.

Perhaps the most rational and comprehensive of the simplified approaches is known as Method 3, published in the Appendix to the 1963 edition of the ACI Code.* The method applies to slabs supported on four sides by walls or relatively stiff beams.† The ratio of short to long sides of a panel may vary between 1.0 and 0.5. Slabs for which the aspect ratio is less than 0.5 may be designed for one-way action. The edge restraint conditions considered are simply supported (torsional resistance negligible) and continuous across or fixed at the supports. Nine separate combinations of restraint are included.

For each set of variables within the stated ranges, coefficients are given that permit the direct calculation of moments. These coefficients are based on elastic analysis, but also account for inelastic redistribution of moments. The design moments in the two directions are computed from the expressions

$$M_a = C_a w l_a^2 \tag{10.4a}$$

$$M_b = C_b w l_b^2 \tag{10.4b}$$

---

* It is unfortunate that the method has been deleted from subsequent editions of the Code; however its validity has not been questioned, and it continues to be a useful tool.

† For cases with more flexible beams, the stiffness of which is of the same order as the slab, or for two-way slabs supported directly on columns with no beams, the methods of Art. 10.12 are appropriate.

where

C_a and C_b = tabulated moment coefficients

w = uniformly distributed load per ft^2

l_a and l_b = length of clear span in short and long directions, respectively, ft

The method provides that each panel be divided, in both directions, into a middle strip whose width is 1/2 that of the panel, and two column strips of 1/4 of the panel width. As noted in Art. 10.3, the moments in both directions are larger in the central region of the slab than in regions close to the edges. Correspondingly, Method 3 provides that the entire middle strip be designed for the full design moments calculated with the tabulated coefficient. In the column strips, this moment is assumed to decrease from its full value at the edge of the middle strip, to 1/3 of this value at the edge of the panel.

Figure 10.5 shows a portion of the floor of a two-way beam-supported slab structure, with middle and column strips in both directions indicated for panel 3. The figure also illustrates certain of the possible edge conditions. Panel 1, for example, has two adjacent discontinuous exterior edges, while the other edges

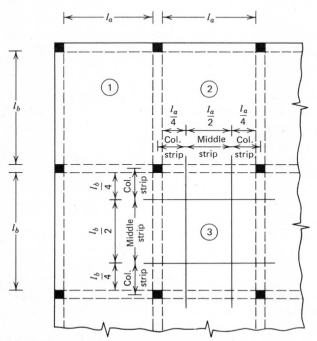

Figure 10.5   Beam-supported two-way slab.

are continuous with neighboring panels. Panel 2 has one discontinuous and three continuous edges. The interior panel 3 has all edges continuous.

Tables 10.1 through 10.4, reproduced from the 1963 ACI Code, give coefficients for moments and shears in two-way slab panels.

In the tables, the effects of dead loads are differentiated from the effects of live loads. The reason for this is that dead loads are always present in all panels of a floor system, while live loads may or may not act, and must be positioned for the maximum effect.

Table 10.1 gives moment coefficients for *negative moments at continuous edges*. Maximum negative edge moments obtain when both panels adjacent to the particular edge carry full dead and live load. The moment is computed for this total load. Clearly, the same coefficients apply in calculating the maximum negative moments due to dead load alone, or to live load only, assumed to be acting on both adjacent panels. Method 3 provides that *negative moments at discontinuous edges* shall be assumed equal to 1/3 of the positive moments for the same direction. One must provide for such moments because some degree of restraint is provided by discontinuous edges, by the torsional rigidity of the edge beam, or by the supporting wall.

For *positive moments*, there will be little, if any, rotation at the continuous edges if *dead load* alone is acting, because the loads on both adjacent panels tend to produce opposite rotations that cancel or nearly cancel. Hence, for this condition, the continuous edges can be regarded as fixed, and the appropriate coefficients for the dead load moments, are given in Table 10.2. On the other hand, the maximum *live load moments* are obtained when the live load is placed only on the particular panel and not on any of the adjacent panels. In this case some rotation will occur at all continuous edges. As an approximation, it is assumed that there is 50 percent restraint for calculating these live load moments, and the corresponding coefficients are given in Table 10.3.

Finally, for computing shear in the slab and loads on the supporting beams, Table 10.4 gives the fractions of the total load w that are transmitted in the two directions.

10.6   DEFLECTION OF TWO-WAY SLABS

Edge-supported slabs are typically thin in relation to their span, and may exhibit excessively large deflections when loaded, even though satisfactory in all other respects. Early in the design, a trial slab depth should be selected such that need for later revision due to deflection restrictions will be unlikely. For prestressed two-way slabs continuous over supported edges, the ratio of average span to total depth may be estimated to be from 45 to 55.

Slab deflections should always be calculated, and the results compared against limit values. Assuming that the slab has been designed for a balanced state under the combined action of prestress plus full dead load, then the deflection at any other load stage within the elastic range, such as at full service load, can be found considering only the incremental loading past the balanced-load stage. Prestressed edge-supported slabs are mostly uncracked at or below the service load stage, and the properties of the gross concrete cross section may be used in the calculations without serious error.

Classical methods of deflection analysis are of very limited use in practical cases, because generally the panel edges are neither fully fixed nor perfectly hinged, but have some intermediate degree of fixity depending on the load and span conditions in the adjacent panels, and on the torsional restraint provided by the edge beams or supporting walls.

However, deflections may be calculated based upon the approximate moment coefficients of Art. 10.5, which include recognition of such effects in a self-consistent way. Such an approximate approach is fully justified here, because it is only the incremental deflection, not the total deflection, that is to be found.

It will be recalled that the moment coefficient method of Art. 10.5 is used to determine *maximum values* of positive and negative moments at the critical sections of slabs. The moment coefficients of Tables 10.1 through 10.3 have been established considering the possibility of loads acting on alternate panels and of other arrangements.

Consequently, in the deflection calculations it would be incorrect to assume that those moments could act simultaneously at positive and negative critical sections.

Because the maximum deflection at the center of a slab panel will normally be obtained when live load acts on that panel, but not on the adjacent panels, deflection calculations should be based on the maximum positive moments found from the coefficients of Table 10.3, together with statically consistent negative moments at the supported edges.

This will be illustrated considering the middle strip of unit width in the long direction of a panel, as shown in Fig. 10.6a. The variation of moment for the uniformly distributed loading is parabolic, and by statics, the sum of the positive moment and the average of the two negative moments must be equal to $\bar{M} = \frac{1}{8}\bar{w}l_b^2$, where $\bar{w}$ is the fractional part of the load transmitted in the long direction of the panel. If full fixity were obtained at the supports, the negative moments would be $\frac{1}{12}\bar{w}l_b^2$, or $\frac{2}{3}\bar{M}$, and the positive moment would be $\frac{1}{24}\bar{w}l_b^2$, or $\frac{1}{3}\bar{M}$. But it has been noted earlier that the coefficients for maximum positive moments were derived assuming not 100 percent fixity, but 50 percent fixity. Accordingly, the moment baseline associated with the maximum positive moment M_{max} is as shown in Fig. 10.6c, and the statically consistent negative moments at the supports are $\frac{1}{2}M_{max}$.

Deflection calculations are thus based on a parabolic moment curve, with maximum ordinate at midspan, and end moments equal to half that maximum.

The midspan deflection d of the slab strip shown in Fig. 10.6b can easily be found using the moment diagram of Fig. 10.6c, in conjunction with the

Table 10.1 Coefficients for Negative Moments in Slabs[a]

$$M_{A\,neg} = C_{A\,neg} \times w \times A^2$$
$$M_{B\,neg} = C_{B\,neg} \times w \times B^2$$

where w = total uniform dead plus live load

Ratio $m = \dfrac{A}{B}$		Case 1	Case 2	Case 3	Case 4	Case 5	Case 6	Case 7	Case 8	Case 9
1.00	$C_{A\,neg}$		0.045		0.050	0.075	0.071		0.033	0.061
	$C_{B\,neg}$		0.045	0.076	0.050			0.071	0.061	0.033
0.95	$C_{A\,neg}$		0.050		0.055	0.079	0.075		0.038	0.065
	$C_{B\,neg}$		0.041	0.072	0.045			0.067	0.056	0.029
0.90	$C_{A\,neg}$		0.055		0.060	0.080	0.079		0.043	0.068
	$C_{B\,neg}$		0.037	0.070	0.040			0.062	0.052	0.025
0.85	$C_{A\,neg}$		0.060		0.066	0.082	0.083		0.049	0.072
	$C_{B\,neg}$		0.031	0.065	0.034			0.057	0.046	0.021
0.80	$C_{A\,neg}$		0.065		0.071	0.083	0.086		0.055	0.075
	$C_{B\,neg}$		0.027	0.061	0.029			0.051	0.041	0.017

		Case 1	Case 2	Case 3	Case 4	Case 5	Case 6	Case 7	Case 8	Case 9
0.75	$C_{A\,neg}$		0.069		0.076	0.085	0.088		0.061	0.078
	$C_{B\,neg}$		0.022	0.056	0.024			0.044	0.036	0.014
0.70	$C_{A\,neg}$		0.074		0.081	0.086	0.091		0.068	0.081
	$C_{B\,neg}$		0.017	0.050	0.019			0.038	0.029	0.011
0.65	$C_{A\,neg}$		0.077		0.085	0.087	0.093		0.074	0.083
	$C_{B\,neg}$		0.014	0.043	0.015			0.031	0.024	0.008
0.60	$C_{A\,neg}$		0.081		0.089	0.088	0.095		0.080	0.085
	$C_{B\,neg}$		0.010	0.035	0.011			0.024	0.018	0.006
0.55	$C_{A\,neg}$		0.084		0.092	0.089	0.096		0.085	0.086
	$C_{B\,neg}$		0.007	0.028	0.008			0.019	0.014	0.005
0.50	$C_{A\,neg}$		0.086		0.094	0.090	0.097		0.089	0.088
	$C_{B\,neg}$		0.006	0.022	0.006			0.014	0.010	0.003

[a] A cross-hatched edge indicates that the slab continues across or is fixed at the support; an unmarked edge indicates a support at which torsional resistance is negligible.

This table is adapted with permission of the American Concrete Institute from ACI Building Code 318–63.

Table 10.2 Coefficients for Dead Load Positive Moments in Slabs[a]

$$M_{A\,pos\,DL} = C_{A\,DL} \times w \times A^2$$
$$M_{B\,pos\,DL} = C_{B\,DL} \times w \times B^2$$
where w = total uniform dead load

Ratio $m = \dfrac{A}{B}$		Case 1	Case 2	Case 3	Case 4	Case 5	Case 6	Case 7	Case 8	Case 9
1.00	$C_{A\,DL}$	0.036	0.018	0.018	0.027	0.027	0.033	0.027	0.020	0.023
	$C_{B\,DL}$	0.036	0.018	0.027	0.027	0.018	0.027	0.033	0.023	0.020
0.95	$C_{A\,DL}$	0.040	0.020	0.021	0.030	0.028	0.036	0.031	0.022	0.024
	$C_{B\,DL}$	0.033	0.016	0.025	0.024	0.015	0.024	0.031	0.021	0.017
0.90	$C_{A\,DL}$	0.045	0.022	0.025	0.033	0.029	0.039	0.035	0.025	0.026
	$C_{B\,DL}$	0.029	0.014	0.024	0.022	0.013	0.021	0.028	0.019	0.015
0.85	$C_{A\,DL}$	0.050	0.024	0.029	0.036	0.031	0.042	0.040	0.029	0.028
	$C_{B\,DL}$	0.026	0.012	0.022	0.019	0.011	0.017	0.025	0.017	0.013
0.80	$C_{A\,DL}$	0.056	0.026	0.034	0.039	0.032	0.045	0.045	0.032	0.029
	$C_{B\,DL}$	0.023	0.011	0.020	0.016	0.009	0.015	0.022	0.015	0.010

Ratio		1	2	3	4	5	6	7	8	9
0.75	$C_{A\,DL}$	0.061	0.028	0.040	0.043	0.033	0.048	0.051	0.036	0.031
	$C_{B\,DL}$	0.019	0.009	0.018	0.013	0.007	0.012	0.020	0.013	0.007
0.70	$C_{A\,DL}$	0.068	0.030	0.046	0.046	0.035	0.051	0.058	0.040	0.033
	$C_{B\,DL}$	0.016	0.007	0.016	0.011	0.005	0.009	0.017	0.011	0.006
0.65	$C_{A\,DL}$	0.074	0.032	0.054	0.050	0.036	0.054	0.065	0.044	0.034
	$C_{B\,DL}$	0.013	0.006	0.014	0.009	0.004	0.007	0.014	0.009	0.005
0.60	$C_{A\,DL}$	0.081	0.034	0.062	0.053	0.037	0.056	0.073	0.048	0.036
	$C_{B\,DL}$	0.010	0.004	0.011	0.007	0.003	0.006	0.012	0.007	0.004
0.55	$C_{A\,DL}$	0.088	0.035	0.071	0.056	0.038	0.058	0.081	0.052	0.037
	$C_{B\,DL}$	0.008	0.003	0.009	0.005	0.002	0.004	0.009	0.005	0.003
0.50	$C_{A\,DL}$	0.095	0.037	0.080	0.059	0.039	0.061	0.089	0.056	0.038
	$C_{B\,DL}$	0.006	0.002	0.007	0.004	0.001	0.003	0.007	0.004	0.002

[a] A cross-hatched edge indicates that the slab continues across or is fixed at the support; an unmarked edge indicates a support at which torsional resistance is negligible.

This table is adapted with permission of the American Concrete Institute from ACI Building Code 318–63.

Table 10.3 Coefficients for Live Load Positive Moments in Slabs[a]

$$\left.\begin{array}{l} M_{A\,pos\,LL} = C_{A\,LL} \times w \times A^2 \\ M_{B\,pos\,LL} = C_{B\,LL} \times w \times B^2 \end{array}\right\} \text{ where } w = \text{total uniform live load}$$

Ratio $m = \dfrac{A}{B}$		Case 1	Case 2	Case 3	Case 4	Case 5	Case 6	Case 7	Case 8	Case 9
1.00	$C_{A\,LL}$	0.036	0.027	0.027	0.032	0.032	0.035	0.032	0.028	0.030
	$C_{B\,LL}$	0.036	0.027	0.032	0.032	0.027	0.032	0.035	0.030	0.028
0.95	$C_{A\,LL}$	0.040	0.030	0.031	0.035	0.034	0.038	0.036	0.031	0.032
	$C_{B\,LL}$	0.033	0.025	0.029	0.029	0.024	0.029	0.032	0.027	0.025
0.90	$C_{A\,LL}$	0.045	0.034	0.035	0.039	0.037	0.042	0.040	0.035	0.036
	$C_{B\,LL}$	0.029	0.022	0.027	0.026	0.021	0.025	0.029	0.024	0.022
0.85	$C_{A\,LL}$	0.050	0.037	0.040	0.043	0.041	0.046	0.045	0.040	0.039
	$C_{B\,LL}$	0.026	0.019	0.024	0.023	0.019	0.022	0.026	0.022	0.020
0.80	$C_{A\,LL}$	0.056	0.041	0.045	0.048	0.044	0.051	0.051	0.044	0.042
	$C_{B\,LL}$	0.023	0.017	0.022	0.020	0.016	0.019	0.023	0.019	0.017

Ratio	Coef.									
0.75	$C_{A\,LL}$	0.061	0.045	0.051	0.052	0.047	0.055	0.056	0.049	0.046
	$C_{B\,LL}$	0.019	0.014	0.019	0.016	0.013	0.016	0.020	0.016	0.013
0.70	$C_{A\,LL}$	0.068	0.049	0.057	0.057	0.051	0.060	0.063	0.054	0.050
	$C_{B\,LL}$	0.016	0.012	0.016	0.014	0.011	0.013	0.017	0.014	0.011
0.65	$C_{A\,LL}$	0.074	0.053	0.064	0.062	0.055	0.064	0.070	0.059	0.054
	$C_{B\,LL}$	0.013	0.010	0.014	0.011	0.009	0.010	0.014	0.011	0.009
0.60	$C_{A\,LL}$	0.081	0.058	0.071	0.067	0.059	0.068	0.077	0.065	0.059
	$C_{B\,LL}$	0.010	0.007	0.011	0.009	0.007	0.008	0.011	0.009	0.007
0.55	$C_{A\,LL}$	0.088	0.062	0.080	0.072	0.063	0.073	0.085	0.070	0.063
	$C_{B\,LL}$	0.008	0.006	0.009	0.007	0.005	0.006	0.009	0.007	0.006
0.50	$C_{A\,LL}$	0.095	0.066	0.088	0.077	0.067	0.078	0.092	0.076	0.067
	$C_{B\,LL}$	0.006	0.004	0.007	0.005	0.004	0.005	0.007	0.005	0.004

[a] A cross-hatched edge indicates that the slab continues across or is fixed at the support; an unmarked edge indicates a support at which torsional resistance is negligible.

This table is adapted with permission of the American Concrete Institute from ACI Building Code 318–63.

Table 10.4 Ratio of Load w in l_a and l_b Directions for Shear in Slab and Load on Supports[a]

Ratio $m = \dfrac{A}{B}$		Case 1	Case 2	Case 3	Case 4	Case 5	Case 6	Case 7	Case 8	Case 9
1.00	W_A	0.50	0.50	0.17	0.50	0.83	0.71	0.29	0.33	0.67
	W_B	0.50	0.50	0.83	0.50	0.17	0.29	0.71	0.67	0.33
0.95	W_A	0.55	0.55	0.20	0.55	0.86	0.75	0.33	0.38	0.71
	W_B	0.45	0.45	0.80	0.45	0.14	0.25	0.67	0.62	0.29
0.90	W_A	0.60	0.60	0.23	0.60	0.88	0.79	0.38	0.43	0.75
	W_B	0.40	0.40	0.77	0.40	0.12	0.21	0.62	0.57	0.25
0.85	W_A	0.66	0.66	0.28	0.66	0.90	0.83	0.43	0.49	0.79
	W_B	0.34	0.34	0.72	0.34	0.10	0.17	0.57	0.51	0.21
0.80	W_A	0.71	0.71	0.33	0.71	0.92	0.86	0.49	0.55	0.83
	W_B	0.29	0.29	0.67	0.29	0.08	0.14	0.51	0.45	0.17

0.75	W_A	0.76	0.76	0.39	0.76	0.94	0.88	0.56	0.61	0.86
	W_B	0.24	0.24	0.61	0.24	0.06	0.12	0.44	0.39	0.14
0.70	W_A	0.81	0.81	0.45	0.81	0.95	0.91	0.62	0.68	0.89
	W_B	0.19	0.19	0.55	0.19	0.05	0.09	0.38	0.32	0.11
0.65	W_A	0.85	0.85	0.53	0.85	0.96	0.93	0.69	0.74	0.92
	W_B	0.15	0.15	0.47	0.15	0.04	0.07	0.31	0.26	0.08
0.60	W_A	0.89	0.89	0.61	0.89	0.97	0.95	0.76	0.80	0.94
	W_B	0.11	0.11	0.39	0.11	0.03	0.05	0.24	0.20	0.06
0.55	W_A	0.92	0.92	0.69	0.92	0.98	0.96	0.81	0.85	0.95
	W_B	0.08	0.08	0.31	0.08	0.02	0.04	0.19	0.15	0.05
0.50	W_A	0.94	0.94	0.76	0.94	0.99	0.97	0.86	0.89	0.97
	W_B	0.06	0.06	0.24	0.06	0.01	0.03	0.14	0.11	0.03

[a] A cross-hatched edge indicates that the slab continues across or is fixed at the support; an unmarked edge indicates a support at which torsional resistance is negligible.

This table is adapted with permission of the American Concrete Institute from ACI Building Code 318–63.

341

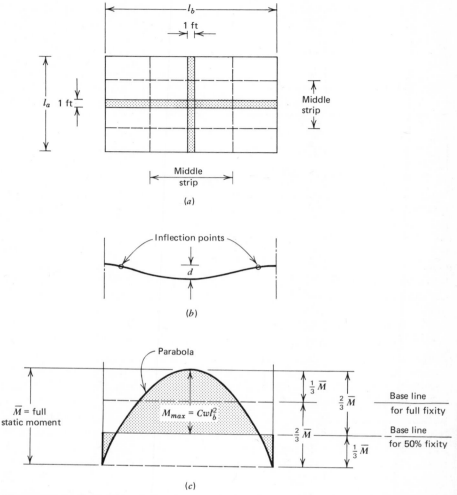

Figure 10.6 Basis for deflection analysis of two-way edge-supported slabs. (*a*) Plan view of slab. (*b*) Deflection curve of unit strip. (*c*) Diagram for maximum positive moment.

moment area principles. For the slab shown, with all edges continuous:

$$d = \frac{3}{32} \frac{M_{max} l_b^2}{E_c I_c} \tag{10.5}$$

where M_{max} is the positive live load moment obtained using the coefficients of Table 10.3, E_c is the elastic modulus of the concrete, and I_c is the moment of inertia of the concrete cross section of unit width, assumed uncracked.

While Eq. (10.5) is based on a unit strip spanning in the long direction of the panel, a similar calculation could as easily have been made in the short direction. The resulting deflections should be the same, although small differences will generally be obtained because of the approximate nature of the moment calculations. A reasonable procedure is to calculate the deflection each way and average the results.

Equation (10.5) was derived for a typical interior panel, with equal restraining moments at each end of the slab strip. Similar equations can easily be derived where one or both edges are discontinuous. Bearing in mind that, according to the approximate method of moment analysis, minimum negative moments at discontinuous edges generally are to be taken equal to 1/3 the positive moment in the same direction, it is clear that the resulting equations will differ very little from Eq. (10.5). For the special case where all edges are completely free of restraint, as for example if a slab were supported on masonry walls, the midspan deflection is

$$d = \frac{5}{48} \frac{M_{max} l_b^2}{E_c I_c} \tag{10.6}$$

If the slab is supported on edge beams for which the deflection is significant, the midspan deflection of the beams on the short side of a slab panel may be added to the center deflection of a unit strip of the slab in the long direction, to obtain the total deflection at the center of the bay. Approximately the same result should be obtained adding the short span slab deflection to the long span beam deflection.

Deflections calculated by the above equations are the initial elastic deflections, resulting immediately upon application of short-term loads. Since the sustained effects of prestress and dead load have been accounted for separately through load balancing, usually only the short term deflection associated with the live load is required. However, if all or part of the incremental loading is sustained in nature, the additional long term deflection may be estimated by multiplying the immediate deflection caused by the sustained load by an appropriate factor. A value of 2.5 has often been used, although this may be unconservative in some cases.

10.7 FLEXURAL STRENGTH OF TWO-WAY SLABS

For slabs, as for other prestressed members, keeping stresses within acceptable limits in the unloaded and service load stages does not insure an adequate degree of safety against collapse. The ultimate strength of slabs for the overload stage should always be determined. Shear strength of edge-supported slabs is usually not critical, although the shear capacity of unit strips may be checked using ordinary beam equations, and compared against the shear strength required, based on the coefficients of Table 10.4. The ultimate flexural strength of slabs is likely to control.

It has been proposed that the yield line theory of ultimate load analysis be applied to prestressed concrete slabs. Basically a two-dimensional version of limit analysis, as is sometimes used for beams and frames, yield line theory assumes the formation of a sufficient number of plastic hinges in an arrangement such as to form a mechanism, leading to collapse of the slab. The formation of such hinges, or yield lines, is accompanied by a redistribution of moments so that the elastic moment ratios are modified (Ref. 10.3).

Questions have been raised relative to the applicability of limit analysis even to reinforced concrete, on the basis that the needed rotation capacity may not be available. The ACI Code permits the designer to assume only a modest amount of moment redistribution. Prestressing steel is less ductile than bar reinforcement, and prestressed concrete members show less rotation at critical sections at failure than do reinforced concrete members. While the application of yield line theory to prestressed slabs is an attractive possibility, it may be concluded that there is as yet insufficient experimental basis for doing so. It is recommended that failure moments be calculated by applying the usual load factors to the moments found from elastic analysis, or from the coefficients of Tables 10.1 through 10.3.

In investigating the ultimate load of slabs, it is no longer appropriate to superimpose load effects, cancelling the effect of prestress uplift against all or part of the surface loading, as is done at the load-balancing stage. Both concrete and steel are likely to be stressed into the nonlinear range, invalidating superposition. The prestressing force changes as the slab is overloaded, and the increase generally is not uniform along the length of the tendons. As the slab deflects for heavy overloads, the lateral distribution of moments across the critical sections changes, further invalidating the load-balancing approach.

The ultimate resisting moments required must be found by applying overload factors to the *total* dead load, including the self-weight of the slab, and the total live load as well. Secondary moments, if any, due to prestressing, must be included, using a load factor of 1.0.

The resisting moment provide by the slab strips is then found, using the methods developed for beams as described in Chs. 3 and 4 and the design modified if necessary to provide the required strength.

10.8   EXAMPLE: TWO-WAY WALL-SUPPORTED SLAB

A rectangular slab measuring 20 × 30 ft in plan is supported on masonry walls on four sides, offering negligible rotational restraint. The general arrangement is shown in Fig. 10.7. The slab is to be designed to carry a superimposed dead load of 9 psf in addition to its own weight, and will be subjected to a service live load of 50 psf. The condition of zero deflection is specified when the full dead load acts. Concrete having 28 day compressive strength of 4000 psi and $E_c = 3.6 \times 10^6$ psi is to be used. Unbonded, post-tensioned single-strand tendons will be used, and losses after anchorage may be taken at 15 percent of the

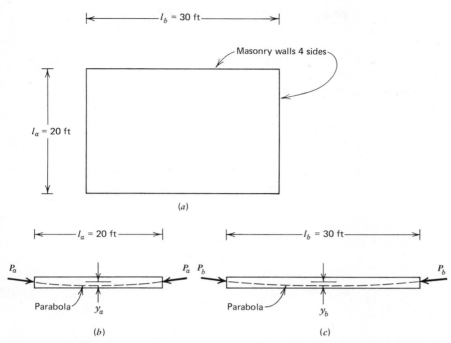

Figure 10.7   Design example: two-way slab. (*a*) Plan view. (*b*) Profile of short span. (*c*) Profile of long span.

initial prestress force. ($l_a = 6.09$ m, $l_b = 9.14$ m, $w_d = 0.43$ kN/m², $w_1 = 2.40$ kN/m², $f'_c = 28$ N/mm², and $E_c = 24.8$ kN/mm².)

A trial slab thickness will be selected based on a span/depth ratio of 45. The average span length may be used for this purpose.

$$h = \frac{(20 + 30)12}{2 \times 45} = 6.67 \text{ in.} \qquad \text{try } h = 6.5 \text{ in. (165 mm)}$$

Since zero deflection is desired for the full dead load stage, the design will be initiated using the load-balancing approach at that stage, although all other significant stages must, of course, be checked. For the trial slab depth, the self-weight is 81 psf, and so the total dead load to be balanced is $w_b = 81 + 9 = 90$ psf (4.3 kN/m²).

It is economical to carry most of the load in the short direction. However a minimum uniform compression of 150 psi in the concrete in the long direction will be used to insure a crack-free structure. Since the balanced load is uniformly distributed, parabolic tendons will be used in both directions, as shown in Figs. 10.7b and 10.7c, with zero eccentricity at the supported edges. Given that a 3/4 in. cover must be maintained below the lowest tendons, according to the Code, and assuming that wrapped tendons will have an outer diameter of about 1/2 in., an average distance from the bottom of slab to the tendon centroid of $1\frac{1}{4}$ in. will be used for calculations. This gives a maximum sag for the tendons of 2 in. from the centroid of the 6.5 in. depth slab.

To maintain the desired average compression of 150 psi in the slab in the long direction, an effective prestress force is required of

$$P_b = 150 \times 6.5 \times 12 = 11{,}700 \text{ lb/ft strip (52 kN)}$$

corresponding to an initial value of 13,800 lb/ft strip. From Eq. (10.1b), with the tendon profile shown, this produces an uplift of

$$w_{pb} = \frac{8 P_b y_b}{l_b^2} = \frac{8 \times 11{,}700 \times 2}{900 \times 12} = 17 \text{ psf}$$

Consequently an uplift of $w_{pa} = 90 - 17 = 73$ psf must be provided by the tendons in the short direction, From Eq. (10.1a):

$$P_a = \frac{w_{pa} l_a^2}{8 y_a} = \frac{73 \times 400 \times 12}{8 \times 2} = 21{,}900 \text{ lb/ft strip (97 kN)}$$

after losses, requiring an initial prestress force of 25,800 lb/ft strip. After losses, this will produce an average compression in the concrete in the short direction of

$$\frac{P_a}{bh} = \frac{21{,}900}{12 \times 6.5} = 280 \text{ psi}$$

Grade 270 unbonded wrapped strand having a diameter of 0.600 in. is selected for each direction (see Appendix B) and tensioned to the full allowed value so as to produce an initial force of 41,000 lb per tendon, at $0.70 f_{pu}$, after strand anchorage. The required spacing in the short direction is

$$s_a = \frac{41{,}000}{25{,}800} = 1.59 \text{ ft} = 19 \text{ in. (483 mm)}$$

and in the long direction

$$s_b = \frac{41{,}000}{13{,}800} = 2.97 \text{ ft} = 36 \text{ in. (914 mm)}$$

These spacings correspond to about 3 and 5.5 times the slab thickness, respectively, confirming that design choices to this point are reasonable.

In addition to the tendons, nonprestressed reinforcement will be added at the end anchorages to avoid splitting of the concrete. Two horizontal No. 4 bars will be placed around the entire perimeter just inside of the anchorages for this purpose (see Art. 10.15).

With the full dead load in place, and prestressing force and arrangement as indicated, a level slab should be obtained, very nearly.

The service live load of 50 psf will now be applied and concrete stresses and slab deflection checked. Making use of the moment coefficients of ACI Method 3, with $l_a/l_b = 20/30 = 0.67$, from Case 1 of Table 10.3 $C_a = 0.072$ and $C_b = 0.014$. Thus the moments per 12 in. strip in the short and long directions, respectively, resulting from application of the live load of 50 psf are

$$M_a = 0.072 \times 50 \times 20^2 = 1440 \text{ ft-lb}$$
$$M_b = 0.014 \times 50 \times 30^2 = 630 \text{ ft-lb}$$

The moment of inertia of a 12 in. strip of the slab is equal to $12 \times 6.5^3/12 = 275$ in.[4] The bending stresses that superimpose on the uniform compression stress already existing in the balanced slab are

$$f_b = \frac{1440 \times 12 \times 3.25}{275} = 204 \text{ psi}$$

in the short direction and

$$f_b = \frac{630 \times 12 \times 3.25}{275} = 89 \text{ psi}$$

in the long direction. The resulting stresses are

$$f_1 = -280 - 204 = -484 \text{ psi}$$
$$f_2 = -280 + 204 = -76 \text{ psi}$$

at the top and bottom surfaces in the short direction and

$$f_1 = -150 - 89 = -239 \text{ psi}$$
$$f_2 = -150 + 89 = -61 \text{ psi}$$

at the top and bottom surfaces in the long direction. This indicates a condition of no tension in the slab for full service load, and maximum compression well below the ACI limit stress of $0.45f'_c$.

Deflection at the center of the panel will be checked for the full live load condition using Eq. (10.6). In the short direction

$$d = \frac{5}{48} \frac{1440 \times 12(20 \times 12)^2}{3.6 \times 10^6 \times 275} = 0.10 \text{ in. (3 mm)}$$

while an independent check using a central strip in the long direction confirms that

$$d = \frac{5}{48} \frac{630 \times 12(30 \times 12)^2}{3.6 \times 10^6 \times 275} = 0.10 \text{ in. (3 mm)}$$

Next the flexural strength of the slab will be determined to confirm that an adequate factor of safety has been incorporated. For a 12 in. strip in the short direction, the required strength, based on ACI load factors, must be at least

$$M_u = 0.072(90 \times 1.4 + 50 \times 1.7)20^2 = 6080 \text{ ft-lb (8.24 kN-m)}$$

Prestressing produces no secondary moments in the present case, as all edges are simply supported.

The resisting moment of the strip will be found using the ACI approximate method. With $A_p = 0.217$ in.[2] on 1.59 ft centers,

$$f_{pe} = \frac{21,900 \times 1.59}{0.217} = 160,000 \text{ psi}$$

$$\rho_b = \frac{0.217}{1.59 \times 12 \times 5.25} = 0.0022$$

and from Eq. (3.21):

$$f_{ps} = f_{pe} + 10,000 + \frac{f'_c}{100\rho_p}$$

$$= 160,000 + 10,000 + 18,200 = 188,200 \text{ psi } (1300 \text{ N/mm}^2)$$

From Eqs. (3.18) and (3.23):

$$a = \frac{A_p f_{ps}}{0.85 f'_c b}$$

$$= \frac{0.217 \times 188,200}{1.59 \times 0.85 \times 4000 \times 12} = 0.63 \text{ in.}$$

$$M_n = A_p f_{ps}\left(d - \frac{a}{2}\right)$$

$$= \frac{0.217}{1.59} \times 188,200(5.25 - 0.32)\frac{1}{12}$$

$$= 10,600 \text{ ft-lb } (14.37 \text{ kN-m})$$

Introducing the strength reduction factor, the design strength is

$$\phi M_n = 0.90 \times 10,600$$
$$= 9540 \text{ ft-lb } (12.94 \text{ kN-m})$$

This is well above the required value of 6080 ft-lb.

Similar calculations in the long direction indicate a required moment capacity of 2660 ft-lb, and an available resisting moment of 5640 ft-lb.

Finally, the shear strength of the slab will be compared against the required capacity. Using the coefficients of Table 10.4, with the total load on the slab of

$$W = (90 \times 1.4 + 50 \times 1.7)20 \times 30 = 126,600 \text{ lb}$$

the shear force applied along the long edge is

$$V_u = \frac{126,600 \times 0.83}{2 \times 30} = 1750 \text{ lb/ft}$$

and along the short edge is

$$V_u = \frac{126,600 \times 0.17}{2 \times 20} = 538 \text{ lb/ft}$$

Using the ACI approximate equation for shear strength, Eq. (5.17),

$$V_c = \left(0.6\sqrt{f'_c} + 700\frac{V_u d}{M_u}\right)b_w d \qquad \text{but} \qquad \geq 2\sqrt{f'_c}b_w d$$

$$\text{and} \qquad \leq 5\sqrt{f'_c}b_w d$$

The last provision controls here and $\phi V_c = 0.85 \times 5\sqrt{4000}(12 \times 5.25)$

$$= 16,900 \text{ lb/ft}$$

Clearly the slab is not shear-critical.

Additional Comments

1. The slab depth was chosen based on an assumed span/depth ratio and was post-tensioned to achieve a zero deflection condition for full dead load. A very low uniform compression in the slab obtained in each direction for that condition.
2. With full service live load superimposed, concrete stresses remained very low and no tensile stress was produced. Deflection at the center of the panel was extremely small.
3. Flexural and shear strengths are well above those required by the Code.
4. It may be concluded that the slab thickness could be reduced somewhat without causing difficulty at any of the significant limit states. However, the prestress force required to balance the specified load would increase as a result. The overall economy of alternate design should be investigated.

10.9 PRESTRESSED FLAT PLATE SLABS

The floor system known as flat plate construction, in which there are no beams or other projections below the bottom surface of the slab, is well suited to prestressed concrete construction. It has been widely used for office buildings, institutional structures, apartment buildings, and hotels. For such cases, loads are not heavy, spans are usually not very long, and the advantages of flat plate construction may be fully exploited.

These advantages are numerous. Forming costs are minimized, because of the lack of beams or drop panels below the bottom face of the slab. Construction depth is the least possible. This permits reduction in the overall height of the structure, with attendant savings in costs of partitions and exterior walls, heating, ventilating and plumbing risers, etc. The smooth undersurface of the slab can be painted directly and left exposed as finish ceiling, or plaster or acoustical material can be applied directly to the concrete.

Many flat plate slabs are cast in place. However, many structures of this type have been built using the lift-slab technique, by which floors and roof slab are cast at ground level, then raised to final position by lifting rods connected to jacks at the tops of the columns. This form of construction is illustrated in Fig. 10.8.

The behavior, design, and construction of prestressed concrete flat plates has been the subject of intensive study by a joint ASCE-ACI committee. Its report, "Tentative Recommendations for Prestressed Concrete Flat Plates" (Ref. 10.4), is a valuable source document. The recommendations contained in that report have been incorporated in the following sections.

Figure 10.8   Lift-slab building under construction.

10.10   BEHAVIOR OF FLAT PLATES

The behavior of a flat plate slab may be understood with reference to Fig. 10.9, which shows a typical interior slab panel, together with portions of the adjacent panels. While, for flat plate slabs, there are no column line beams to provide

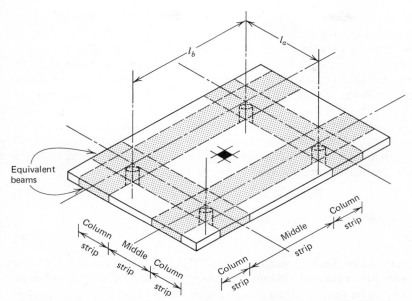

Figure 10.9 Two-way flat plate floor system showing equivalent beams.

edge support for the panels, slab strips centered on the column lines in each direction play the role of the missing beams.

When load is applied, either by curved prestressing tendons or external loads, a flat plate will deform into a double-curved surface, with principal moments acting in the directions parallel to the column lines.

A load applied to the central area, shown darkened in Fig. 10.9, is shared between strips of slab spanning in the short and long directions of the panel. The division of the load between short- and long-direction strips depends on the aspect ratio of the panel, and on the boundary conditions, as was true for edge-supported slabs. The strips of slab each carry their share of the load to the slab column strips, shown shaded, which act as edge-support beams for the panel although their thickness is no greater than that of the central portion of the slab.

Note that the portion of the load that is carried by the middle strip in the long direction is delivered to the column strips spanning in the short direction of the panel. This portion of the total load, plus that carried directly in the short direction by the middle strip, sums up to 100 percent of the load applied to the panel. Similarly the short-direction middle strips deliver a part of the load to the long-direction column strips. This load, plus that carried directly in the long direction by the middle strips, includes 100 percent of the applied load. It is clearly a requirement of statics that, for column-supported slabs, 100 percent of the applied load must be accounted for in *each* direction, jointly by the column strips and middle strips.*

Figure 10.10a shows a flat plate floor supported by columns at *a*, *b*, *c*, and *d*, and carrying load *w* per unit of surface area. Figure 10.10b indicates the moment diagram for the direction of span l_1. In this direction, the slab may be considered as a broad, flat beam of width l_2. Accordingly, the load per unit length of span is wl_2.

In any span of a continuous beam, the sum of the midspan positive moment and the average of the negative moments at adjacent supports is equal to the midspan positive moment of a corresponding simply supported beam. In terms of the slab, this requirement of statics may be written

$$\tfrac{1}{2}(M_{ab} + M_{cd}) + M_{ef} = \tfrac{1}{8}wl_2l_1^2 \tag{10.7a}$$

A similar requirement exists in the perpendicular direction, leading to

$$\tfrac{1}{2}(M_{ac} + M_{bd}) + M_{gh} = \tfrac{1}{8}wl_1l_2^2 \tag{10.7b}$$

These statements disclose nothing about the relative magnitudes of the support moments and span moments. The proportion of the total static moment that is associated with each critical section must be found from an elastic analysis, which considers the relative stiffnesses and loadings of all panels in a continuous strip of floor, as well as the stiffnesses of connected columns. Alternatively, empirical methods that have been found to be reliable under restricted conditions may be adopted.

The moments across the width of critical sections, such as across the lines *ab* or *ef*, are not constant, but vary as shown qualitatively in Fig. 10.10c and 10.10d. Along the column centerlines, where curvatures are greater, moments are greater, while along a line at the centerline of the panel, curvatures are more gradual and the corresponding moments are smaller. For design purposes, it is convenient to divide the panel in each direction as shown, into column strips and middle strips. Within the limits of each, the moment is assumed constant.

It is clear, considering this lateral distribution of moments, that the best distribution of tendons is nonuniform across the width of a slab panel, in either direction. Cables will be rather widely spaced in the middle strips, and closer together in the column strips.

Prestressed concrete flat plates are statically indeterminate structures and, in general, the application of prestressing force produces not only primary moments, but secondary moments, associated with the support reactions resulting from prestressing. This effect is completely analogous to the secondary

---

* This conclusion is not a contradiction of Art. 10.4, in which it was pointed out that the applied load could be assigned more or less arbitrarily to slab strips in either direction, for edge-supported slabs. In that discussion, loads on the edge beams were not considered.

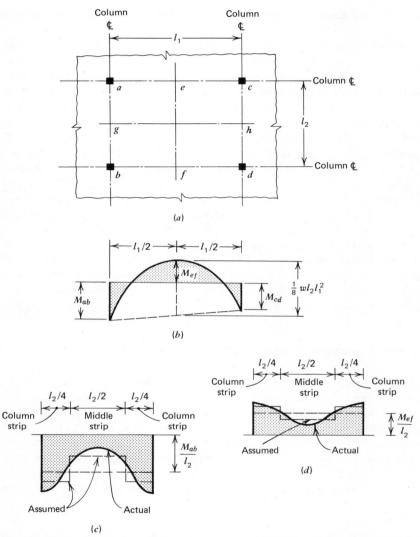

Figure 10.10 Moments in flat plate floors. (*a*) Plan. (*b*) Moments in l_1 direction. (*c*) Variation of moment across width *ab*. (*d*) Variation of moment across width *ef*.

353

moments produced in indeterminate beams by prestressing, as discussed in Ch. 8.

The concept of equivalent load is useful in the design of slabs, as it was for beams, in that the combined primary and secondary moments may be determined based on the equivalent transverse loads from the tendons. Secondary moments may be calculated by deducting the easily determined primary moments from the total moments resulting from the equivalent load analysis.

The load-balancing approach to design, by which the upward equivalent load from prestressing is cancelled against a selected downward load applied to the slab, is also useful. For that special loading, assuming that the applied load, as well as the prestress force, is sustained in nature, the slab is in a state of uniform compression and will deflect neither up nor down. If the load is then increased to full service load, only the effect of the incremental load above the balanced load need be considered, and the stresses and deflections for that incremental load superimposed upon those of the balanced load stage.

At the ultimate load stage, such superposition is not valid, and the design strength of the slab must be compared against the required strength, found by applying the usual load factors to the calculated dead loads and service live loads. At this stage, secondary moments due to prestressing must be considered, just as for continuous beams, with a load factor of 1.0.

10.11   THE BALANCED LOAD STAGE

The load-balancing approach to design is specially useful in treating flat plates. The tendons can be arranged so that a specified loading, for example the total dead load, can be cancelled by the upward equivalent load from prestressing.

An orthogonal grid of parabolic tendons, concave upward, usually is specified for each slab panel. The short, concave downward, transition curves characteristic of each tendon as it passes over the column lines, where tendons pass from one slab panel to the next, produce downward reactions that must be accommodated by special bands of tendons along these column lines, in each direction.

Load-balancing design for a flat plate system may be developed from either of two slightly different points of view. The first derives from the method of analysis of two-way edge-supported plates, while the second treats the slab as a system of broad shallow beams, first in one direction and then the other.

The first approach is illustrated by the rectangular slab of Fig. 10.11, showing a typical interior panel of a flat plate floor. The uniformly distributed load to be balanced is carried by a two-way network of tendons of parabolic shape, uniformly spaced along either side l_1 or l_2. The panel is considered to be supported at its edges along the column lines in each direction. The proportion of the load to be carried in one direction or the other is more or less arbitrary,

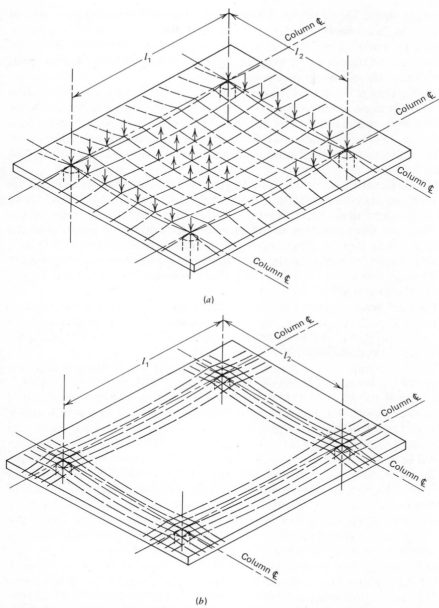

(a)

(b)

Figure 10.11 Load balancing for flat plate as two-way slab. (a) Distributed tendons. (b) Banded tendons.

as for all edge-supported slabs. Assume for the present example that 60 percent of the load is assigned to the short direction l_2 and 40 percent to the long direction l_1. The required tendon network is shown in Fig. 10.11a. Parabolic tendons are used, concave upward, near the top of the slab at the column lines and close to the bottom at midspan.

But the change in slope of the tendons of the primary network, as they cross the column lines, produces a downward reaction on the slab strips along the column lines. A true line loading would be obtained for the sharply bent tendons shown, but such a profile is not practical. In actual cases a transition curve, concave downward, would produce a strip loading of finite width along the column lines.

The downward load on the column strips must be resisted by a second set of tendons, placed along those column strips, as shown in Fig. 10.11b. If 40 percent of the load were carried in the long direction of the slab, then the column strips in the short direction would pick up that load and transmit it to the columns. Note that the 60 percent carried directly the short way by the slab, plus the 40 percent carried by the short direction strips, accounts for 100 percent of the load, as required by statics. A corresponding analysis holds in the perpendicular direction.

The final arrangement of tendons is found by superimposing the arrangements of Figs. 10.11a and 10.11b, resulting in a rather wide spacing of cables in the central part of the panel and a concentrated band of tendons along the column lines in each direction.

The second approach to the analysis treats the slab as an orthogonal system of broad flat beams, each one of full panel width, and makes use directly of the fact that 100 percent of the load to be balanced must be carried in each of the two perpendicular directions. For purposes of analysis in the l_1 direction (Fig. 10.12a) the slab is considered to be supported continuously along the transverse column lines ab and cd. For the usual distributed loading, the designer would be led to select parabolic tendons, with maximum sag controlled by the requirements of cover at the top and bottom of the slab. But it is known, on the basis of elastic analysis and tests as well, that the lateral distribution of bending moments due to applied loading is not uniform across the width of the critical sections, but tends to concentrate near the column lines (see Art. 10.9). According to current information (Refs. 10.4 and 10.5), for simple spans between 55 and 60 percent of the moment will be concentrated in the column strips, while for continuous spans between 65 and 75 percent will be within the column strips, the remainder being placed in the middle strips in each case. Anticipating such a distribution when the slab is subjected to full live load or overloading, the designer is led to distribute the tendons in a like manner. The result is indicated in Fig. 10.12b. The total number of tendons per panel is the same as for Fig. 10.12a, but a large percentage is concentrated in bands along the column lines.

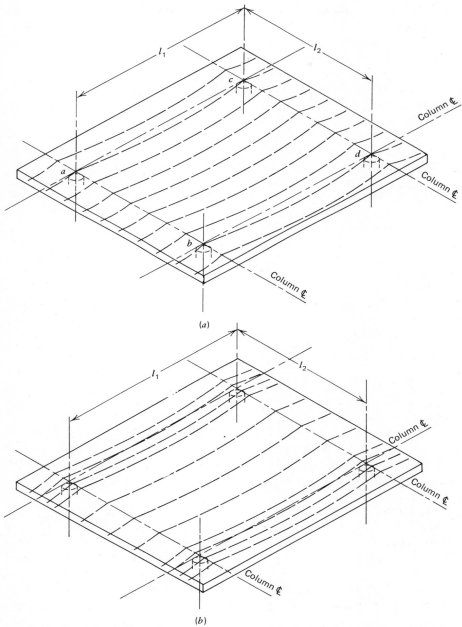

Figure 10.12 Load balancing for flat plate as wide-beam system. (*a*) Tendons uniformly distributed. (*b*) Tendons concentrated in column strips. (*c*) Two-way tendon pattern.

357

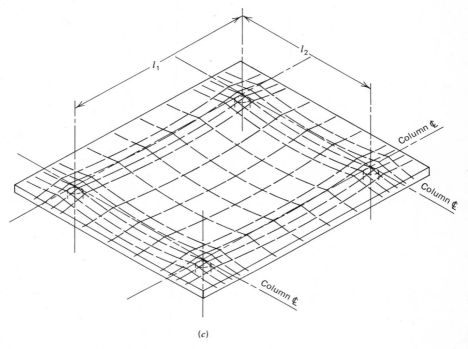

(c)

Figure 10.12 (cont.)

A corresponding situation obtains in the direction l_2, the total number of tendons being sufficient to equilibrate 100 percent of the load to be balanced in that direction also.

The superposition of the tendons in each of the two perpendicular directions is shown in Fig. 10.12c. It is clear that the end results are the same as those of the analysis summarized in Fig. 10.11, although the reasoning is different. The second approach is somewhat simpler to apply in practice, and so is more generally used.

Whichever method is adopted, the fundamentals of load balancing apply. Usually the load selected for balancing consists of the total dead load or, in some cases, the total dead load plus a small percentage of the live load, assumed sustained. The average compression in the concrete in each direction should not be less than 125 psi, and it is desirable to maintain a value of 200 to 250 psi. On the other hand, a high value of average prestress may induce excessive elastic shortening and creep. A maximum value of 500 psi is recommended (Ref. 10.4).

As a general guide, the recommended maximum spacing of tendons in the column strips is about 4 times the slab thickness, and the recommended maximum spacing in the middle strips is about 6 times the slab thickness. However, for very short spans, tendons spacings up to 8 times the slab thickness may be appropriate (Refs. 10.1 and 10.4).

For the full live load stage, moments and stresses are found by superimposing those for the incremental load upon the uniform compressive stress that is obtained for the balanced state. Moment analysis for the full load stage, as well as for overloads, may be based on the equivalent frame method, described in the following articles.

10.12   THE EQUIVALENT FRAME METHOD

When flat plates are acted upon by loads other than the balanced load, deflection results from the unbalanced portion of load, accompanied by curvatures and moments. A refined analysis for such conditions is highly complex, involving not only variations of moments longitudinally and transversely, but requiring consideration of torsional stiffness, moment redistribution, and other effects. Fortunately, there are approximate methods available. The use of such approximate methods is well justified in calculating stresses and deflections for prestressed concrete flat plates designed using the load-balancing approach, because it is only the incremental load that need be considered, and this is but a fraction of the total.

The most widely used approximate method for concrete slabs is the *equivalent frame method* of Ch. 13 of the ACI Code. The equivalent frame method, sometimes known as the beam method, is quite general, and can be applied to two-way slabs supported by beams on column lines, flat slabs with dropped panels or column capitals or both, grid slabs or waffle slabs, and flat plates, including lift slabs. Most prestressed two-way systems are flat plates or lift slabs, and only recommendations pertaining to those forms will be summarized here.

Certain of the provisions of Ch. 13 of the Code are *not* recommended for use in applying the approach to prestressed flat plates (Ref. 10.4). A provision that the live load may be reduced to 3/4 its full value when considering the effects of alternate loadings is based on moment redistribution in reinforced slabs, but should not be applied to prestressed designs. Coefficients for the lateral distribution of design moments across the width of critical sections were developed largely on the basis of tests of reinforced concrete slabs, and other sets of coefficients are appropriate for prestressed construction. Chapter 13 of the Code also includes an alternative method of analysis known as the *direct design method*, based on moment coefficients obtained mainly by testing reinforced concrete slabs. The direct design method should not be used for prestressed concrete.

By the equivalent frame method, the structure is divided for purposes of analysis into continuous frames, centered on the column lines and extending both longitudinally and transversely, as shown by the shaded strips in Fig. 10.13.

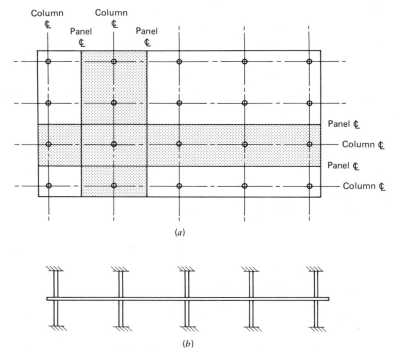

Figure 10.13 Building idealization for equivalent frame analysis. (*a*) Plan. (*b*) Elevation.

Each frame is composed of a row of columns and a broad continuous beam consisting of the portion of slab bounded by panel centerlines on either side of the columns. For vertical loading, each floor with its columns may be analyzed separately; the columns are assumed fixed at the floors above and below. In keeping with the requirements of statics, equivalent beams or frames in each direction must each carry 100 percent of the applied load. To maximize the effect of the live loads, alternate loading positions must be considered as usual for continuous beams and frames.

When columns are relatively slender or not rigidly connected to the slab (as in the case of lift slabs) their stiffness may be neglected and continuous beam analysis applied. For other cases it is necessary to account for the rotational resistance provided by the columns. Figure 10.14 shows the condition at an interior column with the slab spanning in the direction l_1.* According to the Code, the flat plate is to be considered as supported by a transverse slab

* By Code notation l_1 is the span length in the direction that moments are being determined and l_2 is the length of span transverse to l_1.

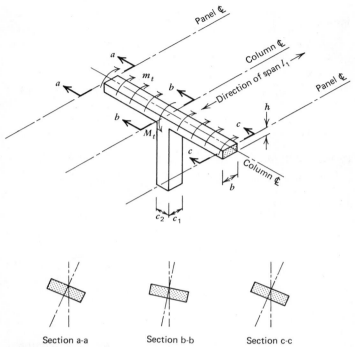

Section a-a   Section b-b   Section c-c

Figure 10.14   Basis of equivalent column. (*a*) Section *a-a*.
(*b*) Section *b-b*. (*c*) Section *c-c*.

strip or beam of width b equal to the dimension of the column in the direction
of the moment analysis, and height h equal to the depth of the slab. The rotational restraint provided for the slab is influenced, not only by the flexural
stiffness of the column, but by the torsional stiffness of the transverse beam
as well, as indicated by the sections. With distributed torque m_t applied by the
slab and resisting torque M_t provided by the column, the outer ends of the
transverse slab strip will rotate to a greater degree than the central section,
due to torsional deformation. To allow for this, the actual column and transverse
slab strip are replaced by an equivalent column, defined so that the total
flexibility (inverse of stiffness) of the equivalent column is the sum of the flexi-
bilities of the actual column and the slab strip. Thus

$$\frac{1}{K_{ec}} = \frac{1}{\sum K_c} + \frac{1}{K_t} \tag{10.8}$$

where

$$K_{ec} = \text{flexural stiffness of equivalent column}$$
$$K_c = \text{flexural stiffness of actual column}$$
$$K_t = \text{torsional stiffness of transverse slab strip}$$

all expressed in terms of moment per unit rotation. The flexural stiffness can be calculated by the usual equations of mechanics and for members having a uniform cross section is equal to $4E_cI/l$. The torsional stiffness of the transverse slab strip can be calculated by the expression

$$K_t = \sum \frac{9E_cC}{l_2 \left(1 - \dfrac{c_2}{l_2}\right)^3} \tag{10.9}$$

where

c_2 = transverse column dimension as shown in Fig. 10.14

C = cross sectional constant for the transverse strip.

The summation applies to the typical case in which there are slab strips on both sides of the column. The constant C pertains to the torsional rigidity of the effective cross section, and for the slab strip shown in Fig. 10.14 is

$$C = \left(1 - 0.63\frac{x}{y}\right)\frac{x^3y}{3} \tag{10.10}$$

where x and y are, respectively, the smaller and larger dimensions of the rectangular cross section (h and b in Fig. 10.14).

With the effective stiffness of the slab strip and the columns found by this procedure, the analysis of the equivalent frame can proceed by any convenient means.

Having found the total moments at positive and negative critical sections from the continuous beam or frame analysis, it still remains to distribute those moments across the width of the critical sections. For this purpose it is convenient to divide the total width of the slab into column strips and middle strips as suggested earlier. The column strip is defined as having a width on either side of the column equal to $1/4$ the smaller of the panel dimensions l_1 or l_2. A middle strip is bounded by two column strips. Moments at positive and negative bending sections are assumed to be constant within the bounds of a middle strip or column strip. For prestressed flat plates the following distribution of moments at the critical sections is recommended (Refs. 10.4 and 10.5):

Simple spans: 55 to 60 percent to the column strip with the remainder to the middle strip

Continuous spans: 65 to 75 percent to the column strip with the remainder to the middle strip

Negative moments obtained from the analysis apply at the centerlines of supports. Since the support provided is not a knife-edge but is a rather broad band of slab spanning in the transverse direction, some reduction in the negative design moment is proper. The critical section for negative bending, in both column and middle strips, may be taken at the face of the supporting column, but in no case at a distance greater than $0.175l_1$ from the center of the column.

Flexural stresses caused by the moments from unbalanced loads, found by the equivalent frame method, may be calculated by the usual equations of mechanics. As tensile and compressive stresses are normally quite low, calculations are usually based on the uncracked section. These stresses are added algebraically to the uniform compressive stresses obtained for the balanced load state.

Limiting concrete stresses at service loads recommended for flat plates differ from the allowable stresses given in the ACI Code for other types of construction in the following respects (Ref. 10.4):

a.   Compression in concrete
     Negative moment areas around columns $0.30f'_c$
b.   Tension in concrete:
     Positive moment areas without the addition of
     non-prestressed reinforcement $2\sqrt{f'_c}$
     Positive moment areas with the addition of
     non-prestressed reinforcement $6\sqrt{f'_c}$
     Negative moment areas without the addition
     of non-prestressed reinforcement   0
     Negative moment areas with the addition of
     non-prestressed reinforcement $6\sqrt{f'_c}$

All other stress limits of the ACI Code apply. The reader is referred to Ref. 10.4 for the background and rationale for these recommendations.

10.13   FLEXURAL STRENGTH OF FLAT PLATES

While the concept of load balancing is of great use up to the service load stage, it has no validity at overload stages. Load balancing makes use of the principle of superposition, which is valid only within the elastic range of behavior. For the overload stage, both steel and concrete are stressed into the inelastic range. Steel stress increases disproportionately to load increase as cracking of the slab occurs. In addition, the increase in steel stress is not uniform along the length of the tendon.

The safety of the structure against collapse must be evaluated by comparing the resisting moment of all critical sections against the maximum moments that would act at those sections, should catastrophic overloads occur.

The flexural strength of slab sections can be calculated by the same procedures used for beams, described fully in Ch. 3. The approximate ACI equations for estimating the stress in the tendons at failure may be used for slabs as well, and capacity reduction factors are applicable as usual. Non-prestressed reinforcement, when used in combination with prestressed steel, may be considered to contribute to the tensile force an amount equal to its area times its yield strength.

The moments that must be resisted at the critical sections are to be based on an elastic analysis, such as the equivalent frame method of Art. 10.11. In this case, the loads are found by applying the usual load factors to the actual dead load (including the self-weight of the slab) and to the service live load.

It has been suggested that the collaspe load for prestressed flat plates can be calculated using yield line theory (Refs. 10.5 and 10.6). Limited experimental evidence suggests that this may be valid. However, the yield line analysis implies a redistribution of elastic moments, which can occur only if adequate rotation capacity is available at the highly stressed sections. There are not sufficient data available at this time to support such an assumption. ACI Committee 423, in its tentative recommendations (Ref. 10.4), makes no mention of yield line theory, but endorses the ACI Code provision for statically indeterminate prestressed structures, that the required ultimate resisting moments should be found from an elastic analysis, with the usual load factors included. Secondary moments, if any, due to prestressing must be included, using a load factor of 1.0. A limited amount of redistribution is permitted for slabs, as it is for beams and frames, provided that the critical sections are sufficiently underreinforced. Specifically, Eq. (8.6) may be applied.

10.14   SHEAR IN FLAT PLATES

Prestressed flat plates are apt to be critical in shear. When two-way slabs are supported directly by columns, there is a high concentration of shear stress near the columns. Tests of flat plate structures confirm that in many practical cases the capacity is governed by shear (Ref. 10.7).

A.   FLAT PLATES WITHOUT SPECIAL SHEAR REINFORCEMENT

There are two kinds of shear that may be critical. The first is the familiar *beam-type shear* leading to diagonal tension failure, as in Fig. 10.15a. Likely to control mainly for long, narrow slabs, this mechanism is based on the slab acting as a wide beam, spanning between supports provided by the perpendicular column strips. A potential diagonal crack extends in a plane across the entire width of the slab as shown. The critical section is taken a distance $h/2$ from the face of the column. As for beams, $V_u \leq \phi V_n$, where V_u is the shear force at factored loads and V_n is the nominal shear strength. The strength reduction factor ϕ is equal to 0.85 as usual for shear calculations. Normally, shear reinforcement is not provided for beam-shear in slabs, and so $V_n = V_c$ where V_c is computed as usual for beams. The effective depth need not be taken less than $0.80h$. The restriction that shear reinforcement must be provided whenever $V_u > \frac{1}{2}\phi V_c$ does not apply to slabs.

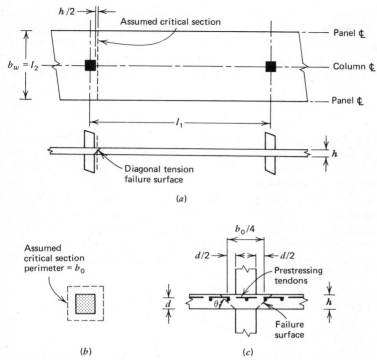

Figure 10.15   Shear failure in flat plates (*a*) Beam shear in rectangular panel. (*b*) Critical section for punching shear. (*c*) Failure surface for punching shear.

Alternatively, failure may occur by *punching shear*, with the potential diagonal crack following the surface of a truncated cone or pyramid around the column, as shown in Figs. 10.15*b* and 10.15*c*. The failure surface extends from the bottom of the slab at the column diagonally upward to the top surface. The angle of inclination with the horizontal, θ, depends on the amount of reinforcement in the slab and the degree of prestressing. It may range from about 20 to 45 degrees.

For design purposes, a critical section for shear is defined, perpendicular to the plane of the slab, and a distance $d/2$ from the face of the column, defining the shear perimeter b_o as shown in Figs. 10.15*b* and 10.15*c*. At that section, the basis for design is that $V_u \leq \phi V_n$ as usual. In the absence of special shear reinforcement, $V_n = V_c$.

At such a critical section, in addition to the shearing stresses and horizontal compression resulting from prestress and bending, vertical or somewhat inclined compressive stress is present due to the reaction of the column. The simultaneous presence of vertical and biaxial horizontal compression increases the strength of the concrete in the area of the column. Tests have indicated that, when punching shear failure occurs, the shear stress computed on the perimeter of the critical section is larger than in beams or one-way slabs, and according to the Code the nominal shear strength may be taken equal to

$$V_c = \left(2 + \frac{4}{\beta_c}\right) \sqrt{f'_c} b_o d \tag{10.11}$$

but not greater than $4\sqrt{f'_c}b_o d$. In Eq. (10.11), β_c is the ratio of the long side to short side of the column.*

B. TYPES OF SHEAR REINFORCEMENT

Special shear reinforcement is usually desirable at the columns for flat plates. It may take several forms. A few of these are shown in Fig. 10.16. The *shearheads* shown in Figs. 10.16a and 10.16c consist of standard structural steel shapes embedded in the slab and projecting beyond the column. They serve to increase the effective perimeter b_o of the critical section. In addition they may contribute to the negative bending resistance of the slab.

The reinforcement shown in (a) is particularly suited for use with concrete columns. It consists of short lengths of I or wide-flange beams, cut and welded at the crossing point, so that the arms are continuous through the column. The prestressing tendons pass over the top of the structural steel. Column bars pass vertically at the corners of the column without interference. The effectiveness of this type of shearhead has been well documented by tests (Ref. 10.8).

The channel frame of (c) is very similar in its action, but is adapted for use with steel columns, as are often used for lift slabs.

The bent bar arrangement of (b) is suited for use with concrete columns. The bars are usually bent at 45 degrees across the potential diagonal crack, and extend along the bottom of the slab a distance sufficient to develop their strength by bond.

The flanged collar of (d) is designed mainly for use with lift slabs. It consists of a flat bottom plate with vertical stiffening ribs. It may incorporate sockets for lifting rods, and usually is used in conjunction with shear pads welded

---

* ACI Committee 423, reporting its views in Ref. 10.4, feels that even this is too restrictive for prestressed concrete flat plates, and recommends that the Code provisions be liberalized. The Committee proposed that the shear strength be taken equal to

$$V_c = (3.5\sqrt{f'_c} + 0.3f_{cc})b_o d + V_p \tag{10.12}$$

where f_{cc} = concrete compressive stress at the centroid of the section
$\quad\quad V_p$ = vertical component of the effective prestress force at the section

This is the same equation presently in use to predict web-shear cracking in beams. For flat plates, it is recommended that f_{cc} not be taken larger than 500 psi and that f'_c not exceed 5000 psi in Eq. (10.12).

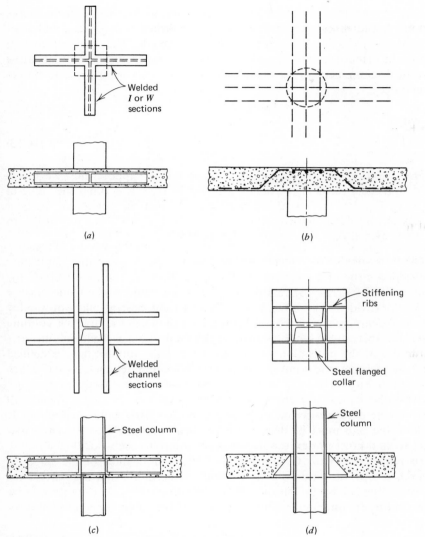

(a)

(b)

(c)

(d)

Figure 10.16   Shear reinforcement for flat plates.

directly to the column surfaces below the collar to transfer the vertical reaction. Moment transfer is generally considered negligible.

C.   DESIGN OF BAR REINFORCEMENT

If shear reinforcement in the form of bars is used (Fig. 10.16b) the nominal shear strength V_n calculated at the critical section a distance $d/2$ from the support face may be increased to $6\sqrt{f'_c}b_od$, according to ACI Code. In this case, the shear resistance of the concrete, V_c is taken equal to $2\sqrt{f'_c}b_od$, and reinforcement must provide for the excess shear above ϕV_c. The total bar area A_v crossing the critical section at a slope angle α is easily obtained by equating the vertical component of the steel force to the excess shear force to be accommodated:

$$A_v f_y \phi \sin \alpha = V_u - \phi V_c$$

from which

$$A_v = \frac{V_u - \phi V_c}{\phi f_y \sin \alpha} \tag{10.13}$$

Successive sections at increasing distances from the support must be investigated, and reinforcement provided wherever V_u exceeds ϕ times the value of V_c given by Eq. (10.11). Only the center 3/4 of the inclined portion of the bent bars can be considered effective in resisting shear, and full development length must be provided past the location of peak stress in the steel.

D. DESIGN OF SHEARHEAD REINFORCEMENT

If embedded structural steel shapes are used (Figs. 10.16a and 10.16c), the limiting value of V_n may be raised to $7\sqrt{f'_c}b_od$ according to the Code. Such a shearhead, provided it is sufficiently stiff and strong, has the effect of moving the critical section out away from the column, as shown in Fig. 10.17. According to the Code, this critical section crosses each arm of the shearhead at a distance equal to 3/4 of the projection beyond the face of the support, and is defined so that the perimeter is a minimum. It need not approach closer than $d/2$ to the face of the support.

Moving the critical section out in this way provides the double benefit of increasing the effective perimeter b_o and decreasing the total shear force V_u for which the slab must be designed. The shear strength $V_n = V_c$ at the new critical section must not exceed $4\sqrt{f'_c}b_od$ according to the Code.

Tests reported in Ref. 10.7 indicate that, throughout most of the length of a shearhead arm, the shear is constant and, furthermore, that the part of the total shear carried by the shearhead arm is proportional to α_v, its relative flexural stiffness, compared with that of the surrounding concrete section:

$$\alpha_v = \frac{E_s I_s}{E_c I_c} \tag{10.14}$$

The concrete section is taken with an effective width of $(c_2 + d)$, where c_2 is the width of the support measured perpendicular to the arm direction. Properies are calculated for the cracked, transformed section, including the shearhead.

The observation that shear is essentially constant, at least up to the diagonal cracking load, implies that the reaction is concentrated largely at the end of the arm. Thus, if the total shear at the support is V, the constant shear force in each arm is equal to $\alpha_v V/4$.

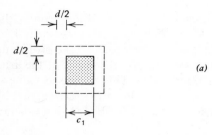

(a)

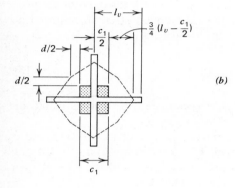

(b)

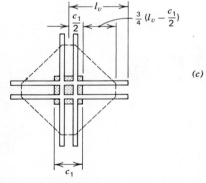

(c)

Figure 10.17 Critical sections for shear in flat plates. (*a*) No shearhead. (*b*) Small shearhead. (*c*) Large shearhead.

369

If load is increased past that which causes diagonal cracking around the column, tests indicate that the increased shear above the cracking shear V_c is carried mostly by the steel shearhead, and that the shear force in the projecting arm within a distance from the column face equal to h_v, the depth of the arm, assumes a nearly constant value greater than $\alpha_v V_c/4$. This increased value is very nearly equal to the total shear per arm, $V_u/4$, minus the shear carried by the partially cracked concrete. The latter term is equal to $(V_c/4)(1 - \alpha_v)$; hence the idealized shear diagram of Fig. 10.18b is obtained.

The moment diagram of Fig. 10.18c is obtained by integration of the shear diagram. If V_c is equal to $V_u/2$, as tests indicate for shearheads of common proportions, it is easily confirmed that the plastic moment strength required at the face of the support, for each arm of the shearhead is such that

$$\phi M_p = \frac{V_u}{8}\left[h_v + \alpha_v \left(l_v - \frac{c_1}{2} \right) \right] \tag{10.15}$$

in which the capacity reduction factor ϕ is taken equal to 0.90 as usual for bending.

According to the Code, the value of α_v must be at least equal to 0.15; more flexible shearheads have proved ineffective. The compression flange must not be more than $0.3d$ from the bottom surface of the slab, and the steel shapes used must not be deeper than 70 times the web thickness.

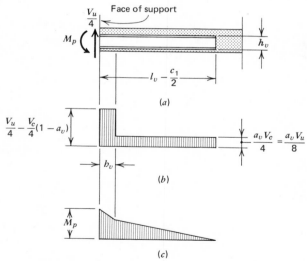

Figure 10.18 Stress resultants in shearhead arm. (a) Shearhead arm. (b) Shear. (c) Moment.

For flexural design of the slab, moments found at the support centerline by the equivalent frame method are reduced to moments at the support face, assumed to be the critical section for moment. If shearheads are used, they have the effect of reducing the design moment in the column strips still further by increasing the effective support width. This reduction is proportional to the share of the load carried by the shearhead, and to its size, and may be estimated conservatively (Figs. 10.18b and 10.18c) by the expression

$$M_v = \frac{\phi \alpha_v V_u}{8}\left(l_v - \frac{c_1}{2}\right) \tag{10.16}$$

where $\phi = 0.90$. According to the Code, the reduction may not be greater than 30 percent of the total design moment for the slab column strip, nor greater than the change in column strip moment over the distance, l_v, nor greater than M_p given by Eq. (10.15).

Limited test information pertaining to shearheads at a slab edge indicates that behavior may be substantially different because of torsional and other effects. If shearheads are used at an edge or corner column, special attention should be given to tendon placement, which should provide concrete compression at the critical section comparable to that obtained for interior columns. To achieve this, tendons usually have to be placed through the columns. Many designers prefer to avoid the special dangers associated with exterior columns by cantilevering flat plates about 1/4 the typical span length beyond the column, creating, in effect, a typical interior column at that location too.

Tests indicate that tendons passing through columns or directly around column edges contribute more to load-carrying capacity than do tendons remote from the columns (Ref. 10.9). For this reason, it is recommended that some tendons should be placed through the columns or at least around their edges. In lift-slab construction, some tendons should be placed over the lifting collars.

E.   EXAMPLE: DESIGN OF SHEARHEAD REINFORCEMENT

A prestressed flat-plate floor slab $7\frac{1}{2}$ in. thick is supported by 10 in. square columns and is reinforced for negative bending with tendons at an average effective depth d of 6 in. The concrete strength f'_c is 3000 psi. The slab must transfer an ultimate shear V_u of 113,000 lb to the column. What special slab reinforcement is required, if any, at the column to transfer the required ultimate shear? ($h = 191$ mm, $d = 152$ mm, columns 254×254 mm, $f'_c = 21$ N/mm^2, and $V_u = 503$ kN.)

The nominal shear strength at the critical section $d/2$ from the face of the column is found from Eq. (10.11) to be

$$V_c = 4\sqrt{3000}(64 \times 6) = 84.1 \text{ kips}$$

and $\phi V_c = 0.85 \times 84.1 = 71.5$ kips. This is less than $V_u = 113$ kips, indicating that shear reinforcement is necessary.

A shearhead similar to Fig. 10.16a will be used, fabricated from I-beam sections with $f_y = 36$ ksi. If we maintain a $\frac{3}{4}$ in. clearance below such steel, clearance at the top of the slab permits use of an I beam of $4\frac{5}{8}$ in. depth; a nominal 4 in. section will be used. With such reinforcement, the upper limit of shear V_n on the critical section is $7\sqrt{3000}(64 \times 6) = 147$ kips, and $\phi V_n = 0.85 \times 147 = 125$ kips, well above the value of V_u to be resisted.

The required perimeter b_o can be found setting $V_u = \phi V_c$ where V_c is given by Eq. (10.11):

$$b_o = \frac{V_u}{4\phi\sqrt{f'_c}d}$$

$$= \frac{113,000}{4 \times 0.85\sqrt{3000}(6)} = 101 \text{ in.}$$

(Note that the actual shear force to be transferred at the critical section is slightly less than 113 kips, because a part of the floor load is within the effective perimeter b_o; however, the difference is small except for very large shearheads.) The required projecting length l_v of the shearhead arm is found from geometry, expressing b_o in terms of l_v.

$$b_o = 4\sqrt{2}\left[\frac{c_1}{2} + \frac{3}{4}\left(l_v - \frac{c_1}{2}\right)\right] = 101 \text{ in.}$$

from which $l_v = 22.2$ in. To determine the required plastic section modulus for the shear arm, it is necessary to assume a trial value of the relative stiffness α_v. Selecting 0.25 for trial, the required moment capacity is found from Eq. (10.15).

$$M_p = \frac{113,000}{8 \times 0.90}[4 + 0.25(22.2 - 5)] = 130,000 \text{ in.-lb}$$

A standard I beam S4 $\times$ 7.7 with a yield stress of 36 ksi provides 126,000 in.-lb resistance, and will tentatively be adopted. The $E_s I_s$ value provided by the beam is 174×10^6 in.^{2}-lb. The effective cross section of the slab strip is shown in Fig. 10.19. If we take moments of the composite cracked section about the bottom surface to locate the neutral axis,

$$y = \frac{8.90 \times 6 + 19.9 \times 2.75 + 8y^2}{8.90 + 19.9 + 16y}$$

from which $y = 2.29$ in. The moment of inertia of the composite section is

$$I_c = \frac{1}{3} \times 16 \times 2.29^3 + 8.90 \times 3.71^2 + 6 \times 9 + 19.9 \times 0.46^2$$
$$= 244 \text{ in.}^4$$

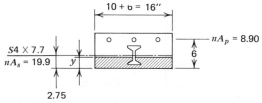

Figure 10.19 Shearhead design example: effective section of slab.

The flexural stiffness of the effective composite slab strip is

$$E_c I_c = 3.1 \times 10^6 \times 244 = 756 \times 10^6 \text{ in.}^2\text{-lb}$$

and from Eq. (10.14),

$$\alpha_v = \frac{174}{756} = 0.23$$

This is greater than the specified minimum of 0.15 and close to the 0.25 value assumed earlier. The revised value of M_p is

$$M_p = \frac{113,000}{8 \times 0.90}[4 + 0.23(22.2 - 5)] = 122,000 \text{ in.-lb}$$

The 4 in. I beam is adequate. The calculated length l_v of 22.2 will be increased to 24 in. for practical reasons. The reduction in column-strip moment in the slab may be based on this actual length. From Eq. (10.16)

$$M_v = \frac{0.90 \times 0.23 \times 113,000}{8}(24 - 5) = 55,600 \text{ in.-lb}$$

This value is less than M_p, as required by specifications, and must also be less than 30 percent of the design negative moment in the column strip, and less than the change in the column strip moment in the distance l_v.

10.15   NONPRESTRESSED REINFORCEMENT

Most prestressed concrete flat plates use unbonded tendons. In general, members with unbonded prestressing steel should also contain a certain amount of bonded reinforcement in the tensile concrete zone. Such reinforcement serves to control and distribute concrete cracks, should they occur in service, and in addition improves the ductility of the member and may increase its flexural strength by avoiding stress concentrations in the concrete at wide cracks. Flexural members using unbonded tendons must, in general, be provided with bonded reinforcement in accordance with Eq. (4.36).

Code provisions for two-way prestressed flat plates are somewhat more liberal, based on successful performance of unbonded prestressed slabs without supplementary steel (Refs. 10.4 and 10.9).

In the positive moment areas of such slabs, if the computed tensile stress in the concrete does not exceed $2\sqrt{f_c'}$, no bonded reinforcement is required. If the tensile stress exceeds that value, then a minimum amount of bonded bar reinforcement or welded wire mesh must be provided equal to

$$A_s = \frac{N_c}{0.5f_y} \tag{10.17}$$

where N_c is the tensile force in the concrete at full service load, and f_y, the yield strength of the steel, is not to exceed 60,000 psi. Such steel is to be uniformly distributed over the precompressed tensile zone, and placed as near to the tensile face as possible. Its length should be 1/3 the clear span length, and it should be centered in the positive moment area.

Bonded reinforcement must always be provided in the negative moment areas of two-way prestressed flat plates, according to the Code. Such reinforcement, which may be in the form of bars or mesh, must have an area not less than

$$A_s = 0.00075hl \qquad (10.18)$$

where l is the slab span length in the direction of such reinforcement. This steel should be concentrated close to the supporting column. According to the Code, it must be placed within a slab width bounded by lines that are $1.5h$ on each side of the column faces. At least four bars or wires must be provided in each direction, and the spacing of the bonded reinforcement must not exceed 12 in. It should extend a distance of 1/6 the clear span on each side of the support.

In addition to nonprestressed reinforcement in the flexural tension regions of flat plates, some bar reinforcement should be added at end anchorages to avoid possible splitting of the concrete. Two No. 4 bars are commonly used continuously around the perimeter of the slab just behind the anchorages for this purpose. For highly prestressed slabs, or where anchorages are concentrated in a narrow slab width, the need for reinforcement to resist horizontal splitting of the slab should be investigated.

Special reinforcement may be necessary around openings, particularly if tendons are terminated. Bar reinforcement may be used, or, in case of larger openings, supplementary post-tensioned tendons may be installed.

10.16 DEFLECTION OF FLAT PLATES

Careful attention must always be paid to the deformation of prestressed flat plates. The use of high strength materials, with prestressing to provide stress control and avoid cracking, and the use of special shearhead reinforcement around the columns, all tend to produce a rather thin slab, which may be satisfactory in all respects other than deflection.

While deflections should be calculated explicitly, for comparison with limiting values (and must be, according to ACI Code), it is useful to base the design initially on a span/depth ratio that is likely to produce a slab of sufficient stiffness, so that later revision may be avoided. For prestressed slabs continuous over two or more spans in each direction, a span/depth ratio (for light live loads, say about 50 psf) of 40 to 45 may be used for floors, and a ratio of 45 to 48 for roofs. These limits may be increased to 48 and 52, respectively, if calculations verify that deflection, camber, and vibration frequency and amplitude are not objectionable, according to ACI Committee 423 (Ref. 10.4).

Generally it is the incremental deflection due to live load that is of interest. This is certainly so for slabs designed for dead load balancing, which should produce a nearly level surface for the balanced load stage. Since only the incremental deflection is to be found, the use of an approximate method is fully justified.

The deflection of a uniformly loaded flat plate may be estimated by the equivalent frame method (Ref. 10.10). Originally developed for reinforced concrete two-way systems, the method is specially appropriate for prestressed flat plates, which are usually uncracked at service loads (Ref. 10.11). The method is fully compatible with equivalent frame method for moment analysis presented in Art. 10.11. The definition of column and middle strips, the longitudinal moment analysis, lateral moment distribution coefficients, and other details are the same as for the moment analysis, and so most of the needed quantities are already at hand.

A slab region bounded by column centerlines is shown in Fig. 10.20. The deflection calculation considers the deformation of such a typical region in one direction at a time after which the contributions in each direction are added to obtain the total deflection at any point of interest. Referring to Fig. 10.20a, the slab is considered to act as a broad, shallow beam of width equal to the panel dimension l_y and having the span l_x. At this stage, the slab is considered to rest on unyielding support lines at $x = 0$ and $x = l_x$. Note that all unit strips in the X direction will not deform identically, because of variation of moment and flexural rigidity across the width of the slab.

The slab is next analyzed for bending in the Y direction (Fig. 10.20b). Once again the effect of variation of moment and flexural rigidity is shown.

The midpanel deflection can now be obtained as the sum of the midspan deflection of the column strip in one direction, and that of the middle strip in the other direction, as shown in Fig. 10.20:

$$d_{max} = d_{cx} + d_{my} \qquad (10.19a)$$

or

$$d_{max} = d_{cy} + d_{mx} \qquad (10.19b)$$

While the floor area bounded by column centerlines (Fig. 10.20) was used to introduce the method, the actual calculations are more easily done for strips of floor in either direction bounded by panel centerlines, as for the moment analysis. Figure 10.21 shows such a strip of floor spanning in the X direction.

The strip is initially considered to have supports that are fully fixed at $x = 0$ and $x = l_x$, permitting neither deflection nor rotation at those support lines. Deflections of the equivalent frame are calculated. The effect of the actual support rotations on midspan deflection is later found, and the total deflection of the equivalent frame spanning in the X direction is taken as the sum of the three parts: that of the panel assumed to have fixed supports, plus that due to the rotation at each of the two support lines in turn.

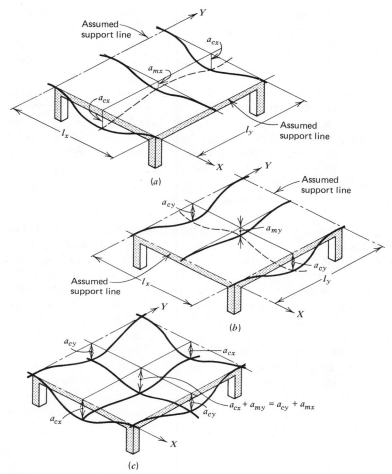

Figure 10.20 Basis of equivalent frame method for deflection analysis. (*a*) *X* direction bending, (*b*) *Y* direction bending, (*c*) Combined bending.

Moment variation across the width of the panel is treated the same approximate way as for the flexural analysis of Art. 10.12. Column strips and middle strips are defined as before, and the moment is assumed to be constant within the bounds of each. As suggested in Art. 10.12, for simple spans 55 to 60 percent of the total moment at critical sections may be assigned to the column strip, while for continuous spans 65 to 75 percent may be assigned to the column strip. In either case, the remaining percentage is assigned to the middle strip.

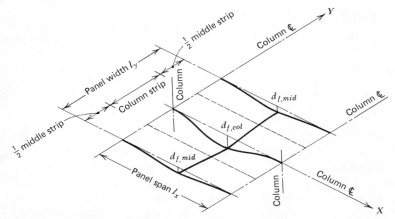

Figure 10.21   Deflection of column and middle strips in X direction.

A "reference" deflection at midspan of the uniformly loaded full-panel-width equivalent frame, with fixed ends, can be established as:

$$d_{f,ref} = \frac{wl^4}{384E_cI_{frame}} \tag{10.20}$$

where w is the load per foot along the span of length l, and I_{frame} is the moment of inertia of the full-panel-width slab. This implies a uniform lateral distribution of moment across the panel width, with the slab deforming into a cylindrical surface. The effect of the actual moment variation, as well as possible difference in width of column strip and middle strip, is accounted for by multiplying the reference deflection by the ratio of M/EI for the strip to that of the frame:

$$d_{f,col} = d_{f,ref} \times \frac{M_{col}}{M_{frame}} \times \frac{E_cI_{frame}}{E_cI_{col}} \tag{10.21a}$$

$$d_{f,mid} = d_{f,ref} \times \frac{M_{mid}}{M_{frame}} \times \frac{E_cI_{frame}}{E_cI_{mid}} \tag{10.21b}$$

The subscripts relate the deflection d, the bending moment M, or moment of inertia I to the column strip, middle strip, or full width frame. Note that the ratio of strip moment to frame moment is simply the lateral distribution factor already used in the flexural analysis.

Next it is necessary to correct for the rotations of the equivalent frame at the supports, which until now were considered fixed. The rotation at the column is equal to the net unbalanced moment applied at the column, divided by the column stiffness:

$$\theta = \frac{M_{net}}{K_{ec}} \qquad (10.22)$$

where θ = angle change in radians

M_{net} = difference in floor moments to left and right of column

K_{ec} = stiffness of equivalent column (see Art. 10.11)

In some cases the connection between floor slab and column transmits negligible moment, as for lift slabs. In such case the flexural analysis will indicate that the net moment applied at the column is zero. The end slopes for the slab may be found, in this case, using the second moment area principle. The slope at the right end of an equivalent frame span, for example, is found by taking moments of the M/EI diagram for that span about the left end, then dividing by the span length.

Once the rotation at each end is known, the associated midspan deflection of the equivalent frame can be calculated. It is easily confirmed that the midspan deflection of a beam experiencing an end rotation of θ radians, the far end being fixed, is

$$d_\theta = \frac{\theta l}{8} \qquad (10.23)$$

Thus the total deflection at midspan of the column strip or middle strip is the sum of the three parts:

$$d_{col} = d_{f,col} + d_{\theta l} + d_{\theta r} \qquad (10.24a)$$
$$d_{mid} = d_{f,mid} + d_{\theta l} + d_{\theta r} \qquad (10.24b)$$

where the subscripts l and r refer to the left and right ends of the span, respectively.

The calculations described above are repeated for the equivalent frame in the second direction of the structure, and the total deflection at midpanel obtained by summing the column strip deflection in one direction and the middle strip deflection in the other, as indicated by Eqs. (10.19).

The midpanel deflection should be the same whether calculated by Eq. (10.19a) or Eq. (10.19b). Actually a difference will usually be obtained because of the approximate nature of the calculations. For very rectangular panels, the main contribution to midpanel deflection is that of the long direction column strip. Consequently the midpanel deflection is best estimated by summing that of the long direction column strip and the short direction middle strip. However, for exterior panels, the most important contribution is from the column strips perpendicular to the discontinuous edge, even though the long side of the panel may be parallel to the edge. Judgment is required.

The deflections found using the procedure described are short-term deflections such as would be caused by a live load intermittently applied. If the unbalanced load is sustained over an extended period, the increase of deflection due to concrete creep must be accounted for. For beams as well as slabs it has long been the practice to estimate long-term deflection as a simple multiplier times the initial elastic deflection. A factor of 2 is often used.

An example of a flat plate deflection calculation is found in the following article.

10.17   EXAMPLE: FLAT PLATE DESIGN

A prestressed flat plate lift slab will be supported by steel columns spaced 25 ft on centers in each direction, as shown in Fig. 10.22a. Loads will be transferred from the slab to the 10×10 in. tubular columns by means of square lifting collars shown in Fig. 10.22b. The collar detail is such as to transmit no significant bending moment to the columns. The load to be carried includes the self-weight of the slab, an additional dead load of 12 psf, and a service live load of 50 psf. A balanced load condition, with zero net deflection, is specified for full dead load. A typical interior panel is to be designed, following the recommendations of ACI Comm. 423 (Ref. 10.4).* Concrete compressive strength $f'_c =$ 5000 psi, and $E_c = 4,030,000$ psi. (Columns 254×254 mm at 7.62 m spacing, $w_d =$ 0.57 kN/m², $w_1 = 2.40$ kN/m², $f'_c = 34$ N/mm², and $E_c = 27.8$ kN/mm².)

A trial depth of slab will be based on a span/depth ratio of 45:

$$h = \frac{25 \times 12}{45} = 6.7 \text{ in.} \qquad \text{try 7 in. (178 mm)}$$

For the 7 in. depth slab, using normal density concrete, the self-weight is 88 psf. Therefore the total dead load, on which load balancing is to be based, is $88 + 12 = 100$ psf. A two-directional network of parabolic tendons will be used. With a 3/4 in. concrete cover required at the top and bottom of the slab, and anticipating the outside diameter of the tendons to be about 1/2 in., the average distance from the slab surface to the top or bottom steel is $1\frac{1}{4}$ in. Thus the maximum sag y for a typical interior span is $7 - 2.5 = 4.5$ in., as shown in Fig. 10.22c. The short transition curve necessary over the column lines will be disregarded in the calculations.

The tendon layout and prestress force will be based on load balancing for a 100 psf dead load, the full load to be carried in each direction. The analysis is based on an equivalent beam of full 25 ft panel width. In each direction, the effective prestress force required per 25 ft strip, from Eq. (4.25), is

$$P_e = \frac{w l_2 l_1^2}{8y} = \frac{100 \times 25 \times 625 \times 12}{8 \times 4.5} = 521,000 \text{ lb (2317 kN)}$$

Assuming 20 percent loss of prestress force, the initial prestress force is 651,000 lb per 25 ft strip. Wrapped 0.600 in. diameter Grade 270 strands will be used, each providing an

---

* The recommendations of ACI Committee 423 are adopted for purposes of the present example because the 1977 ACI Code does not provide detailed provisions for all aspects of the analysis and design of two-way prestressed slab systems.

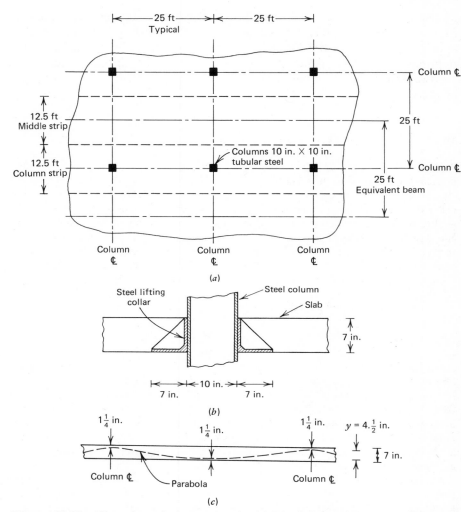

Figure 10.22 Flat plate design example. (*a*) Plan view of floor. (*b*) Detail of steel lifting collars. (*c*) Typical tendon profile.

area of 0.217 in.² For an initial prestress of $0.70f_{pu}$ each cable provides 41.0 kips force (Appendix A); thus the number of tendons required per 25 ft strip is

$$N = \frac{651,000}{41,000} = 15.9 \qquad \text{use } 16$$

The number of these to be placed in the column strip is $0.75 \times 16 = 12$, the remaining 4 to be distributed over the width of the middle strip.

The average compression in the concrete slab at balanced load is

$$f_{c,av} = \frac{521,000}{25 \times 12 \times 7} = 248 \text{ psi } (1.7 \text{ N/mm}^2)$$

which can be considered ideal. The average spacings of the tendons in the column and middle strips, respectively, are

$$s_{col} = \frac{12.5 \times 12}{12} = 12.5 \text{ in.} = 1.8h$$

$$s_{mid} = \frac{12.5 \times 12}{4} = 37.5 \text{ in.} = 5.4h$$

confirming that design decisions to this point are satisfactory.

Next the structure will be analyzed for the effect of applying the 50 psf service live load. Again a 25 ft wide strip provides the basis, the analysis that follows applying in each direction of the structure. Alternate loadings must be considered to maximize moments at negative and positive bending sections. For maximum negative moments at a typical support, the uniform live load of $50 \times 25 = 1250$ plf will be applied to the two adjacent spans, as shown in Fig. 10.23a. The supports second removed from the one under study will be considered fixed, as permitted by ACI Code, and the analysis for moments done by moment distribution, with the results as shown.

For maximum positive moment in a typical span, only that span will be loaded, as in Fig. 10.23b. The resulting live load moment diagram is indicated.

Although not needed for present purposes, a third analysis is shown in Fig. 10.23c for later reference: the effect of dead load of $100 \times 25 = 2500$ plf uniformly distributed over all spans.

Concrete stresses at full service load are found by superimposing the bending stresses due to live load moments on the uniform compression obtained for the balanced dead load.

The negative moments obtained from the live load analysis apply at the column center-lines, and may be reduced for design purposes to those at the support face. The shear at the column centerline resulting from the load that produced the maximum negative moment is (from Fig. 10.23a)

$$V = 1.25 \times \frac{25}{2} + \frac{82 - 32}{25} = 17.6 \text{ kips } (78 \text{ kN})$$

The effective support width is 24 in., based on the use of the lifting collar shown in Fig. 10.22b. Consequently, the negative moment at the face of supports is (see Ref. 10.8, p. 350):

$$M_{neg} = M_{\ell} - \frac{Val}{3} = 81 - 17.6 \times \frac{2}{3} = 69 \text{ ft-kips } (94 \text{ kN-m})$$

The moment assigned to the column strip is $0.75 \times 69 = 52$ ft-kips. The moment of inertia of the column strip is

$$I_c = \frac{1}{12} \times 12.5 \times 12 \times 7^3 = 4290 \text{ in.}^4$$

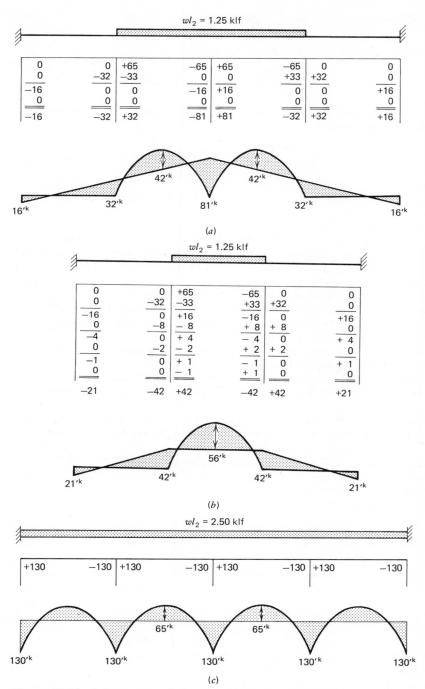

Figure 10.23 Moment analysis at service loads for flat plate example. (*a*) Maximum live load negative moment. (*b*) Maximum live load positive moment. (*c*) Dead load negative and positive moments.

Consequently the bending stress in the concrete in that strip is

$$f_b = \frac{52,000 \times 12 \times 3.5}{4290} = 510 \text{ psi}$$

Thus the concrete stresses at the top and bottom faces of the column strip, at the face of supports, are respectively

$$f_1 = -248 + 510 = +262 \text{ psi} \ (+1.81 \text{ N/mm}^2)$$
$$f_2 = -248 - 510 = -758 \text{ psi} \ (-5.23 \text{ N/mm}^2)$$

According to ACI Committee 423 recommendations, the allowable compression in the concrete is $0.30 \times 5000 = 1500$ psi, and the allowable tension (provided non-prestressed bonded steel is included) is $6\sqrt{5000} = 424$ psi. Both limits are well above the actual stresses.

The negative moment assigned to the middle strip is $0.25 \times 69 = 17$ ft-kips. The low bending stresses in the middle strips, superimposed on the 248 psi compression, produce a variable compressive stress that is not critical.

At the positive moment section, the total moment in each 25 ft strip is 56 ft-kips. Again 75 percent, or 42 ft-kips, will be assigned to the column strip. Thus the bending stresses in the column strip are

$$f_b = \frac{42,000 \times 12 \times 3.5}{4290} = 411 \text{ psi}$$

and the net stresses at the top and bottom of the concrete slab are, respectively,

$$f_1 = -248 - 411 = -659 \text{ psi} \ (-4.54 \text{ N/mm}^2)$$
$$f_2 = -248 + 411 = +163 \text{ psi} \ (+1.12 \text{ N/mm}^2)$$

According to the recommendations, the allowable compression is $0.45 \times 5000 = 2250$ psi and the allowable tension, if bonded steel is added, is 424 psi. The actual stresses are clearly satisfactory.

The middle strip positive moment of 14 ft-kips produces very low bending stress in that region, resulting in variable compression throughout the slab depth. Stresses are not critical at that location.

Non-prestressed bar reinforcement must be provided at the top of the slab in the column region, in the amount

$$A_s = 0.00075 \times 7 \times 25 \times 12 = 1.58 \text{ in.}^2 \ (1019 \text{ mm}^2)$$

Four No. 6 Grade 60 bars will be used in each direction, providing an area each way of 1.77 in.^{2} These will be placed close to the column, and will be $25/3 = 8$ ft long.

Bonded steel must also be placed in the positive bending region of the column strips since the tensile concrete stress there is larger than $2\sqrt{f_c'}$. The amount needed is found from Eq. (10.17). At full service load the concrete stresses at the top and bottom of the slab are, respectively:

$$f_1 = -659 \text{ psi}$$
$$f_2 = +163 \text{ psi}$$

The neutral axis is 1.39 in. from the bottom face of the slab and the total tensile force in the concrete is

$$N_c = \frac{163}{2} \times 12.5 \times 12 \times 1.39 = 17,000 \text{ lb}$$

The required area of bonded steel is

$$A_s = \frac{17,000}{0.5 \times 60,000} = 0.57 \text{ in.}^2 \ (367 \text{ mm}^2)$$

four No. 4 Grade 60 bars will be used in the direction parallel to the column line, providing an area of 0.78 in.^{2}

Beam shear will be checked at a section $h/2$ from the support face, or 15.5 in. from the column centerline (see Fig. 9.22b). The shear force at factored load is

$$V_u = \frac{22.4}{2} (1.4 \times 100 + 1.7 \times 50) \times 25 = 63,000 \text{ lb}$$

By ACI Code the shear strength may be taken as $V_c = 2\sqrt{f'_c} \, b_w d = 2\sqrt{5000} \times 25 \times 12 \times 5.75 = 244,000$ lb. Thus $\phi V_c = 0.85 \times 244,000 = 207,000$ lb, substantially above V_u. Beam shear is not critical here.

Punching shear will be investigated at a critical perimeter $d/2$ from the toe of the lifting collar. The side dimension of the assumed critical section is $24 + 5.8 = 29.8$ in., and $b_0 = 119$ in. (refer to Fig. 10.22b). The shear force to be resisted may be based on the tributary area, neglecting the small reduction for load within the critical perimeter in this case:

$$V_u = 625(1.4 \times 100 + 1.7 \times 50) = 141,000 \text{ lb} \ (627 \text{ kN})$$

According to Eq. (10.11), $V_c = 4\sqrt{f'_c} \, b_o d = 4\sqrt{5000} \times 119 \times 5.75 = 194,000$ lb and $\phi V_c = 0.85 \times 194,000 = 165,000$ lb. It is clear that the slab is satisfactory without supplementary shear reinforcement by either beam-shear or punching-shear criteria.

The flexural strength will be checked for the full width slab strip of 25 ft, in either direction, placing the loads so as to produce maximum moments at the critical sections. Referring to Fig. 10.23, and introducing the usual load factors, the negative moment applied at the column centerline, at factored loads, is*

$$M_{neg} = 1.4 \times 130 + 1.7 \times 81 = 320 \text{ ft-kips} \ (434 \text{ kN-m})$$

and the associated shear force is

$$V = \frac{25}{2} (1.4 \times 2.5 + 1.7 \times 1.25) + \frac{(81 - 32)1.7}{25} = 74 \text{ kips} \ (329 \text{ kN})$$

Consequently the required flexural strength at the face of support is

$$M_{neg} = 320 - 74 \times \tfrac{2}{3} = 271 \text{ ft-kips} \ (367 \text{ kN-m})$$

The positive moment to be resisted is

$$M_{pos} = 1.4 \times 65 + 1.7 \times 56 = 186 \text{ ft-kips} \ (252 \text{ kN-m})$$

* Note that for the present example, a typical interior panel, the application of prestress force produces no secondary moments.

For the full 25 ft strip containing 16 tendons,

$$f_{pe} = \frac{521,000}{16 \times 0.217} = 150,000 \text{ psi}$$

$$A_p = 0.217 \times 16 = 3.472 \text{ in.}^2$$

$$\rho_p = \frac{3.472}{25 \times 12 \times 5.75} = 0.0020$$

and the stress in the unbonded tendons is estimated (Eq. 3.21) to be

$$f_{ps} = f_{pe} + 10,000 + \frac{f_c'}{100\rho_p}$$

$$= 150,000 + 10,000 + \frac{5000}{100 \times 0.0020} = 185,000 \text{ psi } (1276 \text{ N/mm}^2)$$

The contribution of the four No. 6 bars added to meet requirements for bonded non-prestressed steel may be included in ultimate strength calculations. Then

$$a = \frac{A_p f_{ps} + A_s f_y}{0.85 f_c' b} = \frac{3.472 \times 185 + 1.77 \times 60}{0.85 \times 5 \times 300} = 0.59 \text{ in.}$$

$$M_u = 0.90(3.472 \times 185 + 1.77 \times 60)(5.75 - 0.59/2)/12$$

$$= 306 \text{ ft-kips } (415 \text{ kN-m})$$

which is about 13 percent above that required for negative bending. Similar calculations confirm that the positive bending section has adequate flexural strength as well.

The live load deflection at the center of the typical panel will be checked, using the equivalent frame method. The moments of inertia for the full width frame and for the column or middle strips are respectively,

$$I_{frame} = \frac{1}{12} \times 25 \times 12 \times 7^3 = 8580 \text{ in.}^4$$

$$I_{col} = I_{mid} = \frac{8580}{2} = 4290 \text{ in.}^4$$

The reference deflection is found from Eq. (10.20) to be

$$d_{f,ref} = \frac{50 \times 25 \times 25^4 \times 12^4}{384 \times 4,030,000 \times 12 \times 8580} = 0.064 \text{ in.}$$

From Eqs. (10.21a) and (10.21b), the deflections of the column and middle strips, with ends assumed fixed, are

$$d_{f,col} = 0.064 \times 0.75 \times 2 = 0.096 \text{ in.}$$

$$d_{f,mid} = 0.064 \times 0.25 \times 2 = 0.032 \text{ in.}$$

For the present case, with no moment transmitted through the slab-to-column joint, the actual end rotations of the slab strip must be found from the moment diagram for the slab, using moment area principles. Calculations are based on the diagram for maximum live load moment (Fig. 10.23b). The distance of a point on the elastic curve at the left support from a tangent to the elastic curve at the right support is found taking moments of the M/EI area about the left support:

$$\Delta = \frac{1}{EI}\left(98 \times 25 \times \frac{2}{3} \times \frac{25}{2} - 42 \times 25 \times \frac{25}{2}\right) = \frac{7290}{EI}$$

The slope at the right support (the left support slope is the same, of opposite sign) is then easily calculated by dividing by the span length:

$$\theta_r = \frac{7290}{25EI} = \frac{7290 \times 1000 \times 12^3}{25 \times 12 \times 4,030,000 \times 8580} = 0.0012 \text{ radians}$$

From Eq. (10.23) the midspan deflection associated with the end rotation just found is

$$d_\theta = \frac{0.0012 \times 25 \times 12}{8} = 0.045 \text{ in.}$$

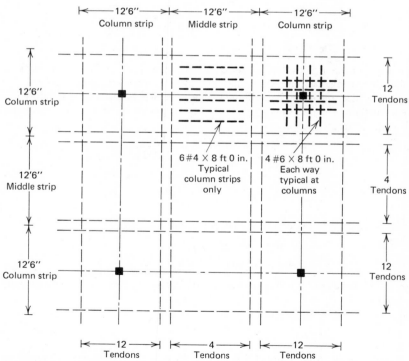

Figure 10.24 Reinforcing and prestress tendon layout for flat plate example.

and from Eqs. (10.24a) and (10.24b) the midspan deflections of the column and middle strips are, respectively,

$$d_{col} = 0.096 + 0.045 \times 2 = 0.186 \text{ in. (5 mm)}$$
$$d_{mid} = 0.032 + 0.045 \times 2 = 0.122 \text{ in. (3 mm)}$$

Finally, from Eq. (10.19a), the live load deflection at the mid-point of the panel is found by summing the deflection of the column strip in one direction and the middle strip in the other:

$$d_{max} = 0.186 + 0.122 = 0.308 \text{ in. (8 mm)}$$

According to ACI Code, the limiting live load deflection is taken as $1/360$ times the span, or 0.833 in. The design is satisfactory in this respect as well as all others.

The complete arrangement of prestressing tendons and non-prestressed bar reinforcement is shown in Fig. 10.24.

REFERENCES

10.1 "Tentative Recommendations for Concrete Members Prestressed with Unbonded Tendons," reported by ACI–ASCE Joint Committee 423, *J. ACI*, Vol. 66, No. 2, February 1969, pp. 81–86.

10.2 Timoshenko, S. and Woinowsky–Krieger, S., *Theory of Plates and Shells*, 2nd Ed., McGraw-Hill, New York, 1959, 580 pp.

10.3 Jones, L. L. and Wood, R. H., *Yield Line Analysis of Slabs*, American Elsevier, New York, 1967, 405 pp.

10.4 "Tentative Recommendations for Prestressed Concrete Flat Plates," reported by ACI Committee 423, *J. ACI*, Vol. 71, No. 2, February 1974, pp. 61–71.

10.5 Scoredelis, A. C., Lin, T. Y., and Itaya, R., "Behavior of a Continuous Slab Prestressed in Two Directions," *J. ACI*, Vol. 56, No. 6, December 1959, pp. 441–460.

10.6 Rice, E. K. and Kulka, F., "Design of Prestressed Lift Slabs for Deflection Control," *J. ACI*, Vol. 56, No. 8, February 1960, pp. 681–693.

10.7 Corley, W. G. and Hawkins, N. M., "Shearhead Reinforcement for Slabs," *J. ACI*, Vol. 65, No. 10, October 1968, pp. 811–824.

10.8 Winter, G. and Nilson, A. H., *Design of Concrete Structures*, 8th Ed., McGraw-Hill, New York, 1972, 615 pp.

10.9 Gerber, L. L. and Burns, N. H., "Ultimate Strength Tests of Posttensioned Flat Plates," *J. PCI*, Vol. 16, No. 6, November–December 1971, pp. 40–58.

10.10 Nilson, A. H., and Walters, D. B., "Deflection of Two-Way Floor Systems by the Equivalent Frame Method," *J. ACI*, Vol. 72, No. 5, May 1975, pp. 210–218.

10.11 Nawy, E. G. and Chakrabarti, P. "Deflection of Prestressed Concrete Flat Plates," *J. PCI*, Vol. 21, No. 2, March–April 1976, pp. 86–102.

PROBLEMS

10.1 A two-way prestressed concrete slab, measuring 60×120 ft overall, is to be provided to carry a tennis court over an underground parking facility. Support will be provided by masonry walls on the perimeter, and steel framing along interior column lines as shown in Fig. P10.1. An asphalt court surface 2 in. thick, weighing 25 psf, will be provided. (a) Design the slab for a balanced load consisting of the self-weight of the slab and the asphalt topping. Determine the required slab thickness, prestress force, and number and spacing of 1/2 in. diameter Grade 250 unbonded post-tensioning tendons. Concrete strengths $f'_c = 5000$ psi and $f'_{ci} = 3500$ psi. (b) Check concrete flexural stresses in the fully loaded stage assuming live load of 100 psf. (c) Check the safety of the slab against flexural failure, applying the usual ACI load factors and strength reduction factors. Modify the design if necessary. (d) What other aspects of the proposed structure should be investigated for a complete structural design?

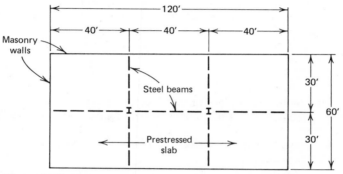

Figure P10.1

10.2 Redesign the structure of Problem 10.1 as a flat plate, with no beams or girders. Walls will be provided at the perimeter as before, but the steel framing will be replaced by two concrete columns 18 in. in diameter at the locations of the steel columns shown in the sketch. Include shear reinforcement at the interior columns if necessary, using either reinforcing bars or shear heads.

CHAPTER 11
AXIALLY LOADED MEMBERS

11.1 INTRODUCTION

The preceding chapters have focused on the analysis and design of flexural members: beams, for which the main loading is normal to the axis of the member, or slabs, with loads acting normal to the surface. Another class of members will now be considered: prismatic elements for which the main loading acts in the direction parallel to the long axis. Included are compression members, such as columns, truss components, or pilings, and tension members such as are used in trusses, for tie rods of arches and rigid frames, or for hangers. While the main loads in all such cases are longitudinal, producing compression or tension, these may be combined with bending loads. Combined loading is normal in columns, for which forces are often applied eccentrically by brackets, or where an equivalent eccentricity results from rigid-jointed continuous-frame action.

This chapter will present the basic features of the analysis and design of tension members and columns, including eccentric columns. Special applications, such as trusses, pilings, foundation anchors, liquid storage tanks, and containment vessels will be described in Ch. 13.

11.2 BEHAVIOR OF PRESTRESSED COLUMNS

If a concrete column were subjected only to axial compression, there would be very little point in prestressing and thereby adding to the compression stress. However, the column that is loaded only with concentric compressive force is most unusual in structural practice. In most cases, columns carry bending moment as well, introduced by eccentric application of the load, as for precast columns with brackets, or by continuous rigid-jointed frame action, which transfers bending moments from the ends of the beam spans into the columns. Wind or earthquake forces often introduce direct tension as well as high bending stresses. Prestressing of columns will often be found advantageous, particularly for situations in which the ratio of bending moment to axial force is high, so as to produce tension over a substantial part of the concrete cross section.

389

Prestressed concrete columns may be categorized as *short* or *long*. In the first case, the strength depends only upon the strength of the steel and concrete, and the geometry of the cross section, while in the second, the strength may be significantly diminished by the effects of slenderness. The effect of slenderness on strength will be studied in Arts. 11.5 and 11.6. The present discussion pertains to short columns, but provides a basis for later study of slender columns as well.

Deflection and cracking of prestressed columns at service loads are almost never serious problems. Furthermore, the investigation of stresses at service loads, based on elastic behavior of the materials, is of limited interest and has little to do with the safety of the column, which is the main consideration. Consequently, present attention will be focused on the analysis to determine *strength* of eccentrically loaded, short, prestressed concrete columns (Refs. 11.1, 11.2, and 11.3).

Figure 11.1a shows such a column, at incipient failure, with ultimate load P_n applied at eccentricity e with respect to the geometric center of the cross section.* Section dimensions b and h are respectively parallel and perpendicular to the axis of bending, as shown in Fig. 11.1b. The prestressing steel is arranged in two layers, each parallel to the axis of bending, and it will be assumed that the cross section is symmetrical, with equal steel areas A_{p1} and A_{p2}. The eccentric load is equilibrated at any section a-a along the length of the member by internal forces producing a net thrust equal and opposite to P_n, and moment M_n equal and opposite to $P_n e$.

Such a column may fail by either of two modes:

a. *For large eccentricities* the prestressing steel on the side of the column farther from the load will reach the yield condition in tension. Continued yielding will shift the neutral axis toward the loaded side of the member, reducing the concrete area available to resist compression, and eventually overloading the concrete. A *secondary* compression failure results when the compressive strain in the concrete becomes equal to the limiting value ε_{cu}.

b. *For small eccentricities* a *primary* compression failure of the concrete will obtain when the maximum concrete strain on the loaded side of column reaches ε_{cu}. The steel on the far side of the column may be well below the yield stress when this occurs.

Clearly, it is also possible, for some unique combination of P_n and M_n (or equivalent eccentricity), to obtain, simultaneously, tension yielding of the steel on the side of the column farther from the load, and crushing of the concrete

---

* Note that a column carrying a concentric load P_n and bending moment M_n may be designed for an equivalent loading consisting of P_n acting at eccentricity $e = M_n/P_n$.

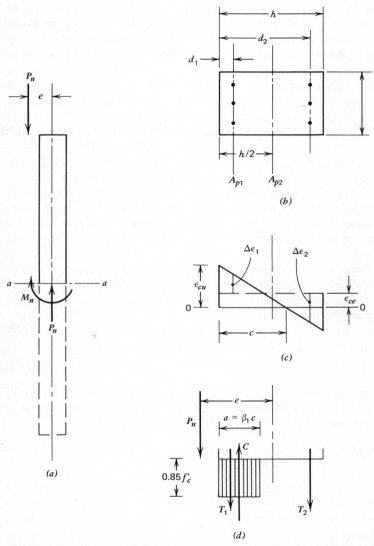

Figure 11.1 Short column with eccentric loading. (*a*) Free body of half-column. (*b*) Cross section. (*c*) Strain distribution. (*d*) Forces and equivalent stresses.

391

in compression on the side nearer the load. Such a situation is referred to as *balanced failure*, occurring at load P_b and moment M_b. For columns, this condition does not have the significance that it did for beams, where a ductile yielding failure could be insured by setting an upper limit on steel ratio. For columns, the nature of the failure, that is, yielding or crushing, is determined by the ratio of the applied moment M_n and thrust P_n, established by analysis of the structure as a whole. The equivalent eccentricity that results may be larger or smaller than the eccentricity e_b for balanced failure, and so failure may be initiated either by concrete crushing or steel yielding in a particular case.

The strains in the concrete at section *a-a* are shown in Fig. 11.1c. A convenient reference strain state corresponds to the effective prestress force P_e, such that after creep, shrinkage, and relaxation have taken place, the concrete strain is uniformly at ε_{ce} compression. Also shown in Fig. 11.1c is the strain distribution in the concrete at incipient failure, when the neutral axis is a distance c from the loaded side of the column, and the concrete strain on that face is equal to the limiting value ε_{cu}.

Forces and stresses corresponding to the strains at incipient failure are given in Fig. 11.1d. The equivalent rectangular stress block, with uniform concrete stress intensity $0.85f'_c$ and depth $a = \beta_1 c$ is substituted for the actual concrete stress variation as usual (see Art. 3.7c).

With reference to Fig. 11.1d, requirements of equilibrium of the free body consisting of the upper half of the column indicate that

$$P_n = C - T_1 - T_2 \tag{11.1}$$

where the concrete compressive stress resultant $C = 0.85f'_c ab$, and T_1 and T_2 are, respectively, the tensile forces provided by the steel areas A_{p1} and A_{p2}. Setting the summation of moments equal to zero indicates that

$$P_n e = C\left(\frac{h}{2} - \frac{a}{2}\right) - T_1\left(\frac{h}{2} - d_1\right) + T_2\left(d_2 - \frac{h}{2}\right) \tag{11.2}$$

Equations (11.1) and (11.2) do not at once permit calculation of the failure load P_n for a given eccentricity e, because the terms C, T_1, and T_2 on the right-hand sides, as well as a, are all dependent upon the still-unknown location of the neutral axis at failure, a distance c from the face of the column (see Fig. 11.1c). The neutral axis dimension, in turn, depends upon the magnitude of the forces C, T_1, and T_2.

One could, theoretically, express all unknowns on the right-hand sides of Eqs. (11.1) and (11.2) in terms of the neutral axis distance c, then, for a given eccentricity e solve the two equations simultaneously for c and P_n. However, the computational difficulties would be substantial.

It is more practical to approach the problem indirectly, through the construction of an *interaction diagram* relating thrust P_n and moment M_n at failure.

A typical diagram of this type is shown in Fig. 11.2. The solid line corresponds to a state of incipient failure for the particular column, while any combination of thrust and moment falling within the area bounded by that line can be carried with some margin of safety.

Radial lines may be drawn in Fig. 11.2 corresponding to discrete values of eccentricity, as shown. As the load is gradually increased from zero, for any eccentricity, the moment increases proportionately. When the load path represented by the radial eccentricity line reaches the solid interaction line, failure is obtained. An eccentricity of zero (vertical eccentricity line) corresponds to a concentric compression failure at P_o, while an infinite eccentricity (horizontal eccentricity line) corresponds to failure at M_o in pure bending with no axial force. It will be seen that in the region of small eccentricity (compression failure) the addition of axial load will reduce the moment that can be carried. Conversely, in the region of high eccentricity (yielding failure) the addition of axial load increases the moment capacity.

A column failure interaction diagram such as Fig. 11.2 may be constructed for a given column geometry, material strengths, and prestress force by choosing successive, arbitrary locations for the ultimate neutral axis. Each choice corresponds to a particular eccentricity, failure load P_n, and failure moment M_n all of which can be found by a strain compatibility analysis as follows.

A convenient starting point for the analysis is the effective prestress stage, prior to application of the external loads, when the prestress force is P_e and the concrete strain is ε_{ce}. Reference again to Fig. 11.1c shows that this compressive concrete strain is uniformly distributed over the depth of the section.

Application of the eccentric load will produce a linearly varying strain in the concrete. When the column is at incipient failure, the concrete strain on the side nearer to load will be ε_{cu} and the neutral axis will be at a distance c from that face, as shown in Fig. 11.1c.

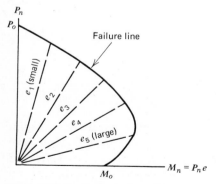

Figure 11.2 Interaction diagram for prestressed column.

The stresses and forces of Fig. 11.1d may be found on the basis of the strain distributions. For the arbitrarily selected value c, the concrete compressive resultant is

$$C = 0.85f'_cab \tag{11.3}$$

Note that while the value of c may be greater than the column dimension h and, in fact, will be equal to infinity for the special case of concentric loading, in all calculations, the upper limit of a is the column dimension h.

The strain in the prestressing steel at effective prestress is

$$\varepsilon_{pe} = \frac{f_{pe}}{E_p} = \frac{P_e}{(A_{p1} + A_{p2})E_p} \tag{a}$$

The *change in strain* in the steel of area A_{p1} as the member passes from effective prestress stage to ultimate load is

$$\Delta\varepsilon_1 = \varepsilon_{cu}\frac{c - d_1}{c} - \varepsilon_{ce} \tag{b}$$

while the corresponding change in strain in the steel of area A_{p2} is

$$\Delta\varepsilon_2 = \varepsilon_{cu}\frac{d_2 - c}{c} + \varepsilon_{ce} \tag{c}$$

The steel forces T_1 and T_2 of Fig. 11.1d may be found based on the net strains in the respective steel areas. If these are below the proportional elastic limit, or yield strain, then

$$T_1 = A_{p1}f_{p1}$$
$$= A_{p1}E_p(\varepsilon_{pe} - \Delta\varepsilon_1)$$
$$T_1 = A_{p1}E_p\left(\varepsilon_{pe} - \varepsilon_{cu}\frac{c - d_1}{c} + \varepsilon_{ce}\right) \tag{11.4}$$

and

$$T_2 = A_{p2}f_{p2}$$
$$= A_{p2}E_{p2}(\varepsilon_{pe} + \Delta\varepsilon_2)$$
$$T_2 = A_{p2}E_p\left(\varepsilon_{pe} + \varepsilon_{cu}\frac{d_2 - c}{c} + \varepsilon_{ce}\right) \tag{11.5}$$

In applying these equations, careful attention must be given to signs, noting that c may be less than d_1 or larger than d_2.

If the strains represented by the quantities in parentheses in Eqs. (11.4) and (11.5) exceed the proportional limit, then the stresses corresponding to the particular strains must be found by reference to the actual stress-strain curve of the steel.

The failure load P_n may now be found by Eq. (11.1), and the failure moment M_n from Eq. (11.2) without difficulty, thus establishing *one point* on the failure interaction curve.

The analysis must be repeated, choosing other values of c, to establish the complete failure line. After the curve is defined in this way, the failure load and moment for any value of eccentricity may be read directly from the graph, moving out the appropriate radial line to the point of intersection with the curve.

For design purposes, according to the ACI Code, the computed values of P_n and M_n must be modified by strength reduction factors ϕ to obtain the reduced values to be used as the design strengths:

$$P_{des} = \phi P_n \qquad (11.6a)$$

$$M_{des} = \phi M_n \qquad (11.6b)$$

The specified value of ϕ is 0.70 for columns with lateral ties (see Art. 11.4) and 0.75 for columns with spiral reinforcement. In either case, the value of ϕ may be increased linearly, according to the Code, to 0.90, as the value of P_n decreases from the balanced load P_b to zero, thus matching at M_o the usual value of $\phi = 0.90$ for beams. In practical cases, the value of P_n corresponding to the maximum moment (Fig. 11.2) may be substituted for P_b.

In addition, according to the Code, the axial load design strength ϕP_n shall not be taken greater than 0.85 (for members with spiral reinforcement) or 0.80 (for members with tie reinforcement) of the axial design strength ϕP_o in pure compression.

It is evident that the design of prestressed concrete columns is essentially a trial-and-error procedure. A trial column must be selected, the strength curve computed, and the capacity of that column compared against the capacity required. The same design approach is followed for ordinary reinforced concrete columns. While certain design aids are available in the form of tables (Ref. 11.4), in most practical cases a strain compatibility analysis such as just described is necessary. A rather simple computer program may be prepared to perform the computations for as many trial designs as required.

11.3 EXAMPLE: CONSTRUCTION OF COLUMN INTERACTION DIAGRAM

The column of Fig. 11.3 measures 12 × 12 in. in cross section and is prestressed using eight 3/8 in. diameter Grade 250 strands in two layers. Total steel area is 0.640 in.^{2} The steel carries an effective prestress, after losses, of 150,000 psi, which, with $E_p = 29,000,000$ psi, corresponds to a strain $\varepsilon_{pe} = 0.0052$. The steel stress-strain curve is as shown in Fig. 2.4. Concrete strength is 6000 psi, and the strain in the concrete when $P_e =$ acts in $\varepsilon_{ce} = 0.0005$. The ultimate compressive strain may be taken as $\varepsilon_{cu} = 0.003$. (Column 305 × 305 mm, $A_p = 413$ mm^2, $f_{pe} = 1034$ N/mm^2, $E_p = 200$ kN/mm^2, and $f'_c = 41$ N/mm^2.) Establish

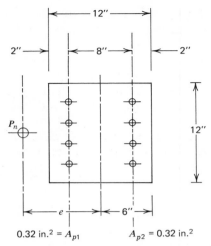

Figure 11.3 Cross section of column.

failure interaction diagram for this column, relating P_n and M_n. Superimpose on the same diagram the line corresponding to the ACI design strength, obtained by application of the appropriate ϕ factors.

The interaction curve will be established by selecting arbitrary values for the neutral axis dimension c, and for each value calculating the axial force and moment producing a state of incipient failure, using Eqs. (11.3), (11.4), (11.5), (11.1), and (11.2). Only representative points will be calculated here. The complete data are summarized in Table 11.1 and plotted in Fig. 11.4.

Table 11.1 Summary of Calculations for Column Design Example

Point	c in.	a in.	P_n kips	M_n in.-kips	ϕ	ϕP_n kips	ϕM_n in.-kips	e in.
1	8	6.0	275	1213	0.70	193	849	4.4
2	10	7.5	376	1125	0.70	263	788	3.0
3	12	9.0	473	899	0.70	331	629	1.9
4	15	11.3	616	319	0.70	431	223	0.5
5	∞	12.0	684	0	0.70	479	0	0
6	6	4.5	177	1151	0.77	136	886	6.5
7	4	3.0	77	944	0.84	65	793	12.3
8	3	2.3	24	777	0.88	21	683	32.4
9	2	1.5	-33	559				-16.9

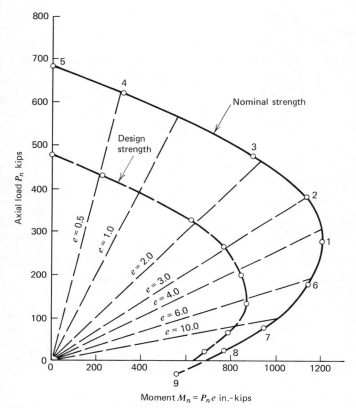

Figure 11.4   Interaction diagram for eccentric column example.

1.   Assume the neutral axis distance c from the left face $= 8$ in. (see Fig. 11.1c). Then $a = 0.75 \times 8 = 6$ in. and the compressive force resultant is found from Eq. (11.3):

$$C = 0.85 \times 6 \times 6 \times 12 = 367 \text{ kips}$$

The resultant force in the steel near the left face is given by Eq. (11.4):

$$T_1 = 0.32 \times 29{,}000(0.0052 - 0.0023 + 0.0005)$$
$$= 32 \text{ kips}$$

while T_2 on the right side is found from Eq. (11.5):

$$T_2 = 0.32 \times 29{,}000(0.0052 + 0.0008 + 0.0005)$$
$$T \ = 60 \text{ kips}$$

Summing vertical forces to determine P_n (Eq. 11.1):

$$P_n = 367 - 32 - 60 = 275 \text{ kips}$$

while the moment M_n is obtained using Eq. (11.2):

$$M_n = 367 \times 3 - 4 \times 32 + 4 \times 60 = 1213 \text{ in-kips}$$

thus determining point (1) on the interaction curve of Fig. 11.4. Other points are found in similar fashion:

5. Assume $c = \infty$; $a = 12$ in. Then

$$C = 0.85 \times 6 \times 12 \times 12 = 734 \text{ kips}$$
$$T_1 = 0.32 \times 29{,}000(0.0052 - 0.0030 + 0.0005) = 25 \text{ kips}$$
$$T_2 = 25 \text{ kips}$$
$$P_n = 734 - 25 - 25 = 684 \text{ kips}$$
$$M_n = 0 - 4 \times 25 + 4 \times 25 = 0$$

6. Assume $c = 6$ in.; $a = 4.5$ in. Then

$$C = 0.85 \times 6 \times 4.5 \times 12 = 275 \text{ kips}$$
$$T_1 = 0.32 \times 29{,}000(0.0052 - 0.0020 + 0.0005) = 34 \text{ kips}$$

In this case the total steel strain in the strand on the right side of the column is 0.0077, exceeding the yield strain shown by Fig. 2.4 for Grade 250 strand. A calculation based on the elastic modulus would be invalid, and steel stress of 200 ksi corresponding to that strain must be read directly from the graph. Then

$$T_2 = 0.32 \times 200 = 64 \text{ kips}$$
$$P_n = 275 - 34 - 64 = 177 \text{ kips}$$
$$M_n = 275 \times 3.75 - 4 \times 34 + 4 \times 64 = 1151 \text{ in.-kips}$$

Similar conditions obtain for points (7) and (8).

9. Assume $c = 2$ in.; $a = 1.5$ in. Then

$$C = 0.85 \times 6 \times 1.5 \times 12 = 92 \text{ kips}$$
$$T_1 = 0.32 \times 29{,}000(0.0052 + 0 + 0.0005) = 53 \text{ kips}$$
$$T_2 = 0.32 \times 225 = 72 \text{ kips}$$
$$P_n = 92 - 53 - 72 = -33 \text{ kips}$$
$$M_n = 92 \times 5.25 - 4 \times 53 + 4 \times 72 = 559 \text{ in.-kips}$$

The negative sign of P_n in this case is an indication that the neutral axis location chosen is possible only if the column is subjected to a tensile load, rather than a compression load. The equivalent eccentricity, having increased to an infinite value at $P_n = 0$, has now changed sign, indicating that the tensile load must be applied on the opposite side of the column. While mainly of academic interest, the last calculation does indicate the generality of the method, which can be applied to eccentric tensile members as well as eccentric compression members.

A total of nine points on the failure interaction line were calculated. All results are summarized in Table 11.1 and are plotted in Fig. 11.4.

Also shown in Fig. 11.4 is the design strength curve, obtained by application of the appropriate ϕ factors to P_n and M_n in accordance with Eqs. (11.6a) and (11.6b). The point of maximum moment on the calculated strength curve matches closely with point (1) for which $P_n = 275$ kips, which may be taken as an approximation of P_b. For higher loads, a ϕ value of 0.70 is applied to thrust and moment to obtain points on the design strength curve, except that a cutoff at $0.80\phi P_o = 383$ kips is applicable. Below point (1), ϕ is permitted to vary linearly to 0.90 as P_n diminishes to zero. Note the discontinuity of slope of the design strength curve that results.

11.4 NON-PRESTRESSED REINFORCEMENT IN COLUMNS

Non-prestressed reinforcement is used in prestressed columns in the form of lateral ties or spirals and, in some cases, as supplementary longitudinal steel.

According to the ACI Code, if compression members have an average prestress, P_e/A_g, less than 225 psi, then longitudinal bar reinforcement must be included. Requirements are the same as for ordinary reinforced concrete columns in this case. Specifically, non-prestressed longitudinal steel must be used having a total area not less than 0.01 and not more than 0.08 times the gross area of the concrete cross section. At least four bars are required when a rectangular arrangement is selected, and at least six bars when the bar pattern is circular. If the average prestress is 225 psi or higher, these provisions do not apply.

Lateral reinforcement should always be provided, just as for reinforced concrete columns. When the main steel is arranged in a circular pattern, normally a continuous spiral winding is used, usually of plain round, underformed steel wire. If the main bars are set in a rectangular pattern, individual lateral ties are provided, spaced at a uniform interval along the column axis.

Such lateral reinforcement serves several important purposes as follows: (1) By resisting the lateral expansion of the concrete that would normally occur because of longitudinal applied load, the transverse steel causes horizontal compression in the concrete. When superimposed on the longitudinal stress, this creates a state of triaxial compression. This not only increases the strength of the column, but improves its toughness by greatly increasing available ductility. (2) If non-prestressed compression steel is used supplementary to the longitudinal prestressing steel, these bars tend to buckle outward when loaded, as would any very slender compression element. Lateral ties or spirals are effective in preventing this type of premature failure. (3) When columns are subjected to horizontal shear forces, as from earthquake action, the lateral reinforcement serves to increase the shear strength substantially. (4) Finally, lateral steel serves the practical function of holding the longitudinal steel in proper alignment and position as the concrete is poured.

Lateral steel is designed on the basis of empirical procedures that have been established by tests. According to ACI Code, if spiral reinforcement is used, the ratio of the volume of spiral steel reinforcement to volume of concrete core (with diameter measured out-to-out of the spiral) should not be less than

$$\rho_s = 0.45 \left(\frac{A_g}{A_c} - 1 \right) \frac{f'_c}{f_y} \tag{11.7}$$

where A_g is the gross concrete area, A_c is the area of the concrete core, and f_y is the specified yield strength of the spiral reinforcement (not to be taken greater than 60,000 psi). For cast-in-place columns the spiral wire is not to be smaller than $\frac{3}{8}$ in. in diameter. In all cases, the pitch of the spiral (advancement in one complete turn) must be between 1 and 3 in. When lateral ties are used, they must be at least $\frac{3}{8}$ in. in diameter. Their spacing must not exceed 18 in., 48 times the tie diameter, or the least dimension of the column, whichever is the smallest. Furthermore, they must be arranged such that every corner and alternate longitudinal bar, wire, or strand has lateral support provided by the corner of a tie having an included angle not greater than 135 degrees.

11.5 BEHAVIOR OF SLENDER COLUMNS

The columns considered in the preceding articles were *short columns*, of such proportions that their strength could be determined on the basis of the geometry of the cross section and the properties of the materials. In practice, many compression members are *long columns*, for which strength is reduced significantly by the effects of slenderness. Prestressed concrete columns, which use higher strength materials, are likely to have smaller cross sections than ordinary reinforced concrete columns, and the possibility of strength reduction due to slenderness should always be investigated (Refs. 11.5, and 11.6).

The idealized case of a perfectly straight, concentrically loaded, slender column was solved by Euler more than 200 years ago. If such a column is free of rotational restraint at its ends, it will fail by lateral buckling at the *critical load*

$$P_c = \frac{\pi^2 EI}{l_u^2} \tag{11.8}$$

where EI is the flexural stiffness of the member, and l_u is the unbraced length. This equation shows that the critical buckling load decreases rapidly as the length increases.

The Euler equation may be generalized to apply to different conditions of end restraint through the introduction of an effective length factor k, applied to the actual length l_u such that

$$P_c = \frac{\pi^2 EI}{(kl_u)^2} \tag{11.9}$$

The value of k depends upon the degree of rotational restraint that exists in a given case, and upon whether or not lateral displacement of the ends of the column is prevented.

In many, if not most, cases concrete structures are braced against sidesway by walls, sufficiently strong and stiff in their own plane effectively to prevent such displacement. These walls may be provided expressly for that purpose, or they may be required otherwise, such as to enclose stairwells, elevator shafts, or utility ducts, for example.

For a column restrained against sway, having hinged ends as shown in Fig. 11.5a, the effective length kl_u is equal to the actual length l_u. When the critical load of Eq. (11.9) is reached, this column will buckle laterally, taking the shape of a half sine wave as shown. In contrast, if the member is restrained against sway and is also fixed against rotation at its ends (Fig. 11.5b) it will buckle into the shape of a full sine wave, with points of inflection at the quarter points of its length. The portion of the column between these inflection points is in precisely the same state as the hinged-end column considered first, and the buckling load of this fixed-ended column can be predicted from Eq. (11.9) with effective length factor $k = 0.5$.

The ends of columns in real structures are seldom either perfectly fixed or perfectly hinged, but rather are restrained by beams, which permit some limited rotation. Consequently, values of k intermediate between 1.0 and 0.5 can be expected for columns that are a part of frames braced against sway.

In some instances, concrete building frames *are* free to sway laterally, the sole resistance to horizontal displacement being provided, in such cases, by the rigid-jointed frame itself. The effective length of the columns is then much greater than before, and the critical buckling load is much less.

This is illustrated by the columns of Figs. 11.5c and 11.5d. If rotation of the column ends is prevented, but translation permitted, as in Fig. 11.5c, the effective length is equal to the actual length, and the effective length factor $k = 1.0$.

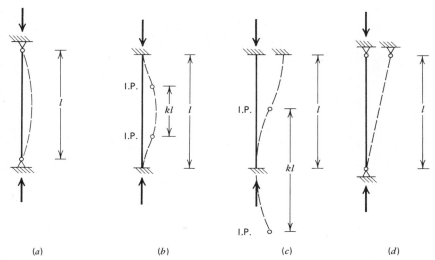

(a)   (b)   (c)   (d)

Figure 11.5 Buckled shapes and effective lengths of axially loaded columns. (*a*) Braced, hinged ends, $k = 1$. (*b*) Braced, fixed ends $k = \frac{1}{2}$. (*c*) Unbraced, fixed ends $k = 1$. (*d*) Unbraced, hinged ends $k = \infty$.

If the ends are provided with no rotational restraint (Fig. 11.5d) the column would topple immediately, that is, the effective length factor is infinite. Thus, for columns in unbraced frames, the effective length factor k may be expected to vary from 1.0 to infinity.

The members considered up to this point were loaded concentrically. Actually, most columns are subjected simultaneously to compression and bending moments, the latter due either to eccentric application of the load or to continuous frame action. The behavior of members subjected to combined loading, too, depends greatly upon slenderness.

Figure 11.6a shows a member carrying axial load P at eccentricity e, producing a *primary moment* $M_o = Pe$, which is constant throughout the length.

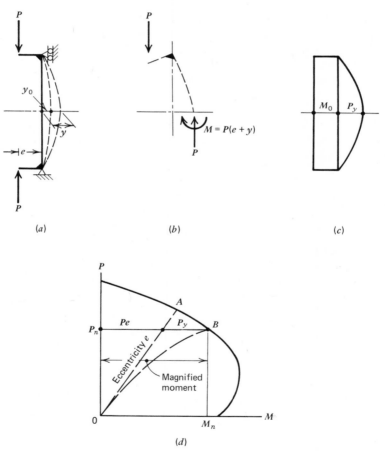

Figure 11.6 Behavior of slender columns. (a) Load and deflection curve. (b) Free body of half-column. (c) Moment diagram. (d) Interaction diagram for failure.

The member deflects laterally an amount y_o due to the moment M_o as shown by the dotted line.

But this lateral displacement causes an increase in bending moment, because of the increased eccentricity of load with respect to the deflected centerline of the column. The column deflects still further due to this increase in moment, which causes an additional moment increase in turn. The behavior is strictly nonlinear.

If the total lateral deflection of the member with respect to its original axis is y, then the final moment is

$$M = M_o + Py \qquad (11.10)$$

The resulting deflected shape is shown by the dashed line of Figs. 11.6a and 11.6b.

Slenderness may be accounted for, in members subject to such combined loading, by what is known as a *second order analysis*, which includes the so-called P-Δ effect, that is, which accounts for the moment increase resulting from lateral displacement. Deflections are calculated for the primary moments. Then the increase in moments that results from these lateral displacements is determined, and the deflections revised accordingly. The process is repeated in an iterative way until satisfactory convergence is obtained. But even with use of a computer, such an analysis is time-consuming and expensive. For ordinary design purposes, a satisfactory approximate solution is possible, based on *magnified moments*, as follows (Ref. 11.7).

The final deflection y of a slender column subjected to eccentric loading can be calculated from the deflection y_o by the following expression:

$$y = y_o \frac{1}{1 - P/P_c} \qquad (11.11)$$

Then from Eqs. (11.10) and (11.11),

$$M_{max} = M_o + Py$$

$$M_{max} = M_o + Py_o \frac{1}{1 - P/P_c} \qquad (11.12)$$

For design purposes, the last equation can be closely approximated by the simplified form:

$$M_{max} = M_o \frac{1}{1 - P/P_c} \qquad (11.13)$$

where $1/(1 - P/P_c)$ is known as a *moment magnification factor*, accounting for the increase in primary moment M_o due to the lateral deflection of the column. Clearly, if the axial force P is much less than P_c, the maximum moment is about equal to the primary moment M_o. If P is close to P_c, the denominator approaches zero, and the maximum moment approaches infinity.

The effect of moment magnification upon the strength of a prestressed concrete column is illustrated by Fig. 11.6d, which shows a typical column strength interaction diagram. A short column loaded with eccentricity e will experience a linear increase of M with increasing P. The loading follows path OA until material failure is obtained at load and moment corresponding to point A. The strength is not diminished by slenderness.

However, if the same column is slender, significant moment magnification will occur. For given eccentricity e, as load is increased, the moment increases in a nonlinear way as indicated by Eq. (11.13) and as shown by Fig. 11.6d. The member fails at a load and moment corresponding to point B.

The direct addition of maximum moment caused by deflection to the full value of primary moment, implied in the preceding paragraphs, does not always obtain. Consider the alternative situations shown in Fig. 11.7. Figure 11.7a shows the load case just described, with eccentricities causing equal and opposite end moments. This is the most unfavorable situation possible, for the

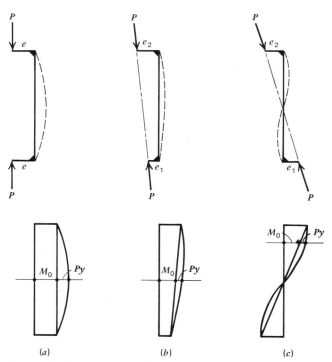

(a) (b) (c)

Figure 11.7 Superposition of primary and deflection moments for slender columns. (a) End moments equal and opposite direction. (b) End moments unequal and opposite direction. (c) End moments same direction.

maximum moment due to lateral deflection superimposes directly on the maximum (in this case constant) moment due to eccentricity. If the end moments act in the opposite sense but are unequal (Fig. 11.7b) then the maximum primary moment occurs at one end of the member, while the maximum moment due to deflection occurs near midlength. This less severe loading case may produce a magnified moment very little greater than the primary moment, as seen. In the third case (Fig. 11.7c) the end moments act in the *same* direction, producing a deflected shape having reverse curvature. In this instance, the magnified moments may or may not be greater than the primary moments, depending upon the relative magnitudes of the primary and deflection moments. The column may, or may not, be weakened by the effect of slenderness.

In practical design methods, such as described in Art. 11.6, the influence of relative magnitude and direction of end moments is accounted for by using an *equivalent uniform moment*, based on the larger of the two end moments, modified to account for the possible alternate loading cases described.

Certain assumptions must be made relative to the effective stiffness of the column. The use of Eq. (11.13) to determine the magnified moment is predicated upon calculation of the critical buckling load P_c from Eq. (11.9). The calculation of P_c depends, in turn, upon the flexural stiffness EI of the column. Prestressed concrete columns are nonhomogeneous, consisting of steel, which is substantially elastic, and concrete, which is not. The concrete is subject to creep, and if the ratio of moment to axial load is high, it is subject to cracking as well. All these factors affect the effective stiffness. While various "exact" methods have been proposed to calculate flexural rigidity taking account of these effects, the calculations are no more accurate than the assumptions on which they are based. It is usually satisfactory to account for such influences in an approximate way, in the calculation of effective EI, by the methods described in Art. 11.6.

11.6   PRACTICAL CONSIDERATION OF SLENDERNESS EFFECTS

The ACI Code does not include provisions relating to the design of slender prestressed concrete columns. However, it has been shown that Code methods intended for *reinforced* concrete columns can be applied to prestressed concrete columns with reasonable accuracy (Refs. 11.8 and 11.9). These provisions are based on the concepts and approaches presented in Art. 11.5.

Axial loads and moments may be determined by a conventional elastic frame analysis. A column is then to be designed for its axial load and a simultaneous *magnified moment* equal to

$$M_c = \frac{C_m M_2}{1 - P_u/\phi P_c} \geq M_2 \qquad (11.14)$$

In this equation, M_2 is the value of the larger end moment, P_u is the axial load obtained from the analysis for factored loads, P_c is the critical buckling load as given by Eq. (11.9), and ϕ is a capacity reduction factor taken equal to 0.75 for spirally reinforced columns and 0.70 for tied columns.

The factor C_m relates the actual moment diagram to an equivalent uniform moment diagram. For members braced against sidesway and without transverse loads between supports, C_m is to be calculated from the equation

$$C_m = 0.6 + 0.4\,\frac{M_1}{M_2} \geq 0.4 \tag{11.15}$$

Here M_2 is the larger of the two end moments and always taken as positive. M_1 is the smaller of the end moments. It is positive if the member is bent in single curvature but negative if it is bent in double curvature. In members not braced against sway, or if subject to transverse loads between supports, C_m is to be taken equal to 1.0.

Values of C_m from Eq. (11.15) are plotted as a function of the moment ratio M_1/M_2 in Fig. 11.8. It is seen that, for a member bent into single curvature by equal end moments, C_m is equal to 1.0. This corresponds to the case shown in Fig. 11.7a, for which no moment reduction is appropriate. For a member subject to moment M_2 at one end only, with $M_1 = 0$ at the far end, an equivalent uniform moment of $0.6M_2$ is to be used. This is the limiting case of the loading shown in Fig. 11.7b. If the member is bent by end moments that cause double curvature, as in Fig. 11.7c, the equivalent moment factor reduces linearly from 0.6 to 0.4 but is not to be taken less than the latter value.

Regardless of the values of the modifying factors applied to M_2 in Eq. (11.14), the value of design moment M_c is not to be taken less than M_2. The need for this limitation is clear from the moment diagrams of Fig. 11.7. In all cases, regardless of the combined effects of slenderness and moment variation along

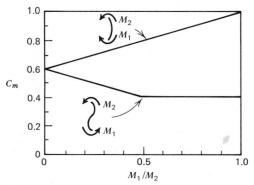

Figure 11.8 Variation of moment factor C_m with ratio of end moments.

the length of a column, a column is at least subject to the full axial load and the primary moment, acting simultaneously, at one end or both.

The denominator of Eq. (11.14) is essentially the same as that of Eq. (11.13). At the ultimate load of present interest, the appropriate value for P is the maximum load that the member can sustain, that is, the *nominal strength* P_n. This is related to the *required strength* P_u by the expression $P_u = \phi P_n$. Consequently the factor P_u/ϕ is substituted for P in Eq. (11.13) to obtain the denominator of Eq. (11.14).

In calculating the critical load P_c for use in Eq. (11.14) due regard must be given to effective length. Limiting cases for frames without and with sidesway, for hinged or fixed ends, were discussed in Art. 11.5 and illustrated by Fig. 11.5. For columns that are a part of rigid frames, the degree of rotational restraint at the column ends depends on whether the rigidities of the beams framing into the column at the top and bottom are large or small compared with the rigidity of the column itself.

An approximate but generally satisfactory way of determining k is by means of the *alignment charts* of Fig. 11.9. The charts are based on isolating the given column plus all members framing into it at top and bottom. The degree of

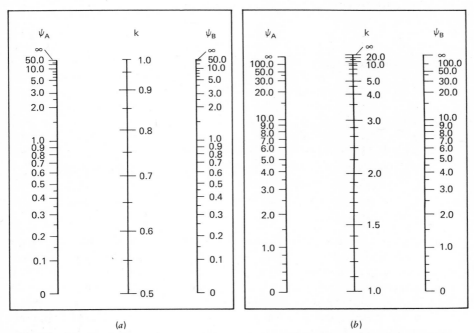

(a)   (b)

Figure 11.9   Alignment charts for effective length factor k. (a) Braced frames. (b) Unbraced frames.

restraint at each end is

$$\psi = \frac{\sum \dfrac{EI}{l} \text{ for columns}}{\sum \dfrac{EI}{l} \text{ for floor members}} \qquad (11.16)$$

Clearly a low value of ψ corresponds to a column almost completely fixed against rotation by much larger floor members, hence k would be close to 0.5 for a braced column and 1.0 for an unbraced one. A high value of ψ corresponds to a column much stiffer than the beams, such that its ends could be considered nearly hinged. The value of k in such case would be near 1.0 for a column in a braced frame, and would approach ∞ for an unbraced column.

In practice the value of ψ may not be the same at both ends of a column. In the use of the interpolation charts of Fig. 11.9, a straight line is drawn between the values of ψ at the A and B ends of a given column, and the appropriate value of k found at the intersection of that line with the k axis.

A final comment is appropriate relative to the value of flexural stiffness EI to be used in the calculation of P_c by Eq. (11.9). On the basis of analytical and experimental studies of *reinforced concrete columns*, the Code permits EI to be determined by either of the following equations:

$$EI = \frac{E_c I_g / 5 + E_s I_s}{1 + \beta_d} \qquad (11.17)$$

or the simpler expression

$$EI = \frac{E_g I_g / 2.5}{1 + \beta_d} \qquad (11.18)$$

where

I_g = moment of inertia of the gross concrete section

I_s = moment of inertia of the reinforcement about the centroidal axis of the concrete section

β_d = ratio of maximum dead load moment to maximum total load moment.

The factor β_d accounts approximately for the effect of creep. That is, the larger the moments caused by sustained dead loads, the larger are the creep deformations and corresponding curvatures. Consequently, the larger the sustained loads relative to the temporary loads, the smaller is the effective rigidity, as correctly reflected in Eqs. (11.17) and (11.18).

Although these equations were developed from study of reinforced concrete columns, their use for prestressed concrete columns may be considered acceptable until further data become available.

11.7 BEHAVIOR OF TENSION MEMBERS

Concrete does not at first seem a natural choice for constructing a member subject dominantly to tensile loads. A *reinforced concrete* tensile member will crack at relatively low loading, after which the reinforcing bars must carry all of the tension. The concrete, subsequent to cracking, serves mainly to provide some measure of corrosion protection for the steel. If cracking is extensive, even this function is not well served.

By prestressing the concrete, however, a tension member may be constructed that is superior in all respects to a reinforced concrete unit and, in several important ways, is superior to a comparable all-steel member.

It is evident that, by applying an appropriate amount of compressive prestress, a tension member may be designed that will be free of concrete cracking under normal service conditions. This is of particular importance for tie members, which may be buried underground between arch foundations, for example.

Of greater significance, in many cases, is the fact that a prestressed concrete tension member will display much less elongation when loaded than will a comparable all-steel member designed for the same load. Prior to concrete cracking, the strain per unit load will be much less, because of the much larger effective cross section. After cracking, the steel tendon must carry all of the tension. However, the tendon has been "prestretched" during the prestressing of the concrete, and the additional elongation as the concrete is relieved of its compressive stress by the external loading is likely to be very small.

This point will be illustrated by Fig. 11.10. The bare steel strand of Fig. 11.10a, if stressed by the specified service load Q, as shown in Fig. 11.10b, would exhibit an increase in length of the amount Δl directly proportional to the steel stress and inversely proportional to the modulus of elasticity. If the otherwise efficient, economical, high tensile strength wire or strand were to be used, and if length l is substantial, an unacceptably large elongation could be expected.

However, if the wire were "prestretched" by a force P equal to Q, and if concrete were poured between suitable end bearing plates, and furthermore, if the force P were then released after the concrete had hardened, then shortening of the strand would be largely prevented by the concrete, as seen in Fig. 11.10c. The length of the prestressed concrete member, with no external load applied, would be slightly less than the length $(l + \Delta l)$, because of elastic shortening of the concrete. (This would also reduce the prestress force to a value somewhat less than P).

If the external load Q is now applied, as in Fig. 11.10d, the member would elongate only by the amount $\Delta' l$, much less than the elongation Δl of Fig. 11.10b, because in this case elongation is governed by the transformed cross section of concrete rather than the area of the strand alone. In the service load stage, the concrete stress would be diminished to zero, and the force in the steel would be equal to Q.

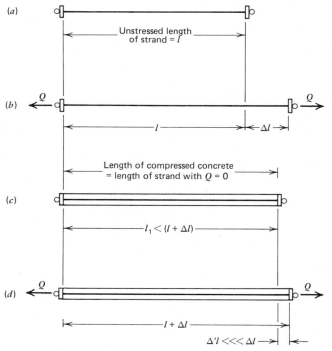

Figure 11.10 Use of prestressed concrete to limit tensile deformation.

This simplified example neglects such factors as creep and shrinkage of the concrete and relaxation of the steel, but serves to illustrate the deformation control possible for prestressed tension members.

A question that may be raised relative to prestressing tension members is whether or not the member, which typically will be rather long and slender, is vulnerable to buckling because of the prestress compression load. It can be shown analytically, and it has been confirmed experimentally that, in the case of post-tensioning, if the tendon is in close contact with the inside of the duct, then no tendency to buckle will result. Any slight lateral displacement of the concrete is accompanied by a corresponding displacement of the steel which provides the force producing the compression and, consequently, no bending moment is obtained. This is in contrast with the condition in the typical Euler column analysis, in which a slight lateral displacement of the member axis introduces bending moment as a result of the eccentricity of loading that accompanies that displacement.

The same argument obviously applies to pretensioned members as well; the prestressing forces cause no tendency to buckle. For post-tensioned elements in which the tendon is contained in an unusually large duct or in a hollow box section, however, a buckling tendency does exist and calculations should always be made to insure that no problems will arise.

As long as both materials are stressed only in the elastic range, stresses and deformations may be found based on the net or transformed cross section, whichever is applicable. The following notation will be used:

P_i = initial prestress force, after anchorage but before time-dependent losses

P_e = effective prestress force, after all losses

A_g = gross area of concrete cross section

A_p = area of steel tendon

A_c = net area of concrete cross section

A_t = transformed area of concrete cross section

n = modular ratio = E_p/E_c

The stress in the concrete immediately after transfer and anchorage is

$$f_{ci} = -\frac{P_i}{A_c} \tag{11.19}$$

After time-dependent losses have occurred, this stress is reduced to

$$f_{ce} = -\frac{P_e}{A_c} \tag{11.20}$$

while the stress in the steel is

$$f_{pe} = \frac{P_e}{A_p} \tag{11.21}$$

Because tensile loads applied to the member after this time cause equal elongation and tensile strain in both the concrete and steel, stress changes due to subsequent loading, prior to cracking, may be found using the transformed section approach.* If we replace the actual steel area A_p with its equivalent tensile concrete area, the transformed section is

$$A_t = A_g + (n-1)A_p \tag{11.22}$$

The stress changes in the concrete and steel, as an external tension Q is applied (up to the cracking load), are respectively

$$\Delta f_c = \frac{Q}{A_t} \tag{11.23}$$

$$\Delta f_p = \frac{nQ}{A_t} \tag{11.24}$$

---

* This statement applies to both bonded and unbonded tension members. In practice most tension members are bonded, being either pretensioned or grouted after post-tensioning.

When superimposed on the stresses already present, these produce

$$f_c = -\frac{P_e}{A_c} + \frac{Q}{A_t} \tag{11.25}$$

$$f_p = f_{pe} + \frac{nQ}{A_t} \tag{11.26}$$

The cracking load Q_{cr} may be predicted using Eq. (11.25), by setting the concrete stress equal to the direct tensile strength of the material. This is generally in the range from $3\sqrt{f'_c}$ to $5\sqrt{f'_c}$ for normal density concrete and from $2\sqrt{f'_c}$ to $3.5\sqrt{f'_c}$ for lightweight concrete.

After cracking, the concrete is ineffective, and the entire tension must be resisted by the steel tendon. Denoting f_{pu} the tensile strength of the steel, the nominal strength of the tension member is

$$Q_n = A_p f_{pu} \tag{11.27a}$$

For design purposes this is reduced by the factor $\phi = 0.90$, giving the design strength

$$\phi Q_n = \phi A_p f_{pu} \tag{11.27b}$$

Deformations will be found with respect to the original, unstressed length of the concrete. If we assume for present purposes that the member will be post-tensioned and grouted, the reduction in length as the concrete is initially stressed to P_i is

$$\Delta_i = -\frac{P_i l}{A_c E_c} \tag{11.28}$$

Creep deformation takes place while the prestress force reduces gradually from P_i to P_e. For most practical purposes it will be sufficient to use an average value of force $(P_i + P_e)/2$ to compute total displacement after an extended time period:

$$\Delta_e = -\frac{l}{A_c E_c}\left[P_e + \left(\frac{P_i + P_e}{2}\right)C_u\right] \tag{11.29}$$

where C_u is the creep coefficient. Values of C_u and suitable modifying factors will be found in Ch. 2. If greater accuracy is required, an improved estimate of long term deformation may be had using a time-step incremental approach, similar to that described in Ch. 9, in which the force causing creep during any time step is that computed, after losses, at the end of the preceding time step.

Assuming that the member has been designed to avoid cracking at service load, then the change in length at service load, with respect to the prestressed but unloaded length of the concrete member, is

$$\Delta_s = \frac{Ql}{A_t E_c} \tag{11.30}$$

11.8 EXAMPLE: BEHAVIOR OF PRESTRESSED CONCRETE TENSION ELEMENT

A concrete tension member 100 ft long has a cross section 10 in. square. It is post-tensioned with a force $P_i = 103$ kips using a single 12 wire tendon of Grade 250 steel, with total steel area $A_p = 0.589$ in.^{2} The wires are contained in a 1.5 in. diameter conduit, and are grouted after post-tensioning. Separate calculations indicate that after losses the prestress force will be $P_e = 88$ kips. Using values of $C_u = 2.0$, $E_p = 29 \times 10^3$ ksi, $E_c = 3.64 \times 10^3$ ksi, $n = 8$, and $f'_t = 0.475$ ksi, find

a.   The maximum tensile force Q that can be resisted without causing tension in the concrete.
b.   The cracking load.
c.   The failure load.
d.   The safety factor against cracking and failure, if service load is defined to be the zero-tension load of part (a).
e.   The elongation at P_i, P_e, and full service load

($l = 30.5$ m, $b = h = 254$ mm, $P_i = 458$ kN, $P_e = 391$ kN, $A_p = 380$ mm^2, conduit 38 mm diameter, $E_p = 200$ kN/mm^2, $E_c = 25.1$ kN/mm^2, $f'_t = 3.28$ N/mm^2.)

Elastic stress calculations will require use of the transformed section. In the present case

$$A_g = 10 \times 10 = 100 \text{ in.}^2$$

$$A_c = 100 - \pi \times \frac{1.5^2}{4} = 98 \text{ in.}^2$$

$$A_t = A_g + (n - 1)A_p$$
$$= 100 + 7 \times 0.589 = 104 \text{ in.}^2$$

The zero-tension load, defined here as the service load, can be found setting f_c in Eq. (11.25) equal zero and solving for Q:

$$Q_o = \frac{A_t}{A_c} \times P_e$$

$$= \frac{104}{98} \times 88 = 93 \text{ kips (414 kN)}$$

Note that Q_o required to produce zero concrete tension is larger than the effective prestress force P_e. The reason for this is that the force P_e was applied to the *net section* of concrete, while the force Q_o required to return the concrete to the zero stress state is applied to the transformed section.

If we assume elastic behavior, the cracking load is also found using Eq. (11.25), in this case setting the concrete stress equal to 475 psi. Thus

$$Q_{cr} = \left(f_c + \frac{P_e}{A_c} \right) A_t$$

$$= \left(0.475 + \frac{88}{98} \right) 104$$

$$= 142 \text{ kips (632 kN)}$$

But, assuming that the stress-strain curve of Fig. 2.4 for Grade 250 steel is applicable, the resulting steel stress of $142/0.589 = 240$ ksi is somewhat above the yield stress of 215 ksi. In all probability, cracking of the concrete would initiate soon after yielding of the steel and therefore the cracking tension will be taken equal to

$$Q_{cr} = 215 \times 0.589 = 127 \text{ kips (565 kN)}$$

The design strength is easily found using Eq. (11.27b):

$$\phi Q_n = 0.90 \times 0.589 \times 250$$
$$= 132 \text{ kips (587 kN)}$$

On the basis of these calculations, the safety factors against cracking and failure, with respect to the zero-tension load, are, respectively,

$$F_{cr} = \frac{127}{93} = 1.37$$

$$F_u = \frac{132}{93} = 1.42$$

The relatively small spread between cracking and failure is typical of prestressed tension members, and illustrates well the dangers of basing designs on permissible tensile stress in the concrete. This point will be further discussed in the following article.

Deformations will next be calculated. Upon initial post-tensioning the concrete shortening is found from Eq. (11.28):

$$\Delta_i = -\frac{103 \times 1200}{98 \times 3.64 \times 10^3} = -0.346 \text{ in. } (-9 \text{ mm})$$

After all losses have occurred, the total displacement with respect to the original length is found from Eq. (11.29):

$$\Delta_e = -\frac{1200}{98 \times 3.64 \times 10^3}\left[88 + \left(\frac{103 + 88}{2}\right)2\right]$$
$$= -0.939 \text{ in. } (24 \text{ mm})$$

When the full service load acts, the deformation with respect to the prestressed but unloaded length is found from Eq. (11.30):

$$\Delta_s = \frac{93 \times 1200}{104 \times 3.64 \times 10^3} = 0.294 \text{ in. } (7 \text{ mm})$$

It is of great relevance to compare this deformation with that which would be obtained if the bare steel tendon had been used to carry the same load, without prestressing. In such case, the deformation at 93 kips would have been

$$\Delta_s = \frac{Ql}{A_p E_p} = \frac{93 \times 1200}{0.589 \times 29 \times 10^3} = 6.53 \text{ in. } (166 \text{ mm})$$

This is 22 *times* the length increase associated with the prestressed concrete tie member.

11.9 DESIGN OF TENSION MEMBERS

It was illustrated by the preceding example that a tension member designed on the basis of an allowable concrete stress may show a dangerously low factor of safety against failure. This suggests that the most direct route to the final design of such a structural component may well start with the consideration of strength, rather than stress limitations.

In most such cases, the design considerations, in order of importance, are as follows:

a. To provide a member having the strength adequate to resist a specified degree of overloading.
b. To control the elongation of the member at full service load, with reference to its unloaded length.
c. To provide crack control at service load, usually specifying zero concrete tension at this stage.

Accordingly, a suggested design procedure for tension members is as follows:

a. Select the steel area on the basis of the required strength, disregarding the presence of concrete, which will be cracked at ultimate load. Thus

$$Q_u = F_1 Q_d + F_2 Q_l$$

where Q_d and Q_l are the tensile forces corresponding to dead loads and service live loads, respectively, and F_1 and F_2 the required load factors (e.g., 1.4 and 1.7, according to ACI Code). Then from Eq. (11.27a), $Q_n = A_p f_{pu} = Q_u/\phi$ and the required steel area is

$$A_p = \frac{Q_u}{\phi f_{pu}} \qquad (11.31)$$

b. Next a maximum elongation Δ_s at full service load $Q_d + Q_l$ is established, based, for example, on maximum acceptable moments in a rigid frame if support diaplacement were to occur. Based on Eq. (11.30)

$$A_t = \frac{(Q_d + Q_l)l}{\Delta_s E_c} \qquad (11.32)$$

giving the required transformed section area, from which

$$A_g = A_t - (n - 1)A_p$$

and

$$A_c = A_g - A_{duct}$$

c. The amount of prestress is finally determined, so as to provide the desired crack control. For the common case when zero tension is specified at service load, from Eq. (11.25):

$$P_e = \frac{A_c}{A_t}(Q_d + Q_l) \tag{11.33}$$

A design that is carried out in this order will be satisfactory for all specified conditions and will be completed without unnecessary repetition of effort.

11.10 EXAMPLE: DESIGN OF RIGID FRAME TIE MEMBER

An athletic field house roof is supported by concrete rigid frames of 120 ft span as shown in Fig. 11.11a. When subjected to dead load plus full service live load, the frames will impose an outward thrust at each footing of $Q_d = 50$ kips and $Q_l = 85$ kips. A maximum outward displacement of 0.333 in. is acceptable under that loading. Using load and capacity reduction factors in accordance with ACI Code, design an appropriate prestressed tie member to connect the frame footings. The following data are given: $E_p = 27 \times 10^3$ ksi, $E_c = 3.64 \times 10^3$ ksi, $n = 8$, Grade 250 steel. ($l = 36.6$ m, $Q_d = 222$ kN, $Q_1 = 378$ kN, $d = 8$ mm, $E_p = 186$ kN/mm², and $E_c = 25.1$ kN/mm².)

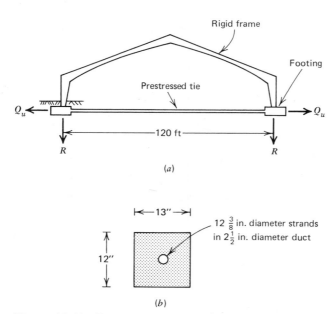

Figure 11.11 Prestressed tension tie for rigid frame. (a) Transverse section through building. (b) Cross section of footing tie.

The required area of steel is found using Eq. (11.31):

$$A_p = \frac{1.4 \times 50 + 1.7 \times 85}{0.90 \times 250} = 0.96 \text{ in.}^2 \ (619 \text{ mm}^2)$$

A single multistrand tendon consisting of 12 $\frac{3}{8}$ in. diameter strands is selected, providing a total steel area just equal to 0.96 in.^{2} The strands are enclosed in a 2.5 in. diameter duct.

From Eq. (11.32) the transformed area necessary to limit the elongation to the desired value is

$$A_t = \frac{(50 + 85) \times 120 \times 12}{0.333 \times 3.64 \times 10^3} = 160 \text{ in.}^2 \ (103 \times 10^3 \text{ mm}^2)$$

Thus

$$A_g = 160 - 7 \times 0.96 = 153 \text{ in.}^2 \ (99 \times 10^3 \text{ mm}^2)$$

A 12 × 13 in. gross cross section will be specified, as shown in Fig. 11.11b, providing $A_g = 156$ in.^{2} and $A_t = 163$ in.^{2} With a 2.5 in. diameter duct the net concrete area is

$$A_c = 156 - \frac{\pi}{4}(2.5)^2 = 151 \text{ in.}^2 \ (97 \times 10^3 \text{ mm}^2)$$

From Eq. (11.33) the prestress force necessary to insure zero concrete tension at full service load is

$$P_e = \frac{151}{163}(50 + 85) = 125 \text{ kips (556 kN)}$$

Losses will be estimated based on $\varepsilon_{sh} = 800 \times 10^{-6}$, $C_u = 2.35$, and relaxation of 3.5 percent. The change in length due to creep of the concrete is based on a constant force assumed 15 percent larger than P_e:

$$\begin{aligned}
\Delta_{cr} &= \frac{1.15 P_e l C_u}{A_c E_c} \\
&= \frac{1.15 \times 125 \times 120 \times 12 \times 2.35}{151 \times 3.64 \times 10^3} \\
&= 0.88 \text{ in. (22 mm)}
\end{aligned}$$

while the length change due to shrinkage is

$$\begin{aligned}
\Delta_{sh} &= \varepsilon_{sh} l \\
&= 800 \times 10^{-6} \times 120 \times 12 \\
&= 1.15 \text{ in. (29 mm)}
\end{aligned}$$

Accordingly the loss in tension from these two causes is

$$\begin{aligned}
\Delta P &= \frac{(\Delta_{cr} + \Delta_{sh})}{l} E_p A_p \\
&= \frac{2.03}{120 \times 12} \times 27 \times 10^3 \times 0.96 \\
&= 37 \text{ kips (165 kN)}
\end{aligned}$$

Allowing also for relaxation of 3.5 percent:

$$P_i = \frac{P_e - \Delta P}{1 - 0.035}$$

$$= \frac{125 + 37}{0.965} = 168 \text{ kips (747 kN)}$$

As a check on the force used for the creep calculations:

$$\frac{P_i + P_e}{2} = \frac{125 + 168}{2} = 147 \text{ kips (654 kN)}$$

very nearly the same as the value used of $1.15 \times 125 = 144$ kips. No revision is required. The final design is shown in Fig. 11.11.

REFERENCES

11.1 Zia, P. and Moreadith, F. L., "Ultimate Load Capacity of Prestressed Concrete Columns," *J. ACI*, Vol. 63, No. 7, July 1966, pp. 767–788.

11.2 Zia, P. and Guillermo, E. C., "Combined Bending and Axial Load in Prestressed Concrete Columns," *J. PCI*, Vol. 12, No. 3, June 1967, pp. 52–59.

11.3 Wilhelm, W. J. and Zia, P., "Effects of Creep and Shrinkage on Prestressed Concrete Columns," *J. Struct. Div. ASCE*, Vol. 96, No. ST10, October 1970, pp. 2103–2123.

11.4 *PCI Design Handbook*, Prestressed Concrete Institute, Chicago, 1971.

11.5 Aroni, S., "The Strength of Slender Prestressed Concrete Columns," *J. PCI*, Vol. 13, No. 2, April 1968, pp. 19–33.

11.6 Nathan, N. D., "Slenderness of Prestressed Concrete Beam-Columns," *J. PCI*, Vol. 17, No. 6, November–December 1972, pp. 45–57.

11.7 Winter, G. and Nilson, A. H., *Design of Concrete Structures*, 8th Ed., McGraw-Hill, New York, 1972, 615 pp.

11.8 Nathan, N. D., "Applicability of ACI Slenderness Computations to Prestressed Concrete Sections," *J. PCI*, Vol. 20, No. 3, May–June 1975, pp. 68–85.

11.9 "Recommended Practice for the Design of Prestressed Concrete Columns and Bearing Walls," reported by PCI Committee on Prestressed Concrete Columns, *J. PCI*, Vol. 21, No. 6, November–December 1976, pp. 16–45.

PROBLEMS

11.1 The precast concrete column shown in Fig. P11.1 is pretensioned with eight 3/8 in. diameter Grade 250 strands tensioned to a stress which, after losses, reduces to $f_{pe} = 150,000$ psi. The steel has stress-strain characteristics as shown in Fig. 2.4. The concrete used has strength $f'_c = 5500$ psi, and ultimate strain capacity $\varepsilon_{cu} = 0.0035$. At effective prestress, the concrete strain is 0.0007. Plot a failure interaction diagram for this member relating P_n and M_n with bending taking place about the strong axis as indicated in the figure. Calculate no fewer than 10 well-spaced points along the curve. Show the "balanced failure" point on your diagram. Show also

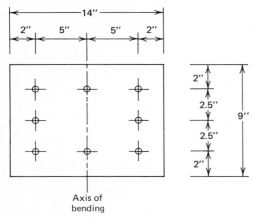

Axis of
bending

Figure P11.1

the curve of design strength, obtained by application of ACI strength reduction
factors.

11.2 An alternative design is considered for the column of Problem 11.1, identical in all
respects except that the prestress in the steel is reduced to $f_{pe} = 75,000$ psi. The
corresponding strain in the concrete is 0.00035. Construct the interaction curve for
this alternative design and compare with previous results.

CHAPTER 12
PRECAST CONSTRUCTION

12.1 INTRODUCTION

Over the past several decades, development of prestressed concrete in Europe and in the United States has taken place along quite different lines. In Europe, where the ratio of labor cost to material cost has been relatively low, innovative one-of-a-kind projects were economically feasible. Sophisticated design and construction techniques were used to achieve the ultimate in material savings. In the United States, where by contrast, the demand for skilled on-site building labor often exceeded the supply, economic conditions were such as to favor the greatest possible standardization of construction, replacing site labor by factory production of precast parts.

There are signs that conditions of practice here are changing. Construction labor is no longer so scarce, and material costs are ever increasing. Advanced design and construction concepts are more often employed, both to save material and to extend the range of prestressed concrete beyond previous limits.

The advantages of precasting are clearly established, however. Because of mass production, less labor is required per unit, and unskilled local labor, much less expensive than skilled mobile construction labor, may be used. High quality, high strength concrete is more easily attained. Complex section shapes are made economically feasible by the repeated use of metal or fiberglass forms. The work can proceed with greater independence from weather and season. On-site construction time is reduced because of the prefabrication of parts, an important consideration in congested localities.

Thus the operation of centrally located permanent precasting plants, supplying standard members within a shipping radius of several hundred miles, will comprise an important part of the total United States construction effort in the years ahead, as it has in the past.

Many future designs are likely to combine precasting with cast-in-place concrete to provide composite action or to develop continuity. The combination of pretensioning and post-tensioning has proved economically advantageous in many instances.

In addition, one can expect the greater use of temporary precasting yards, set up at the site of heavy construction, to produce members specially designed for particular projects. An example is the production of precast cellular segments for long-span bridges. In other cases, site precasting will be used to

421

reduce forming costs and speed construction, as for lift slabs or for construction of shell roofs.

Many types of precast members have been developed, and much thought has been given to the design of connections for precast members, such that structural requirements are met and erection procedures simplified to the maximum degree. For economy, standard members and connections are used where possible. In other cases, when special components and details are justified, close collaboration is needed between the engineer and builder to develop the best arrangement.

The following articles describe some of the more common precast members and connections. Because of the many variations and important differences in design details, the discussion is generally descriptive. However, the shear-friction theory, which has broad applicability in the design of connections and precast members, is described in detail in Art. 12.4. Special Code provisions and reinforcement details for corbels, which are frequently used in precast structures, are found in Art. 12.5.

12.2 PRECAST MEMBERS FOR BUILDINGS

Certain more-or-less standard forms of precast units have been developed for buildings. Though not completely standardized at this time, they are widely available with minor local variations. At the same time, the precasting process is sufficiently adaptable so that special shapes can be produced economically, provided the number of repetitions of each unit is sufficiently large. This is particularly important for exterior wall panels, for example, for which a great variety of architectural treatment is needed.

A. FLOOR AND ROOF UNITS

Perhaps the most common of the standard shapes for buildings is the double-tee floor or roof plank shown in Figs. 12.1a and 1.3. These are available in 4 and 8 ft widths, with depths ranging from 8 to 24 in. The double-tee is highly functional, as it not only meets structural requirements, but also provides a flat useful surface. Often a 2 in. cast-in-place concrete topping slab is used over the top flange to provide a smooth finished surface. The topping bonds to the precast units, the top of which are deliberately left rough. Resulting composite action increases both stiffness and strength. Spans of about 30 ft are common, but longer spans, to about 60 ft, may be attained with deep sections.

Also widely employed for floors and roofs are the various types of hollow-core slabs. A representative panel cross section is shown in Fig. 12.1b. Slab panels are ordinarily available in depths from 4 to 12 in., and widths from 2 to 8 ft. The 4 ft width is most common. Spans may range from 15 to about 30 ft. With these panels, too, a topping slab is often used.

The single-tee section of Fig. 12.1c has been employed frequently for longer spans and heavier loads in buildings such as parking garages, auditoriums,

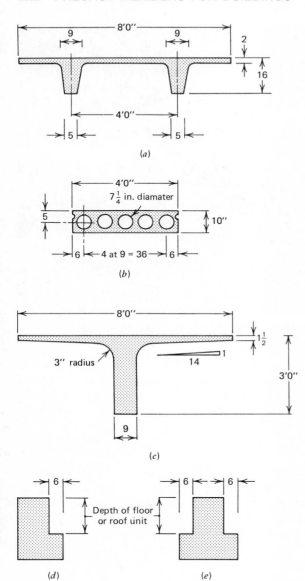

Figure 12.1   Typical standard sections. (*a*) Double-tee. (*b*) Hollowcore plank. (*c*) Single-tee. (*d*) L-section. (*e*) Inverted-tee.

Figure 12.2   Long span single-tee beams used over parking garage.

gymnasiums, and dining halls. Stem widths vary from 8 to 12 in. as a rule, and flange widths are usually 8 or 10 ft, although narrower flanges are easily cast, simply by blocking out the forms. Depths range from 24 to 48 in. Topping slabs are generally used. Floor and roof spans to 120 ft are not uncommon for members of this type. Figure 12.2 shows a typical example of long-span single-tee beams used over a garage.

When concrete is cast against smooth steel or fiberglass formwork, as is generally the case for members of the types just described, and when care is taken in proportioning the mix and vibrating after placement, the resulting member has a surface that is very smooth and hard. Often this is left exposed in the completed structure with no additional finish other than paint. Flat plank provides a smooth ceiling overhead. Single- and double-tees, too, may be left exposed and incorporated in the basic architectural scheme.

B. BEAMS AND GIRDERS

Beams and girders of many shapes have been produced for the main framing members of precast prestressed concrete buildings. The shape and dimensions of these members are not so standard as was the case for deck units. Cross section geometry is dictated not only by requirements of load and span, but often by the need to provide a shelf, or continuous corbel, for the end support of precast deck units framing in at right angles. Typical L and inverted T cross sections are seen in Figs. 12.1*d* and 12.1*e*.

Special attention should be given to detailing of reinforcement for sections of this type. Auxiliary web steel should project into the flange to provide for the vertical reactions from floor units. This steel may be designed using the shear-friction approach (Art. 12.4). Longitudinal prestressing steel, in the case of unsymmetrical L beams, should have its centroid in the same vertical plane as the centroid of the concrete section, to avoid lateral warping due to prestress force.

Typical use of L section beams to carry a double-tee floor system is shown in Fig. 12.3.

Figure 12.3 Commonwealth Title Building in Tacoma, showing floor and roof system composed of precast double-tee beams supported by precast L-section girders (courtesy Concrete Technology Corporation, Tacoma, Washington).

C. COLUMNS

Columns, as well as floor beams and girders, are often precast. They may be prestressed (see Ch. 11) but more often are conventionally reinforced, even though the rest of the work is prestressed. Rectangular cross sections are most common, but unusual shapes have been employed for special purposes. Columns are precast in the horizontal position, greatly simplifying formwork and facilitating the placement of concrete.

A variety of column details has been developed to support beams and girders. Corbels such as described in Art. 12.5 and illustrated in Fig. 12.15 are used extensively in industrial construction, but may be visually or functionally objectionable in apartments or schools, for example. Alternative beam support details will be discussed in Art. 12.3.

An unusual example of precast columns with corbels is shown in Fig. 12.4. Reinforced, but not prestressed, these 93 ft members were precast in one piece, each weighing 41 tons. Floor members are 9 ft width and 36 in. depth single tees resting on individual column haunches at each level.

Figure 12.4   Crown Street Parking Garage, New Haven, showing 93 ft long precast tree columns carrying 36 in. depth single-tee deck girders (courtesy Blakeslee Prestress, Inc.).

D.   EXTERIOR WALL PANELS

Many types of precast wall panels have been used to enclose multi- as well as single-story buildings. These may serve only as cladding, but often the walls are load bearing, and provide vertical support for floors and roofs. In addition, with proper attention to details, they can be effective in providing resistance to lateral forces on buildings.

The same double-tee forms used to produce floor deck plank can be employed to manufacture wall panels. Widths are normally 4 or 8 ft, and typical surface thickness 2 or 3 in., with ribs 8 to 16 in. in depth. Such units provide vertical support for floors and roofs by means of continuous corbels on the inside face, or by steel shelf angles anchored to inserts cast into the concrete.

Flat wall panels are often used as well, such as illustrated in Fig. 12.5. These may have various surface treatments, including exposed aggregate and patterned surfaces. Flat panels are sometimes cast with an internal layer of 2 to 4 in. of foam-insulating material, with structural concrete faces, inside and out, connected by shear clips.

The unusually large bearing wall panels shown in Fig. 12.6 are continuous over four stories of building height, carrying floor and roof loads directly to the foundation wall.

E.   LARGE PANEL CONSTRUCTION

Large panel construction is the name given to the broad class of structural systems, some patented, in which precast floor panels span freely between precast interior and exterior wall panels. Generally no columns or beams are used. The walls serve to enclose and subdivide the space, provide vertical support, and in addition resist lateral loads. Wall panels are reinforced and may be pretensioned. They may serve as forms for cast-in-place reinforced concrete columns. In some cases, the completed assemblage is post-tensioned, permitting the structure to act in an integrated sense in resisting horizontal loads due to wind or seismic action.

Figure 12.7 shows a variation of large-panel construction used for a 21-story hotel. Except for the service units, the structure consisted entirely of box-shaped, room-sized modules, completely prefabricated, and stacked on top of each other. In Europe, such precast modules, with plumbing, wiring, and heating preinstalled, are widely used for multistory apartment buildings, as an alternative to making similiar apartment structures in precast wall, roof, and floor panels, which are more easily shipped but less easily erected than box-shaped modules.

Perhaps the best-known example of precast modular design is Habitat 67 at Montreal, shown in Fig. 12.8. Post-tensioning tendons lock the residential units together, permitting dramatic cantilevers and open space in the seemingly random arrangement of boxes. The project may be regarded as a prototype in the development of industrialized housing that retains a large measure of uniqueness in the final result.

Figure 12.5 Tai Tung Village in Boston, with precast bearing walls and floor units joined by post-tensioning (Sepp Firnkas and Associates, Engineers; photograph courtesy of Prestressed Concrete Institute).

Figure 12.6 Precast, prestressed concrete load-bearing wall units having total height 62 ft and weighing 35 tons each (courtesy Prestressed Concrete Institute).

Figure 12.7 Precast room-size modules for 21 story hotel (courtesy Portland Cement Association).

Figure 12.8 Habitat Village at Montreal, constructed as part of Expo 67 (courtesy of Portland Cement Association).

12.3 CONNECTION DETAILS

By their very nature, cast-in-place concrete structures tend to be monolithic and continuous. Connections, in the sense of joining two otherwise separate pieces, rarely occur in that type of construction. Precast structures, on the other hand, resemble steel construction in that the final structure consists of an assemblage of a large number of prefabricated elements that are connected together on the site.

For precast concrete structures, as for steel structures, connections can be detailed to transmit gravity forces only, or gravity and horizontal forces, or moments in addition to these forces. In the latter case, a continuous structure is obtained much as in cast-in-place construction, and connections that achieve such continuity by appropriate use of special hardware, rebars, and concrete to transmit all tension, compression, and shear stresses are sometimes called *hard connections*. In contrast, connections that transmit reaction in one direction only, analogous to rockers or rollers in steel structures, but permit a limited amount of motion to relieve other forces such as horizontal reaction components, are known as *soft connections.*

In many precast connections, bearing plates, suitably anchored into the connected members, are used to insure distribution and reasonable uniformity of bearing pressures. If these bearing plates are of steel and the plates of the connected members are joined by welding, a hard connection is obtained in the sense that at least horizontal, as well as vertical, forces are transmitted. On the other hand, bearing details are common that permit relief of horizontal forces, such as by use of tetrafluorethylene (TFE) pads, which effectively eliminate bearing friction, or of pads with low shear rigidity (elastomeric or rubber pads of various types) that permit sizable horizontal movements.

Precast concrete structures are subject to dimensional changes from creep and shrinkage, in addition to temperature, while in steel structures only temperature changes produce dimensional variations. Early in the development of precast construction there was a tendency to use soft connections extensively in order to permit these dimensional changes to occur without causing restraint forces. More recent experience with soft connections indicates that the resulting structures tend to have insufficient resistance to lateral forces, such as those due to earthquake. For this reason the present trend is toward the use of hard connections with a high degree of continuity. In connections of this sort, provision must be made for resistance to the restraint forces that are caused by volume changes.

Few specific recommendations are found in the ACI Code pertaining to the design of connections for precast members, for the reason that such construction is still regarded as somewhat special. A substantial amount of work has been done by industry-oriented groups toward formulating design recommendations and establishing more-or-less standard connection details. Of particular interest are the recommendations of the PCI Committee on Connection Details contained in Ref. 12.1 (see also Ref. 12.2).

In the design of connections, it is prudent to select load factors that exceed those required for the members being connected. This is so because connections are generally subject to high stress concentrations, which preclude the attainment of much ductility should overloading occur. In contrast, the members connected are apt to show substantial deformation when loaded near the ultimate, and will give warning of impending collapse. In addition, imperfections in connections, as built, may cause large changes in the magnitude of stresses from what was assumed in the design.

In general, in designing members according to the ACI Code, load factors of 1.4 and 1.7 are applied to dead and live loads, D and L respectively, to determine the required strength. When volume change effects T are considered, they are normally treated as dead load, and the ultimate load effect U is calculated from the equation $U = 0.75(1.4D + 1.4T + 1.7L)$. The overall reduction factor of 0.75 is introduced, recognizing that simultaneous occurence of worst effects is not likely.

However, for the design of brackets and corbels the Code provides that the tensile force resulting from volume change effects should be included with the live load. Thus a load factor of 1.7 is to be used. No overall reduction factor is used for corbels and brackets. PCI recommendations for load factors are still more conservative. In view of the importance of connections, and to further insure that, should failure occur, it will be in the members connected rather than in the connections themselves, the PCI Committee has recommended that an additional load factor of 4/3 be applied in designing all connections. This is equivalent to an overall load factor of about 2 in. in typical cases. Others have noted that, for connections which may be particularly sensitive to imperfections, an overall factor of 2.5 is not excessive (Ref. 12.3).

Many types of connections have been developed for use with precast concrete members, with details varying depending upon the forces to be transferred, plant facilities available, and the particular construction techniques and sequences to be followed. Certain of the more common types will be described below.

A. COLUMN BASE CONNECTIONS

Figure 12.9a shows a column base detail with projecting base plate. Four anchor bolts are used, with double nuts facilitating erection and leveling of the

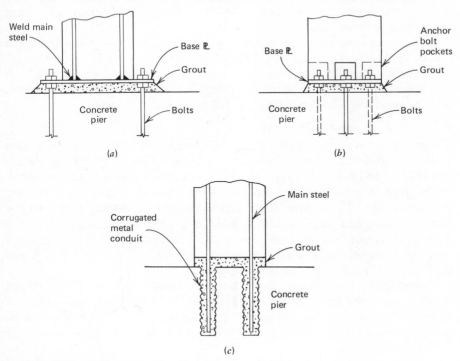

Figure 12.9 Column base connections.

column. Typically about 2 in. of nonshrink grout is used between the top of the pier, footing, or wall and the bottom of the steel base plate. Column reinforcement is welded to the top face of the base plate. Tests have confirmed that such column connections can transmit the full moment for which the column is designed, if properly detailed (Ref. 12.4).

An alternative base plate detail is shown in Fig. 12.9b, with the dimensions of the base plate the same as, or in some cases less than, the outside column dimensions. The advantage of this type is that the column can be cast using long-line forms, without need for special modification to accommodate the projecting base plates of Fig. 12.9a. Anchor bolt pockets are provided, either centered on the four column faces as shown, or located at the corners. Ordinarily a double-nut system is used to facilitate leveling of the column, and nonshrink grout is placed after the column is set. Bolt pockets too are grouted, after the nuts are tightened. Column reinforcement, not shown here, would be welded to the top face of the plate as before.

In Fig. 12.9c, the main column reinforcement projects from the end of the precast member a sufficient distance to develop its strength by bond. The projecting rebars are inserted into grout-filled cold-formed steel conduits, which are embedded in the foundation when it is poured. Temporary bracing may be used to position the column until the grout has set and hardened, or temporary erection angles may be provided, bolted to two opposite column faces using inserts cast in the concrete.

In all cases described, confinement steel should be provided around the anchor bolts in the form of closed ties. A minimum of four No. 3 ties is recommended, placed at 3 in. centers near the top surface of the pier or wall in addition to the normal pattern of tie steel. Tie reinforcement in the columns, not shown in Fig. 12.9 for clarity, should be provided as usual.

B.　BEAM-TO-COLUMN CONNECTIONS

Several alternative means for interconnecting beams and columns are illustrated in Fig. 12.10. In all cases, rectangular beams are shown, but similar details would apply to I beams or single tees. The figure shows only the basic geometry of the joint in each case, and auxiliary reinforcement, anchors, and ties are omitted for the sake of clarity. Such steel is crucially important to the integrity of connections, and careful attention must be given to detailing. The design of such reinforcement may be based on the shear friction approach in most cases (Art. 12.4). Specific suggestions for steel details will be found in Ref. 12.1 and other sources listed at the end of this chapter.

Figure 12.10a shows a joint detail with a concealed haunch. Well anchored bearing angles are provided at the column seat and the beam end. This type of connection may be used to provide vertical and horizontal reaction components only, or with the addition of nonshrink grout and post-tensioning at the top of the beam as shown, will serve as a moment connection as well. The tendon, in such case, passes through the column and is jacked and anchored

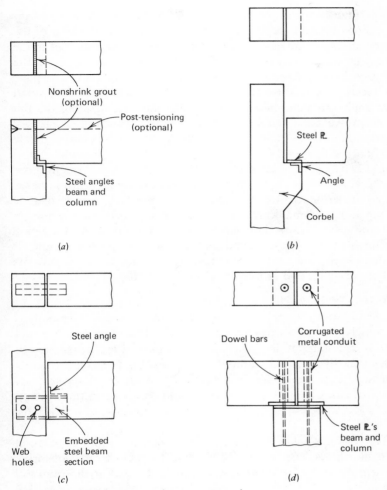

Figure 12.10 Beam-to-column connections.

from the outside. It may be continuous through the entire beam span, may be terminated in an internal anchor, or may be curved downward and anchored at the bottom face of the beam.

Figure 12.10b shows a typical corbel connection, common for industrial construction where the projecting bracket is not architecturally offensive. The seat angle at the upper corner of the corbel is welded to reinforcing bars anchored into the column, and special ties and moment bars provided in the corbel. A steel bearing plate is used at the bottom corner of the beam, anchored into the concrete. Design considerations for corbels will be discussed in detail in Art. 12.5.

The embedded steel shape shown in Fig. 12.10c is used when it is necessary to avoid projections beyond the face of column or below the bottom of the beam. The steel, often a short piece of wide-flanged beam, is embedded in the column and projects outward a distance sufficient to provide the proper bearing for the beam. A socket is formed in casting the beam, with steel angle or plate at its top, to receive the beam stub. Alternately, a dapped-end beam detail may be used, similar to that shown but with the cutout extending the full width of the beam. Auxiliary reinforcement is specially critical in such cases. Holes provided in the web of the steel beam stub help to insure good concrete consolidation between flanges (Ref. 12.5).

Finally, Fig. 12.10d shows a doweled connection with bars projecting from the column into cold-formed steel tubing or conduit embedded in the beam ends. The tubes are grouted after the beams are in position. A steel plate is shown at the top of the column, with bearing plates also provided at the bottom faces of the beams. The connection may be made continuous by providing nonshrink grout between the beam ends, after which top post-tensioning is introduced. Alternately, non-prestressed rebars may be placed in blockout slots along the top of the beams and grouted in place (Ref. 12.6).

C. COLUMN-TO-COLUMN CONNECTIONS

Figure 12.11 shows several typical column-to-column splices. Generally a non-shrink grout is used between column members, and often a double-nut system is used to facilitate leveling of the upper column. Base plates may be slightly smaller than the external column dimensions if architectural requirements so indicate. Tie steel and main steel have been omitted from the sketches for clarity, in most cases. Closely spaced ties should be placed in the columns immediately above and below the joint, as described earlier, in addition to the usual ties.

Figure 12.11a shows a detail using anchor bolt pockets and a double-nut system with anchor bolts. The bolt pockets would be packed with nonshrink grout after assembly of the parts. Bolts can also be located at the center of the column faces, as in Fig. 12.9b.

The detail of Fig. 12.11b permits the main steel to be lap-spliced with that of the column below. Generally clip angles would be provided, attached to inserts cast into the column faces, to permit positioning of the upper column during erection.

One of many possibilities for splicing a column through a continuous beam is shown in Fig. 12.11c. Main reinforcement in both upper and lower columns should be welded to steel cap and base plates to transfer their load, and anchor bolts should be detailed with the same consideration. Closely spaced ties must be provided in the columns, and in this case in the beam as well, to transfer the load between columns.

The various types of connections shown and described are representative, but countless variations may be developed to suit the special circumstances in any given instance. Many details are suggested in Ref. 12.1.

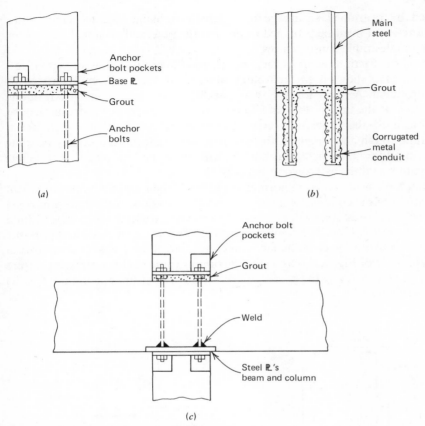

Figure 12.11   Column-to-column connections.

12.4 SHEAR-FRICTION METHOD FOR CONNECTION DESIGN

Chapter 5 dealt with shear in prestressed concrete beams in the context of flexural and torsional loading. In such cases, shear is used merely as a convenient measure of diagonal tension, which is the real concern. In contrast, there are circumstances such that direct shear may cause failure. Such situations occur commonly in precast concrete members, particularly in the vicinity of connections. Potential failure planes can be established along which direct shear stresses are high, and failure to provide adequate reinforcement across such planes may produce disastrous results.

The necessary reinforcement in such cases may be determined on the basis of the *shear-friction theory* (Refs. 12.7 and 12.8). The basic approach is to assume that the concrete may crack in an unfavorable manner. In some cases, such a crack may already exist for reasons unrelated to shear, such as tension forces caused by restrained shrinkage or volumetric change due to temperature. Reinforcement must be provided to prevent the potential or actual crack from having undesirable consequences.

The shear-friction theory is very simple, and the behavior is easily visualized. Figure 12.12a shows a cracked block of concrete, with the crack crossed by reinforcement. A shear force V_n acts parallel to the crack, and the resulting tendency for the upper block to slip relative to the lower is resisted largely by friction along the concrete interface at the crack. Since the crack surface is naturally rough and irregular, the effective coefficient of friction may be quite high. In addition, the irregular surface will cause the two blocks of concrete to separate slightly, as shown in Fig. 12.12b.

If reinforcement is present normal to the crack, then slippage and subsequent separation of the concrete will stress the steel in tension. Tests have confirmed that well-anchored steel will be stressed to its yield strength when shear failure is obtained (Ref. 12.9). The resulting tensile force sets up an equal and opposite pressure between the concrete faces on either side of the crack. It is clear from the free body of Fig. 12.12c that the maximum value of this interface pressure is $A_{vf}f_y$, where A_{vf} is the total area of steel crossing the crack, and f_y is its yield strength.

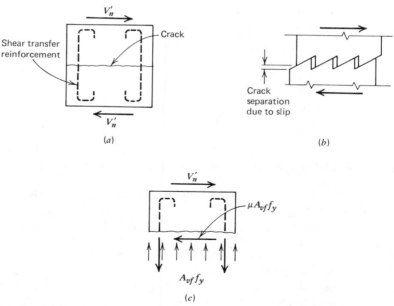

Figure 12.12 Basis of shear-friction theory (a) Applied shear. (b) Enlarged representation of crack surface. (c) Free body of concrete above crack.

The concrete resistance to sliding may be expressed in terms of the normal force times a coefficient of friction μ. By setting the summation of horizontal forces equal to zero:

$$V_n = \mu A_{vf} f_y \tag{12.1}$$

Defining the steel ratio $\rho = A_{vf}/A_c$ where A_c in this case is the area of the cracked surface, Eq. (12.1) may be rewritten in terms of the nominal shear stress v_n:

$$v_n = \mu \rho f_y \tag{12.2}$$

The relative movement of the concrete on opposite sides of the crack also subjects the individual reinforcing bars to shearing action, and the dowel resistance of the bars to this shearing action also contributes to shear resistance. However, it is customary to neglect the dowel effect for simplicity in design, and to compensate for this by using an artificially high value of the friction coefficient.

Based on early tests, μ may be taken equal to 1.4 for cracks in monolithic concrete, but V_n should not be assumed greater than $0.2f'_c A_c$ or $800 A_c$ lb (Ref. 12.7).

In Fig. 12.13 the shear transfer strength predicted by Eq. (12.2) is compared with experimental values obtained in more recent tests conducted at the University of Washington (Refs. 12.9 and 12.10). It is evident that Eq. 12.2 gives a conservative estimate of shear strength. It is also clear that strength considerably in excess of the upper limit of 800 psi can be developed if appropriate reinforcement is provided. It has been proposed (Ref. 12.10) that a modified form of Eq. (12.2) be adopted when ρf_y exceeds 600 psi, as follows:

$$v_n = \mu \rho f_y \left(\frac{300}{\rho f_y} + 0.5 \right) \tag{12.3}$$

The strengths predicted by Eq. (12.3) (indicated by the dashed line in Fig. 12.13), appear to give a satisfactory correlation with experimental results for concrete strengths greater than 2500 psi. Pending further data, it is recommended that an upper limit of $v_n = 1300$ psi be imposed for Eq. (12.3).

The provisions of the ACI Code are based on Eq. (12.1). The design strength is to be taken equal to ϕV_n where $\phi = 0.85$ for shear-friction design, and V_n is not to exceed the smaller of $0.2f'_c A_c$ or $800 A_c$ lb. Recommendations for friction factor μ are as follows:

For concrete placed monolithically	1.4
For concrete placed against hardened concrete	1.0
For concrete placed against as-rolled structural steel	0.7

The design strength of the reinforcement is not to exceed 60,000 psi. Direct tension across the crack, if present, is to be provided for by additional reinforcement. When shear is transferred between concrete placed against hardened

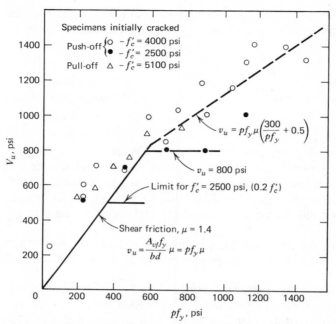

Figure 12.13 Calculated vs. experimental shear transfer strength for initially cracked specimens (Ref. 12.10).

concrete, the interface shall be rough with a full amplitude of approximately 1/4 in. When shear is transferred between as-rolled steel and concrete, the steel shall be clean and without paint, according to the Code.

If V_u is the shear force to be resisted at factored loads, then the required steel area is found by suitable transposition of Eq. (12.1):

$$A_{vf} = \frac{V_u}{\phi \mu f_y} \tag{12.4}$$

Certain precautions should be observed in applying the shear-friction method in design. Reinforcement should be at least approximately perpendicular to the potential crack. It should be sufficiently well anchored to develop the yield strength of the bars, either by full development length or by hooks or bends. The concrete should be well-confined, and the liberal use of hoops has been recommended (Refs. 12.7 and 12.11). Care must be taken to consider all possible failure planes, and to provide sufficient well-anchored steel across these planes.

In certain circumstances it is necessary to calculate the shear force that can be transferred across a crack arbitrarily inclined with respect to the reinforcement direction. An extension of the shear-friction method to apply to such cases is described in Ref. 12.12.

EXAMPLE Design of Beam Bearing Detail

A precast pretensioned beam must be designed to resist a support reaction, at factored loads, of $V_u = 125$ kips applied to a 3×3 steel angle as shown in Fig. 12.14. In lieu of a calculated value, a horizontal force T_u, due to restrained volume change, will be assumed at 20 percent of the vertical reaction, or 25 kips. Determine the required auxiliary reinforcement, using steel of yield strength $f_y = 60,000$ psi. Concrete design strength $f_c' = 5000$ psi. ($V_u = 556$ kN, $T_u = 111$ kN, $f_y = 522$ N/mm², and $f_c' = 34$ N/mm².)

A potential crack will be assumed at 20 degrees, initiating at a point 4 in. (102 mm) from the end of the beam, as shown in Fig. 12.14a. The total required steel A_{vf} is the sum

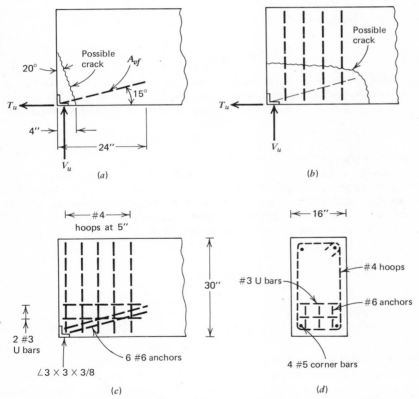

Figure 12.14 Design at beam bearing shoe. (*a*) Diagonal crack. (*b*) Horizontal crack. (*c*) Reinforcement. (*d*) Cross section.

of that required to resist the effects of V_u and T_u. Equation (12.4) is modified accordingly:

$$A_{vf} = \frac{V_u \cos 20°}{\phi \mu f_y} + \frac{T_u \cos 20°}{\phi f_y}$$

$$= \frac{125 \times 0.940}{0.85 \times 1.4 \times 60} + \frac{25 \times 0.940}{0.85 \times 60}$$

$$= 1.65 + 0.46$$

$$= 2.11 \text{ in.}^2 \ (1361 \text{ mm}^2)$$

Six No. 6 bars will be used, providing an area of 2.65 in.^{2} They will be welded to the 3×3 angle and will extend into the beam a sufficient distance to develop the yield strength of the bars. According to the Code, the development length for a No. 6 bar is 12 in. However, considering the uncertainty of the exact crack location, the bars will be extended twice the development length, or 24 in., into the beam as shown in Fig. 12.14a. If we follow the recommendations made in Ref. 12.11, the bars will be placed at an angle of 15 degrees with the bottom face of the member.

The area of the cracked interface is

$$A_c = 16 \left(\frac{4}{\sin 20°} \right) = 187 \text{ in.}^2$$

Thus, according to the Code, the maximum nominal shear strength of the surface is not to exceed $V_n = 0.2 f'_c A_c = 187$ kips or $V_n = 800 A_c = 150$ kips. The maximum design strength to be used is $\phi V_n = 0.85 \times 150 = 128$ kips. The applied shear on the interface at factored loads is

$$V_u = 125 \cos 20° + 25 \sin 20° = 126 \text{ kips}$$

and so the design is judged satisfactory to this point.

A second possible crack must be considered, as shown in Fig. 12.14b, resulting from the tendency of the entire anchorage weldment to pull horizontally out of the beam. The required steel area A_{sh} and the concrete shear stress will be calculated based on the development of the full yield tension in the bars A_{vf}. (Note that the factor ϕ need not be used here because it has already been introduced in computing A_{vf}.)

$$A_{sh} = \frac{A_{vf} f_y \cos 15°}{\mu f_y}$$

$$= \frac{2.11 \times 0.966}{1.4}$$

$$= 1.46 \text{ in.}^2 \ (942 \text{ mm}^2)$$

Four No. 4 hoops will be used, providing an area of 1.57 in.^{2}

The maximum shear force that can be transferred, according to the Code limits, will be based conservatively on a horizontal plane 24 in. long. No strength reduction factor need be included in the calculation of this maximum value because it was already introduced in determining the steel area A_{vf} by which the shear force is applied. Accordingly

$$V_n \le 800 \times 16 \times 24 = 308 \text{ kips}$$

The maximum shear force that could be applied in the given instance is

$$V_n = 2.11 \times 60 \cos 15° = 122 \text{ kips}$$

well below the specified maximum.

Additional confinement steel is recommended in Ref. 12.11, in the amount $V_u/8f_y$, to be placed in the form of hoops or hairpin bars confining the concrete near the bottom and end faces of a precast beam at the reaction. In the present case

$$A_{cv} = A_{ch} = \frac{125}{8 \times 60}$$

$$= 0.26 \text{ in.}^2 \ (168 \text{ mm}^2)$$

One additional No. 4 hoop will be placed as near as possible to the end face, and two U-shaped No. 3 bars will be added parallel to the bottom of the beam as shown in Figs. 12.14c and 12.14d. Also shown in Fig. 12.14d are four No. 5 corner bars that will provide anchorage for the hoop steel.

12.5 CORBELS

Corbels, or brackets, as shown in Fig. 12.15, are widely used in precast concrete construction for supporting beams at columns or walls. They are designed mainly to provide vertical reactions for beams but, unless special precautions are taken to avoid horizontal forces due to restrained shrinkage, creep, or temperature change, they must also resist horizontal forces. According to the ACI Code, unless such special precautions are taken, a tensile force not less than 20 percent of the vertical reaction shall be assumed to act. Such tensile

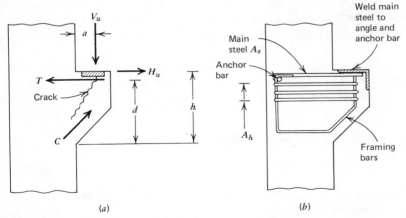

(a)   (b)

Figure 12.15   Typical reinforced concrete corbel.

force is to be regarded as live load, and a basic load factor of 1.7 applied. Other recommendations for load factors for connection design are as stated in Art. 12.3.

Steel bearing plates are generally used at the top face of corbels to provide a uniform contact surface and to distribute the reaction. Their outer edge should be no closer than 2 in. from the outer edge of the corbel, to prevent cracking off the corner. A corresponding steel bearing plate or angle is usually provided at the lower corner of the supported beam. If the two plates are welded, clearly horizontal forces must be allowed for in the design. These may be avoided by use of TFE or elastomeric bearing pads. The vertical force should be assumed to act at the outer third point of the bearing plate.

The structural performance of a corbel is fairly complex, but may be approximately visualized from Fig. 12.15. A correctly designed corbel, when overloaded, develops a crack as shown in Fig. 12.15a. The applied forces V_u and H_u (if present) are then equilibrated in a trusslike fashion by the tension force T developed in the main tensile reinforcement near the top of the corbel, and the compression force C that develops in the concrete compression strut outside of the crack, To counteract cracking, either of the kind shown or closer to the root section, horizontal stirrups must be placed in the upper portion of the corbel.

Typical corbel reinforcement is shown in Fig. 12.15b. Often a confinement angle is used as shown, rather than a flat plate. Because corbel dimensions are small, special attention must be paid to providing proper anchorage for the steel.

The main tensile reinforcement A_s is welded to the confinement angle (or plate) and to a special transverse anchor bar at the far end. Horizontal stirrups of area A_h are in the form of closed hoops, and framing bars are provided, of about the same diameter as the stirrups, to improve stirrup anchorage. Main tensile steel, for cases where only vertical force V_u acts, may be computed for the moment $V_u a$ by the usual methods, with $\phi = 0.9$. If horizontal tension H_u is to be resisted, the main steel must be increased by the amount $H_u/\phi f_y$, where $\phi = 0.85$.

Present Code provisions for the design of corbels have been developed from extensive tests (Ref. 12.13). They apply to brackets and corbels with shear span ratio a/d of 1.0 or less. The distance d is measured at the column face, but must not be taken greater than twice the depth of the corbel at the outside edge of the bearing area.

At the critical section, the design basis is

$$V_u \leq \phi V_n \tag{12.5}$$

where all terms are as previously defined and $\phi = 0.85$. The nominal strength V_n must not exceed the following values:

a. For brackets and corbels subject to tension due to restrained creep and shrinkage:

$$V_n = [6.5 - 5.1\sqrt{N_{uc}/V_u}][1 - 0.5a/d]$$
$$\times (1 + [64 + 160\sqrt{(N_{uc}/V_u)^3}]\rho)\sqrt{f'_c}b_w d \qquad (12.6)$$

where ρ shall not exceed $0.13f'_c/f_y$ and N_{uc}/V_u shall not be taken less than 0.20.

b. When provisions are made to avoid tension due to restrained creep and shrinkage, so that the bracket or corbel is subject to shear and moment only

$$V_n = 6.5(1 - 0.5a/d)(1 + 64\rho_v)\sqrt{f'_c}b_w d \qquad (12.7)$$

where

$$\rho_v = \frac{A_s + A_h}{bd}$$

but not greater than $0.20f'_c/f_y$, and A_h shall not exceed A_s.

Closed stirrups or ties parallel to the main tensile steel, with a total area A_h not less than $0.50A_s$, shall be uniformly distributed within 2/3 of the effective depth adjacent to the main steel. The main steel ratio $\rho = A_s/bd$ shall not be less than $0.04f'_c/f_y$.

Brackets and corbels with shear span ratio of 1/2 or less may be designed according to the shear-friction theory, according to ACI Code, except that all limitations on quantity and spacing of reinforcement given above shall apply. It has further been proposed that a modified shear friction theory be used for all brackets with shear span of 1.0 or less. (Ref. 12.14, 12.15.)

12.6   LIFT SLAB CONSTRUCTION

A form of on-site precast construction that has been widely exploited employs what is known as the lift-slab technique. An example is shown in Fig. 12.16. A casting bed, often doubling as the ground floor slab, is poured, columns are erected and braced, and at ground level successive slabs, which will later become upper floors, are cast. A membrane or sprayed parting agent is laid down between successive pours so that each slab can be lifted in its turn. Jacks placed atop the columns are connected to threaded rods extending down the faces of the columns and connecting, in turn, to lifting collars embedded in the slabs.

Columns may be steel or concrete. Often tubular steel sections are used. When a slab is in its final position, shear keys are welded to the column to transfer vertical reactions from the slab.

Life slab construction almost invariably implies flat plate construction (see Art. 10.9) with no beams, dropped panels, or column capitals, for obvious

Figure 12.16 Construction of office building for Douglas Aircraft Company in Long Beach, California using the lift-slab method. To facilitate lifting, each floor was divided into 8 sections of about 12,000 ft^2 each (courtesy Post-Tensioning Institute).

reasons. The slabs are usually post-tensioned using unbonded wire or strand, either coated with bituminous mastic and paperwrapped, or encased in plastic tubing. Special shear reinforcement is often incorporated in the slab at the columns.

Typically, slab-to-column connections in lift-slab buildings can transfer little moment, and so frame stability against lateral loading must be provided by other resisting elements. Stairwells, elevator shafts, and utility shafts may be used for this purpose.

12.7 STANDARD BRIDGE GIRDERS

The precasting of bridge girders is particularly attractive because it permits the erection of a bridge superstructure with little or no interference with the traffic passing below. For spans up to about 140 ft, it is common practice to cast the main carrying girders in one piece, either in a precasting plant or in a temporary yard established at the construction site, then to lift these into position with truck cranes. Placed side-by-side, these provide support for temporary form-work to construct a cast-in-place deck slab. The completed slab spans trans-versely between girders, carrying wheel loads to those girders. In addition, composite action is developed in the main span direction between the precast girders and the cast-in-place slab, so that the slab provides the main part of the compression flange for the girders. Special precautions are taken to insure that longitudinal slip between the components is prevented. This requires that the top of the precast unit be left rough-screeded, rather than trowelled smooth, and that vertical stirrups placed in the precast unit for conventional shear reinforcement be extended into the slab to further lock the parts together.

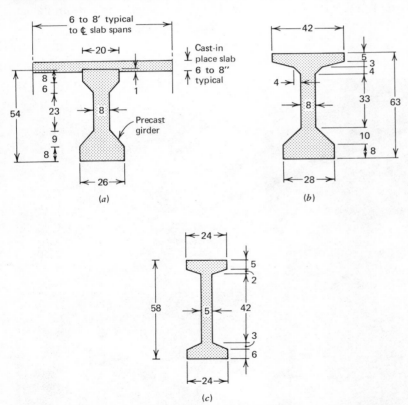

Figure 12.17   Precast bridge girder cross sections (all dimensions inches or as noted). (*a*) AASHTO Type IV girder with slab. (*b*) AASHTO Type V girder. (*c*) Washington State Standard Bridge Girder—100 ft span.

A variety of standard bridge girders exists. The most common are the AASHTO standard girders, of depths varying from 28 to 72 in. A typical AASHTO girder, with cast-in-place slab, is shown in Fig. 12.17a. Such girders are usually cast with solid end blocks to accommodate post-tensioning anchorages. In many cases pretensioning and post-tensioning are combined.

Other AASHTO sections are shown and dimensioned in Appendix A, Table A.11. Types I through IV are best described as unsymmetrical I beams. The large bottom flange provides for heavy initial prestress force. The section proportions were selected with a view toward composite action with the slab, which provides most of the compression area needed in the service load and overload stages. Spans for AASHTO Types I through IV range from about 35 to 100 ft.

For longer spans, up to about 140 ft, AASHTO sections of Types V and VI may be used. The section shown in Fig. 12.11b is typical. The bottom flange,

Figure 12.18   Standard highway girder, State of Washington (courtesy Concrete Technology Corporation, Tacoma, Washington).

similar in proportion to that of the previous girders, is designed to resist heavy compression force in the initial stage. The wider top flange provides improved bond slip resistance to meet requirements in the service load and overload stages, and provides substantial compression area, supplementing that provided by the slab.

In all AASHTO girders, web reinforcing steel is carried into the slab to improve horizontal shear transfer by dowel action and by shear friction.

Other standard highway girder cross sections have been adopted by some states. The State of Washington has established a series of five standard I beams having proportions as shown, for example, by the 58 in. depth section in Fig. 12.17c. Depths for this series range from 32 to 73.5 in., used on spans from about 40 to 120 ft. These members, too, are intended for composite action with a cast-in-place deck.

Figure 12.18 shows a number of Washington State standard girders in a precasting yard. Note the mild steel shear reinforcement extending upward for later embedment in the deck slab. The beam being lifted has one post-tensioning tendon stressed to facilitate handling, while those on the ground to the left have both tendons stressed. In addition, straight pretensioned strands were used in the bottom flanges. Note also the flared end blocks that are used to provide for post-tensioning anchorages and to reduce local compressive stresses in the anchorage regions. The girder in the main part of each span has web width of only 5 in., as shown by Fig. 12.17c.

12.8   SEGMENTALLY PRECAST BRIDGE CONSTRUCTION

There is a clear trend toward the use of longer spans for highway bridge construction, resulting from the combination of requirements relating to safety, economy, function, and esthetics. The practical upper limit for the precast girders described in Art. 12.7 is about 120 to 140 ft. While this range may be extended somewhat by adopting post-tensioned continuous spans or by combining precast units with cast-in-place haunched sections, even with such schemes spans in excess of about 160 ft do not appear feasible. Where longer clear spans are needed, the concrete box girder offers many advantages.

This form of construction results in a very compact structural member with high resistance to bending, torsion, and shear. It is suitable for spans upward from 140 ft, and a bridge over the Rhine at Bendorf, in Germany, has a main span of 682 ft.

Two examples of precast box girder bridge cross sections are shown in Fig. 12.19. The Oleron Viaduct, in France, is shown in Fig. 12.19a. It is a single cell box girder, continuous over sixteen 130 ft spans and twenty-six 260 ft spans. Segments having total width of 35 ft and a length of 10.8 ft were prestressed transversely and after placement the segments were post-tensioned longitudinally.

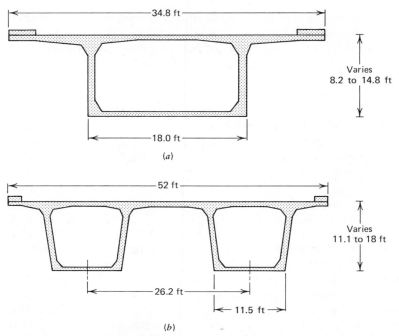

Figure 12.19 Segmentally precast bridges. (*a*) Oleron viaduct. (*b*) Pont Aval.

The superstructure of the Pont Aval in Paris (Fig. 12.19*b*) consists of a pair of single cell box girders, with upper slabs rigidly connected by an 8 in. cast-in-place joint, and tied together by transverse post-tensioning. Individual precast segments were 52 ft wide and 12.5 ft long.

The segments of box girder bridges may be cast-in-place, but with increasing frequency they are precast, either in a permanently located precasting plant or in a temporary yard set up adjacent to the bridge site. Often segments are "countercast," that is, each succeeding segment is cast against the leading face of the preceding segment before the latter is removed from the casting bed. This provides excellent dimensional control of alignment and provides closely fitting surfaces between segments for epoxy resin joints. Each segment, after it is placed, is post-tensioned to the construction already in place, the work usually proceeding in a balanced cantilever manner without the need of false-work. After the span is completed, continuous post-tensioning cables provide continuity.

Long-span prestressed bridges are only now being introduced in the United States. The first application of the precast segmental construction method was the Corpus Christi Bridge in Texas, having spans of 100, 200, and 100 ft. A number of other designs using this construction method are now in preparation, some of major span, and it is certain that much of this type of work will be seen here in the years ahead.

REFERENCES

12.1   *PCI Manual on Design of Connections for Precast Prestressed Concrete*, Prestressed Concrete Institute, Chicago, 1973, 99 pp.

12.2   "Supplement to PCI Manual on Design of Connections for Precast Prestressed Concrete," Report by PCI Technical Activities Committee, *J. PCI*, Vol. 20, No. 3, May–June 1975, pp. 17–21.

12.3   Shemie, M., "Bolted Connections in Large Panel Systems Buildings," *J. PCI*, Vol. 18, No. 1, January–February 1973, pp. 27–33.

12.4   LaFraugh, R. W. and Magura, D. D., "Connections in Precast Concrete Structures—Column Base Plates," *J. PCI*, Vol. 11, No. 6, December 1966, pp. 18–39.

12.5   Raths, C. H., "Embedded Structural Steel Connections," *J. PCI*, Vol. 19, No. 3, May–June 1974, pp. 104–112.

12.6   Burns, N. H., "Development of Continuity Between Precast Prestressed Concrete Beams," *J. PCI*, Vol. 11, No. 3, June 1966, pp. 23–36.

12.7   Birkeland, P. W. and Birkeland, H. W., "Connections in Precast Concrete Construction," *J. ACI*, Vol. 63, No. 3, March 1966, pp. 345–368.

12.8   Mast, R. F., "Auxiliary Reinforcement in Precast Concrete Connections," *J. Struct. Div.*, ASCE, Vol. 94, No. ST6, June 1968, pp. 1485–1504.

12.9   Hofbeck, J. A., Ibrahim, I. O., and Mattock, A. H., "Shear Transfer in Reinforced Concrete," *J. ACI*, Vol. 66, No. 2, February 1969, pp. 119–128.

12.10   Mattock, A. H. and Hawkins, N. M., "Shear Transfer in Reinforced Concrete—Recent Research," *J. PCI*, Vol. 17, No. 2, March–April 1972, pp. 55–75.

12.11   *PCI Design Handbook*, Prestressed Concrete Institute, Chicago, 1971.

12.12   Mattock, A. H., *Shear Transfer in Concrete Having Reinforcement at an Angle to the Shear Plane*, "Shear in Reinforced Concrete," ACI Special Publication SP-42, Detroit, 1974, pp. 17–42.

12.13   Kriz, L. B. and Raths, C. H., "Connections in Precast Concrete Structures—Strength of Corbels," *J. PCI*, Vol. 10, No. 1, February 1965, pp. 16–47.

12.14   Mattock, A. H., Chen, K. C., and Soongswang, K., "The Behavior of Reinforced Concrete Corbels," *J. PCI*, Vol. 21, No. 2, March–April 1976, pp. 52–77.

12.15   Mattock, A. H., "Design Proposals for Reinforced Concrete Corbels," *J. PCI*, Vol. 21, No. 3, May–June 1976, pp. 18–42.

12.16   Pastore, P. R., "Crown Street Parking Garage: Design, Fabrication, and Erection of Tree Columns," *J. PCI*, Vol. 17, No. 1, January–February 1972, pp. 21–28.

CHAPTER 13
APPLICATIONS

13.1 INTRODUCTION

Yves Guyon remarked many years ago that there is probably no structural problem to which prestress cannot provide a solution, and often a revolutionary one. The diverse applications of prestressed concrete described recently in the technical literature and in the general press confirm the truth of this observation. Prestressing is more than a technique; it is a general principle.

The members and structures that will be described in the following pages serve to illustrate the variety of design circumstances in which prestressed concrete may be employed advantageously. Because of space limitations, specific applications will be described only in the most general terms. However, an extensive list of references is included, which will provide an entry into the literature for those seeking details.

13.2 BRIDGES

Prestressed concrete has proved to be technically advantageous, economically competitive, and esthetically superior for bridges, from very short span structures using precast standard components to cable-stayed girders and continuous box girders with clear spans of nearly 1000 ft. Nearly all concrete bridges, even those of relatively short span, are now prestressed. Precasting, cast-in-place construction, or a combination of the two methods may be used. Both pretensioning and post-tensioning are employed, often on the same project.

In the United States, highway bridges generally must meet loading, design, and construction requirements of the AASHTO Specification (Refs. 13.1 and 13.2). The design and construction of railway bridges are governed by provisions of the *AREA Manual for Railway Engineering* (Ref. 13.3). Design requirements for pedestrian crossings and bridges serving other purposes may be established by local or regional codes and specifications. ACI Code provisions are often incorporated by reference, and in most cases serve as model provisions for other governing documents.

Bridge spans to about 100 ft often consist of precast integral-deck units such as shown in cross section in Fig. 13.1. These units offer low initial cost,

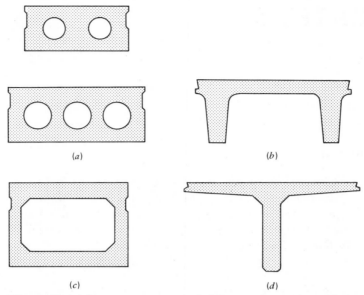

Figure 13.1 Short span precast bridge sections. (*a*) Voided slabs. (*b*) Channel-section. (*c*) Box beam. (*d*) Single-tee.

minimum maintenance, and fast easy construction, with minimum traffic interruption. Such girders are generally pretensioned. The units are placed side by side, and are often post-tensioned laterally at intermediate diaphragm locations, after which shear keys between adjacent units are filled with non-shrinking mortar. For highway spans, an asphalt wearing surface may be applied directly to the top of the precast concrete. In some cases, a cast-in-place slab is placed to provide composite action.

The voided slabs shown in Fig. 13.1*a* are commonly available in depths from 15 to 21 in. and widths of 3 or 4 ft. For a standard highway HS20 loading (Ref. 13.1), they are suitable for spans to about 50 ft. Standard channel sections (Fig. 13.1*b*) are available in depths from 21 to 35 in. in a variety of widths, and are used for spans between about 20 and 60 ft. The hollow box beams and single-tee girders shown in Figs. 13.1*c* and 13.1*d*, respectively, are intended for longer spans up to about 100 ft. The box section shown has been adopted as a standard railway trestle member by AREA, a typical design using four 3 ft wide sections, side by side, on 28 ft simple spans (Ref. 13.3).

In all cases, details and dimensions vary slightly depending upon the local source of supply. Cross section properties for typical members are given in Ref. 13.4.

For medium-span highway bridges, to about 120 ft, AASHTO standard I beams are generally used. These have already been described in Ch. 12 and typical cross sections are found in Figs. 12.17*a* and 12.17*b*. They are intended for use with a composite cast-in-place roadway slab. Such girders often combine pretensioning of the precast member with post-tensioning of the composite beam after the deck is placed. In an effort to obtain improved economy, some states have adopted more refined designs, such as the State of Washington standard girder shown in Fig. 12.17c.

The use of specially designed precast girders to carry a monorail transit system is illustrated in Fig. 13.2. The finished guideway features a series of segments, each consisting of six simply supported pretensioned beams, post-tensioned together to form a continuous structure. Typical spans are 100 to 110 ft. Approximately half of the 337 beams used have some combination of vertical and horizontal curvatures and variable superelevation. All beams are hollow, a feature achieved by inserting a styrofoam void in the curved beams and by using a moving mandrel in straight beam production.

Precast girders may not be used for spans much in excess of 120 ft because of the problems of transporting and erecting large, heavy units. On the other hand, there is a clear trend toward the use of longer spans for bridges. Highway safety is improved by eliminating central piers and moving outer piers away

Figure 13.2   Walt Disney World Monorail (courtesy ABAM Engineers, Inc., copyright Walt Disney Productions).

from the edge of divided highways. For elevated urban expressways, long spans facilitate access and minimize obstruction to activities below. Concern for environmental damage has led to the choice of long spans for continuous viaducts. For river crossings, intermediate piers may be impossible because of requirements of navigational clearance.

Such requirements have led to the development in Europe, and more recently in the western hemisphere, of long span segmental prestressed concrete box girder bridges of the type shown under construction in Fig. 13.3. In typical construction of this type, piers are cast-in-place, often using the slip-forming technique. A "hammerhead" section of box girder is then cast at the top of the pier, and construction proceeds in each direction by the balanced cantilever method. The construction is advanced using either cast-in-place or precast segments, each post-tensioned to the previously completed construction. Finally, after the closing cast-in-place joint is made at midspan, the structure is further post-tensioned for full continuity. Shear keys may be used on the vertical faces between segments, and precast units are glued with epoxy resin (Refs. 13.5, 13.6, 13.7, and 13.8).

Figure 13.3 Construction view of Knight Street Bridge, Vancouver-Richmond, British Columbia (courtesy Post-Tensioning Institute).

The use of precast segments, up to about 20 ft long, has become the more common method for construction of this type of bridge. Often a casting yard is established at the construction site. Special forms are made to permit variable depth sections and variable wall thicknesses, and each unit is cast using the immediately preceding unit as end form, thus insuring perfect alignment.

Many special techniques have been developed to place the precast segments. The use of a launching girder is illustrated in Fig. 13.4 (Ref. 13.5). Such a girder has a length slightly greater than the maximum span length and consists essentially of: (a) a main truss-type beam of which the bottom chords act as

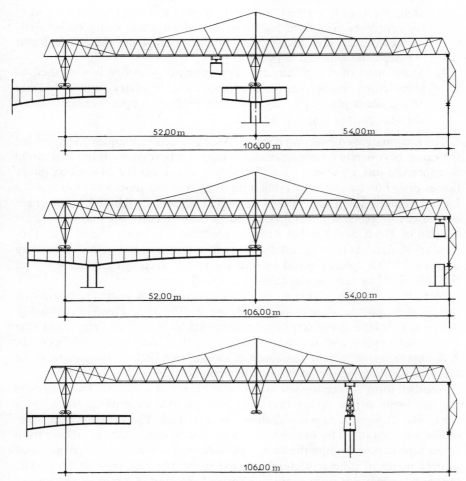

Figure 13.4 Operational phases of a launching girder: (*a*) placing of standard segments, (*b*) partial translation and placing of the pier segment, (*c*) translation of the girder (courtesy of Freyssinet International).

rolling tracks, (b) three leg frames, fixed or not to the main beam, with the rear and central frames allowing sufficient free internal width for the passage of the segments, and (c) a segment placing trolley that travels along the main beam and that is capable of longitudinal and vertical displacement as well as horizontal rotation. In the course of normal operations, the girder takes up three successive positions, as shown in Fig. 13.4:

1. Placing of standard segments: the central leg frame rests directly over a pier and the rear frame is seated toward the end of the previously completed deck cantilever.
2. Placing of the segment over the following pier: the girder advances along the completed deck until the central leg frame reaches the end of the cantilever. The front leg frame, seated on a temporary corbel fixed to the pier, ensures the stability of the girder while the pier segment is placed and adjusted in position.
3. Translation of the girder: the segment-placing trolley is now used as a launching cradle with the assistance of an auxiliary support bearing on the newly placed pier segment. The auxiliary support is removed and segment placing may recommence.

The imaginative engineering demonstrated by such techniques has extended the range of concrete construction for bridges far beyond anything that could be conceived just a few years ago. The record at present (1977) is a box girder bridge of 787 ft clear span carrying a highway over the mouth of Hamana-Ko Lake 150 miles southwest of Tokyo (Ref. 13.9). In the United States, twin curved cast-in-place segmental box girders have recently been completed for of span of 310 ft over the Eel River in northern California (Ref. 13.10). Preliminary design has been completed for twin continuous box girders consisting of central 550 ft spans flanked by 390 ft side spans, carrying route 408 over the Illinois River near Springfield (Ref. 13.11).

Not all bridges are suited to precast construction. A particularly striking cast-in-place post-tensioned span is shown in Fig. 13.5. This river crossing, designed by Pierre Tremblet, met requirements for a roadway alignment that was curved in plan, with superelevation, and with vertical grade of 6.7 percent. A double tee cross section was adopted, closing to a hollow box section at the negative bending regions at intermediate supports.

Another form of prestressed concrete bridge well suited to long spans is the cable-stayed box girder (Ref. 13.12). A notable example is the Chaco-Corrientes Bridge in Argentina, shown in Fig. 13.6. The bridge's main span of 804 ft is supported by two A-frame towers, with cable stays stretching from tower tops to points along the deck. The deck itself consists of two parallel box girders made of precast sections erected using the cantilever method. The tensioned cables not only provide a vertical reaction component to support the deck, but also introduce horizontal compression to the box girders, adding to the post-tensioning force in those members (Ref. 13.13).

Figure 13.5 Cast-in-place prestressed bridge over the river Viege in Switzerland, designed by Pierre Tremblet, Geneva.

Figure 13.6 Chaco-Corrientes Bridge in Argentina. Cable-stayed box girder with maximum span 804 ft (courtesy Ammann and Whitney Consulting Engineers).

Bridge designs of the type just described are developments of a design concept originated by the noted Italian engineer Ricardo Morandi. The Morandi designs, similar in general appearance to the structure of Fig. 13.6, make use of concrete encased steel stays, rather than bare steel, to minimize deffection under load (Ref. 13.14. See also Art. 11.7.). Four such structures have been built including one of record 940 ft span in northern Libya.

A type of structure well suited to light loads and long spans is the stress-ribbon bridge, pioneered many years ago by the German engineer Ulrich Finsterwalder (Refs. 13.15 and 13.16). The stress-ribbon bridge shown in Fig. 13.7 carries a pipeline and pedestrians over the Rhine River with a span of 446 ft. The superstructure erection sequence was to (a) erect two pairs of cables, (b) place precast slabs forming a sidewalk deck and a U channel under each of the sets of cables, and (c) cast-in-place concrete within the two U's. The pipeline is placed atop supports at railing height, off to one side, which greatly increases the critical wind speed of the structure (Ref. 13.17).

Figure 13.7 Stress-ribbon bridge of 446 ft span carrying pedestrian traffic and pipeline over the Rhone River near Lignon-Loex (courtesy *Civil Engineering*).

It is appropriate in discussing bridge forms to mention structural esthetics. The time is past when structures could be designed on the basis of minimum cost and technical advantages alone. Bridge structures in particular are exposed for all to see. To produce a structure that is visually offensive, as has occurred all too often in the past, is an act of professional irresponsibility. Particularly for major spans, but also for more ordinary structures, architectural advice should be sought early in the conceptual stage of the design process (Ref. 13.18).

13.3 SHELLS AND FOLDED PLATES

In a well-designed shell structure the loads are for the most part resisted by membrane forces acting in the plane tangent to the shell surface at any point. Principal tensile stresses, where they exist, are likely to cause cracking in the concrete shell, and may adversely affect its performance. It is an obvious idea to cancel these tensile stresses by prestressing, and the optimum arrangement of the tendons is along the lines of the principal tensile stress trajectories.

Figure 13.8   Concrete hyperbolic paraboloid shells.

Advantages of shell prestressing are important. By avoiding cracking at the service load stage, the shell more nearly satisfies the assumption usually made in analysis that the structure is uncracked and elastic. By prestressing, deflections may be minimized with the result that secondary stresses are avoided. Required steel is more conveniently placed in the form of high tensile tendons than ordinary bar reinforcement. Not only are steel areas smaller, and thus more easily accommodated within the usually small thickness of the shell, but full-length reinforcement is possible without the need for bar splices, which are often a source of trouble when heavy reinforcing bars are used.

Concrete shells such as the hyperbolic paraboloids shown in Fig. 13.8 resist their loads mainly by membrane stresses, although in certain regions, such as near the projecting tips and near the edge beams, bending moments are significant. Prestressing tendons are used to cancel the membrane tensile stresses, which act in the direction of the concave-upward parabolic curvature, and also serve to minimize deformation of the loaded shell, thus reducing the secondary bending of the shell surface.

Concrete-folded plate roofs, which may be regarded as prismatic shells, have also been prestressed to good advantage. Figure 13.9 shows a hangar facility recently constructed at Logan Airport in Boston, in which a record 255 ft span was achieved (Ref. 13.19).

Figure 13.9 Folded plate hangar for Allegheny Airlines at Logan Airport in Boston (courtesy Sepp Firnkas Engineering Inc.).

13.4 TRUSSES AND SPACE FRAMES

Prestressed concrete has not often been used for truss-type structures, but a few strikingly successful designs have been produced. The prestressing of axial tension members has been discussed in Ch. 11, and it was pointed out that not only can tensile stresses and cracking be avoided at service load, but also the elongation when loaded is very small compared with the elongation that would result if a steel member had been used. This great increase in stiffness has been used to good advantage for long span roof trusses.

Perhaps the most remarkable structure of this type is the aircraft service depot designed by A. J. and J. D. Harris Engineers for Transair, Ltd. at Gatwick, near London. A view of a part of the roof structure is shown in Fig. 13.10. Secondary "triangulated beams," or space trusses span 105 ft front-to-back of the hanger, and are carried across the front of the structure by a main beam, also triangulated, continuous on two 140 ft spans. Precast components making up the secondary trusses were assembled at ground level, then post-tensioned and hoisted into position. The main carrying beam was then made up in place by installing precast elements between the end frames of the secondary beams, after which the parabolic main cables were positioned and post-tensioned. Connections were detailed to be virtually free from bending, so as to eliminate secondary stresses.

The resulting structure is an inspiring example of the strength and elegance that can be achieved by a combination of precasting and prestressing (Ref. 13.20).

Figure 13.10 Prestressed concrete space trusses for aircraft service depot at Gatwick, England (courtesy of A. J. Harris, P. W. Abeles, and the Cement and Concrete Association).

13.5   **WATER STORAGE TOWERS**

Elevated water storage tanks are a common feature of the skylines of communities, large and small. Too often they are designed solely based on utility and economics. Besides performing its function, a well-designed water tower can be an esthetic asset for any region. This fact is widely recognized in European countries, especially Sweden, Finland, and France (Refs. 13.21 and 13.22). A dramatic tower may become the symbol of a city and the source of great community pride.

It has been estimated that the exceptional esthetics of Finnish water towers, for example, add about 15 to 20 percent to their cost (Ref. 13.23). In many instances the incremental expense may be at least partially recovered through the income from restaurants and observation decks incorporated in the design.

A fine example of the merging of function and esthetics is the 58 m high tower at Orebro in Sweden, seen in the photograph of Fig. 13.11 and shown in section in Fig. 13.12. The structure consists of a conical shell of 46 m external diameter, supported on a tall shaft. Atop the tank itself is an observation platform covered by an umbrellalike conical shell. The shell of the main tank is circumferentially prestressed using 206 Freyssinet cables each containing 12 wires of 7 mm diameter. Sixteen vertical ribs were provided for architectural reasons, and also serve to anchor the prestressing cables, each one of which

Figure 13.11   Water tower of 9000 m^3 capacity at Orebro, Sweden.

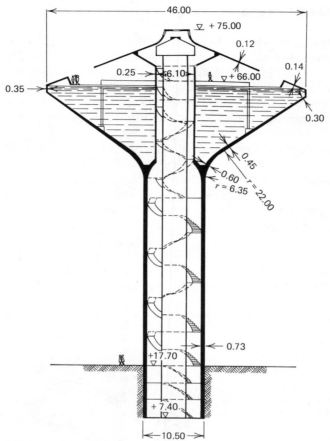

Figure 13.12 Section through the Orebro tower (adapted from Ref. 13.22).

extends halfway around the tank circumference. Typical of many such structures, the tank was cast at ground level and raised to its final position by hydraulic jacks placed on the circumference of the tower and fixed to the bottom face of the tank base ring. Construction of the tower proceeded as the tank was raised.

13.6 NUCLEAR CONTAINMENT VESSELS

The development of nuclear energy for electric power generation has resulted in new applications for prestressed concrete. Two types of post-tensioned pre-stressed concrete reactor structures are used. In the first type, the complete pressure circuit embracing reactor and heat exchangers is placed within a prestressed concrete reactor vessel, always with massive concrete walls, placed in triaxial compression through post-tensioning. The second type of reactor structure is a containment vessel, designed to protect the environment from radioactive release in case of an accident to the plant. In this type of design, the reactor is contained in a steel pressure vessel connected by external ducts to heat exchangers. The complete system is then surrounded by the larger containment structure (Ref. 13.24).

A typical nuclear containment vessel of 40 m diameter and 54 m height is shown in Fig. 13.13. The shell is prestressed vertically and circumferentially

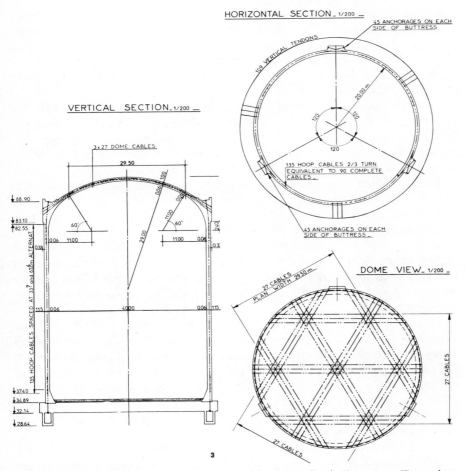

Figure 13.13 Nuclear containment vessel in Asco, Spain (courtesy Freyssinet International).

in the cylindrical wall, and the dome is prestressed by tendons arranged at 120 degrees.

The circumferential or hoop prestressing force required for a typical secondary vessel is about 700 kips per foot. To apply this large force economically, post-tensioning tendons of much larger capacity than normal have been developed (Ref. 13.25).

13.7 PAVEMENTS

Constantly increasing traffic volume and weight on concrete pavement slabs, both for highways and airports, call for improvement in pavement design and construction. Conventional pavements are designed on the basis of the concrete's low modulus of rupture; thus the high compressive strength of the material cannot be utilized. When steel is included, it is intended to control and distribute cracking of the concrete, but not to eliminate it. On the other hand, experience indicates that pavement deterioration usually starts at the cracks and transverse joints.

In longitudinally prestressed concrete pavements, fluctuating stresses due to passing wheel loads remain in the compressive range. Cracking is eliminated and transverse joints are decreased in number or eliminated completely, resulting in longer pavement life and smoother riding characteristics. In addition, costs may be reduced through reduction in slab thickness. Recent experience with experimental and prototype prestressed pavements has confirmed that they are practical and economically competitive (Refs. 13.26, 13.27, and 13.28).

Techniques for longitudinal prestressing of pavements vary, but some details of a recent project in Pennsylvania are of interest (Ref. 13.29). Unbonded coated tendons of 0.68 in. diameter were used, placed 24 in. on centers and located slightly below the middle of the 6 in. thick slab. A slipform concrete paver was modified so as to feed the 12 tendons into the slab as it passed. Polyethelyne sheets were used on the base under the slab so the slab could contract during tensioning

The typical length between transverse expansion joints was 600 ft. Four foot long blockouts at joint locations provided space for jacking the tendons, which were stressed to 46,000 lb each to provide compression in the concrete of about 320 psi. A typical joint detail, shown in Fig. 13.14, provides for the transfer of anchorage force from temporary anchors "A" to final anchors "B" after the 4 ft blockouts had been concreted. Anchors "C" provide for the dead end restraint of tendons in the next segment of slab. The expansion joint provided for a total movement of 3.5 in.

The resulting slab is expected to be virtually maintenance-free for 40 years, while conventional pavement requires heavy maintenance usually after 20 years. Compared with a competing design of ordinary reinforced concrete, the thickness of the pavement was reduced from 9 to 6 in., and the amount of steel was reduced 90 percent by weight.

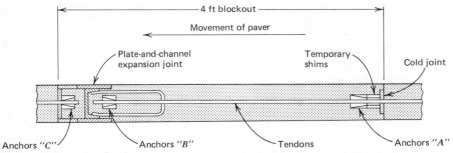

Figure 13.14 Prestressed concrete pavement (adapted from Ref. 13.29).

13.8 MARINE STRUCTURES

Prestressed concrete has found frequent application in recent years in marine structures of all types. These range from routine seawall constructions to prestressed concrete tanker ships and the massive "Ekofisk" oil storage and tanker-loading caisson recently built in Norway and towed to its permanent location in the North Sea (Refs. 13.30, 13.31, and 13.32).

Figure 13.15 Floating liquified petroleum gas vessel being towed to its destination in Indonesia (courtesy ABAM Engineers and Concrete Technology Corporation).

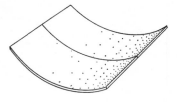

a. Match Castings of Shell Segments

b. Setting of Shells in Graving Dock

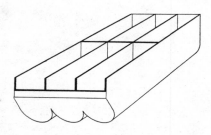

c. In-place Casting of Longitudinal Bulkheads,
   Saddles and Transverse Bulkheads

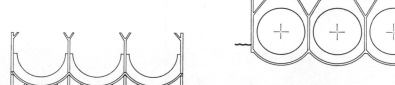

d. Launching Stage

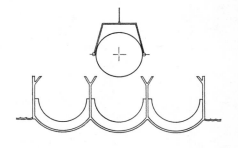

e. Placing Hull Tanks

f. In-place Casting of "Δ" Plates
   and Deck

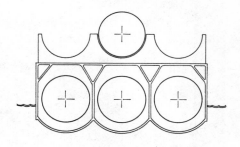

g. Placing Deck Tanks and Final
   Outfitting

Figure 13.16   Construction sequence floating LPG terminal (from Ref. 13.34).

470

Indicative of the possibilities of offshore structures is the giant precast, prestressed concrete floating liquified petroleum gas (LGP) facility shown in Fig. 13.15 (Ref. 13.33). This remarkable structure of 461 ft total length and 65,000 ton displacement, was constructed in Tacoma, Washington and towed 10,000 miles across the Pacific Ocean to the Ardjuna oil and gas field in the Java Sea. It provides for storage of liquified petroleum gas in 12 insulated steel tanks, 6 above deck and 6 below, having a total capacity of 375,000 barrels. The entire facility includes tanks, refrigeration machinery, an electric power plant, accommodations for a 50 man crew, crane service for maintenance, and lifeboats and heliport.

The entire hull structure was precast in segments. With reference to Fig. 13.16, the hull bottom is made of precast concrete shell segments (a), which are delivered to the graving dock (b). Vertical side shell and longitudinal bulkheads are cast in place (c). The partially completed hull is launched (d). When afloat, the lower six tanks are installed (e) and remaining hull concrete in cast in place (f). Finally, deck tank supports and tanks are installed (g). Precast elements were reinforced and provided with ducts for both longitudinal and transverse tendons. During assembly of the shell segments, each joint was coated with epoxy adhesive, after which the segment was promptly post-tensioned to its neighbor.

In comparing construction of prestressed concrete for the facility with an alternative design in steel, the following advantages were noted:

a.   Lower initial construction cost.
b.   Superior durability in sea water environment.
c.   Ductile behavior when severely overloaded.
d.   Freedom from damage under fatigue loading.
e.   Excellent properties at extremely low temperatures.
f.   Superior behavior when exposed to fire.
g.   Ease of repair when damaged by collision.
h.   Freedom from need for drydocking at regular intervals for inspection, repair, and maintenance.

Based on this pioneering venture, prospects for future development of offshore facilities using prestressed concrete are most favorable.

13.9 MISCELLANEOUS STRUCTURAL ELEMENTS

A. PILING

Prestressed concrete has been used extensively for bearing and friction piles as well as for sheet piling, and offers the advantages of low cost and a high degree of permanence. While they are primarily compression members, piles are subjected to tensile stresses caused by bending during lifting and placing, as well as in service and, in addition, must withstand tensile forces during driving. A prestress force producing axial compression of about 700 psi in the concrete is often used, almost always produced by pretensioning (Refs. 13.34, 13.35, and 13.36).

Typical foundation pile cross sections are shown in Fig. 13.17. The square solid section of Fig. 13.17a is economical for load ranges between about 60 and 80 tons, while for loads to about 125 tons the octagonal pile of Fig. 13.17b, of 14 to 18 in. flat dimension, is more suitable. The voided octagonal pile of Fig. 13.17c, usually of 24 in. dimension, has been widely used for waterfront construction. Very large size cylindrical piles (Fig. 13.17d) of diameters 36, 54, and 60 in. have been employed for the supports for major bridge piers, and may develop capacities in excess of 800 tons.

When length requirements dictate, prestressed concrete piles may be spliced using non-prestressed reinforcing bars cast into the end of the upper section and thrust into grout-filled sockets provided in the section below.

(a)

(b)

(c)

(d)

Figure 13.17 Typical prestressed concrete piling sections. (a) Square solid section. (b) Octagonal solid section. (c) Voided octagonal section. (d) Cylindrical section.

Sheet piling (Ref. 13.37) is used to resist earth pressure or hydrostatic pressure through flexural resistance, and may also carry vertical loads. Watertightness, if required, is achieved through specially designed interlocking joints. The complete installation of such piling may also include horizontal support beams, backstays and anchorages.

B.   ROCK AND SOIL ANCHORS

Where sheet pile walls or unstable rock formations must be anchored to firm subsoil or rock, prestressed anchors are suitable. The restraining force provided by the highly stressed ties places the exposed material in compression, preventing lateral displacement and slides (Ref. 13.38).

A typical installation is shown in Fig. 13.18. The hole to receive the stressing rod is drilled in rock or augered into the soil, after which the prestressing rod, containing a core hole, is placed to full depth. High strength grout is forced into the top under pressure, flowing out the base of the stressing rod and filling the drilled hole to a sufficient length to develop the tensile strength of the steel by bond. Deformed bars may be used to reduce the required development length, and in some cases the base of the drilled hole may be belled to a larger diameter to further insure against pullout. After the wall has been constructed and the grout has achieved sufficient strength, the rod is stressed by post-tensioning jacks, and wedge anchorages or nuts placed at the bearing plate.

C.   RAILROAD TIES

With the long-delayed, but much-needed, reconstruction of the United States railroads, there appears to be a promising opportunity to rebuild substandard track using prestressed concrete ties or sleepers. These have been in use in

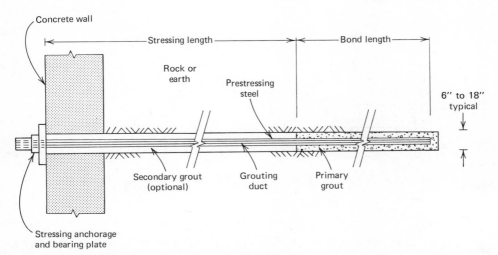

Figure 13.18   Prestressed anchor in drilled hole.

Europe for several decades and have proved both economical and practical (Refs. 13.39, 13.40, 13.41, 13.42.). Well over one million prestressed concrete ties are already in use in the United States.

The design of such ties has been standardized by the Association of American Railroads. While there are several alternative designs, the AAR Type I tie shown in Fig. 13.19 has been used almost exclusively in United States construction. The top surface of the tie is flat to accept the indirect fixation rail fastening assembly. The ties are characterized by a wedge shape at the bottom of the center 3 ft. Weight is about 620 lb. The ties are pretensioned with four 7/16 in. strands to an initial prestress force that totals 81,600 lb. After losses this is

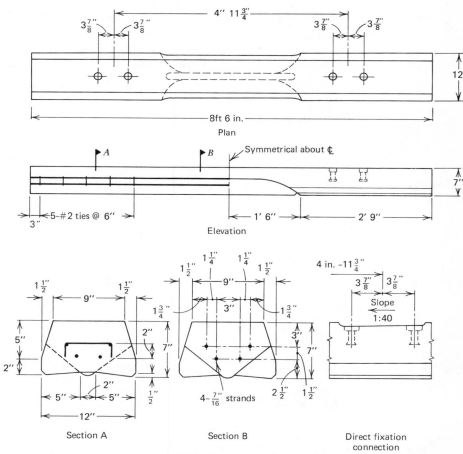

Figure 13.19 Prestressed concrete railroad tie, AAR Type E, Association of American Railroads.

Figure 13.20 Prestressed concrete railway ties awaiting installation in a test project in California (courtesy Santa Fe Railway).

estimated to be 69,000 lb. Designed for a cracking moment of 150,000 in.-lb under the rail, they must be able to withstand 200,000 in.-lb of bending moment for 2 million cycles of load without failure.

A prestressed cross tie of somewhat different design, installed on an experimental basis in California, is shown in Fig. 13.20 (Ref. 13.41).

D. UTILITY POLES

Prestressed concrete utility poles are widely used in Europe, where timber is not plentiful, and are increasingly used in the United States as well. They are usually pretensioned, although post-tensioning is sometimes employed. The shape of the poles depends on the purpose to be served and the loading conditions anticipated. Thus poles intended for overhead contact wires on electrified railways are usually of I section since bending will be about one axis mainly, while free-standing transmission poles, which must resist bending about both axes as well as torsional loading, are normally circular or octagonal (Refs. 13.42, 13.43, and 13.44).

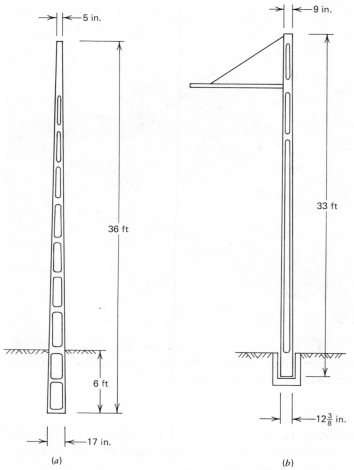

Figure 13.21   Prestressed concrete poles (from Ref. 13.43).
(*a*) Vierendeel mast. (*b*) Standard British Railways mast.

Fig. 13.21*a* shows a vierendeel mast of I section with web open except for intermittent ribs connecting the flanges. This mast was concentrically pre-stressed with a uniform concrete compression of 2400 psi. Although cracking was greatly delayed, the section was overreinforced and subject to brittle failure. It was concluded that a section with substantially less prestress would permit greater energy absorption when subject to impact loadings, and the design was later revised.

Figure 13.21*b* shows a type of mast developed for the British Railways. In this case, the bending moment in one direction was greater than in the other, and so eccentric prestressing was used. The prestress in the concrete was relatively low. Load tests confirmed that complete recovery resulted after loading to about twice the cracking load.

13.10   TOWERS AND MASTS

The use of prestressed concrete in very tall towers to support restaurants, observation decks, and radio and television facilities originated in 1953 with the famous Stuttgart Tower designed by Fritz Leonhardt. With a total height of 211 m, that structure features a high-level 170 seat restaurant.

While a number of towers similar in concept have been constructed since, none can rival the remarkable CN Tower in Toronto, designed for Canadian National Railways by Nicolet, Carrier, Dressel and Associates, Ltd. of Montreal. An overall view of the recently completed tower is shown in Fig. 13.22.

Having a total height of 1815 ft, the CN tower is the tallest self-supporting structure in the world. At the 1100 ft level, a seven story pod 140 ft in diameter

Figure 13.22   CN Tower, Toronto, the world's tallest self-supporting structure at 1815 ft (copyright CN Tower Ltd. 1973).

Figure 13.23 View of CN Tower at elevation 1100 ft. Structure contains broadcast facilities, observation decks, and revolving restaurant (copyright CN tower Ltd. 1973).

contains four floors for broadcast facilities, two floors for observation decks, and one floor for a 400 seat revolving restaurant as shown in Fig. 13.23.

The tower, cast in a continuous slip-forming operation, contains 150 vertical post-tensioning tendons. Some individual 1/2 in. diameter strands are nearly 1500 ft in length. The mast rests on an 18 ft thick cellular raft foundation, which was itself post-tensioned in 16 stages as the tower construction proceeded.

Space limitations do not permit an adequate description of the design and execution of this landmark structure, which ranks with the most remarkable achievements of the structural engineering profession. Additional details will be found in Ref. 13.45.

REFERENCES

13.1 *Standard Specifications for Highway Bridges*, 11th Ed., American Association of State Highway and Transportation Officials (AASHTO), Washington, 1973, 469 pp.

13.2 *Interim Specifications—Bridges—1975*, AASHTO Subcommittee on Bridges and Structures, AASHTO, Washington, 1975, 100 pp.

13.3 *Manual for Railway Engineering*, American Railway Engineering Association (AREA), Washington, 1973.

13.4 *Short Span Bridges—Spans to 100 Feet*, Prestressed Concrete Institute, Chicago, 1975, 34 pp.

13.5 *Precast Segmental Cantilever Bridge Construction*, Europe Etudes, Boulogne, France, 1973, 26 pp.

13.6 Libby, J. R., "Segmental Box Girder Bridge Superstructure Design," *J. ACI*, Vol. 73, No. 5, May 1976, pp. 279–290.

13.7 "Recommended Practice for Segmental Construction in Prestressed Concrete," Report by PCI Committee on Segmental Construction, *J. PCI*, Vol. 20, No. 2, March–April 1975, pp. 23–41.

13.8 Hugenschmidt, F., "Epoxy Adhesives in Precast Prestressed Concrete Construction," *J. PCI*, Vol. 19, No. 2, March–April 1974, pp. 112–124.

13.9 "Fishy Issues Spawn Record Box Girder Bridge," *Engineering News-Record*, February 19, 1976, p. 14.

13.10 "Contractor Saves $220,000 on Bridges," *Engineering News-Record*, January 8, 1976, pp. 22–23.

13.11 *Preliminary Design of the Prestressed Concrete Segmental Bridges on FA Route 408 over the Illinois River*, Post-Tensioning Division Bridge Report, Prestressed Concrete Institute, Chicago, 1975, 9 pp.

13.12 Podolny, W., Jr., "Cable-Stayed Bridges of Prestressed Concrete," *J. PCI*, Vol. 18, No. 1, January–February 1973, pp. 68–79.

13.13 Rothman H. B. and Chang, F. K., "Longest Precast-Concrete Box Girder Bridge in Western Hemisphere," *Civil Engineering*, March 1974, pp. 56–60.

13.14 "Rigid Stays Slim Box Girder Bridge and Reduce Deflection," *Engineering News-Record*, June 20, 1974, p. 58.

13.15 Finsterwalder, U., "Prestressed Concrete Bridge Construction," *J. ACI*, Vol. 62, No. 9, September 1965, pp. 1037–1046.

13.16 Wilson, A. J. and Wheen, R. J., "Direct Design of Taut Cables Under Uniform Loading," *J. Struct. Div. ASCE*, Vol. 100, No. ST3, March 1974, pp. 565–578.

13.17 World's Top Prestressed Structures—1970–74, *Civil Engineering*, August 1974, pp. 68–71.

13.18 Leonhardt, F., "Aesthetics of Bridge Design," *J. PCI*, Vol. 13, No. 1, February 1968, pp. 14–31.

13.19 Firnkas, S., "Prestressed Folded Plate Hangar for Allegheny Airlines—Design and Construction," *J. PCI*, Vol. 16, No. 2, March–April 1971, pp. 43–62.

13.20 Haines, W. J. M. and Harris, A. J., "Structure of Aircraft Service Depot at Gatwick for Transair Ltd.," *J. PCI*, Vol. 4, No. 3, December 1959, pp. 46–60.

13.21 Leonhardt, F., *Prestressed Concrete Design and Construction*, 2nd Ed., Wilhelm Ernst and Son, Berlin, 1964, pp. 647–648.

13.22 Abeles, P. W., *Introduction to Prestressed Concrete*, Vol. 2, Concrete Publications, Ltd., London, 1966, pp. 600–601.

13.23 Klus, J. P. and Wortley, C. A., Finns Emphasize Esthetics in Water Towers, *Civil Engineering*, September 1973, pp. 84–87.

13.24 *Prestressed Concrete in Nuclear Power*, Europe Etudes, Boulogne, France, 1974, 29 pp.

13.25 Schupack, M., "Large Post-tensioning Tendons," *J. PCI*, Vol. 17, No. 3, May–June 1972, pp. 14–28.

13.26 Sargious, M. and Wang, S. K., "Economical Design of Prestressed Concrete Pavements," *J. PCI*, Vol. 16, No. 4, July–August 1971, pp. 64–79.

13.27 Pasko, T. J., "Prestressed Highway Pavement at Dulles Airport for Transpo 72," *J. PCI*, Vol. 17, No. 2, March–April 1972, pp. 46–54.

13.28 Huyghe, G. and Celis, R., "Joint-Free Experimental Prestressed Pavement," *J. PCI*, Vol. 17, No. 1, January–February 1972, pp. 58–72.

13.29 "Prestressed Concrete Pavement No Longer Seen as Experimental," *Engineering News-Record*, May 23, 1974, pp. 16–17.

13.30 Gerwick, Jr., B. C., "Concrete Structures: Key to Development of the Oceans," *J. ACI*, Vol. 71, No. 12, December 1974, pp. 611–616.

13.31 Moe, J., "Feasibility Study of Prestressed Concrete Tanker Ships," *J. ACI*, Vol. 71, No. 12, December 1974, pp. 617–626.

13.32 *Ekofisk Prestressed Concrete Oil Storage Caisson*, Europe Etudes, Boulogne, France, 1972, 15 pp.

13.33 Anderson, A. R., "World's Largest Prestressed LPG Floating Vessel," *J. PCI*, Vol. 22, No. 1, January–February 1977, pp. 12–31.

13.34 *PCI Design Handbook*, Prestressed Concrete Institute, Chicago, 1971, pp. 4.10–4.12.

13.35 Goble, G. G., Fricke, K., and Likens, G. E., Jr., "Driving Stresses in Concrete Piles," *J. PCI*, Vol. 21, No. 1, January–February, 1976, pp. 70–88.

13.36 Anderson, A. R. and Moustafa, S. E., "Dynamic Driving Stresses in Prestressed Concrete Piles," *Civil Engineering*, August 1971, pp. 55–58.

13.37 Li, S. T. and Ramakrishnan, V., "Optimum Prestress, Analysis, and Ultimate Strength Design of Prestressed Concrete Sheet Piles," *J. PCI*, Vol. 16, No. 3, May–June 1971, pp. 60–81.

13.38 Leonhardt, F., *Prestressed Concrete*, 2nd Ed., Wilhelm Ernst and Son, Berlin, 1964, pp. 601–606.

13.39 Weber, J. W., "Concrete Crossties in the United States," *J. PCI*, Vol. 14, No. 1, February 1969, pp. 46–61.

13.40 Kaar, P. H. and Hanson, N. W., "Bond Fatigue Tests of Beams Simulating Pretensioned Concrete Crossties," *J. PCI*, Vol. 20, No. 5, September–October 1975, pp. 65–80.

13.41 "Concrete Railway Ties Tested in California," *J. ACI*, Vol. 69, No. 3, March 1972, p. N5.

13.42 Abeles, P. W., *Introduction to Prestressed Concrete*, Vol. 1, Concrete Publications Ltd., London, 1964, pp. 298–300.

13.43 Leonhardt, F., *Prestressed Concrete*, 2nd Ed. Wilhelm Ernst and Son, Berlin, 1964, pp. 572–575.

13.44 Rodgers, T. E., Jr., "A Utility's Development and Use of Prestressed Concrete Poles," *J. PCI*, Vol. 17, No. 3, May–June 1972, pp. 8–13.

13.45 Slipformed Tower Post-Tensioned to Record Height of 1,805 Ft., *Engineering News-Record*, May 23, 1974, pp. 18–20.

APPENDIX A

DESIGN AIDS

Table A.1 Properties of Prestressing Steels

Seven-Wire Strand Grade 250						
Nominal diameter, in.	$\frac{1}{4}$	$\frac{5}{16}$	$\frac{3}{8}$	$\frac{7}{16}$	$\frac{1}{2}$	0.600
Area, A_p, in.^{2}	0.036	0.058	0.080	0.108	0.144	0.215
Weight, plf	0.12	0.20	0.27	0.37	0.49	0.74
$0.7f_{pu}A_p$, kips	6.3	10.2	14.0	18.9	25.2	37.6
$0.8f_{pu}A_p$, kips	7.2	11.6	16.0	21.6	28.8	43.0
$f_{pu}A_p$, kips	9.0	14.5	20.0	27.0	36.0	54.0

Seven-Wire Strand Grade 270				
Nominal diameter, in.	$\frac{3}{8}$	$\frac{7}{16}$	$\frac{1}{2}$	0.600
Area, A_p, in.^{2}	0.085	0.115	0.153	0.217
Weight, plf	0.29	0.39	0.52	0.74
$0.7f_{pu}A_p$, kips	16.1	21.7	28.9	41.0
$0.8f_{pu}A_p$, kips	18.4	24.8	33.0	46.9
$f_{pu}A_p$, kips	23.0	31.0	41.3	58.6

Round Wire				
Diameter	0.192	0.196	0.250	0.276
Area, A_p, in.^{2}	0.0289	0.0302	0.0491	0.0598
Weight, plf	0.098	0.10	0.17	0.20
Ultimate strength, f_{pu}, ksi	250	250	240	235
$0.7f_{pu}A_p$, kips	5.05	5.28	8.25	9.84
$0.8f_{pu}A_p$, kips	5.78	6.04	9.42	11.24
$f_{pu}A_p$, kips	7.22	7.55	11.78	14.05

Round Bars   Grade 145

Nominal diameter, in.	$\frac{3}{4}$	$\frac{7}{8}$	1	$1\frac{1}{8}$	$1\frac{1}{4}$	$1\frac{3}{8}$
Area, A_p, in.^{2}	0.442	0.601	0.785	0.994	1.227	1.485
Weight, plf	1.50	2.04	2.67	3.38	4.17	5.05
$0.7f_{pu}A_p$, kips	44.9	61.0	79.7	100.9	124.5	150.7
$0.8f_{pu}A_p$, kips	51.3	69.7	91.0	115.3	142.3	172.2
$f_{pu}A_p$, kips	64.1	87.1	113.8	144.1	177.9	215.3

Round Bars   Grade 160

Nominal diameter, in.	$\frac{3}{4}$	$\frac{7}{8}$	1	$1\frac{1}{8}$	$1\frac{1}{4}$	$1\frac{3}{8}$
Area, A_p, in.^{2}	0.442	0.601	0.785	0.994	1.227	1.485
Weight, plf	1.50	2.04	2.67	3.38	4.17	5.05
$0.7f_{pu}A_p$, kips	49.5	67.3	87.9	111.3	137.4	166.3
$0.8f_{pu}A_p$, kips	56.6	77.0	100.5	127.2	157.0	190.1
$f_{pu}A_p$, kips	70.7	96.2	125.6	159.0	196.3	237.6

Deformed Bars

Nominal diameter, in.	$\frac{5}{8}$	$\frac{5}{8}$S	1	1	$1\frac{1}{4}$	$1\frac{1}{4}$	$1\frac{3}{8}$
Area, A_p, in.^{2}	0.28	0.31	0.85	0.85	1.25	1.25	1.56
Weight, plf	0.98	1.09	3.01	3.01	4.39	4.39	5.56
Ultimate strength, f_{pu}, ksi	157	230	150	160	150	160	150
$0.7f_{pu}A_p$, kips	30.5	49.5	89.5	95.4	131.0	140.0	163.8
$0.8f_{pu}A_p$, kips	34.8	56.5	102.2	109.1	150.0	160.0	187.2
$f_{pu}A_p$, kips	43.5	70.5	127.8	136.3	187.5	200.0	234.0

[a] The bar designated $\frac{5}{8}$S is made from a newly developed heat treated steel with an ultimate strength of 230 ksi. Information on the properties of this steel in regard to stress corrosion, cracking, hydrogen embrittlement, and relaxation is available from the supplier.

Table A.2   Designations, Areas, Perimeters, and
Weights of Reinforcing Bars

Bar No.[a]	Diameter, in.	Cross-Sectional Area, A in.^{2}	Perimeter, in.	Unit Weight per foot, lb
2	$\frac{1}{4} = 0.250$	0.05	0.79	0.167
3	$\frac{3}{8} = 0.375$	0.11	1.18	0.376
4	$\frac{1}{2} = 0.500$	0.20	1.57	0.668
5	$\frac{5}{8} = 0.625$	0.31	1.96	1.043
6	$\frac{3}{4} = 0.750$	0.44	2.36	1.502
7	$\frac{7}{8} = 0.875$	0.60	2.75	2.044
8	$1 = 1.000$	0.79	3.14	2.670
9	$1\frac{1}{8} = 1.128^b$	1.00	3.54	3.400
10	$1\frac{1}{4} = 1.270^b$	1.27	3.99	4.303
11	$1\frac{3}{8} = 1.410^b$	1.56	4.43	5.313
14	$1\frac{3}{4} = 1.693^b$	2.25	5.32	7.650
18	$2\frac{1}{4} = 2.257^b$	4.00	7.09	13.600

[a] Based on the number of eighths of an inch included in the nominal diameter of the bars. The nominal diameter of a deformed bar is equivalent to the diameter of a plain bar having the same weight per foot as the deformed bar. Bar No. 2 is available in plain rounds only. All others are available in deformed rounds.
[b] Approximate to the nearest $\frac{1}{8}$ in.

Table A.3   Areas of Groups of Reinforcing Bars, in.^{2}

Bar No.	Number of Bars												
	2	3	4	5	6	7	8	9	10	11	12	13	14
4	0.39	0.58	0.78	0.98	1.18	1.37	1.57	1.77	1.96	2.16	2.36	2.55	2.75
5	0.61	0.91	1.23	1.53	1.84	2.15	2.45	2.76	3.07	3.37	3.68	3.99	4.30
6	0.88	1.32	1.77	2.21	2.65	3.09	3.53	3.98	4.42	4.86	5.30	5.74	6.19
7	1.20	1.80	2.41	3.01	3.61	4.21	4.81	5.41	6.01	6.61	7.22	7.82	8.42
8	1.57	2.35	3.14	3.93	4.71	5.50	6.28	7.07	7.85	8.64	9.43	10.21	11.00
9	2.00	3.00	4.00	5.00	6.00	7.00	8.00	9.00	10.00	11.00	12.00	13.00	14.00
10	2.53	3.79	5.06	6.33	7.59	8.86	10.12	11.39	12.66	13.92	15.19	16.45	17.72
11	3.12	4.68	6.25	7.81	9.37	10.94	12.50	14.06	15.62	17.19	18.75	20.31	21.87
14	4.50	6.75	9.00	11.25	13.50	15.75	18.00	20.25	22.50	24.75	27.00	29.25	31.50
18	8.00	12.00	16.00	20.00	24.00	28.00	32.00	36.00	40.00	44.00	48.00	52.00	56.00

Table A.4   Perimeters of Groups of Reinforcing Bars, in.

Bar No.	Number of Bars												
	2	3	4	5	6	7	8	9	10	11	12	13	14
4	3.1	4.7	6.2	7.8	9.4	11.0	12.6	14.1	15.7	17.3	18.8	20.4	22.0
5	3.9	5.9	7.8	9.8	11.8	13.7	15.7	17.7	19.5	21.6	23.6	25.5	27.5
6	4.7	7.1	9.4	11.8	14.1	16.5	18.8	21.2	23.6	25.9	28.3	30.6	33.0
7	5.5	8.2	11.0	13.7	16.5	19.2	22.0	24.7	27.5	30.2	33.0	35.7	38.5
8	6.3	9.4	12.6	15.7	18.9	22.0	25.1	28.3	31.4	34.6	37.7	40.9	44.0
9	7.1	10.6	14.2	17.7	21.3	24.8	28.4	31.9	35.4	39.0	42.5	46.0	49.6
10	8.0	12.0	16.0	20.0	23.9	27.9	31.9	35.9	39.9	43.9	47.9	51.9	55.9
11	8.9	13.3	17.7	22.2	26.6	31.0	35.4	39.9	44.3	48.7	53.2	57.6	62.0
14	10.6	16.0	21.3	26.6	31.9	37.2	42.6	47.9	53.2	58.5	63.8	69.2	74.5
18	14.2	21.3	28.4	35.5	42.5	49.6	56.7	63.8	70.9	78.0	85.1	93.2	100.3

Table A.5   Areas of Reinforcing Bars in Slabs, in.^{2} per ft

Spacing, in.	Bar No.								
	3	4	5	6	7	8	9	10	11
3	0.44	0.78	1.23	1.77	2.40	3.14	4.00	5.06	6.25
$3\frac{1}{2}$	0.38	0.67	1.05	1.51	2.06	2.69	3.43	4.34	5.36
4	0.33	0.59	0.92	1.32	1.80	2.36	3.00	3.80	4.68
$4\frac{1}{2}$	0.29	0.52	0.82	1.18	1.60	2.09	2.67	3.37	4.17
5	0.26	0.47	0.74	1.06	1.44	1.88	2.40	3.04	3.75
$5\frac{1}{2}$	0.24	0.43	0.67	0.96	1.31	1.71	2.18	2.76	3.41
6	0.22	0.39	0.61	0.88	1.20	1.57	2.00	2.53	3.12
$6\frac{1}{2}$	0.20	0.36	0.57	0.82	1.11	1.45	1.85	2.34	2.89
7	0.19	0.34	0.53	0.76	1.03	1.35	1.71	2.17	2.68
$7\frac{1}{2}$	0.18	0.31	0.49	0.71	0.96	1.26	1.60	2.02	2.50
8	0.17	0.29	0.46	0.66	0.90	1.18	1.50	1.89	2.34
9	0.15	0.26	0.41	0.59	0.80	1.05	1.33	1.69	2.08
10	0.13	0.24	0.37	0.53	0.72	0.94	1.20	1.52	1.87
12	0.11	0.20	0.31	0.44	0.60	0.78	1.00	1.27	1.56

Table A.6 Development Length in Tension, in.

For No. 11 bars or smaller: $l_d = 0.04 A_b f_y / \sqrt{f'_c}$ but $\geq 0.0004 d_b f_y$

For No. 14 bars: $\qquad\qquad l_d = 0.085 f_y / \sqrt{f'_c}$

For No. 18 bars: $\qquad\qquad l_d = 0.11 f_y / \sqrt{f'_c}$

(Minimum length 12 in. in all cases.)

		f'_c							
		3000		4000		5000		6000	
Bar No.	f_y	Basic l_d	Top Bars $1.4 l_d$	Basic l_d	Top Bars $1.4 l_d$	Basic l_d	Top Bars $1.4 l_d$	Basic l_d	Top Bars $1.4 l_d$
2	40	12	12	12	12	12	12	12	12
	50	12	12	12	12	12	12	12	12
	60	12	12	12	12	12	12	12	12
3	40	12	12	12	12	12	12	12	12
	50	12	12	12	12	12	12	12	12
	60	12	13	12	13	12	13	12	13
4	40	12	12	12	12	12	12	12	12
	50	12	14	12	14	12	14	12	14
	60	12	17	12	17	12	17	12	17
5	40	12	14	12	14	12	14	12	14
	50	13	18	13	18	13	18	13	18
	60	15	21	15	21	15	21	15	21
6	40	13	18	12	17	12	17	12	17
	50	16	22	15	21	15	21	15	21
	60	19	27	18	25	18	25	18	25
7	40	18	25	15	21	14	20	14	20
	50	22	31	19	27	18	25	18	25
	60	26	37	23	32	21	29	21	29
8	40	23	32	20	28	18	25	16	23
	50	29	40	25	35	22	31	20	29
	60	35	48	30	42	27	38	24	34
9	40	29	41	25	35	23	32	21	29
	50	37	51	32	44	28	40	26	36
	60	44	61	38	53	34	48	31	43

Table A.6 (*cont.*)

Bar No.	f_y	f'_c							
		3000		4000		5000		6000	
		Basic l_d	Top Bars $1.4l_d$	Basic l_d	Top Bars $1.4l_d$	Basic l_d	Top Bars $1.4l_d$	Basic l_d	Top Bars $1.4l_d$
10	40	37	52	32	45	29	40	26	37
	50	46	65	40	56	36	50	33	46
	60	56	78	48	67	43	60	39	55
11	40	46	64	39	55	35	49	32	45
	50	57	80	49	69	44	62	40	56
	60	68	96	59	83	53	74	48	68
14	40	62	87	54	75	48	67	44	61
	50	78	109	67	94	60	84	55	77
	60	93	130	81	113	72	101	66	92
18	40	80	113	70	97	62	87	57	80
	50	100	141	87	122	78	109	71	99
	60	121	169	104	146	93	131	85	119

Table A.7 Properties of Welded Wire Mesh

Style Designation	Spacing of Wires, in. Longit.	Trans.	Size of Wires, AS and W Gage Longit.	Trans.	Sectional Area, in.^{2} per ft Longit.	Trans.	Weight lb per 100 ft^2
Two-Way Types							
2 × 2-10/10	2	2	10	10	0.086	0.086	60
2 × 2-14/14[a]	2	2	12	12	0.052	0.052	37
2 × 2-12/12[a]	2	2	14	14	0.030	0.030	21
3 × 3-8/8	3	3	8	8	0.082	0.082	58
3 × 3-10/10	3	3	10	10	0.057	0.057	41
3 × 3-12/12[a]	3	3	12	12	0.035	0.035	25
3 × 3-14/14[a]	3	3	14	14	0.020	0.020	14
4 × 4-4/4	4	4	4	4	0.120	0.120	85
4 × 4-6/6	4	4	6	6	0.087	0.087	62
4 × 4-8/8	4	4	8	8	0.062	0.062	44
4 × 4-10/10	4	4	10	10	0.043	0.043	31
4 × 4-12/12[a]	4	4	12	12	0.026	0.026	19
6 × 6-0/0	6	6	0	0	0.148	0.148	107
6 × 6-2/2	6	6	2	2	0.108	0.108	78
6 × 6-4/4	6	6	4	4	0.080	0.080	58
6 × 6-4/6	6	6	4	6	0.080	0.058	50
6 × 6-6/6	6	6	6	6	0.058	0.058	42
6 × 6-8/8	6	6	8	8	0.041	0.041	30
6 × 6-10/10	6	6	10	10	0.029	0.029	21
One-Way Types							
2 × 12-0/4	2	12	0	4	0.443	0.040	169
2 × 12-2/6	2	12	2	6	0.325	0.029	124
2 × 12-4/8	2	12	4	8	0.239	0.021	91
2 × 12-6/10	2	12	6	10	0.174	0.014	66
2 × 12-8/12	2	12	8	12	0.124	0.009	46
3 × 12-0/4	3	12	0	4	0.295	0.040	119
3 × 12-2/6	3	12	2	6	0.216	0.029	87
3 × 12-4/8	3	12	4	8	0.159	0.021	64
3 × 12-6/10	3	12	6	10	0.116	0.014	46
3 × 12-8/12	3	12	8	12	0.082	0.009	32
4 × 8-8/12	4	8	8	12	0.062	0.013	27
4 × 8-10/12	4	8	10	12	0.043	0.013	20
4 × 12-0/4	4	12	0	4	0.221	0.040	94
4 × 12-2/6	4	12	2	6	0.162	0.029	69
4 × 12-4/8	4	12	4	8	0.120	0.021	51
4 × 12-6/10	4	12	6	10	0.087	0.014	36
4 × 12-10/12	4	12	10	12	0.043	0.009	19
6 × 12-00/4	6	12	00	4	0.172	0.040	78
6 × 12-0/4	6	12	0	4	0.148	0.040	69
6 × 12-2/2	6	12	2	2	0.108	0.054	59
6 × 12-4/4	6	12	4	4	0.080	0.040	44
6 × 12-6/6	6	12	6	6	0.058	0.029	32

[a] Usually furnished only in galvanized wire.

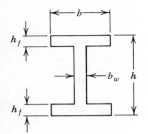
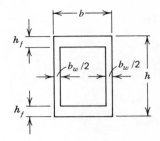

Table A.8 Section Properties of Symmetrical I and Box Beams

b_w/b	h_f/h	A_c	I_c	c_1	c_2	r^2
0.1	0.1	$0.280bh$	$0.0449bh^3$	$0.500h$	$0.500h$	$0.160h^2$
0.1	0.2	0.460	0.0671	0.500	0.500	0.146
0.1	0.3	0.640	0.0785	0.500	0.500	0.123
0.2	0.1	0.360	0.0492	0.500	0.500	0.137
0.2	0.2	0.520	0.0689	0.500	0.500	0.132
0.2	0.3	0.680	0.0791	0.500	0.500	0.117
0.3	0.1	0.440	0.0535	0.500	0.500	0.121
0.3	0.2	0.580	0.0707	0.500	0.500	0.122
0.3	0.3	0.720	0.0796	0.500	0.500	0.111
0.4	0.1	0.520	0.0577	0.500	0.500	0.111
0.4	0.2	0.640	0.0725	0.500	0.500	0.113
0.4	0.3	0.760	0.0801	0.500	0.500	0.105

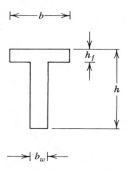

Table A.9   Section Properties of T Beams

b_w/b	h_f/h	A_c	I_c	c_1	c_2	r^2
0.1	0.1	$0.190bh$	$0.0179bh^3$	$0.286h$	$0.714h$	$0.0945h^2$
0.1	0.2	0.280	0.0192	0.244	0.756	0.0688
0.1	0.3	0.370	0.0193	0.245	0.755	0.0520
0.2	0.1	0.280	0.0283	0.371	0.629	0.1010
0.2	0.2	0.360	0.0315	0.322	0.678	0.0875
0.2	0.3	0.440	0.0319	0.309	0.691	0.0725
0.3	0.1	0.370	0.0365	0.415	0.585	0.0985
0.3	0.2	0.440	0.0408	0.374	0.626	0.0928
0.3	0.3	0.510	0.0417	0.355	0.645	0.0819
0.4	0.1	0.460	0.0440	0.441	0.559	0.0954
0.4	0.2	0.520	0.0486	0.408	0.592	0.0935
0.4	0.3	0.580	0.0499	0.391	0.609	0.0860

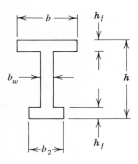

Table A.10　Section Properties of Unsymmetrical I Beams

$b_2/b = 0.30$

b_w/b	h_f/h	A_c	I_c	c_1	c_2	r^2
0.1	0.1	$0.210bh$	$0.0260bh^3$	$0.350h$	$0.650h$	$0.1236h^2$
0.1	0.2	0.320	0.0345	0.325	0.675	0.1080
0.1	0.3	0.430	0.0387	0.328	0.672	0.0900
0.2	0.1	0.290	0.0316	0.390	0.610	0.1090
0.2	0.2	0.380	0.0378	0.353	0.647	0.0994
0.2	0.3	0.470	0.0402	0.345	0.655	0.0856

$b_2/b = 0.50$

b_w/b	h_f/h	A_c	I_c	c_1	c_2	r^2
0.1	0.1	$0.230bh$	$0.0326bh^3$	$0.403h$	$0.597h$	$0.1420h^2$
0.1	0.2	0.360	0.0464	0.389	0.611	0.1288
0.1	0.3	0.490	0.0535	0.394	0.606	0.1090
0.2	0.1	0.310	0.0373	0.428	0.572	0.1204
0.2	0.2	0.420	0.0488	0.405	0.595	0.1160
0.2	0.3	0.530	0.0540	0.401	0.599	0.1020
0.3	0.1	0.390	0.0430	0.443	0.557	0.1103
0.3	0.2	0.480	0.0510	0.418	0.582	0.1065
0.3	0.3	0.570	0.0553	0.408	0.592	0.0970

$b_2/b = 0.70$

b_w/b	h_f/h	A_c	I_c	c_1	c_2	r^2
0.1	0.1	$0.250bh$	$0.0381bh^3$	$0.446h$	$0.554h$	$0.1525h^2$
0.1	0.2	0.400	0.0560	0.440	0.560	0.1391
0.1	0.3	0.550	0.0651	0.443	0.557	0.1182
0.2	0.1	0.330	0.0425	0.460	0.540	0.1290
0.2	0.2	0.460	0.0578	0.448	0.552	0.1258
0.2	0.3	0.590	0.0657	0.447	0.553	0.1113
0.3	0.1	0.410	0.0467	0.466	0.534	0.1140
0.3	0.2	0.520	0.0598	0.454	0.546	0.1150
0.3	0.3	0.630	0.0663	0.450	0.550	0.1051

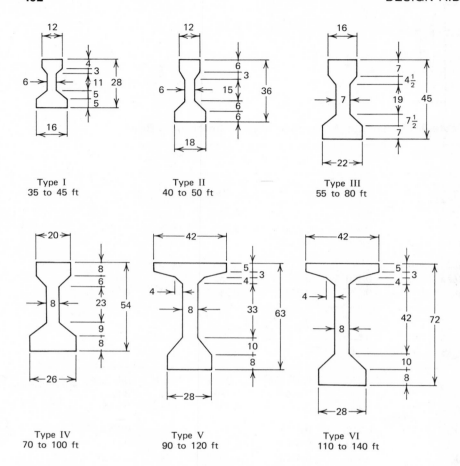

Table A.11 Section Properties of AASHTO Bridge Girders

Type	h in.	A_c in.^{2}	I_c in.^{4}	c_1 in.	c_2 in.	r^2 in.^{2}	w_0 plf
I	28	276	22,750	15.41	12.59	82	288
II	36	369	50,979	20.17	15.83	138	384
III	45	560	125,390	24.73	20.27	224	583
IV	54	789	260,741	29.27	24.73	330	822
V	63	1013	521,180	31.04	31.96	514	1055
VI	72	1085	733,320	35.62	36.38	676	1130

POST-TENSIONING HARDWARE

Inryco CONA Single-Strand Post Tensioning System

Inland-Ryerson single strand tendons use the Cona wedge anchor system developed by the designers of the BBRV system. Tendons employ cold drawn, stress relieved, seven-wire strands of 0.5" or 0.6" diameter, conforming to ASTM A-416.

Cona Single strand tendons are normally used in un-bonded construction, but may be used as bonded tendons where specifications require. The small diameter strand bundle is particularly suited for use in thin, one-way slabs, two-way flat plates and flat slabs and topping slabs.

Differentiae of the Cona single-strand system are:

- Very small tendon diameter allows optimum eccentricities, hence efficient use of P-T steel.
- Small anchor plate meets edge-size restrictions of thin slabs and light structural shapes. (0.5" Anchors require only 3½" concrete thickness; 0.6" Anchor require 4¼" concrete thickness.)
- Oversize anchor plates are available to accommodate stressing at low concrete strengths.
- Like all wedge-grip, strand systems, anchorage develops slightly less than ultimate capacity of the tendon, but two-piece wedge design reduces seating losses to a minimum.

- Design of anchor components and stressing equipment allows accurate overstress and back-off to lock-off force without premature, uncontrolled seating of wedges.
- Coupling is never necessary. There are essentially no length restrictions, and tension can be applied separately to successive sections of total length by stressing at any intermediate point, and then continuing the same strand.
- No large pockets to form and patch. Re-usable pocket-former comes with anchor hardware; attaches to formwork for quick positioning of anchor, and creates small, clean, stressing void that's, easily patched.
- Tendons are "built" at the job site from pre-assembled anchor components and wrapped lengths of strand. (Excess can be burned off.) So special accuracy in cutting to length and fabricating is not required.
- Stressing equipment is small and light — easily handled by one man.

Exploded view of Cona Single Strand stressing anchor, Type CM, from left to right: plastic nut, plastic pocket former (reusable), steel wedge, anchor casting, plastic connector and seven-wire strand. Plastic pocket former may be replaced by gasket for intermediate stressing anchor, Type IM.

Exploded view of Cona Single Strand anchor, Type EM, from left to right: plastic cap, steel wedges, anchor casting, plastic connector and button-headed seven-wire strand.

CONA SINGLE
STRAND ANCHOR

**Type CM
(stressing)**

Anchor Designation		0.5 CM	0.6 CM
Base Plate Size (inches)	(A)	4½ x 2¼	5⅜ x 2¾
	(B)	6¼ x 2¼	7⅛ x 2¾
Pocket Former O.D. (inches)		2¼	2¾
Pocket Former Length (inches)		1⅜	1⅝
Bundle O.D. (inches)		0.5	0.6

The fixed Cona anchors, Types EM and EG, are identical in basic design and size to the stressing anchors. The end of the strand is button-headed. Wedges are hydraulically power seated, providing a positive non-slip, fixed-end anchorage.

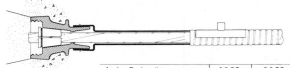

**Type CG
(stressing)**

Anchor Designation		0.5 CG	0.6 CG
Base Plate Size (inches)	(A)	4½ x 2¼	5⅜ x 2¾
	(B)	6¼ x 2¼	7⅛ x 2¾
Pocket Former O.D. (inches)		2¼	2¾
Pocket Former Length (inches)		1⅜	1⅝
Conduit O.D. (inches)		1	1⅛

Also available on special order is Type LM anchorage for special applications or repair work. It consists of a wedge grip contained within a short steel collar, backed by a steel bearing plate.

Bearing plate "A" is designed to accommodate stressing at a concrete compressive strength of 2,500 to 3,000 psi, depending on the geometry of the concrete and tendon spacing. Bearing plate "B" designed to accommodate stressing at concrete strength of 1,500 to 2,000 psi, depending on geometry of concrete and tendon spacing.

TYPICAL CONA SINGLE STRAND
TENDON INSTALLATION

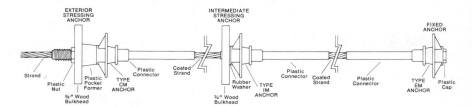

Inryco CONA Multi-Strand Post Tensioning System

The Cona Multi-Strand anchor system was developed by the Swiss engineers who created the BBRV wire system (pp. 16-20) and introduced to the U.S. market by Inland-Ryerson in 1970. It is most applicable to heavy beams or to structures requiring large-capacity tendons — cases where a structure's irregularity dictates the use of post-tensioning tendons of varying size and length, or where accurate determination of length is not possible.

The system is made up of multiple units of seven-wire strands, each 0.5″ or 0.6″ in diameter. Steel wedges anchor each strand and all strands of a given tendon are stressed simultaneously.

An important feature of the system is the capability to hydraulically power-seat all wedges of the stressing anchor (WG) to assume a uniform initial force and to control seating loss.

Cona Multi-Strand tendons are usually grouted and are especially suited for the pass-through method of tendon installation. In this procedure, only empty rigid ducts are placed in forms prior to concreting. Site-fabricated tendons are pulled through the ducts, and are stressed and grouted in one continuous operation. Tendons can also be shop-fabricated.

Anchorages using 0.5″ dia. strands are available in 7, 12, 19, 31 and 55 strand units. Tendons using 0.6″ dia. strands, are available in 4, 7, 12, 19 and 31 strand units.

Type WG stressing anchor.

CONA MULTI-STRAND ANCHORS

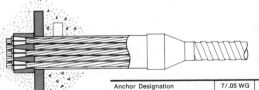

Type WG (stressing)

Anchor Designation	7/.05 WG	12/0.5 WG	19/0.5 WG	31/0.5 WG	55/0.5 WG
No. of 0.5″ Strands (max.)	7	12	19	31	55
Anchor Designation	4/0.6 WG	7/0.6 WG	12/0.6 WG	19/0.6 WG	31/0.6 WG
No. of 0.6″ Strands (max.)	4	7	12	19	31
Bearing Plate Size (inches)	8½ x 8½	11 x 11	14 x 14	17½ x 17½	24 x 24
Trumpet O.D. (inches)	3¼	4½	5¾	7½	10
Trumpet Length (inches)	8	16	20	26	36
Conduit O.D. (inches) — Pull-through	2⅜	2¾	3⅜	4⅜	5¾
Conduit O.D. (inches) — Assembled	2	2⅜	3	3¾	5¼

Type WG used as fixed anchorage for pull through tendon installations. Wedges are pressed into anchorhead by special retaining plate.

Type FG (fixed)

Anchor Designation		7/0.5 FG	12/0.5 FG	19/0.5 FG	31/0.5 FG	55/0.5 FG
No. of 0.5″ Strands (max.)		7	12	19	31	55
Anchor Designation		4/0.6 FG	7/0.6 FG	12/0.6 FG	19/0.6 FG	31/0.6 FG
No. of 0.6″ Strands (max.)		4	7	12	19	31
Bearing Plate Size (inches)	(A)	8 x 8	10½ x 10½	13½ x 13½	17 x 17	22½ x 22½
	(B)	4¾ x 14¼	6¼ x 18¾	8 x 24	9⅞ x 29½	13 x 39

Type FG anchorage used for fixed anchorage where tendon is plant fabricated and is cast in concrete. Strand ends are buttonheaded.

BBRV
tendons and anchors

BBRV post tensioning was developed in 1949 by four Swiss engineers, Birkenmeier, Brandestini, Ros and Vogt, whose initials give the system its name. Use of the BBRV system has spread rapidly throughout the free world, and in the United States it is now probably the most widely used method of post tensioning.

A BBRV tendon consists of several (or many) parallel lengths of ¼" high-strength wire with each end of each wire terminating in a cold-formed buttonhead, after the wire passes separately through a machined anchorage fixture. The system provides for the simultaneous stressing of all the wires in a tendon and the buttonheads allow development of ultimate tendon forces.

Tendons are produced for either bonded or unbonded installation. They can be furnished in practically any length and in a range of sizes and force capacities from 8 to 52 wires for building construction. For heavy construction, such as nuclear containment vessels, tendons with 90-170 wires are commonly used. Engineering data for such sizes is available on request.

In the bonded or grout-type tendons, the wires are encased in flexible metal conduit. The unbonded BBRV tendons are generally mastic-coated and wrapped in heavy paper but in certain applications conduit-encased tendons are also used ungrouted. In these instances the conduit is filled with grease after the tendon has been installed and stressed.

Type SG
fixed
anchor

Type BG
stressing
anchor

Differentiae of the BBRV system are:

- Button-head terminals for every wire give positive, no-slip anchorage and eliminate seating losses, making it possible to develop the full potential force of every tendon.

- Tendons are precisely engineered and completely shop fabricated which minimizes field labor and allows more exact control of quality and accuracy. This feature may result in a higher *initial* cost-per-lb. of tendon than with other systems, but not necessarily in a higher *installed* cost. And often the highest initial cost may yield the *lowest cost-per-lb. of force delivered.*

- Tendons may be fabricated in long lengths when desirable (we have supplied them over 400 ft. long).

- Long tendons present no problems in fabrication or in shipping since they are furnished coiled on "lazy susan" racks 6 ft. in diameter. This method of shipment also reduces job-site storage requirements, makes on-the-job handling of any length tendon easy and minimizes exposure to transit damage.

- Coupling of BBRV tendons is easily accomplished, with no loss of forces.

- Curved or draped positioning of tendons within a structural member, often desirable from a design standpoint, is readily achieved because of the small diameter (¼") of the steel elements. For the same reason, however, BBRV tendons positioned vertically require substantial support.

- Developed force can be closely matched to design requirements with no waste of prestress steel because BBRV tendons are available in a wide range of size-force units — with each single-wire increment adding 7 kips of force.

- BBRV can provide much the greatest force from single tendons because of multi-wire, high-strength steel construction. But take into account the fact that large-capacity tendons require large, less-easily-handled field equipment. Also remember that this type of tendon and anchor requires relatively large blockouts.

The BBRV anchorages illustrated here are the standard types. But special types can be developed to meet unusual requirements and any anchorage can be produced with any number of wires (up to the hardware's maximum capacity) needed to produce a specified prestressing force.

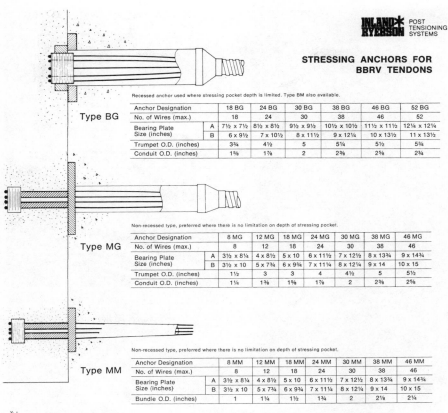

INLAND RYERSON POST TENSIONING SYSTEMS

STRESSING ANCHORS FOR BBRV TENDONS

Recessed anchor used where stressing pocket depth is limited. Type BM also available.

Type BG

Anchor Designation		18 BG	24 BG	30 BG	38 BG	46 BG	52 BG
No. of Wires (max.)		18	24	30	38	46	52
Bearing Plate Size (inches)	A	7½ x 7½	8½ x 8½	9½ x 9½	10½ x 10½	11½ x 11½	12¼ x 12¼
	B	6 x 9½	7 x 10½	8 x 11½	9 x 12¼	10 x 13½	11 x 13½
Trumpet O.D. (inches)		3¾	4½	5	5¼	5½	5¾
Conduit O.D. (inches)		1⅝	1⅞	2	2⅜	2⅝	2¾

Non-recessed type, preferred where there is no limitation on depth of stressing pocket.

Type MG

Anchor Designation		8 MG	12 MG	18 MG	24 MG	30 MG	38 MG	46 MG
No. of Wires (max.)		8	12	18	24	30	38	46
Bearing Plate Size (inches)	A	3½ x 8¼	4 x 8½	5 x 10	6 x 11½	7 x 12½	8 x 13¾	9 x 14¾
	B	3½ x 10	5 x 7¾	6 x 9¾	7 x 11¼	8 x 12¼	9 x 14	10 x 15
Trumpet O.D. (inches)		1½	3	3	4	4½	5	5½
Conduit O.D. (inches)		1¼	1⅜	1⅝	1⅞	2	2⅜	2⅝

Non-recessed type, preferred where there is no limitation on depth of stressing pocket.

Type MM

Anchor Designation		8 MM	12 MM	18 MM	24 MM	30 MM	38 MM	46 MM
No. of Wires (max.)		8	12	18	24	30	38	46
Bearing Plate Size (inches)	A	3½ x 8¼	4 x 8½	5 x 10	6 x 11½	7 x 12½	8 x 13¾	9 x 14¾
	B	3½ x 10	5 x 7¾	6 x 9¾	7 x 11¼	8 x 12¼	9 x 14	10 x 15
Bundle O.D. (inches)		1	1¼	1½	1¾	2	2⅛	2¼

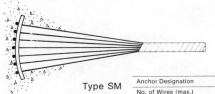

FIXED ANCHORS FOR BBRV TENDONS

Type SM

Anchor Designation	8 SM	12 SM	18 SM	24 SM	30 SM	38 SM	46 SM	52 SM
No. of Wires (max.)	8	12	18	24	30	38	46	52
Bearing Plate Size (inches)	3½ x 8	5 x 8	5 x 10	6 x 11½	7 x 12½	8 x 13¾	9 x 15	10 x 15

Engineering data on BBRV tendon systems for heavy construction, with 170 wire capacity, available on request.

Type SG anchor for grouted installations is similar to Type SM.

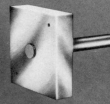

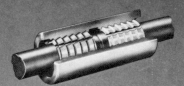

STRESSTEEL BARS

STRESSTEEL Bars are available in diameters from ¾" to 1⅜", in increments of ⅛".* Bars can be ordered in any length to 100'. Lengths greater than 100' are obtained by use of couplers.

These bars are manufactured from specially selected hot rolled alloy steels. Each bar is cold stretched, which uniformly cold works the cross section and develops high yield strength. The bar is then stress relieved in a gas fired furnace, insuring ductility and uniform stress-strain characteristics. This carefully controlled process provides high strength bars ideal for prestressing.

* Smaller and larger bars are available on special order. Ultimate strengths and physical properties of these bars vary from those indicated. Inquire for specific information.

The cold stretching process, in addition, proof stresses each bar to 100% of its minimum guaranteed yield stress. Proof stressing eliminates all bars with surface imperfections or metallurgical defects detrimental to the strength of the steel. It guarantees that every bar possesses the necessary properties to perform as required.

STRESSTEEL Bars are manufactured in two grades: REGULAR STRESSTEEL with a guaranteed minimum ultimate strength of 145,000 psi, and SPECIAL STRESSTEEL with a guaranteed minimum ultimate strength of 160,000 psi.

DESIGN PROPERTIES OF STRESSTEEL BARS

Nominal Bar Size Ø"	Nominal Weight Pounds Lin/Ft.	Nominal Area Square Inches	Ultimate Strength Guaranteed Minimum		Recommended Initial Tensioning Load—0.7 f's†		Maximum Recommended Final Design Load—0.6 f's†	
			REGULAR 145 ksi	SPECIAL 160 ksi	REGULAR 101.5 ksi	SPECIAL 112 ksi	REGULAR 87 ksi	SPECIAL 96 ksi
			(All units in values of 1000 pounds)					
¾	1.50	.442	64	71	45	50	39	42
⅞	2.04	.601	87	96	61	67	52	58
1	2.67	.785	114	126	80	88	68	75
1⅛	3.38	.994	144	159	101	111	87	95
1¼	4.17	1.227	178	196	125	137	107	118
1⅜	5.05	1.485	215	238	151	166	129	143

† Design properties indicated are in accordance with ACI Building Code 318-63, Sections 2606 and 2607. Temporary jacking stresses up to 0.8f's are permitted to overcome losses due to tendon friction, anchorage seating and elastic shortening. Losses due to creep, shrinking and steel relaxation should be deducted from the recommended initial tensioning load to obtain actual final design load. Actual final design load, after losses are accounted for, may be less than 0.6f's.

BAR ANCHORAGE DETAILING INFORMATION

Wedges and Nuts

WEDGE W—

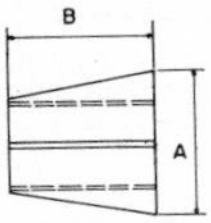

NUT N—

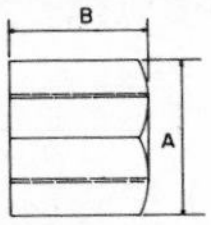

GRIP NUT G—

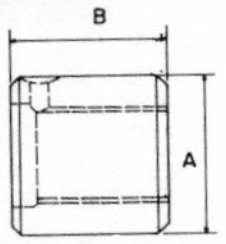

BAR Ø"	WEDGES Part No.	A	B	Wt. # Ea.	NUTS* Part. No.	A	B	Wt. # Ea.	GRIP NUTS Part. No.	A	B	Wt. # Ea.
¾	W6	1⅜	1¼	.2	N6	1⅜	1¼	.5	G6	1⅞	1¾	1.0
⅞	W7	1¾	1½	.3	N7	1⅝	1 7/16	.7	G7	2 1/16	2	1.5
1	W8	1¾	1½	.5	N8	1⅞	1⅝	1.0	G8	2¼	2¼	2.5
1⅛	W9	2	1¾	.7	N9	2⅛	1 13/16	1.5	G9	2½	2½	2.7
1¼	W10	2¼	2	.8	N10	2¼	2	2.0	G10	2¾	2⅝	3.2
1⅜	W11	2⅜	2 3/16	1.1	N11	2⅜	2	2.0	G11	3	2⅞	4.2

All data subject to revision as new developments are made.

* 3/16" washer shipped with each nut.

All dimensions in inches

Couplers

THREADED COUPLERS TC—

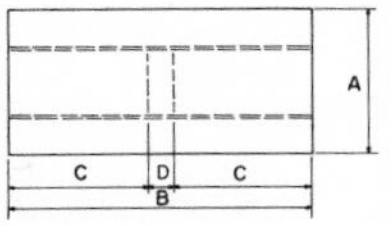

GRIP COUPLERS GC—

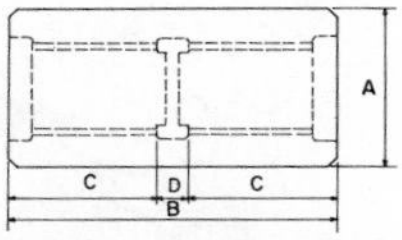

BAR Ø"	Part No.	THREADED COUPLERS A	B	C	D	I.D." Coupler Shield	Wt. # Ea.	Part No.	GRIP COUPLERS A	B	C	D	I.D." Coupler Shield	Wt. # Ea.
¾	TC6	1¼	3	1⅜	¼	1½	1.1	GC6	1⅞	3⅜	1 7/16	⅜	2¼	2.0
⅞	TC7	1½	3½	1⅝	¼	2	1.8	GC7	2⅛	3⅞	1¾	⅜	2¼	3.0
1	TC8	1¾	3¾	1¾	¼	2	1.9	GC8	2¼	4¼	1 15/16	⅜	2¾	3.5
1⅛	TC9	2	4¼	1⅞	½	2½	2.5	GC9	2½	4⅝	2⅛	⅜	3	4.9
1¼	TC10	2¼	4¾	2⅛	½	2½	3.7	GC10	2¾	5⅛	2⅜	⅜	3	6.2
1⅜	TC11	2¼	5	2¼	½	2½	3.5	GC11	3	5⅝	2⅝	⅜	3½	8.1

All data subject to revision as new developments are made.

All dimensions in inches

Bar Anchorage Detailing Information (cont'd)

Plates

CAST-IN-PLACE PLATE

DRY PLACED PLATE

BAR Ø"	Part No. WP.-TP. or P.*	No. of Holes	DIMENSIONS IN INCHES						Wt. Lbs. Ea.
			A	B	C	D	E	T	
¾	6	1	4	4	2	—	2	1	4.5
⅞	7	1	5	4½	2½	—	2¼	1½	9.5
1	8	1	5½	5	2¾	—	2½	1½	11.9
1⅛	9	1	6	6	3	—	3	1¾	17.8
1¼	10	1	7	6	3½	—	3	1¾	20.8
1⅜	11	1	7½	7	3¾	—	3½	2	29.7
2 @ 1	8-2	2	11	5	3	5	2½	1½	23.4
2 @ 1⅛	9-2	2	11½	6	3¼	5	3	1¾	32.2
2 @ 1¼	10-2	2	12	7	3½	5	3½	1¾	41.6
2 @ 1⅜	11-2	2	14½	7	4¼	6	3½	2	57.5

* Precede part number by using appropriate letter designation: WP = Wedge Plate; TP = Threaded Plate; EP = Plate with Drilled Hole; Hole ¼" larger than bar Ø.

NOTES:
1. Standard Plate sizes shown, when used with regular grade bars, conform to allowable bearing stresses of ACI Building Code 318-63, Section 2605, assuming that f'c = 5000 psi and Ab'/Ab = 1.0. For lower strength concrete a larger bearing area should be provided. For higher strength concrete, or where Ab'/Ab exceeds 1.0, smaller plates may be used. Consult our Engineering Department for recommendations on plate design.

2. Standard Plates are fabricated from AISI C-1040 Steel.

3. Plates to anchor a larger number of bars, plates to anchor bars of different diameters, or plates of non-rectangular shape may be designed to meet the specific needs of the engineer.

JACKS

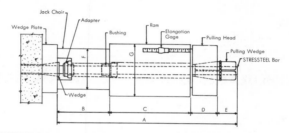

TYPE	DIMENSIONS IN INCHES							Wt. of Heaviest Part (lbs.)
	*A	B	C	D Closed	E	F	G	
30 Ton — 6" Travel	21½	6¼	9¾	3¼	2¼	5	6½	36
60 Ton — 3" Travel	21⅜	6¼	9⅝	3¼	2¼	5	6½	63
60 Ton — 10" Travel	30¼	6¼	18½	3¼	2¼	5	6½	120
100 Ton — 3" Travel	23½	6¼	10½	3¾	2¾	5**	7½	95
100 Ton — 6" Travel	25¼	6¼	12¼	3¾	2¾	5**	7½	114
100 Ton — 10" Travel	29½	6¼	16½	3¾	2¾	5**	7½	145

* Minimum Bar Length Necessary for Jacking, outside of plate.
** 6½" for 1⅜" Ø bars.
NOTE 1. Special adaptations can be made to fit unusual applications. Consult Sales Department for special design jacking components.
NOTE 2. Bushings are provided to center pulling head and rams. 6" and 10" Travel Rams have hydraulic return; 3" Travel Rams have spring return.

General Arrangement of Hydraulic Components

6" Travel, 100-ton STRESSTEEL Hydraulic Jacking Unit with electric pump. Note jack chair and wedge seating ram with connection to hand operated hydraulic pump.

Processing methods, anchorages and coupling devices described in this manual are protected by U.S. Patents and Patent Applications.

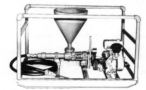

Grouting

Grouting is done through previously formed openings. The grout mix should be specified by the engineer and grouting performed at his direction. For grout mix and method recommendations see PCI Recommended Practice on Grouting.

Standard STRESSTEEL Grout Pump with gas or electric motor will develop 150 psi grout pressure.

The Westrand Mono-System

Tendons and Anchors

Mono-System tendons use ½″ diameter seven-wire strand in single or multiple groups. The strand is stress relieved and conforms to ASTM A-416. Features of the Mono-System are:

- Rectangular anchor plate provides flexibility to meet the restrictions of thin slabs or narrow beams.

- Fixed end anchorages are attached and pre-set at factory to reduce field labor and prevent strand slippage at the fixed end.

- Coupling is never necessary since tension can be applied separately to successive sections of total length by stressing at any intermediate point, and then continuing the same strand.

- No large pockets to form and patch. Re-usable pocket former comes with anchor. The entire assembly attaches to form work and when removed after concreting, leaves a small, clean stressing pocket that is easily patched.

- Stressing equipment is small and light-weight, easily handled by one man. Operation is semi-automatic and fast.

The advantages of the Westrand Mono-System of post-tensioning place the flexibility of prestressing within the scope of any project. With this flexibility long spans, cantilevers and heavy loading are no longer a problem.

Design Data

Strand Area	.153	in²
Maximum Jacking Force 0.80 f's	33.0	Kips
Maximum Anchoring Force 0.70 f's	28.9	Kips
Maximum Effective Force 0.60 f's	24.8	Kips
Anchor Castings are 2¼″ x 5″		

Short Form Specification

1.0 Material

1.1 Strand used in post-tensioning shall conform to ASTM A416 (Specification for uncoated seven-wire stress relieved strand for prestressed concrete.)

1.2 Strand anchorages shall develop at least 95% of the minimum specified ulimate strength of the prestressing steel without exceeding anticipated set.

1.3 Sheathing shall have sufficient strength to resist damage during transport, storage at jobsite, and during installation. It shall prevent the intrusion of cement paste and the escape of coating material.

2.0 Placing

2.1 Anchorage assemblies shall be securely fastened to the edge forms and shall be perpendicular to the longitudinal axis of the tendon.

2.2 Post-Tensioning tendons shall be secured at regular intervals to prevent vertical or lateral movement during the placement of the concrete.

3.0 Stressing

3.1 Post-Tensioning shall not be started until the concrete has attained a minimum strength of 3,000 psi.

3.2 The strand may be temporarily stressed up to 80% of f's to overcome friction.

3.3 The anchor force shall not exceed 70% of f's.

3.4 The effective force shall be assumed to be 60% of f's assuming losses of 10%, unless there is data to prove otherwise.

Stressing Equipment

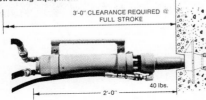

3′-0″ CLEARANCE REQUIRED @ FULL STROKE

40 lbs.

2′-0″

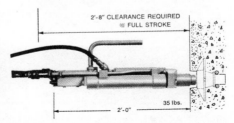

2′-8″ CLEARANCE REQUIRED @ FULL STROKE

35 lbs.

2′-0″

ELECTRICAL POWER REQUIREMENTS
60 Hertz
110 Volts
20 Amps per jack

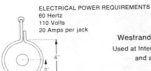

Westrand Center Hole Jack
Used at Stressing End

4″

2″

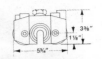

Westrand Open-Throat Jack
Used at Intermediate Stressing End
and at Stressing End

3⅜″

1⅛″

5¾″

Mono-System Installation

1. All Westrand Mono-System tendons are fabricated and coiled in multiples whenever possible to facilitate field placement; by this method up to 4 tendons are placed in a single operation.

2. Intermediate and fixed end anchors are attached to the tendon in the factory so that only the required portion of a particular tendon need be uncoiled for each pour.

3. The stressing anchor is attached to the edge form by means of a pocket former, spindle and hex nut. The anchor is now ready to receive the stressing end of the tendon which is easily pushed through the entire assembly.

4. Once the concrete sets, the hex nuts, spindles, edge form and pocket formers are removed. Upon reaching the required strength, generally about 5 days, stressing proceeds.

5. The stressing ram is placed over the tendon and set against the anchor. The tendon is then gripped and pulled to the specified elongation and force. As the hydraulic pressure is released the ram automatically seats the wedges and then retracts. The stressing time is approximately 30 seconds per tendon.

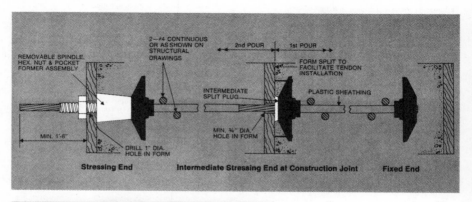

Stressing End   **Intermediate Stressing End at Construction Joint**   **Fixed End**

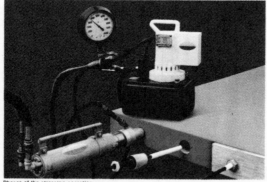

Phases of the stressing operation

The Westrand Multi-System

The Westrand Multi-System provides post-tensioning for a wide range of force requirements from the 99K four strand system to the 1189K forty eight strand system. This system, commonly used with grouted tendons, has many applications.

- Cast-in-place and precast, continuous, long span bridges.
- Transverse deck post-tensioning in cast-in-place or precast bridge construction
- Beams or girders in commercial structures where grouted tendons are advantageous or desirable.
- Tanks or containment structures as either circumferential or vertical tendons.
- Tension rings used to support domes or arches of any type of construction.

Anchorage Assembly		**4s**	**12s**	**16s**	**20s**	**24s**	**28s**	**48s**
Number of ½″ Dia. 270ᵏ Strands		4	12	16	20	24	28	48
Strand Area (Based on 0.153 in²)		.612	1.836	2.448	3.060	3.672	4.284	7.344
Maximum Jacking Force 0.80 f's	(Kips)	132	396	529	661	793	925	1586
Maximum Anchoring Force 0.70 f's	(Kips)	116	347	463	578	694	810	1388
Maximum Effective Force 0.60 f's	(Kips)	99	297	396	496	595	694	1189
Rigid Duct Diameter	O.D. (In)	1¾	2⅝	3	3 9/16	3 9/16	3 15/16	5 1/16
Square Bearing Plate	A (In)	6¾	10⅞	13	14¼	15¼	16⅜	21¾
Square Wedge Plate	B (In)	3¾	6	8	8	8	8	13
Wedge Plate Thickness	C (In)	1¾	2¾	3	4	4	4	5
Bearing Plate Thickness	D (In)	1	1½	1¾	2	2½	2¾	3
Transition Length	E (In)	12	22	35	35	35	31	54
Maximum Transition Diameter	F (In)	2¾	4⅜	6¾	6¾	6¾	6¾	9¾
Stressing Clearance	G (Ft)	3′-0″	8′-0″	8′-0″	8′-0″	8′-0″	8′-0″	8′-0″
Stressing Clearance	H (In)	4	12	12	12	12	12	16
Stressing Equipment		30ᵀ	200ᵀ	500ᵀ	500ᵀ	500ᵀ	500ᵀ	1000ᵀ

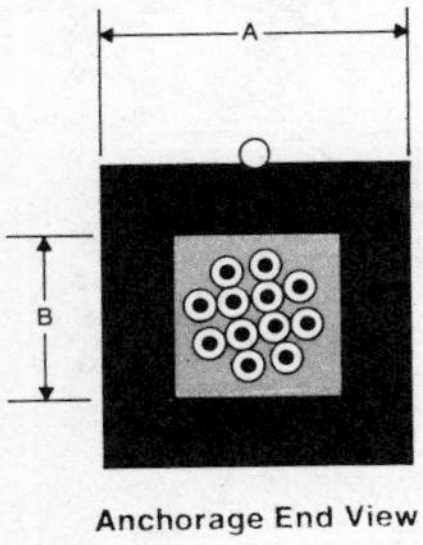

Anchorage End View

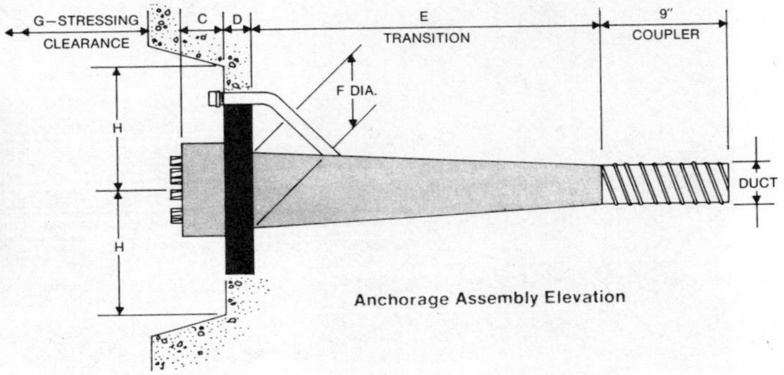

Anchorage Assembly Elevation

VSL POST-TENSIONING For Circular Structures

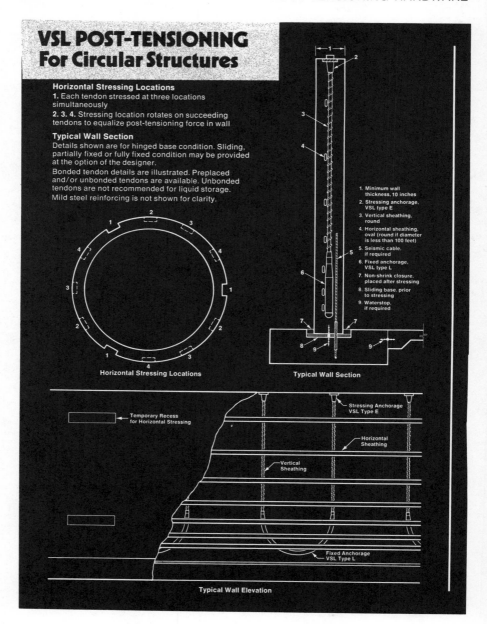

Horizontal Stressing Locations
1. Each tendon stressed at three locations simultaneously
2. 3. 4. Stressing location rotates on succeeding tendons to equalize post-tensioning force in wall

Typical Wall Section
Details shown are for hinged base condition. Sliding, partially fixed or fully fixed condition may be provided at the option of the designer.

Bonded tendon details are illustrated. Preplaced and/or unbonded tendons are available. Unbonded tendons are not recommended for liquid storage.

Mild steel reinforcing is not shown for clarity.

1. Minimum wall thickness, 10 inches
2. Stressing anchorage, VSL type E
3. Vertical sheathing, round
4. Horizontal sheathing, oval (round if diameter is less than 100 feet)
5. Seismic cable, if required
6. Fixed anchorage, VSL type L
7. Non-shrink closure, placed after stressing
8. Sliding base, prior to stressing
9. Waterstop, if required

Horizontal Stressing Locations

Typical Wall Section

Temporary Recess for Horizontal Stressing

Stressing Anchorage VSL Type E

Horizontal Sheathing

Vertical Sheathing

Fixed Anchorage VSL Type L

Typical Wall Elevation

Horizontal Prestressing

Stressing Anchorage VSL Type Z

This anchorage allows seating of grippers in two directions, thus providing a continuous, self-anchored horizontal tendon. To reduce friction loss, normally three anchorages are provided for each 360° tendon. Stressing points for succeeding tendons are rotated to equalize the circumferential force at any vertical section. The VSL Z5 anchorage produces compression in the wall without concentrated bearing. Cost of additional formwork, concrete, and mild steel reinforcing, associated with external pilasters, is eliminated. If pilasters are desired, the VSL E5 anchorage is used.

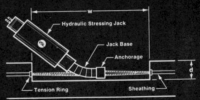
Plan - Temporary Recess

Recess to be filled with non-shrink grout after stressing.

Elevation - Temporary Recess

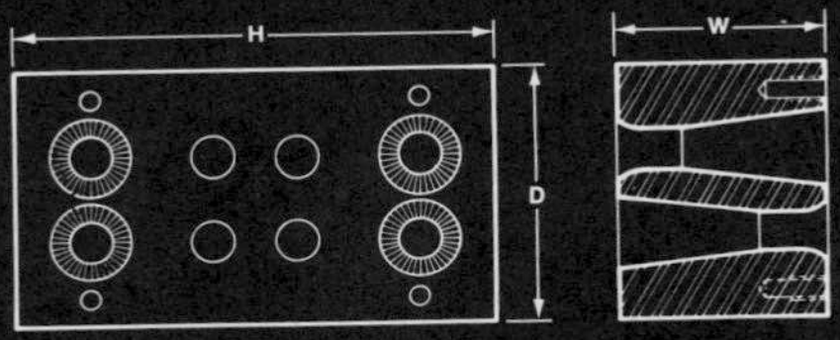

Applicable Dimensions — Inches

Unit	H	D	W	h	d	w
Z5-4	6¼	3½	2⅞	7	5¼	30
Z5-6	7⅞	5¼	3½	8½	6⅞	42
Z5-12	11	5½	5½	12½	7¼	60

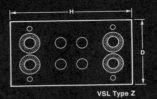

VSL Type Z

Vertical Prestressing

Fixed Anchorage VSL Type L

The advantage of this anchorage is that tendon sheathing can be embedded in concrete prior to the installation of prestressing steel. Prestressing steel can be installed in an "inaccessible" or "dead-end" location using the "pull-through" method. Prestressing force is transferred to the concrete along the pre-flattened intrados of the loop.

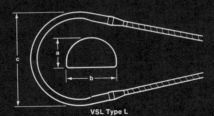
VSL Type L

Stressing Anchorage VSL Type E

The stressing anchorage, a VSL type E, consists of an anchor head, VSL grippers, bearing plate and sleeve. Bearing plates shown are standard and are based on a bearing stress of 3,000 psi at working force. Compressive strength of concrete at the time of initial prestress $f'_{ci} = 3,500$ psi.

Applicable Dimensions — Inches

Unit	a	b	c
L5-3	2½	3	48
L5-4	2½	3	48
L5-7	2½	3	48
E5-3	5¼ x 5¼	3½	4
E5-4	6⅛ x 6⅛	3½	4½
E5-7	8 x 8	3½	8

Other sizes are available.

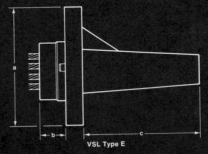
VSL Type E

FREYSSINET
post tensioning

Description

Most Freyssinet strand tendons are composed of twelve strands, but fewer strands — six, eight or nine — are also used. Available strand diameters are limited to ½″ and 0.6″. All Freyssinet strand tendons conform to ASTM A-416, latest edition.

Each Freyssinet strand tendon is coded to indicate the number of strands in the tendon, strand diameter, and steel quality.

Tendon Sizes

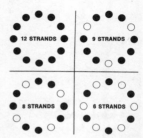

Half-Inch Diameter Tendons

250 KSI Grade	270 KSI Grade
6/500 = 6 strands	6/500K = 6 strands
8/500 = 8 strands	8/500K = 8 strands
9/500 = 9 strands	9/500K = 9 strands
12/500 = 12 strands	12/500K = 12 strands

0.6-Inch Diameter Tendons

6/600 = 6 strands	6/600K = 6 strands
8/600 = 8 strands	8/600K = 8 strands
9/600 = 9 strands	9/600K = 9 strands
12/600 = 12 strands	12/600K = 12 strands

The largest ultimate capacity tendons currently available are 12/500K (495.6 kips) and 12/600K (703.2 kips).

Tensioning

A variety of techniques are available to meet all possible site needs. The Freyssinet system accommodates almost any construction technique and provides safe and effective recovery procedures from unexpected site conditions.

The load in the tendon is easily controllable to any required level by relaxing, partial tensioning, retensioning, or detensioning. Freyssinet tendons may be tensioned to 80% of the guaranteed steel strength to overcome friction.

Recovering anchorage set. If the anchorage set affects the final required prestressing force, the set may be adjusted with a jacking chair and shims. External anchorages with bearing plates are used to do this (see illustrations).

Detensioning. Freyssinet strand tendons may be detensioned at any stage either to remove entirely the prestressing force in the tendon or to reduce the force to meet some special need of the project.

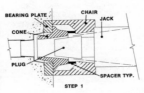

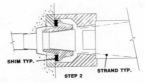

Upswept tendons. Tendons may be anchored in the top surface of a member. The minimum angle of rise, 25°, and the recess dimensioned at the right is for internal half-inch strand anchorages. However, all Freyssinet anchorages may be used in this manner.

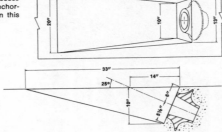

Cast-in-Place anchorages. Anchorages that have been cast into a structure and are completely inaccessible thereafter are called "Dead End Anchorages." The illustration to the right shows a typical standard detail for a Dead End Anchorage.

The Freyssinet engineering staff should be consulted when any special situation is encountered.

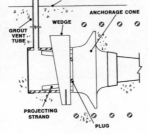

4

Table A—Tendon Characteristics

STRAND SIZE	½" DIAMETER				0.6" DIAMETER			
Ultimate Strength of One Strand	41,300 lbs.				58,600 lbs.			
Nominal Steel Area of One Strand	0.1531 in².				0.217 in².			
Number of Strands in Tendon	6	8	9	12	6	8	9	12
Nominal Steel Area (In²)	0.92	1.22	1.38	1.84	1.30	1.74	1.95	2.60
Ultimate Tendon Strength (Kips)	247.8	330.4	371.7	495.6	351.6	468.8	527.4	703.2
Maximum Jacking Force — 80% f'ₛ (Kips)	198.2	264.3	297.4	396.5	281.3	375.0	421.9	562.6
Maximum Force After Anchoring — 70% f'ₛ (Kips)	173.5	231.3	260.2	346.9	246.1	328.2	369.2	492.2
Maximum Effective Force — 60% f'ₛ (Kips)	148.7	198.2	223.0	297.4	211.0	281.3	316.4	421.9
Tendon Weight — Without Sheath (lbs/ft)	3.15	4.20	4.73	6.30	4.38	5.84	6.57	8.76
Sheath Diameter — I.D. (In)	1⅞	2¼	2¼	2⅝	2¼	2⅝	2⅝	3
A (IN)	9	9½	10	10	10	10	10	12
B (IN)	9	10½	11	13½	10	13	14½	15
C (IN)	1	1¼	1¼	1½	1¼	1½	1½	1¾
D (IN)	6½	7	7	8	—	—	—	—
E (IN)	9	9	10	11	—	—	—	—
F (No.)	5	6	6	7	—	—	—	—
G (IN)	2	1¾	1¾	1½	—	—	—	—

Notes

- 250,000 psi quality strand of ½" or 0.6" diameter may be used when required.
- The dimensions A & B have been calculated using A-36 steel or equal and a bearing stress in accordance with current ACI Building Code Specifications.
- The dimensions A & B may be varied to suit concrete strength and end block dimensions providing the minimum plate widths of 9" and 10" for ½" and 0.6" strand tendons, respectively, are maintained.
- Two or more anchorages may be placed on a common bearing plate. Bearing plates may assume special shapes to meet unique site conditions.
- Our engineering staff is available at all times to adapt the Freyssinet system to your particular needs.
- For external anchorage applications, minimum concrete cover shall be two inches.

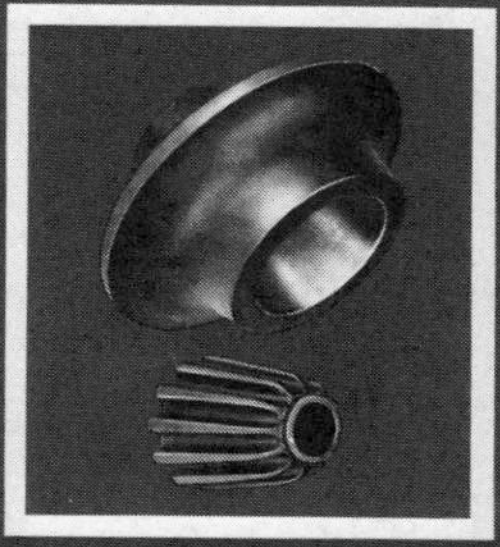

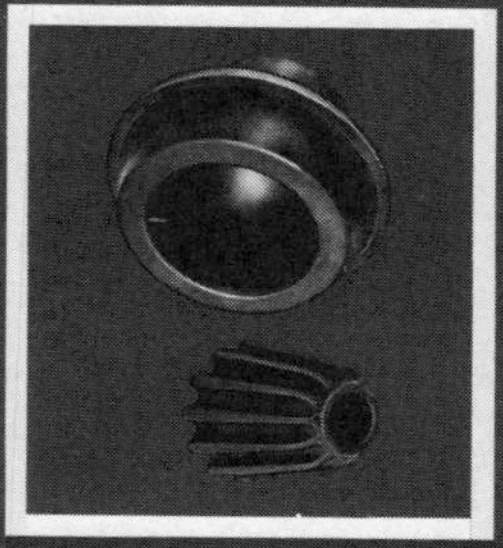

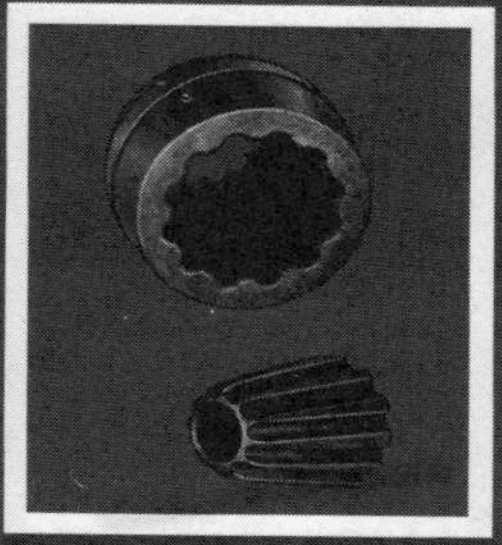

Anchorage Details

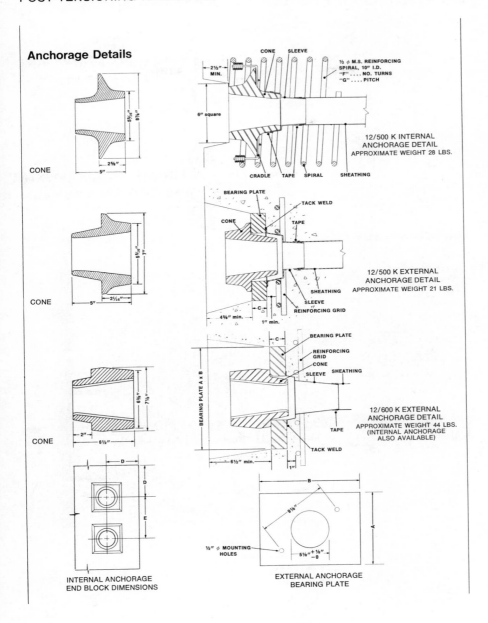

CONE

CONE

CONE

INTERNAL ANCHORAGE
END BLOCK DIMENSIONS

12/500 K INTERNAL
ANCHORAGE DETAIL
APPROXIMATE WEIGHT 28 LBS.

12/500 K EXTERNAL
ANCHORAGE DETAIL
APPROXIMATE WEIGHT 21 LBS.

12/600 K EXTERNAL
ANCHORAGE DETAIL
APPROXIMATE WEIGHT 44 LBS.
(INTERNAL ANCHORAGE
ALSO AVAILABLE)

EXTERNAL ANCHORAGE
BEARING PLATE

DYWIDAG Single-bar tendon

Bell Anchorage

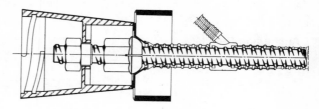

Anchorage with Solid Plate
(square or rectangular)

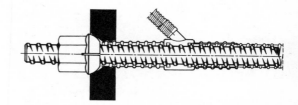

Tendon Characteristics

Nominal Diam.	in.	5/8"	5/8" S	1"	1"	1 1/4"	1 1/4"	1 3/8"
Actual Diam.	mm.	15.0	16.0	26.5	26.5	32.0	32.0	36.0
Ultimate Strength	KSI	157	230	150	160	150	160	150
Area	sq. in.	0.28	0.31	0.85	0.85	1.25	1.25	1.58
Ultimate load f_{pu}	KIP	43.5	70.5	127.5	136.0	187.5	200.0	237.0
0.8 f_{pu}	KIP	34.8	56.5	102.0	108.8	150.0	160.0	189.6
0.7 f_{pu}	KIP	30.5	49.5	89.3	95.2	131.0	140.0	165.9
0.6 f_{pu}	KIP	26.1	42.3	76.5	81.6	112.5	120.0	142.2
Weight	lbs/ft	0.98	1.09	3.01	3.01	4.39	4.39	5.56
Min. elastic bending radius*	ft	26	15	52	49	64	60	72

* For smaller radii bars are cold prebent

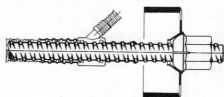

Anchorage Details

Bar Diameter	5/8	5/8 S'	1	1 1/4	1 3/8
Bell Inchor O. D. in	3 1/4 Φ × 1 1/2	4 Φ × 2 1/4	5 1/2 Φ × 2 5/8	6 3/4 Φ × 2 5/8	7 3/4 Φ × 3 1/8
Plate Anchor Solid	3×3×3/4 / 2×5×1	4×4×1 / 3×5×1	5×5 1/2×1 1/4 / 4×6 1/2×1 1/4	6×7×1 1/2 / 5×8×1 1/2	7×7 1/2×1 3/4 / 5×9 1/2×1 3/4
Nut Extension	1	1 5/8	1 7/8	2 1/2	2 3/4
Bar Protrusion	2	3	2 1/2	3	3 1/2

Pocket Former

	5/8	5/8 S'	1	1 1/4	1 3/8
Height in.	4 3/8	4 3/8	7	8	8 5/8
Max. O. D. in	3 1/8	3 1/8	5 1/8	6 1/2	6 1/2

Coupling Details

	5/8	5/8 S'	1	1 1/4	1 3/8
Length in.	3 1/2	5 1/2	5 1/2	6 3/4	8 5/8
Diameter O. D. in.	1 1/8	1 1/4	2	2 3/8	2 5/8

Sheathing

Bar Sheathing O. D.	5/8	5/8 S'	1	1 1/4	1 3/8
in	1	1	1 1/2	1 3/4	2
I. D. in	3/4	3/4	1 1/4	1 1/2	1 3/4
Coupling Sheathing O. C. in	1 3/4	1 3/4	2 3/4	3 1/4	3 3/4
I. D. in.	1 3/8	1 3/8	2 3/8	2 7/8	3 3/8

APPENDIX C

SI CONVERSION FACTORS AND EQUIVALENT SI DESIGN EQUATIONS

CONVERSION FACTORS—U.S. CUSTOMARY UNITS TO S.I. METRIC UNITS

OVERALL GEOMETRY

Spans	1 ft = 0.3048 m
Displacements	1 in. = 25.4 mm
Surface area	1 ft^2 = 0.0929 m^2
Volume	1 ft^3 = 0.0283 m^3
	1 yd^3 = 0.765 m^3

STRUCTURAL PROPERTIES

Cross-sectional dimensions	1 in. = 25.4 mm
Area	1 in.^{2} = 645.2 mm^2
Section modulus	1 in.^{3} = 16.39 × 10^3 mm^3
Moment of inertia	1 in.^{4} = 0.4162 × 10^6 mm^4

MATERIAL PROPERTIES

Density	1 lb/ft^3 = 16.03 kg/m^3
Modulus and stress	1 lb/in.^{2} = 0.006895 N/mm^2
	1 kip/in.^{2} = 6.895 N/mm^2

LOADINGS

Concentrated loads	1 lb = 4.448 N
	1 kip = 4.448 kN
Density	1 lb/ft^3 = 0.1571 kN/m^3
Linear loads	1 kip/ft = 14.59 kN/m
Surface loads	1 lb/ft^2 = 0.0479 kN/m^2
	1 kip/ft^2 = 47.9 kN/m^2

STRESSES AND MOMENTS

Stress	1 lb/in.^{2} = 0.006895 N/mm^2
	1 kip/in.^{2} = 6.895 N/mm^2
Moment or torque	1 ft-lb = 1.356 N-m
	1 ft-kip = 1.356 kN-m

511

S.I. METRIC EQUIVALENTS OF LIMITING VALUES*

UNITS

	U.S. Customary	S.I. Metric
Area	in.^{2}	mm^2
	ft^2	m^2
Density	lb/ft^3	kg/m^3
Load	lb	N
Size	in.	mm
	ft	m
Stress	lb/in.^{2}	MPa $=$ N/mm^2

STRESS

U.S. Customary	S.I. Metric
$\sqrt{f'_c}$	$0.08\sqrt{f'_c}$
$0.5\sqrt{f'_c}$	$0.04\sqrt{f'_c}$
$0.6\sqrt{f'_c}$	$0.05\sqrt{f'_c}$
$2/3\sqrt{f'_c}$	$0.06\sqrt{f'_c}$
$1.1\sqrt{f'_c}$	$0.091\sqrt{f'_c}$
$1.2\sqrt{f'_c}$	$0.10\sqrt{f'_c}$
$1.25\sqrt{f'_c}$	$0.10\sqrt{f'_c}$
$1.5\sqrt{f'_c}$	$0.13\sqrt{f'_c}$
$1.6\sqrt{f'_c}$	$0.13\sqrt{f'_c}$
$1.7\sqrt{f'_c}$	$0.14\sqrt{f'_c}$
$1.9\sqrt{f'_c}$	$0.16\sqrt{f'_c}$
$2.0\sqrt{f'_c}$	$0.17\sqrt{f'_c}$
$2.4\sqrt{f'_c}$	$0.20\sqrt{f'_c}$
$3.0\sqrt{f'_c}$	$0.25\sqrt{f'_c}$
$3.3\sqrt{f'_c}$	$0.27\sqrt{f'_c}$
$3.5\sqrt{f'_c}$	$0.29\sqrt{f'_c}$
$4.0\sqrt{f'_c}$	$0.33\sqrt{f'_c}$
$4.4\sqrt{f'_c}$	$0.37\sqrt{f'_c}$
$5.0\sqrt{f'_c}$	$0.42\sqrt{f'_c}$
$5.5\sqrt{f'_c}$	$0.46\sqrt{f'_c}$
$6.0\sqrt{f'_c}$	$0.50\sqrt{f'_c}$
$6.3\sqrt{f'_c}$	$0.52\sqrt{f'_c}$
$6.5\sqrt{f'_c}$	$0.54\sqrt{f'_c}$
$7.0\sqrt{f'_c}$	$0.58\sqrt{f'_c}$
$7.5\sqrt{f'_c}$	$0.62\sqrt{f'_c}$
$8.0\sqrt{f'_c}$	$0.67\sqrt{f'_c}$
$10.0\sqrt{f'_c}$	$0.83\sqrt{f'_c}$
$12.0\sqrt{f'_c}$	$1.00\sqrt{f'_c}$

* All section numbers and table numbers refer to ACI Code (318–77).

U.S. Customary	S.I. Metric

Sec. 7.12.2 (ACl Code)

$$\frac{0.0018 \times 60,000}{f_y} \qquad\qquad \frac{0.0018 \times 410}{f_y}$$

Sec. 8.5.1

$$w_c^{1.5}33\sqrt{f'_c} \qquad\qquad w_c^{1.5}0.043\sqrt{f'_c}$$
$$57,000\sqrt{f'_c} \qquad\qquad 4,730\sqrt{f'_c}$$

Table 9.5(a) footnotes (a) and (b)

$$(1.65 - 0.005w_c) \geq 1.09 \qquad\qquad (1.65 - 0.0003w_c) \geq 1.09$$

$$0.4 + \frac{f_y}{100,000} \qquad\qquad 0.4 + \frac{f_y}{690}$$

Sec. 10.5.1

$$\frac{200}{f_y} \qquad\qquad \frac{1.38}{f_y}$$

Sec. 10.6.4

175 kips/in.   30.6 MN/m
145 kips/in.   25.4 MN/m

Sec. 11.2.1.1

$$\frac{f_{ct}}{6.7} \leq \sqrt{f'_c} \qquad\qquad \frac{f_{ct}}{6.7} \leq 0.083\sqrt{f'_c}$$

Sec. 11.6.6.2

$$\left(1 + \frac{1}{500}\frac{N_u}{A_q}\right) \qquad\qquad \left(1 + 0.29\frac{N_u}{A_q}\right)$$

Sec. 11.7.4

$$800A_c \qquad\qquad 5.5A_c$$

Sec. 12.2.2

$$\frac{0.04A_b f_y}{\sqrt{f'_c}} \qquad\qquad \frac{0.02A_b f_y}{\sqrt{f'_c}}$$

$$0.0004d_b f_y \qquad\qquad 0.06d_b f_y$$

$$\frac{0.085f_y}{\sqrt{f'_c}} \qquad\qquad \frac{26f_y}{\sqrt{f'_c}}$$

U.S. Customary	*S.I. Metric*

Sec. 12.2.2 (*cont.*)

$$\frac{0.11f_y}{\sqrt{f'_c}} \qquad\qquad\qquad \frac{34f_y}{\sqrt{f'_c}}$$

$$\frac{0.03d_b f_y}{\sqrt{f'_c}} \qquad\qquad\qquad \frac{0.36d_b f_y}{\sqrt{f'_c}}$$

Sec. 12.2.3

$$2 - \frac{60{,}000}{f_y} \qquad\qquad\qquad 2 - \frac{410}{f_y}$$

$$\frac{6.7\sqrt{f'_c}}{f_{ct}} \qquad\qquad\qquad \frac{0.56\sqrt{f'_c}}{f_{ct}}$$

Sec. 12.3.2

$$\frac{0.02f_y d_b}{\sqrt{f'_c}} \qquad\qquad\qquad \frac{0.24f_y d_b}{\sqrt{f'_c}}$$

$$0.0003f_y d_b \qquad\qquad\qquad 0.04f_y d_b$$

Table 12.5.1 — ξ values

$f_h = \xi\sqrt{f'_c}$	$f_h = \xi\sqrt{f'_c}$
220	18
330	28
360	30
420	35
450	37
480	40
540	45

Sec. 12.8.2

$$\frac{0.03d_b(f_y - 20{,}000)}{\sqrt{f'_c}} \qquad\qquad\qquad \frac{0.36d_b(f_y - 140)}{\sqrt{f'_c}}$$

$$0.20\,\frac{A_w}{s_w}\,\frac{f_y}{\sqrt{f'_c}} \qquad\qquad\qquad 2.4\,\frac{A_w}{s_w}\,\frac{f_y}{\sqrt{f'_c}}$$

Sec. 12.9

$$0.27\,\frac{A_w}{s_w}\,\frac{f_y}{\sqrt{f'_c}} \qquad\qquad\qquad 3.3\,\frac{A_w}{s_w}\,\frac{f_y}{\sqrt{f'_c}}$$

U.S. Customary	*S.I. Metric*
Sec. 12.10.1	
$(f_{ps} - \frac{2}{3}f_{se})d_b$	$0.145(f_{ps} - \frac{2}{3}f_{se})d_b$
Sec. 12.11.5.2	
$\dfrac{60b_w s}{f_y}$	$\dfrac{0.41b_w s}{f_y}$
Sec. 12.17.1	
$0.0005f_y d_b$	$0.073f_y d_b$
$(0.0009f_y - 24)d_b$	$(0.13f_y - 24)d_b$
Sec. 17.5.4.1 and 17.5.4.2	
$80b_v d$	$0.55b_v d$
Sec. 17.5.4.3	
$350b_v d$	$2.41b_v d$
Sec. 19.5.1	
$\dfrac{7.2hf'_c}{f_y}$	$\dfrac{600hf'_c}{f_y}$
$29,000\,\dfrac{h}{f_y}$	$16,660\,\dfrac{h}{f_y}$
Sec. A.5.2	
$\dfrac{200}{f_y}$	$\dfrac{1.38}{f_y}$

S.I. METRIC CONVERSIONS OF NONHOMOGENEOUS EQUATIONS*

Eq. (8-1)

$$\rho_b = 0.85\beta_1 \frac{f'_c}{f_y} \frac{600}{600 + f_y}$$

Eq. (9-10)

$$h = \frac{l_n(800 + 0.73f_y)}{36,000 + 5,000\beta \left[\alpha_m - 0.5(1 - \beta_s)\left(1 + \dfrac{1}{\beta}\right)\right]}$$

* All equation numbers refer to ACI Code (318–77).

Eq. (9-11)

$$h = \frac{l_n(800 + 0.73f_y)}{36,000 + 5000\beta(1 + \beta_s)}$$

Eq. (9-12)

$$h = \frac{l_n(800 + 0.73f_y)}{36,000}$$

Eq. (11-3)

$$V_c = 0.17\sqrt{f_c'}b_w d$$

Eq. (11-4)

$$V_c = 0.17\left(1 + 0.073\frac{N_u}{A_q}\right)\sqrt{f_c'}b_w d$$

Eq. (11-5)

$$V_c = \frac{0.17\sqrt{f_c'}}{\sqrt{1 + \left(2.5C_t\dfrac{T_u}{V_u}\right)^2}}$$

Eq. (11-6)

$$V_c = \left(0.16\sqrt{f_c'} + 17.2\rho_w\frac{V_u d}{M_u}\right)b_w d$$

Eq. (11-8)

$$V_c = 0.29\sqrt{f_c'}b_w d\sqrt{1 + 0.29\frac{N_u}{A_q}}$$

Eq. (11-9)

$$V_c = 0.17\left(1 + 0.29\frac{N_u}{A_g}\right)\sqrt{f_c'}b_w d$$

Eq. (11-10)

$$V_c = \left(0.05\sqrt{f_c'} + 4.8\frac{V_u d}{M_u}\right)b_w d$$

Eq. (11-11)

$$V_{ci} = 0.05\sqrt{f_c'}b_w d + V_d + \frac{V_i M_{cr}}{M_{max}}$$

Eq. (11-12)

$$M_{cr} = \frac{I}{y_t}(0.5\sqrt{f_c'} + f_{pe} - f_d)$$

Eq. (11-13)

$$V_{cw} = (0.29\sqrt{f'_c} + 0.3f_{pc})b_w d + V_p$$

Eq. (11-14) and (11-16)

$$A_v = 0.35\frac{b_w s}{f_y}$$

$$A_v + 2A_t = 0.35\frac{b_w s}{f_y}$$

Eq. (11-22)

$$T_c = \frac{0.2\sqrt{f'_c}}{\sqrt{1 + \left(\dfrac{0.4V_u}{C_t T_u}\right)^2}}$$

Eq. (11-25)

$$A_l = \left[\frac{2.76xs}{f_y}\left(\frac{T_u}{T_u + \dfrac{V_u}{3C_t}}\right) - 2A_t\right]\left(\frac{x_1 + y_1}{s}\right)$$

$$0.35\frac{b_w s}{f_y} \quad \text{for} \quad 2A_t$$

Eq. (11-27)

$$V_n = 0.055\left(10 + \frac{l_n}{d}\right)\sqrt{f'_c}b_w d$$

Eq. (11-29)

$$V_c = \left(3.5 - 2.5\frac{M_u}{V_u d}\right)\left(0.16\sqrt{f'_c} + 17\rho_w\frac{V_u d}{M_u}\right)b_w d$$

Eq. (11-31)

$$V_n = \left(6.5 - 5.1\sqrt{\frac{N_{uc}}{V_c}}\right)\left(1 - 0.5\frac{a}{d}\right)$$

$$\left[1 + \left(64 + 160\sqrt{\left(\frac{N_u}{V_u}\right)^3}\right)\rho\right]0.083\sqrt{f'_c}b_w d$$

Eq. (11-32)

$$V_n = 0.540\left(1 - 0.5\frac{a}{d}\right)(1 + 64\rho_v)\sqrt{f'_c}b_w d$$

Eq. (11-33)

$$V_c = 0.274\sqrt{f'_c}hd + \frac{N_u d}{4l_w}$$

Eq. (11-34)

$$V_c = \left[0.05\sqrt{f'_c} + \frac{l_w\left(0.1\sqrt{f'_c} + 0.2\dfrac{N_u}{l_w h}\right)}{\dfrac{M_u}{V_u} - \dfrac{l_w}{2}} \right]hd$$

Eq. (11-37)

$$V_c = 0.083\left(2 + \frac{4}{\beta_c}\right)\sqrt{f'_c}b_o d$$

Eq. (18-4)

$$f_{ps} = f_{se} + 69 + \frac{f'_c}{100\rho_p}$$

Eq. (A-3)

$$A_s = \left(\frac{1.38}{f_y}\right)hd$$

Eq. (B-2)

$$v_c = 0.09\left(1 + 0.58\frac{N}{A_g}\right)\sqrt{f'_c}$$

Eq. (B-3)

$$v_c = 0.08\sqrt{f'_c} + 9\rho\frac{V_d}{M}$$

Eq. (B-4)

$$v_c = 0.091\left(1 + 0.087\frac{N}{A_g}\right)\sqrt{f'_c}$$

Eq. (B-5)

$$A_v = 0.35\frac{b_w s}{f_y}$$

Eq. (B-10)

$$v_c = 0.08\left(1 + \frac{2}{\beta_c}\right)\sqrt{f'_c}$$

METAL REINFORCEMENT

Reinforcing Bars

Bar Size	U.S. Customary			Metric		
	Nominal Diameter in.	Nominal Area in.^{2}	Nominal Weight lb/ft	Nominal Diameter mm	Nominal Area mm^2	Nominal Mass kg/m
3	0.375	0.11	0.376	9.525	71	0.560
4	0.500	0.20	0.668	12.700	129	0.994
5	0.625	0.31	1.043	15.875	200	1.552
6	0.750	0.44	1.502	19.050	284	2.235
7	0.875	0.60	2.044	22.225	387	3.042
8	1.000	0.79	2.670	25.400	510	3.973
9	1.128	1.00	3.400	28.651	645	5.060
10	1.270	1.27	4.303	32.258	819	6.404
11	1.410	1.56	5.313	35.814	1,006	7.907
14	1.693	2.25	7.650	43.002	1,452	11.385
18	2.257	4.00	13.600	57.328	2,581	20.240

Wire Reinforcement

W and D Size Smooth	Deformed	U.S. Customary			Metric		
		Nominal Diameter in.	Nominal Area in.^{2}	Nominal Weight lb/ft	Nominal Diameter mm	Nominal Area mm^2	Nominal Mass kg/m
W31	D31	0.628	0.310	1.054	15.951	200.0	1.569
W30	D30	0.618	0.300	1.020	15.697	193.6	1.518
W28	D28	0.597	0.280	0.952	15.164	180.7	1.417
W26	D26	0.575	0.260	0.934	14.605	167.7	1.390
W24	D24	0.553	0.240	0.816	14.046	154.8	1.214
W22	D22	0.529	0.220	0.748	13.437	141.9	1.113
W20	D20	0.504	0.200	0.680	12.802	129.0	1.012
W18	D18	0.478	0.180	0.612	12.141	116.1	0.911
W16	D16	0.451	0.160	0.544	11.455	103.2	0.810
W14	D14	0.422	0.140	0.476	10.719	90.3	0.708
W12	D12	0.390	0.120	0.408	9.906	77.4	0.607
W11	D11	0.374	0.110	0.374	9.500	71.0	0.557
W10.5		0.366	0.105	0.357	9.296	67.7	0.531
W10	D10	0.356	0.100	0.340	9.042	64.5	0.506
W9.5		0.348	0.095	0.323	8.839	61.3	0.481
W9	D9	0.338	0.090	0.306	8.585	58.1	0.455
W8.5		0.329	0.085	0.289	8.357	54.8	0.430

Wire Reinforcement (*cont.*)

W and D Size Smooth Deformed		Nominal Diameter in.	Nominal Area in.²	Nominal Weight lb/ft	Nominal Diameter mm	Nominal Area mm²	Nominal Mass kg/m
		U.S. Customary			Metric		
W8	D8	0.319	0.080	0.272	8.103	51.6	0.405
W7.5		0.309	0.075	0.255	7.849	48.4	0.380
W7	D7	0.298	0.070	0.238	7.569	45.2	0.354
W6.5		0.288	0.065	0.221	7.315	41.9	0.329
W6	D6	0.276	0.060	0.204	7.010	38.7	0.304
W5.5		0.264	0.055	0.187	6.706	35.5	0.278
W5	D5	0.252	0.050	0.170	6.401	32.3	0.253
W4.5		0.240	0.045	0.153	6.096	29.0	0.228
W4	D4	0.225	0.040	0.136	5.715	25.8	0.202
W3.5		0.211	0.035	0.119	5.359	22.6	0.177
W3		0.195	0.030	0.102	4.953	19.4	0.152
W2.9		0.192	0.029	0.098	4.877	18.7	0.146
W2.5		0.178	0.025	0.085	4.521	16.1	0.127
W2		0.159	0.020	0.068	4.039	12.9	0.101
W1.4		0.135	0.014	0.049	3.429	9.0	0.073

Prestressing Tendons

Type	Nominal Diameter in.	Nominal Area in.²	Nominal Weight lb/ft	Nominal Diameter mm	Nominal Area mm²	Nominal Mass kg/m
	U.S. Customary			Metric		
Seven-wire strand (Grade 250)	$\frac{1}{4}$ (0.250)	0.036	0.12	6.350	23.2	0.179
	$\frac{5}{16}$ (0.313)	0.058	0.20	7.950	37.4	0.298
	$\frac{3}{8}$ (0.375)	0.080	0.27	9.525	51.6	0.402
	$\frac{7}{16}$ (0.438)	0.108	0.37	11.125	69.7	0.551
	$\frac{1}{2}$ (0.500)	0.144	0.49	12.700	92.9	0.729
	(0.600)	0.216	0.74	15.240	139.4	1.101
Seven-wire strand (Grade 270)	$\frac{3}{8}$ (0.375)	0.085	0.29	9.525	54.8	0.432
	$\frac{7}{16}$ (0.438)	0.115	0.40	11.125	74.2	0.595
	$\frac{1}{2}$ (0.500)	0.153	0.53	12.700	98.7	0.789
	(0.600)	0.215	0.74	15.240	138.7	1.101
Prestressing wire	0.192	0.029	0.098	4.877	18.7	0.146
	0.196	0.030	0.10	4.978	19.4	0.149
	0.250	0.049	0.17	6.350	31.6	0.253
	0.276	0.060	0.20	7.010	38.7	0.298

Prestressing Tendons (*cont.*)

Type	U.S. Customary			Metric		
	Nominal Diameter in.	Nominal Area in.^{2}	Nominal Weight lb/ft	Nominal Diameter mm	Nominal Area mm^2	Nominal Mass kg/m
Prestressing bars (smooth)	$\frac{3}{4}$	0.44	1.50	19.050	283.9	2.232
	$\frac{7}{8}$	0.60	2.04	22.225	387.1	3.036
	1	0.78	2.67	25.400	503.2	3.973
	$1\frac{1}{8}$	0.99	3.38	28.575	638.7	5.030
	$1\frac{1}{4}$	1.23	4.17	31.750	793.5	6.206
	$1\frac{3}{8}$	1.48	5.05	34.925	954.8	7.515
Prestressing bars (deformed)	$\frac{5}{8}$	0.28	0.98	15.875	180.6	1.458
	$\frac{3}{4}$	0.42	1.49	19.050	271.0	2.217
	1	0.85	3.01	25.400	548.4	4.480
	$1\frac{1}{4}$	1.25	4.39	31.750	806.5	6.535
	$1\frac{3}{8}$	1.56	5.56	34.925	1006.5	8.274

INDEX

523